BASIC STATISTICAL METHODS FOR ENGINEERS AND SCIENTISTS

The authors of the first edition of this book were listed as Neville and Kennedy, the order of the names having been decided by chance and therefore not being significant. Since chance is a fickle jade, the order of names in this edition is Kennedy and Neville.

BASIC STATISTICAL METHODS FOR ENGINEERS AND SCIENTISTS

Third Edition

John B. Kennedy
University of Windsor

Adam M. Neville
University of Dundee

1817

HARPER & ROW, PUBLISHERS, New York
Cambridge, Philadelphia, San Francisco,
London, Mexico City, São Paulo, Singapore, Sydney

Sponsoring Editor: Peter Richardson
Cover Design: Wanda Lubelska Design
Text Art: Vantage Art, Inc.
Production: Jeanie Berke
Compositor: Syntax International Pte. Ltd.
Printer and Binder: The Maple Press Company

Basic Statistical Methods for Engineers and Scientists, Third Edition

Library of Congress Cataloging in Publication Data

Kennedy, John B.
   Basic statistical methods for engineers and
scientists.

   Includes index.
   1. Engineering—Statistical methods. 2. Science—
Statistical methods.   I. Neville, Adam M.   II. Title.
TA340.K37   1985   620'.0028   84–791
Regular edition ISBN: 0-06-046633-6
International edition ISBN: 0-06-350372-7

85 86 87 88 9 8 7 6 5 4 3 2 1

To N. K. and L. N.

CONTENTS

16 COMPARISON OF VARIANCES AND THEIR PROPERTIES   334

17 REGRESSION AND METHOD OF LEAST SQUARES   365

18 CORRELATION   407

23 INTRODUCTION TO THE DESIGN OF EXPERIMENTS   511

NOTATION

ANOVA	analysis of variance
AQL	acceptable quality level
A_w, A_A	factors given in Table A-19 for mean control charts
$_nC_r$	number of combinations of r items from n items
Cov(x, y)	covariance of two random variables x and y
d	range coefficient (given in Table A-13)
d_m	mean absolute deviation
$D_{WU}, D_{WL}, D_{AU}, D_{AL}$	factors given in Table A-20 for range control charts
$E(x)$	expected value of a random variable x
$f(F)$	probability density of the F statistic
$f(t)$	probability density of the t statistic
$f(z)$	standardized probability density of the normally distributed random variable z
$f(\chi^2)$	probability density of the χ^2 statistic
$F(z)$	area under normal probability curve between $z = 0$ and $z = z$
F_{v_1, v_2} (or F)	random variable statistic defined in Chapters 6 and 16
H_a	alternative hypothesis
H_0	null hypothesis
MS	mean square = sum of squares divided by degrees of freedom
MSA	$= \dfrac{\text{SS}A}{(a - 1)}$
MSAB	$= \dfrac{\text{SS}AB}{(a - 1)(b - 1)}$
MSB	$= \dfrac{\text{SS}B}{(b - 1)}$
MSE	$= \dfrac{\text{SSE}}{N - ab} = \dfrac{\text{SSE}}{ab(n - 1)}$
MTTF	mean time to first failure
MWL (MAL)	mean warning (action) limits
n	sample size or number of observations
np	mean number of population of defectives

$n\hat{p}$	estimate of np, calculated from sample
$\left(\dfrac{n}{r}\right)$	number of combinations of r items from n items
N	population size
p	probability of success of an event
$p(x)$	probability density of variable x
$P(A)$	probability of event A occurring
$P(\bar{A})$	probability of the complement of event A occurring $[=1 - P(A)]$
$P(A\|B)$	conditional probability of event A occurring given that event B has occurred
$_nP_r$	number of permutations of r items from n items
P_r	$= P(x = x_r)$
$P(x)$	cumulative distribution function of variable x
q	probability of failure of an event $= (1 - p)$
r	sample correlation coefficient
r_{ij}	correlation coefficient between two variables X_i and X_j
r^2	coefficient of determination
R	range
$\bar{R}$	mean range
$R(t)$	reliability function
RWL (RAL)	range warning (action) limits
s	estimate of σ calculated from sample
s^2	estimate of σ^2 calculated from sample
s_c^2	estimate of the combined population variance
$s_{\bar{x}}$	estimate of $\sigma_{\bar{x}}$ calculated from the sample
$s_{y_P}^2$	estimate of variance of a single individual value of y
S_t	cumulative sum of deviations at any instant t
SSA	sum of squares of deviations due to factor A
SSAB	sum of squares of deviations due to interaction between factors A and B
SSB	sum of squares of deviations due to factor B
SSE	sum of squares of deviations due to random chance error
SSR	sum of squares of deviations accounted for by regression
SST	total sum of squares of deviations
SSTr	sum of squares of deviations accounted for by treatment(s)
t_v (or t)	standardized random variable statistic defined in Chapters 6 and 15
T	random variable statistic in a Dixon-type test for an outlier (Chapter 12), or Wilcoxon statistic (Chapter 15)

$T\ldots$	$= \displaystyle\sum_{i=1}^{a} \sum_{j=1}^{b} \sum_{k=1}^{n} y_{ijk}$
$T_{i..}$	$= \displaystyle\sum_{j=1}^{b} \sum_{k=1}^{n} y_{ijk}$
$T_{ij.}$	$= \displaystyle\sum_{k=1}^{n} y_{ijk}$
$T_{.j.}$	$= \displaystyle\sum_{i=1}^{a} \sum_{k=1}^{n} y_{ijk}$
V	coefficient of variation
$\text{Var}(x)$	variance of the random variable x
x or (X)	random variable
$\bar{x}$	sample mean or estimate of population mean μ
$\bar{\bar{x}}$	mean of sample means
$\bar{x}_g$	geometric mean
$\bar{x}_h$	harmonic mean
$\bar{x}_s$	sample mean
X	$= (x - \bar{x})$
$\bar{y}\ldots$	$= \dfrac{T\ldots}{N} = \dfrac{T\ldots}{abn}$
$\bar{y}_{i..}$	$= \dfrac{T_{i..}}{jk}$
$\bar{y}_{.j.}$	$= \dfrac{T_{.j.}}{ik}$
$\hat{y}_i$	estimate of μ_i from the sample
z	normally distributed random variable statistic with mean $= 0$ and variance $= 1$
Z	$= \frac{1}{2} \log_e \dfrac{1 + r}{1 - r}$
$Z(t)$	instantaneous failure rate or hazard rate
α	level of significance; probability of committing a Type I error
β	probability of committing a Type II error
$\Gamma(k)$	$= \int_0^{\infty} x^{k-1} e^{-x}\, dx = $ gamma function. If k is a positive integer, $\Gamma(k) = (k - 1)!$
λ	$= \dfrac{\lvert \mu - \mu_0 \rvert}{\sigma}$
μ	true (or population) mean
μ_i	$= \mu_{y\mid x} = $ mean of population of y at $x = x_i$
v	number of degrees of freedom

ρ	population correlation coefficient
σ	true (or population) standard deviation
σ^2	true (or population) variance
$\sigma_{\bar{x}}$	standard deviation of variable $\bar{x}$: standard error of the variable $\bar{x}$
$\sigma_{\bar{x}}^2$	variance of the variable $\bar{x}$
σ_y^2	$= \sigma_{y|x}^2 =$ variance of population of y at $x = x_i$
$\sigma_{\hat{y}}^2$	variance of $\hat{y}$
χ_v^2 (or χ^2)	random variable statistic defined in Chapters 6 and 14
$\hat{\ }$	circumflex denotes estimate of a parameter

PREFACE

We should explain at the outset that we are not mathematicians but engineers. This should not, however, be construed as an apology, because this book is written to satisfy, we hope, the needs of engineers and scientists who, as is always the case, need statistics but not necessarily the full treatment of the underlying mathematical theory.

We believe that in order to understand better engineering and scientific problems and to be able to draw correct inferences from experiment, a knowledge of statistics is essential in the very early stages of a university or college program. This book makes the acquisition of such knowledge possible since it does not build upon rigorous mathematics but rather uses an intuitive approach and common sense. Clearly, then, this is *not* a book on mathematical statistics but neither is it a cookbook of ready-to-apply formulae. Jargon is down to a minimum; explanation, though full, is kept simple; and there is a large number of illustrative solved problems both in the text and at the end of each chapter.

The first edition of the book was written as a textbook either for a one-semester course or as a basis for a one-year junior course taken at a comfortable rate. The second and third edition have enlarged the scope of the book, but the arrangement of the material is such that some of the more advanced chapters can be omitted. Thus the book, with a suitable selection, is still suitable for a shorter or a longer course, and of course the remainder of the material may well be of use beyond student days. Indeed, we have endeavored to make the book suitable also for engineers or scientists who want to teach themselves the basic statistical methods, as well as for occasional use by the person who is presented with a specific problem requiring statistical treatment, be it in research, in laboratory, or in production. We hope to have satisfied these aims since the book is written largely from the practical point of view. The manuscript was understood by our wives, which makes us confident that it can be understood by anybody.

The continued demand for the book has indicated, we believe, that our simple exposition of statistical methods has been found useful in the training of engineers and scientists. But a practical book needs periodic updating and revision. The third edition includes new material on probability, statistical inference, and goodness of fit, and also contains an improved collection of problems.

We have removed most of the errors (the probability of removing them all is very small!), clarified ambiguities, and improved explanations in a number of places. We have refrained, however, from inserting too much new material, which would change the character of the book from its simple format, because we continue to believe that this is what the majority of engineers and scientists need. In keeping with the modern trend, the Système International d'Unités (SI units) has been used throughout the book.

We wish to acknowledge our obvious debt to the authors of numerous books on statistics from which we ourselves learned the art. We are also indebted for specific help to Dr. June Adam and Professor T. Lewis, as well as to those who suggested alterations to the earlier editions, especially Professors Clayborn, Hall, Mischke, Stratton, Stolte, and Mrs. O. Delvecchio.

Reproduced material is acknowledged wherever appropriate. We are indebted to the Imperial Chemical Industries Ltd., London, and to Messrs. Oliver and Boyd Ltd., Edinburgh, for permission to reprint Table G from their book by Davies: *Statistical Methods in Research and Production,* and to the Literary Executor of the late Sir R. A. Fisher, FRS, Cambridge, and Dr. F. Yates, FRS, and the same publishers for permission to reprint Tables II, III, IV, and XXXIII from their book *Statistical Tables for Biological, Agricultural and Medical Research.*

We acknowledge the secretarial assistance of Mrs. J. Assef, Miss A. Bartlett, and the proofreading by Mr. R. J. Philips. Our particular debt is to Miss C. A. Green for her most valuable help in checking and generally preparing the third edition for printing, and to Miss A. C. Ranby for overall handling of the proofs. Last, but not least, we are grateful to Elizabeth Neville who performed the experiment discussed on page 146.

John B. Kennedy
Adam M. Neville

Chapter 1

Introduction

It is a truism to say that an improvement in the knowledge of the world around us requires an ever-increasing use of statistical methods and inferences. Almost everyone needs some knowledge of statistics. However, because of the width and depth of the subject, we have to select the field of knowledge and methods relevant to a particular purpose. This book is primarily concerned with basic applications in engineering and in science, although much of the knowledge of basic applied statistics is of use to workers and students in other fields of study.

What is statistics? Statistics is the science concerned with problems involving *chance* variations that result from a large number of small and independent influences operating on each measured result we obtain. More specifically, statistics is concerned with making decisions from data influenced by these chance variations in such a way that the reliability of conclusions based on the data is evaluated by means of probability. In general, we can say that statistics is a science that deals with the collection, tabulation, analysis, and interpretation of quantitative and qualitative data. This process includes determining the actual attributes or qualities (such as size or color), making estimates (e.g., of the average size of a number of items), as well as hypotheses about *probable* values (e.g., that a certain size of item will be exceeded in some future consignment).

Statistical methods are used to enable us to draw conclusions from *limited* data, as for instance when we want to estimate the average height of women in a certain country without actually determining the height of all of them. The need for, and use of, information based on what we might call incomplete data is frequently encountered, and such information carries with it uncertainty and risk of being incorrect.

Examples of such situations are numerous. For instance, a survey of a sample of men can be used to determine the proportion of left-handed golf clubs to be purchased by a sports goods store. Intuitively, we know that the larger the number of those in the sample the "better," that is, the more reliable, our conclusion. Also, we know that the sample must be drawn from the potential customers and not from an irrelevant population. This example introduces us to the concepts of *sample* and *population*. The latter is the totality of all possible data or measurements; the former is the set of data or measurements selected from the population and actually determined or tested.

POPULATION AND SAMPLE

Let us define these concepts more formally. The term population or universe denotes the entire number of items or measurements theoretically possible. This can be, for instance, the total number of ball bearings manufactured by a given machine in a given period. Since the number is definite the population is said to be *finite*. Another example is the totality of temperature measurements which could be made in a given period; this is clearly *infinite*. The practical difference between the two may be of no importance because, if the finite population is very large, we can treat it as if it were infinite. This would be the case, for instance, if we were interested in the strength of concrete in a gravity dam: the strength is determined by tests on specimens (cores) taken out of the dam. Theoretically, all the concrete could be taken out as cores.

What is important is that the population is properly defined by the *common* characteristic of all its members, for example, all precast concrete beams made by a given machine or in a given factory or in a given period or from a given material. Alternatively, we can have a population of measurements taken by one operator or obtained from one testing machine. In the case of, for instance, a concrete dam, the population would be all the concrete of the same specified composition.

In a great many practical problems we cannot or do not want to test or observe all of the items involved, and therefore we have to resort to sampling. A sample is a selection from the population, and it is on this selection that measurements are made. In practice, we take measurements on a sample and not on the whole population, either because it is infinite or very large, or because the test is expensive or destructive. An example of the latter is the test to determine the life of an electric bulb: once the life has been measured, the bulb is useless. Likewise, in the case of a population consisting of all the concrete in a dam, if we remove all the concrete by taking it out as cores for testing, there will be no dam left. What we do then is to measure the properties of a sample for the purpose of estimating the properties of all the items (population) from which the sample was drawn.

A property descriptive of the population is called a *parameter;* the corresponding property derived from a sample is called an *estimator*. Since samples are used for the purpose of estimating the properties of the parent population they must be representative of the latter. They have, therefore, to be drawn in a random manner.[1] A *random sample* is one selected in such a way that every element in the population has an equal chance of being selected. (See Chapter 6 for a more formal definition.) Inference from samples is of tremendous value in many fields, varying from assessing whether a consignment of goods conforms to specification to the prediction of election results. Experience with the latter type of problem makes us realize that not only must the sample be properly taken so as to be representative of the underlying population, but also that our conclusion is only *probably* correct; certainty on the basis of sampling is not possible (except in trivial cases). This is so because samples from the same population vary among themselves, and variation is inherent in all natural phenomena and in all manufacturing operations. For this reason, all statistical inference is presented in terms of *probability* statements.

USE OF STATISTICS IN ENGINEERING
AND SCIENCE

In the fields of engineering and experimental sciences the use of statistics is almost invariably required in routine testing in the laboratory, in research work, and in production and construction. In the laboratory, we may want to know whether our testing is "precise," or whether the variability of our results is greater than in some other test. In research, we may want: to know whether a change in an ingredient affects the properties of the resulting material; to compare the efficiency of processes or of testing machines; to determine whether the results fit a suspected or postulated form; or to design an experiment that will enable us to separate out the variation due to different causes.

The latter problem also arises in production, as the knowledge of variation in observations caused by a certain factor enables us to decide whether it is economic to control this factor more closely. We may want: to know the probability of obtaining a strength above or below a certain value; to check whether the production has altered so as to change this probability; to determine the proportion of items that have a certain attribute; or to know the size of the sample that we have to use in order that our conclusions will have a specified reliability. Probability is a measure of what is expected to happen if a given event is repeated a large number of times under identical conditions; in other words, it is the relative frequency of occurrence of a given event in the long run. Probability plays an important role in all problems in our daily lives which involve an element of uncertainty, be it engineering, science, or business. Indeed, probability is the basis of judgment when certainty is not available or not possible.

In many engineering and scientific activities we obtain a collection of measurements or other data. A simple inspection of such a collection, especially if large, rarely enables us to draw sound conclusions. For instance, when we have

[1] This does not apply in stratified sampling, which is outside the scope of this book.

two sets of measurements, values in one set may appear at first glance to be generally higher than in the other set but some individual values do not follow this pattern. How can we tell whether one set really represents a population of higher values than the other? We have to organize the data, hypothesize about the parameters of the populations which they represent, and test the hypothesis using statistical methods, which determine the reliability of our conclusions about the data. The main object of using statistics is to be able to generalize from a given set of data to a more broadly applicable statement. This, of course, involves an uncertainty about the validity of the generalization, and statistics enables us to estimate the degree of uncertainty. In this manner, we apply specific and rigorous techniques to data affected by chance.

Although the greater part of this book is concerned with the use of statistics in extracting information from the results of experiments that have already been carried out, we must not forget the importance of statistics in planning experiments. With an appropriate testing program, we can obtain more information from a given experimental effort than if the observations are made in a haphazard manner and the use of statistics is brought in only *a posteriori*. For this reason, we should view statistics not merely as an aid in the interpretation of experimental results but as an integral part of the design of experiments.

CONTINUOUS AND DISCRETE VARIABLES

There are two basic types of variables with which we are concerned: *continuous variables*, which may differ from each other by infinitesimal amounts, and *discrete variables*, which can have only specified values but not intermediate values between the specified values. These concepts are familiar from a study of mathematics but some very simple examples may be usefully given. Time elapsed can be a given number of whole seconds or any fraction of a second, however small, provided we have sensitive enough equipment to measure it; these measurements represent a continuous variable. On the other hand, the numbers of rivets in similar structural elements can differ from one another only by an integer so that solely discrete values are possible. The two types of variables are of interest as they generally follow different *frequency distributions*. By frequency distribution we mean the frequency with which different observed values occur. (This topic is developed in Chapter 2.)

These "different values" occur in three ways. We may measure a certain property, for example, a dimension of one particular thing, a number of times. Because of errors in measurement we shall not record exactly the same value every time. The second case occurs when we manufacture items all of which are to have a certain property, for example, a dimension, the same. Because of variations in manufacture, as well as errors in measurement, the resulting values vary. The third possibility is that there is an inherent variability in the quantity measured, for example, rainfall. In all these cases, if we take a number of observations, we obtain results that vary among themselves, and it is one of the main functions of statistics to evaluate information of this type so that we can estimate the "best" value of the quantity being measured and assess the precision of our estimate. By means of statistics we attempt to define and control the extent of the uncertainty that is due to the inevitable variability of the data.

The distribution of discrete variables is of interest primarily in problems involving items that have or have not a certain attribute: balls that are black or not black, manufactured items that are defective or not defective, specimens that have or have not a strength in excess of a required value, and so on.

We should note that, for the purpose of statistical analysis, the discrete and continuous variables are not irrevocably separated from one another. If values of a variable that is continuously distributed are grouped in intervals and further treated in the grouped form, the treatment becomes essentially one of discrete variables. Conversely, when a discrete variable consists of a large number of classes and is determined a large number of times, its distribution approximates that of a continuous variable, and the use of such an approximation is often convenient. However, the character of the underlying variable must not be forgotten.

DESCRIPTIVE AND INFERENCE PROBLEMS

Statistics is concerned with two basic types of problems: descriptive problems and inference problems. The former include presentation of sets of observations in such a manner that they can be comprehended and interpreted. The numerical characteristics used to describe the set are called *statistics*.[2] Inference problems are those that involve inductive generalizations, for example, from the statistics of the sample actually tested to the parameters of the population from which the sample was drawn. Statistical inference enables us to obtain the maximum amount of accurate information from a given effort of testing; in other words, the use of statistics makes testing more efficient.

Although statistics is a branch of mathematics, it is different from pure mathematics in the following sense. In pure mathematics, values are exact, that is, either a variable has a particular value (the probability of this being so is unity, since we are certain) or it does not have that particular value (the probability in this case being zero, since we are certain that the variable does not have that value). In statistical analysis, however, the variable can take on many possible values, and there is a definite probability that it acquires each such value. This probability can have any value between 0 and 1. The variable may be the original one or a derived quantity such as the mean of samples (considered in Chapter 3), their standard deviation (considered in Chapter 4), or other quantities.

Since many test results or other measurements are affected by chance variations, one is tempted to ask how an engineer or a scientist can make inferences about the population represented by the sample tested and, even more

[2] Singular: a statistic.

so, how he can take decisions on the basis of sample results. Statistical methods make such inference making and decision taking possible because they utilize a certain orderliness which exists in statistical measurements. We use here the concept of *frequency*, that is, of the number of occurrences of a given value, and of *frequency distribution*, that is, of the relative frequency of different values. (These are considered in Chapter 2.)

In a practical situation of a set of data related to a physical measurement, a pattern is discerned from their frequency distribution and is related to a theoretical and mathematically defined distribution. Examples of such distributions in practice and of mathematically defined distributions (described by probability models[3]), given in Figs. 2.1 to 2.3, help to understand why probability theory is used in statistical work. Using the probability model, one can apply the probability approach to estimate the population parameters from random sample statistics. The choice of a proper *probability distribution* to represent the given data comes with experience of the use of statistical methods coupled with a knowledge of the underlying physical phenomena. The correctness of the probability distribution adopted is tested by using certain statistical hypotheses (considered in Chapter 6). The results of these tests are themselves expressed with a certain probability of correctness; a certainty of being right, or of being wrong, is not possible. The degree of uncertainty can, however, be controlled (as we shall see in Chapter 7). The important link between empirical and probability distributions is discussed further in Chapter 2.

STATISTICS AND PROBABILITY

It is clear from what has been mentioned already that the subjects of statistics and probability are fundamentally interrelated. While statistics is largely concerned with drawing conclusions from samples affected by random variations or uncertainties, it is only through the probability theory that we can express these uncertainties in our results. Variations are said to be *random* when they have no pattern of behavior or regularity.

The relation between a sample and the population might elucidate further the distinction between statistics and probability. Such a relation is relevant in two general problems: the testing of a statistical hypothesis and the estimation of a parameter or parameters characteristic of the population. In the former problem, we are concerned with testing whether it is reasonable to conclude that an observed sample belongs to a particular population (the hypothesis) or whether it is not reasonable to reach such a conclusion. Because of the inherent chance variations in the sample, we cannot be 100 percent sure of our conclusion and hence we must couple our conclusion with a probability statement.

---

[3] A model takes the form of a mathematical equation. A probability model is an equation that predicts the relative frequencies (or probabilities) for the various possible outcomes of an experiment.

In the problem of estimation, we are attempting to estimate a parameter of the population from a sample by means of some "best" single value; again, because of the inherent variation from sample to sample we cannot be certain of our estimate and hence we must assign a probability band about our estimate. Such a band will give us a specified degree of confidence that the true value of the population parameter lies between the confidence limits.

In certain problems, a simplified distinction between statistics and probability is possible. If the parameter of the population is known from an earlier record, we can deduce the behavior of the components, or samples, assumed to be part of the population; this then is a probability problem. For example, if we know that a coin is true (unbiased), we can calculate the probability of obtaining a certain number of "heads" in a given number of throws of the coin.

However, if the parameter of the population is unknown, and it has to be estimated from the sample, then we have a statistical problem. An example of this would be the estimate, based on test results from samples, of the number of ball bearings exceeding a certain size in a consignment. It should be mentioned that the theory of probability is based on laws of chance or randomness; hence, samples must be random in composition (as discussed in Chapter 6). Obviously, if we are to judge the population (whole) from a sample (part), the sample must be as representative of the population as possible.

Another way of putting the foregoing is to say that in problems involving probability we make statements about the chances that various events will take place, on the basis of an assumed *model*. On the other hand, in problems involving statistics we have some observed data (random sample) and wish to determine a model that can be used to describe the entire data (population). For example, let us imagine that from numerous past tests we know the mean life expectancy of a particular type of electric bulb, μ; furthermore, the life behavior pattern (distribution) is also known and can be modeled mathematically. The *probability theory* enables us to calculate the chance (or probability) of obtaining some given mean life $\bar{x}$ in a sample or in a particular system. This then is a probability problem: we know the parameters of the population (in this case μ) and we wish to deduce the behavior of the actual system (in this case $\bar{x}$) from the mathematical model describing the known distribution. On the other hand, if we do not know the mean life μ of the population of bulbs, then we can resort to testing a random sample of bulbs, giving a mean life of, say, $\bar{x}$. Hence, by means of *statistical theory*, we would be able to estimate the value of the population of bulbs, μ. We can see thus that in a probabilistic model, the probability is completely specified. In a statistical model, the exact probability distribution is unknown; what are specified are some general characteristics of the probability distribution. Figure 1.1 presents some of the concepts discussed above. We should remember that a parameter of a population, such as μ, is a constant that is generally unknown, whereas the statistic of a sample, such as $\bar{x}$, is a random variable since it is derived from random variables (measurements) forming the sample.

Finally, it may be useful to note that the opposite of a probabilistic situation is a *deterministic* one. Here, we know the values of a variable, and no

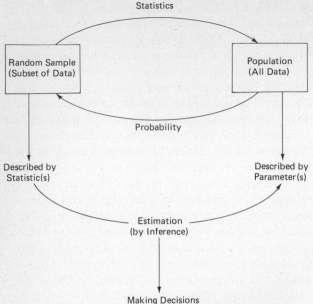

Figure 1.1 Relation between sample and population; probability and statistics; parameter(s) and statistic(s); and estimation (by inference) and making decisions.

uncertainty attaches to our conclusions drawn from the data. Sometimes, although there are inherent errors, we ignore them and assume the values obtained to be precise. These cases, of course, are not our concern as the present book deals with probabilistic situations.

SUMMARY

The main function of statistical methods is to *provide information* about a particular population. To achieve this objective the experimenter:

Descriptive Statistical Methods
1. Makes observation of relevant facts by defining the problem, the variables and their range, and so on, all associated with the population under study.
2. Conducts experiment(s) and gathers data based on random sample(s) from the population, presenting the results in the form of frequency distribution, and describing the data by a few statistics, for example, mean.
3. By induction (i.e., reasoning from the particular facts to the general) formulates a theory relating the data to some common pattern of behavior based on laws of chance, that is, probability distributions.

Inference Statistical Methods

4. Based on his theory, deduces or predicts results of subsequent experiments, for example, population parameters and their limits.
5. Then collects facts to verify or to deny the truth of his predictions by means of hypothesis testing.
6. This process continues either by developing the main theory, for example, using established control charts to check future production, or by formulating a new one, for example, establishing *new* control charts.

In the next chapter we shall start with the descriptive statistical methods.

Chapter 2

Empirical Frequency Distributions

We mentioned in Chapter 1 the variability of engineering and scientific measurements arising from inaccuracies known as errors. Errors associated with the accuracy and precision of measurements are dealt with later on in this chapter, and at this stage we are concerned only with the fact that if we measure something repeatedly we obtain different observations or results, even if our determination of the measured value is made under as closely similar conditions as possible. This is due to variation, however small, in temperature, pressure, potential, instrument setting, and so on . By a similar argument it can be seen that there are differences between supposedly similar items manufactured by the same process. If we measure some property of the various items of the same type, we obtain a collection of data, but without an intelligent treatment, interpretation of such data is well-nigh impossible.

We should stress that we have ignored the possibility of a mistake in our measurements and are concerned only with a number of "equally good" observations that are truly representative of the measured quantity.

We shall now consider the methods of representing the data collected in an experiment.

DISPLAYING DATA

In summarizing Chapter 1, we mentioned that a main function of statistical methods is to provide information by means of descriptive techniques; these techniques enable the engineer or scientist to describe a collection of data in a form that is more concise and convenient than the original collection and to do it in a manner that makes the data easier to comprehend and communicate. Such descriptions can be accomplished both by graphical and by numerical techniques; the latter are discussed in Chapters 3 and 4, where certain statistics, important for statistical inference, are computed. Using graphical techniques, discussed in this chapter, the data under analysis are displayed in some convenient form which not only helps us gain some practical insight into the way the variable seems to behave but also helps in selecting an appropriate theoretical model for the random variable under study. This important feature is explained further in the next section.

The graphical display, mentioned earlier, is accomplished by arranging the data in a *frequency distribution*. We divide the overall range of the values in our set of data into a number of classes and count the number of observations that fall into each of these classes. It should be emphasized that a frequency distribution summarizes the data from a sample while a *probability distribution* models the behavior of the corresponding population from which the sample is drawn. The terms *probability* and *probability distribution* are explained in Chapter 5.

In general, the graphical representation of empirical distributions aids the experimenter in that it:

1. gives him a good idea of how the values of the random variable under investigation are distributed;
2. pinpoints important features which may not be immediately apparent from the raw data;
3. enables him to choose an appropriate theoretical model in the form of a probability distribution to represent the data (see also next section);
4. provides him with a basis for taking corrective action when departures from the norm appear, for example, when a departure from a stable condition in a manufacturing process is observed and the fault is diagnosed early and rectified before an excessive number of defectives has been manufactured.

RELATION BETWEEN FREQUENCY
AND PROBABILITY DISTRIBUTIONS

It is important to elaborate the advantage under item 3 above. It has been noted that statistical measurements, when gathered, frequently exhibit orderliness in the change in their frequencies, for example, small at the lower end of the range, maximum in the central portion, and diminishing toward zero at the upper end of the range. Thus measurements grouped together show conformity not apparent from individual measurements. In fact, in many activities, there is a general pattern of behavior. For example, Fig. 2.1 shows the experimental results (empirical frequency distribution), based on a sample of people, of the

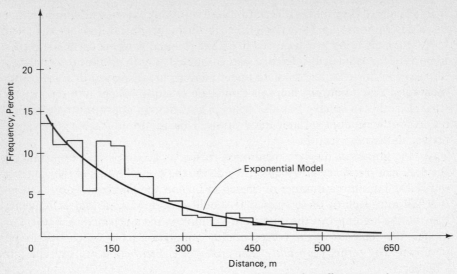

Figure 2.1   Frequency distribution of walking distances for off-street parkers.

pattern of behavior for a sample of individuals' walking distance from car parks to their places of business. The plotted results are used to identify the appropriate model that best describes the behavior of the random variables studied; in the present case, this is an exponential probability model (whose form we know). Figures 2.2 and 2.3 show other experimental results.

It is this existence of patterns that enables us to apply the probability theory to statistical data. Clearly, if conformity or pattern of behavior is absent it is *not* possible to make any inferences at all; fortunately, it is found that random errors in engineering and scientific experiments are quite often dis-

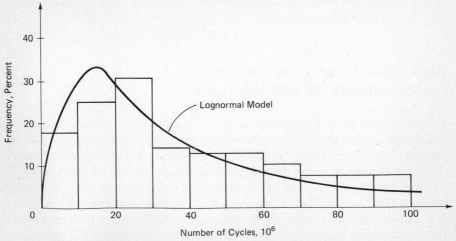

Figure 2.2   Frequency distribution of fatigue life of an aluminum alloy.

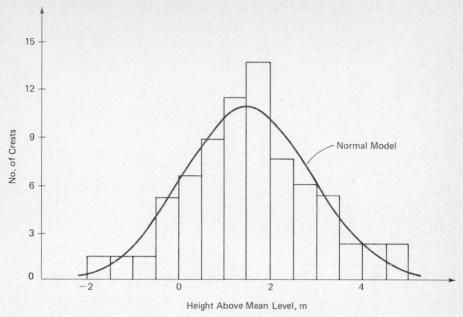

Figure 2.3 Frequency diagram of wave heights above mean sea level.

tributed according to simple laws of chance represented by probability distributions, described by known probability models.

The procedure for making inferences is as follows. After gathering the data presented in a frequency distribution, a few sample statistics (e.g., mean) are calculated. In a physical situation, if a pattern of behavior is discerned from the frequency distribution of the data, the most appropriate probability distribution (as described by a known model) is chosen to represent the empirical data, the parameter(s) of such a probability distribution being estimated from the random sample statistics. A check on the correctness of the probability distribution adopted can be carried out by applying a particular test. The procedure is explained in Chapter 7.

TABULATION OF DATA

Imagine that we have a collection of measurements, each represented by a number, which gives us information about the quantity being determined. As an example, let us consider the results of tests on the transverse strength of 270 bricks from one plant, given in Table 2.1. Some of the numbers occur only once, others are repeated several times. The test results are written down in the order in which they occur, and are said to be in the form of *ungrouped data*. This form enables us to study the sequence of the values, for example, of "high" or "low" values, and, hence, possibly to discover some of the causes of variation.

TABLE 2.1   TRANSVERSE STRENGTH OF 270 BRICKS FROM
ONE SOURCE, MPa

5.93	9.10	5.66	7.17	6.89	6.96	8.20	8.14	7.45	7.58	7.79
6.34	7.58	8.62	10.20	7.93	5.10	7.45	5.93	6.89	5.58	6.89
8.27	5.66	7.58	6.14	1.86	7.38	5.72	9.51	6.62	9.38	5.03
5.86	6.34	6.48	9.03	9.17	7.03	9.58	5.72	5.66	6.76	9.17
6.34	7.38	11.24	4.62	7.93	8.07	6.34	7.72	8.07	8.00	7.52
7.52	4.83	6.27	8.07	5.52	6.62	7.03	7.52	13.86	6.14	6.41
5.72	6.07	6.00	9.24	5.79	8.14	5.10	6.07	5.45	7.58	8.69
7.17	7.45	7.17	6.76	8.55	5.52	5.93	6.96	7.79	6.69	7.86
10.41	7.31	5.79	6.48	7.65	8.55	8.89	6.00	8.69	7.24	6.21
5.10	8.48	7.03	7.31	6.83	7.03	5.66	7.03	5.93	5.86	6.14
7.93	5.93	7.58	5.79	7.31	7.10	6.83	7.58	7.45	7.45	6.69
6.89	4.96	5.52	8.07	6.69	4.76	7.10	6.14	4.83	6.07	7.93
7.86	7.45	6.83	3.93	5.45	7.38	5.66	4.00	5.66	7.31	6.76
7.10	6.62	6.00	5.52	7.17	5.66	8.14	9.31	8.14	6.55	7.58
4.83	5.93	4.55	8.14	5.38	8.48	6.55	6.21	5.24	9.51	6.21
6.34	7.58	7.45	6.76	5.24	5.72	8.41	7.58	7.52	9.51	8.75
5.93	6.83	6.14	6.48	6.27	7.65	7.03	9.51	6.96	7.10	6.55
6.55	6.07	6.69	6.89	6.83	5.72	5.86	4.34	4.90	6.21	6.14
7.03	5.17	7.38	6.34	6.00	6.96	8.48	5.38	6.89	7.93	9.38
8.96	6.69	5.52	4.48	8.14	5.93	7.93	9.65	6.07	5.03	5.72
6.14	7.10	7.31	11.10	8.20	9.65	5.86	6.96	6.96	8.55	
7.38	6.69	6.62	8.14	7.24	6.27	7.65	5.38	5.38	8.20	
6.27	7.58	6.00	6.76	5.03	5.52	5.52	7.86	6.48	6.76	
6.00	6.69	6.27	5.72	7.10	7.24	4.90	6.14	6.96	7.72	
5.58	7.38	7.58	3.17	5.93	7.38	6.07	8.55	6.48	5.93	

Source: Report of Committee on Manual on Presentation of Data, *Proc. ASTM*, vol. 33, 1933, Part 1, p. 454. The
original data were in psi units.

However, because arithmetical processing of ungrouped data is cumbersome
and because we often need a rapid impression of the data, we usually resort to
tabulation. Table 2.2 shows the data of Table 2.1 ranked in an increasing order
of magnitude, that is, in *rank order;* such a form is sometimes called *ungrouped
frequency distribution.*

FREQUENCY GROUPING

However, even this form is rather difficult to take in at a glance. For this
reason, if there are more than about 40 observations, a more compact representation is advantageous. This is obtained by arranging the results into *class
intervals*, usually of equal width, and recording the number of items in each
interval, this number being called the *class frequency*. For example, we can
choose a class width of 1.00 MPa, with the midpoint of the lowest interval at
2.00 MPa. Such a choice is quite arbitrary, but it is usually convenient to have
5 to 20 intervals. If too many class intervals are used, the class frequencies are
low and the saving in computational effort is small. Conversely, with too few
class intervals the true character of the distribution may be obscured and information may be lost.

TABLE 2.2 DATA OF TABLE 2.1 ARRANGED IN RANK (ASCENDING) ORDER

1.86	5.38	5.72	6.00	6.34	6.69	7.03	7.38	7.58	8.14	9.03
3.17	5.38	5.72	6.07	6.34	6.76	7.03	7.38	7.58	8.14	9.10
3.93	5.38	5.72	6.07	6.34	6.76	7.03	7.38	7.58	8.14	9.17
4.00	5.45	5.79	6.07	6.34	6.76	7.03	7.38	7.58	8.14	9.17
4.34	5.45	5.79	6.07	6.34	6.76	7.03	7.38	7.65	8.14	9.24
4.48	5.52	5.79	6.07	6.41	6.76	7.03	7.38	7.65	8.14	9.31
4.55	5.52	5.86	6.07	6.48	6.76	7.03	7.38	7.65	8.14	9.38
4.62	5.52	5.86	6.14	6.48	6.83	7.10	7.45	7.72	8.20	9.38
4.76	5.52	5.86	6.14	6.48	6.83	7.10	7.45	7.72	8.20	9.51
4.83	5.52	5.86	6.14	6.48	6.83	7.10	7.45	7.79	8.20	9.51
4.83	5.52	5.93	6.14	6.48	6.83	7.10	7.45	7.79	8.27	9.51
4.83	5.52	5.93	6.14	6.55	6.83	7.10	7.45	7.86	8.41	9.51
4.90	5.58	5.93	6.14	6.55	6.89	7.10	7.45	7.86	8.48	9.58
4.90	5.58	5.93	6.14	6.55	6.89	7.17	7.45	7.86	8.48	9.65
4.96	5.66	5.93	6.14	6.55	6.89	7.17	7.52	7.93	8.48	9.65
5.03	5.66	5.93	6.21	6.62	6.89	7.17	7.52	7.93	8.55	10.20
5.03	5.66	5.93	6.21	6.62	6.89	7.17	7.52	7.93	8.55	10.41
5.03	5.66	5.93	6.21	6.62	6.89	7.24	7.52	7.93	8.55	11.10
5.10	5.66	5.93	6.21	6.62	6.96	7.24	7.58	7.93	8.55	11.24
5.10	5.66	5.93	6.27	6.69	6.96	7.24	7.58	7.93	8.62	13.86
5.10	5.66	6.00	6.27	6.69	6.96	7.31	7.58	8.00	8.69	
5.17	5.72	6.00	6.27	6.69	6.96	7.31	7.58	8.07	8.69	
5.24	5.72	6.00	6.27	6.69	6.96	7.31	7.58	8.07	8.75	
5.24	5.72	6.00	6.27	6.69	6.96	7.31	7.58	8.07	8.89	
5.38	5.72	6.00	6.34	6.69	6.96	7.31	7.58	8.07	8.96	

The number of class intervals should be governed by the amount and scatter of the data present: a small sample or a uniform distribution (i.e., one which has a constant frequency) of values would suggest that fewer class intervals are needed. When the number of observations is increased, the width of the class intervals can be decreased as there will be more observations in any particular interval. Sturges[1] suggested a practical guide to derive an estimate for the number of class intervals, k, as a function of the number of observations, n:

$$k = 1 + 3.3 \log_{10} n. \tag{2.1}$$

It is generally preferable to choose class intervals in such a way that no result falls on the *class boundary*. Since in the present case the results are given to the nearest 0.01 MPa, the class intervals may be chosen as 1.50–2.49, 2.50–3.49, and so on. For simplicity, class intervals such as 1.50–2.50, 2.50–3.50, and 3.50–4.50, are sometimes written, it being understood that the upper boundary is exclusive; this is the same as when using the appropriate inequality signs. Other ways of dealing with the boundary between class intervals exist, such as selecting class intervals which have more significant places than the data, but no fundamental point is involved; what is essential is that there is no

[1] H. A. Sturges, "The Choice of a Class Interval," *J. Am. Statist. Assoc.*, vol. 21, 1926, pp. 65–66.

TABLE 2.3 GROUPED FREQUENCY TABLE FOR DATA OF TABLE 2.1

Class interval	Class midpoint, x_i	Class frequency, f_i	Cumulative frequency, F	Relative cumulative frequency, F/n	$f_i x_i$
1.5–2.5	2.00	1	1	0.00370	2.00
2.5–3.5	3.00	1	2	0.00741	3.00
3.5–4.5	4.00	4	6	0.0222	16.00
4.5–5.5	5.00	24	30	0.111	126.00
5.5–6.5	6.00	81	111	0.411	486.00
6.5–7.5	7.00	78	189	0.700	546.00
7.5–8.5	8.00	51	240	0.889	408.00
8.5–9.5	9.00	18	258	0.956	162.00
9.5–10.5	10.00	9	267	0.989	90.00
10.5–11.5	11.00	2	269	0.996	22.00
11.5–12.5	12.00	0	269	0.996	0
12.5–13.5	13.00	0	269	0.996	0
13.5–14.5	14.00	1	270	1.000	14.00
Totals		$\sum f_i = 270 = n$			$\sum f_i x_i = 1869.00$

gap and no overlap between classes. In the numerical examples given in the book, the class boundaries are in all cases assumed to be such that the interval to either side is allocated one-half of the values falling on the boundary. This method has the advantage of leading to simple numerical values, desirable in a textbook.

Arrangement of observations in class intervals, with the class frequencies tallied, produces a *grouped frequency distribution*. The concept of frequency distribution is of importance since it makes it convenient to use a graphical approach to probability distributions. Table 2.3 gives the grouped frequency distribution for the data of Table 2.1. The advantages of this presentation are clear: we can see whether values near the extremes occur frequently or whether the observations cluster near some central value, and specifically which class intervals contain the most values.

If instead of actual frequency we consider the frequency of each interval divided by the total number of observations, we obtain results in terms of relative frequency; we then deal with a *relative frequency distribution*.

CUMULATIVE FREQUENCY

Furthermore, we may be interested (to continue with our example) in the number of bricks whose strength is higher or lower than a specified value. This is given by the *cumulative frequency* F column of Table 2.3. The "lower than" F is a sum of the frequencies of all class intervals below the specified value; for example, $1 + 1 + 4 + 24 = 30$ bricks have a strength lower than 5.50 MPa. A "not lower than" F is similarly obtained by summing frequencies of intervals from the highest; for example, $1 + 0 + 0 + 2 + 9 = 12$ bricks have a strength not lower than 9.50 MPa. It is not possible to say how many bricks have a strength higher than 9.50 MPa because bricks whose strength is exactly 9.50 MPa are included in the interval 9.50–10.50 MPa.

In many cases, the proportion of results rather than their number is of interest; to obtain this, the cumulative frequency is simply divided by the total number of results n, the quotient being known as relative or *fractional cumulative frequency*. The calculated values are given in Table 2.3, and it can be seen, for example, that the proportion of bricks whose strength is lower than 5.50 MPa is $\frac{30}{270} = 0.11$.

GRAPHICAL REPRESENTATION

A grouped frequency distribution may be represented diagrammatically in several ways. The most common of these is the *histogram*. Here, the class intervals are set out on a horizontal axis, and the vertical direction is used to represent the frequency in a given interval, marked by means of a horizontal line across the width of the class interval; the scale chosen is quite arbitrary. Figure 2.4 shows a histogram for the data of Table 2.3. Strictly speaking, it is the area of each rectangle that represents the frequency in that interval, and the total area under the histogram represents the total number of results to an appropriate scale. In the case where the width of all class intervals is the same, the heights and areas are proportional to one another. The two approaches differ only in

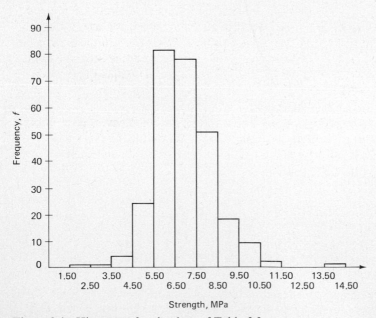

Figure 2.4 Histogram for the data of Table 2.3.

the markings on the vertical scale. However, if the class intervals are not all of the same width, the ordinates must be plotted so that the area of each rectangle is proportional to the class frequency. Thus the ordinate no longer represents the frequency but a ratio of frequency to the class width, called density. The concept of density is of importance and will be encountered again in Chapter 12.

    The choice of the class width is governed by the same considerations as in the case of grouping for computational purposes only. If too many intervals are used, the histogram becomes irregular, and no clear pattern of frequency distribution can be seen. This is illustrated in Fig. 2.5(a). By contrast, Fig. 2.5(b) shows a histogram for the same data but with a class width twice that in Fig. 2.5(a).

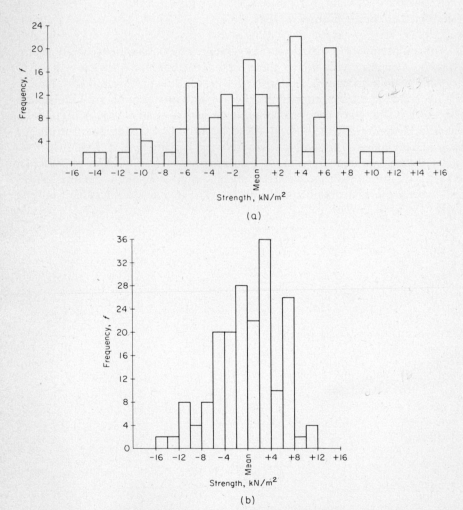

Figure 2.5 (a) Histogram for strength of mortar cubes with grouping in class intervals of too small a width; (b) histogram for the same data as (a) but with a class width of twice the size.

Sometimes the frequency within a class interval is plotted as a point whose abscissa is that of the class midpoint. If adjacent points are connected, a *frequency polygon* is obtained, as shown in Fig. 2.6 for the data of Fig. 2.4. When plotting a frequency polygon, it is usual to indicate the values of the class midpoints rather than class boundaries as in the case of a histogram. The line between the points has no significance, and intermediate values must not be read off the line. Generally, frequency polygons are not applicable to observations on discrete variables. However, with continuous variables, frequency polygons are useful when we want to compare visually two or more frequency distributions: superimposed relative frequency polygons give a clearer picture than histograms.

If we are interested in proportions of results within various class intervals, we plot the relative frequency, that is, frequency divided by the total number of results. *Percentage frequency*, which is simply relative frequency multiplied by 100, is particularly convenient. The difference between histograms showing the frequency and those showing the relative or percentage frequency lies in the scale of the ordinates only; the form of the diagram is the same in either case.

In the case of a histogram showing relative frequency, if the total number of results is increased indefinitely so that the class width can be correspondingly decreased, the histogram becomes transformed, in the limiting case, into a *probability distribution*. The ordinate then represents the probability density.

Cumulative frequency can also be represented graphically. The class intervals are set out horizontally as before, and the cumulative frequency is plotted as the ordinate at the right-hand end of each interval. This ordinate thus represents the area to the left of the corresponding ordinate in a histogram. The

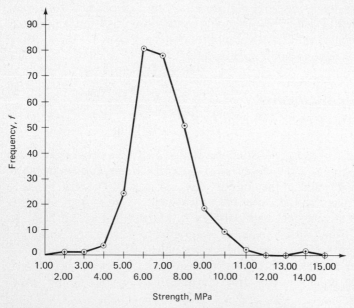

Figure 2.6   Frequency polygon for the data of Fig. 2.1.

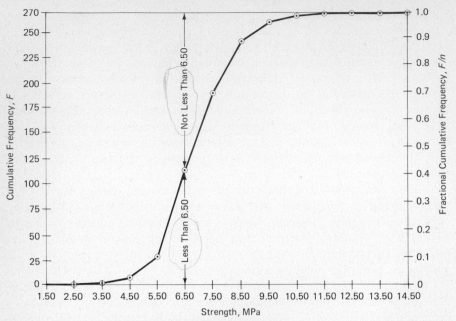

Figure 2.7 Cumulative frequency and fractional cumulative frequency curve for the data of Table 2.3.

cumulative frequency curve is also called an *ogive*.[2] Figure 2.7 shows the "less than" curve for the data of Table 2.3, the ordinates giving both the cumulative frequency and the fractional cumulative frequency. The number or the fraction of results below or above any strength can easily be read off such a diagram, but care is required in distinguishing between fractions "less than" and "not greater than" a specified value. The cumulative frequency curve for the so-called normal distribution is considered in Chapter 11.

ACCURACY AND PRECISION
OF MEASUREMENTS

In dealing with measurements, a distinction should be drawn between accuracy and precision. *Accuracy* is the closeness or nearness of the measurements to the "true" or "actual" value of the quantity being measured. The term *precision* (or *repeatability*) refers to the closeness with which the measurements agree with each other. To make this distinction clear, we refer to Fig. 2.8. Here, we have the readings from four tachometers being used to measure the speed of a constant-speed motor. Five measurements are made with each tachometer. It is observed that tachometer I has good precision (the five speeds are closely grouped) as well as good accuracy (the representative value for all five speeds

---

[2] Pronounced *ō-jīv*.

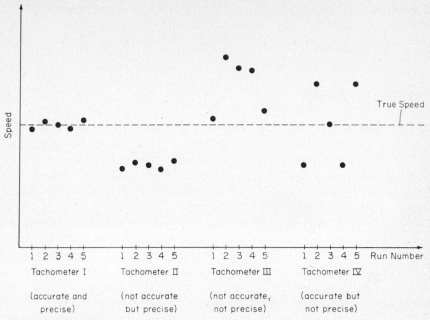

Figure 2.8 Precision and accuracy of four tachometers.

(arithmetic mean[3]) is close to the true value). Tachometer II is precise but not very accurate (the representative value for the five speeds deviates from the true speed). Following the same reasoning, we can see that neither good precision nor good accuracy is exhibited by tachometer III, whereas tachometer IV shows good accuracy but poor precision (wide scattering among the five speeds). Furthermore, comparing tachometer I with tachometer IV we note that both are accurate but the former is more precise than the latter; therefore, we can conclude that tachometer I is more reliable than tachometer IV because it possesses good precision as well as good accuracy.

Precision errors are sometimes called *random* or *accidental* errors, which are usually assessed by applying certain statistical concepts and techniques. Accuracy errors are referred to as *systematic* errors and are usually reduced through *calibration*, which will improve the performance of a measuring device that has poor accuracy and good precision. In cases where a systematic error is not completely eliminated, it then becomes part of the random error or uncertainty and is therefore assessed as such; it is measured by means of the standard deviation, a quantity of immense importance in statistical methods, discussed in Chapter 4.

For example, a new rifle cannot be used for tasks requiring precision if test firing indicates that the standard deviation in distance from a fixed target (precision) is large. On the other hand, if the standard deviation is small, but the average distance of shots from the target (accuracy) is large, it is possible

---

[3] Considered in Chapter 3.

to incorporate an aiming correction that will center the shots on the target. If this correction can be made without increasing the deviation, the rifle will be both accurate and precise. A further discussion of errors can be found in Chapter 10.

SIGNIFICANT FIGURES

The correct handling of significant figures is important in the processing and analyzing of collected data from an experiment. If we use too few significant figures we may lose important accuracy during processing. Conversely, too many significant figures require more effort in calculations and, what is more important, may lead us astray in that the outcome would suggest an experimental accuracy that did not actually exist.

If there is any doubt, it is better to use *more* rather than fewer significant figures in calculations since too few can cause accumulated "rounding errors." Significant figures (or digits) are the accurate digits, not counting zeros before the first nonzero digit, required to locate the decimal point. For example, 32.95 has 4 significant figures; 64.9 has 3 significant figures; 9.3500 has 5 significant figures; $0.00029 = 29 \times 10^{-5}$ has 2 significant figures; while $0.000290 = 290 \times 10^{-6}$ has 3 significant figures. In operations involving multiplication, division, and extraction of roots of numbers, the *final* result can have no more significant figures than the number with the fewest significant figures used in the calculation. For example:

$$17.2 \times 6.0 = 1.0 \times 10^2; \qquad \frac{0.824}{0.023} = 36; \qquad \sqrt{348.3} = 18.66.$$

In operations of addition and subtraction of numbers, the *final* result can have no more significant figures after the decimal point than the number with the fewest significant figures after the decimal point. For example: $5.92 + 7.5 = 13.4$; $52.95 - 46 = 7$.

SOLVED PROBLEM

2-1. In a test on 35 glue-laminated beams, the following values of the spring constant (in MN/m) given in Table 2.4 were found.

TABLE 2.4

Spring constant/100						
6.72	6.77	6.82	6.70	6.78	6.70	6.62
6.75	6.66	6.66	6.64	6.76	6.73	6.80
6.72	6.76	6.76	6.68	6.66	6.62	6.72
6.76	6.70	6.78	6.76	6.67	6.70	6.72
6.74	6.81	6.79	6.78	6.66	6.76	6.72

   a. Obtain a frequency table.
   b. Draw a histogram and a frequency polygon.
   c. Draw a cumulative frequency diagram.
   d. Estimate the fraction of beams that will have a constant of less than 6.71
       × 100 MN/m. Estimate also the spring constant which is not exceeded by 80
       percent of the beams tested.

Solution
   a. We shall assign the observations to 6 classes. The lowest and highest values
in Table 2.4 are 6.62 and 6.82. The difference is 0.20 which gives, when divided by 6,
approximately 0.04. We shall, therefore, adopt 0.04 as class width, the lowest boundary
being 6.61. Table 2.5 gives the frequency and cumulative frequency for the various class
intervals.
   b. The histogram and the frequency polygon are shown in Fig. 2.9.

TABLE 2.5

Class interval	Frequency, f_i	Cumulative frequency, F
6.61–6.65	3	3
6.65 6.69	6	9
6.69–6.73	9	18
6.73–6.77	9	27
6.77–6.81	6	33
6.81–6.85	2	35
Total	$\sum f_i = 35$	

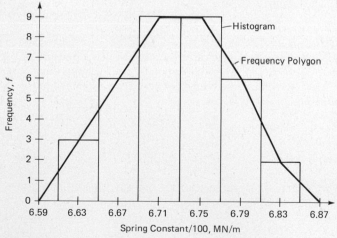

Figure 2.9

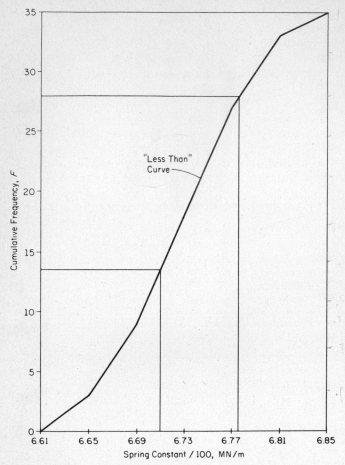

Figure 2.10

c. The cumulative frequency diagram is shown in Fig. 2.10.

d. From the cumulative frequency diagram it is estimated that 13 beams have a constant of less than 6.71×100 MN/m, which corresponds to a fractional cumulative frequency of $\frac{13}{35} = 0.37$. Eighty percent of the beams (28 beams) are estimated to have a spring constant of less than 6.776×100 MN/m.

PROBLEMS

2-1. The annual precipitation (in centimeters) at some city is listed in Table 2.6.
a. Arrange the data in (ascending) rank order.
b. Prepare a frequency table. Take a class width of 1.0 cm and commence with the lower boundary of the first class interval of 9.0 cm.
c. Draw a histogram, a frequency polygon, and a cumulative frequency diagram.

TABLE 2.6

Year	Precipitation	Year	Precipitation	Year	Precipitation
1904	19.5	1923	18.8	1942	21.0
1905	10.9	1924	9.3	1943	13.5
1906	12.6	1925	15.9	1944	14.0
1907	10.4	1926	13.6	1945	13.3
1908	14.1	1927	17.0	1946	16.2
1909	15.9	1928	12.9	1947	13.6
1910	11.1	1929	9.0	1948	10.2
1911	19.4	1930	11.5	1949	15.5
1912	16.7	1931	11.6	1950	16.3
1913	13.5	1932	10.1	1951	16.4
1914	12.7	1933	9.8	1952	10.7
1915	10.5	1934	9.9	1953	13.4
1916	17.4	1935	17.8	1954	20.4
1917	10.3	1936	11.3	1955	15.4
1918	12.7	1937	10.7	1956	13.7
1919	13.4	1938	18.0	1957	10.1
1920	15.2	1939	15.7	1958	11.7
1921	21.0	1940	12.9	1959	13.4
1922	11.4	1941	10.3	1960	10.2

d. From the cumulative frequency diagram, estimate the number of years in which the annual precipitation exceeded 14.5 cm and the number of years in which the annual precipitation was lower than 11.0 cm.

2-2. The frequency distribution of 500 television components tested at a certain company is as follows:

Lifetime (hours)	400–499	500–599	600–699	700–799	800–899	900–999	1000–1099	1100–1199
Number of components	25	65	79	108	92	76	34	21

a. Construct a histogram, a frequency polygon, and a cumulative frequency diagram.
b. Find the percentage of tubes whose lifetimes do not exceed 700 hours.
c. Find the percentage of tubes whose lifetimes are at least 600 but not more than 1000 hours.

2-3. The moisture content in percent of 44 samples of clay was measured as follows: 10.3, 10.7, 9.2, 11.4, 11.5, 8.4, 10.3, 10.2, 9.8, 10.2, 11.4, 10.4, 11.6, 10.3, 11.4, 10.3, 7.8, 8.7, 11.7, 9.3, 9.8, 11.4, 10.4, 9.3, 10.4, 11.2, 10.6, 9.8, 10.1, 13.1, 10.5, 12.2, 9.6, 7.0, 12.3, 12.3, 12.3, 9.7, 10.7, 11.5, 10.6, 13.0, 13.0, 9.0.
a. Obtain a grouped frequency distribution for these results, taking a class width of 1.0 percent moisture content and starting with a class interval of 7.0 to 8.0.
b. Draw a histogram.
c. Draw a frequency polygon and cumulative frequency diagram.

TABLE 2.7

Number of defective bolts	0	1	2	3	4	5	6	7	8	9	10	11	12
Number of lots	55	108	80	56	34	21	19	11	8	4	1	2	1

TABLE 2.8

1.740	1.731	1.740	1.730	1.741	1.735	1.732	1.736	1.738	1.737
1.746	1.742	1.744	1.727	1.734	1.742	1.735	1.724	1.732	1.729
1.740	1.735	1.735	1.736	1.731	1.729	1.741	1.735	1.733	1.736
1.727	1.732	1.732	1.734	1.736	1.736	1.738	1.739	1.728	1.732
1.730	1.743	1.735	1.739	1.733	1.738	1.734	1.728	1.735	1.737
1.735	1.736	1.737	1.726	1.739	1.725	1.733	1.734	1.745	1.730

2-4. The distribution of the number of defective bolts found in 400 lots of manufactured bolts is shown in Table 2.7.

3/400

    a. Determine the percentage of the lots containing more than 10 defective bolts.

    b. Determine the relative frequency of the lots containing 5 or fewer defective bolts.

    c. What are the class boundaries?

    d. Construct a histogram and a cumulative frequency diagram.

2-5. The diameters in centimeters of a sample of 60 ball bearings manufactured by a company are given in Table 2.8.

    a. Using appropriate class intervals, calculate the frequency distribution of the diameters. (HINT: Take a class width of 0.02 cm and commence with the class interval of 1.724 to 1.726.)

    b. Draw a histogram, a frequency polygon, and a cumulative frequency diagram.

    c. Find the percentage of bearings whose diameters do not exceed 1.735 cm.

2-6. The dielectric strengths (measured in V/mm) of 200 paper samples were measured and the resulting frequency distribution is shown in Table 2.9.

    a. Draw a histogram, a relative frequency diagram, and a cumulative frequency diagram.

    b. Find the percentage of paper samples whose dielectric strengths exceed 550 V/mm.

TABLE 2.9

Dielectric strength (V/mm)	475–490	490–505	505–520	520–535	535–550	550–565	565–580	580–595	595–610	610–625
Number of paper samples	2	4	16	28	45	40	38	18	6	3

Chapter 3

Characteristics of Distributions: Central Tendency

In Chapter 2 we explained how to arrange a collection of observations in a frequency distribution form. We shall now proceed with statistical analysis using a numerical technique in order to learn how to present information about the distribution in a clear and concise form.

There are two obvious features of the data that can be characterized in a simple form and yet give a very meaningful description of a set of observations: *central tendency* and *dispersion*. The central tendency is described by averages; these are measures of location and are "typical" of the data. The measure of dispersion is concerned with scatter about the average and is dealt with in Chapter 4. It should be emphasized that the concepts of central tendency and dispersion are applied to empirical data or distributions. On the other hand, the concepts of expectation (average in the long run) and variance discussed in Chapter 5 are used to describe probability distributions in a concise manner.

AVERAGES

Averages are commonly used in everyday life to give a *typical* representation of a group as a whole, possibly as a basis for comparison with other groups. It has been said that averages help the human mind to comprehend with a single effort the significance of the whole, but of course the average is only one feature of the totality of data.

In many cases, the data in hand refer to a sample drawn from a larger body of data—for example, we may take a number of rock specimens from some stratum and measure their density. The tested specimens are referred to collectively as a *sample*, and the whole body of rock as the parent *population*.

We measure the average density of the sample for the purpose of obtaining information about the average density of the population. This type of problem is dealt with in Chapter 6.

It may be relevant to note that if we take repeated measurements of a quantity, the average does not represent a "true" value of the quantity. In many cases the term "true value" has no meaning (e.g., the time taken by jet planes to fly between New York and San Francisco); in other cases, we may never be able to determine the true value but can determine only the most probable value (e.g., the difference in level between two points on the ground).

There are several types of averages, which will now be discussed; the appropriate one to use depends on the problem in hand.

ARITHMETIC MEAN

This is the most common type of average, often referred to simply as the *average* or *mean*. The latter term will be used here.

The mean is a value such that the sum of deviations of observations from it is zero, that is,

$$\sum_{i=1}^{n} (x_i - \bar{x}) = 0 \tag{3.1}$$

where x_i = an observation or measurement,
 n = the total number of observations,
 $\bar{x}$ = the mean.

The mean is thus the sum of the observations divided by their number.

$$\bar{x} = \frac{1}{n} \sum_{i=1}^{n} x_i. \tag{3.1a}$$

The mean of a set of empirical data may be designated as the "point of balance" of the sample data analagous to the centroid in mechanics. The term "first moment" is therefore sometimes used to describe the mean.

The concept of mean is so well known that no further discussion is needed, but at this stage a brief note on the notation for the mean may be of help. The true mean of a population is usually denoted by μ. The mean of a sample is written as $\bar{x}$. The values of $\bar{x}$ and μ become identical when the sample is, in fact, the total finite population; in such a case either symbol may be used.

A simple example will be given to illustrate some shortcuts in computation.

EXAMPLE

The solids content of water, in parts per million (ppm), was measured in 11 samples, the following results being obtained: 4520, 4570, 4520, 4490, 4540, 4570, 4500, 4520, 4520, 4500, and 4590. Hence, from Eq. (3.1a),

$$\text{mean} = \bar{x} = \frac{\sum \text{above values}}{11} = 4530.9 \text{ ppm.}$$

TABLE 3.1

(1)	(2)	(3)	(4)	(5)
Solids content, ppm, x_i	(-4400)	$(\div 10)$ x_i'	Frequency, f_i	$x_i' f_i$
4490	90	9	1	9
4500	100	10	2	20
4520	120	12	4	48
4540	140	14	1	14
4570	170	17	2	34
4590	190	19	1	19
Totals			$\sum f_i = 11$	$\sum x_i' f_i = 144$

When the frequency of some of the observations is greater than 1, computation may be simplified by setting the data in a tabular form, such as in Table 3.1, and using frequency grouping. If f_i is the frequency of any value x_i, then the mean can be written as

$$\bar{x} = \frac{\sum f_i x_i}{\sum f_i}. \tag{3.2}$$

A further saving in effort is effected by reducing all the observations by a constant value, and possibly also by dividing them by a factor such as 10. This transformation of the original variable is known as *coding*. In our case we can thus subtract 4400 (column 2) and divide by 10 (column 3).

Hence, from Eq. (3.2),

$$\bar{x}' = \tfrac{144}{11} = 13.09$$

and $\bar{x} = 10\bar{x}' + 4400 = 4530.9$ ppm, as before.   ■ ■

When dealing with a large number of observations, or a large sample, the computation of the mean can be shortened considerably, with only a small loss of accuracy, by using the class-interval method explained in Chapter 2. Instead of considering each individual observation, we treat all observations within a class interval as a group and assume that, in any class, the observations are uniformly distributed throughout the interval so that the class frequency may be assumed to be concentrated at the class midpoint x_i'. The procedure is then as follows:

1. Take the first class midpoint x_0 as an arbitrary origin for the purpose of calculating the fictitious (or coded) mean.
2. Calculate deviations X_i' from this origin, expressed in terms of the class width w, that is,

$$X_i' = \frac{(x_i' - x_0)}{w}.$$

3. Find the product of class frequency f_i and X_i'.

4. Obtain the fictitious mean

$$\bar{X}' = \frac{\sum f_i X_i'}{\sum f_i}.$$

5. Convert $\bar{X}'$ to the true mean $\bar{x}$:

$$\bar{x} = \text{arbitrary origin} + (\text{fictitious mean}) \times (\text{class width}).$$

That is,

$$\bar{x} = x_0 + \frac{\sum f_i X_i'}{\sum f_i} \times w = x_0 + \bar{X}'w. \tag{3.3}$$

As an example, the short method of computing the mean will be used for the data of Table 2.1. The class width, as in Table 2.3, is $w = 1.00$ and the origin is taken at $x_0 = 2.00$ MPa. From Table 3.2 the fictitious mean (in terms of class width) is

$$\bar{X}' = \frac{\sum f_i X_i'}{\sum f_i} = \frac{1329}{270} = 4.92.$$

Using Eq. (3.3), we find that the true mean is

$$\bar{x} = 2.00 + 4.92 \times 1.00$$
$$= 6.922 \text{ MPa}.$$

Giving the correct number of significant figures, we report the value as 6.92 MPa.

TABLE 3.2 CALCULATION OF THE MEAN FOR DATA OF TABLE 2.3 USING THE CLASS-INTERVAL METHOD

Class midpoint	Class frequency, f_i	Deviation from origin in terms of class width, X_i'	$f_i X_i'$	$f_i X_i'^2$
2.00	1	0	0	0
3.00	1	1	1	1
4.00	4	2	8	16
5.00	24	3	72	216
6.00	81	4	324	1296
7.00	78	5	390	1950
8.00	51	6	306	1836
9.00	18	7	126	882
10.00	9	8	72	576
11.00	2	9	18	162
12.00	0	10	0	0
13.00	0	11	0	0
14.00	1	12	12	144
Totals	$\sum f_i = 270$		$\sum f_i X_i' = 1329$	$\sum f_i X_i'^2 = 7079$

The exact mean of the measurements in Table 2.1 is 6.89 MPa. For many purposes the difference between the two is not significant.

The value that we have found is the mean of the values comprising our sample of bricks, but if we took another sample from the same source, it would, in all likelihood, have a different mean. Thus, so far as the population of all bricks manufactured by the given plant is concerned, the mean as determined from samples is a variable quantity, but much less variable than the strength of the individual bricks. This applies, of course, to measurements in all problems of this type. In general terms, we can state that statistics derived from a random sample are also random variables.

As we saw earlier, the arithmetic mean is the average that is most commonly used, but it is not the only one of importance; we shall now consider the other averages.

MEDIAN

The median of a set of observations is the middle observation when the observations are ranked or arranged in order of magnitude. The term *middle observation* refers to the count from the extremes in rank order and not to the numerical value. More precisely, if the number of observations is odd, say $2m + 1$, the median is the $(m + 1)$th value; if the number of observations is even, say $2m$, the "middle" values of the set are the mth and $(m + 1)$th, and their arithmetic mean is taken as the median. For example, the numbers 21, 22, 31, 34, 31, 22, 17, and 26 when arranged in ascending order of magnitude are 17, 21, 22, 22, 26, 31, 31, and 34, with 22 and 26 being the two "middle" values. The median in this case is $(22 + 26)/2 = 24$. If, however, the last value 34 were not present, the median would be 22.

Since the area of a histogram is proportional to the number of observations, it follows from the above definition that the median divides a histogram into two equal areas.

As an example, let us calculate the median for the data of Table 2.3; the class width is $w = 1$ MPa and the number of observations is $n = 270$. Now, one-half of the area of the histogram $= wn/2 = 135w$. Referring to Table 2.3, we can say therefore that the median will fall in the interval containing the cumulative frequency 135. The position of the median within this interval is some distance, say x, to the right of the class interval below, that is, to the right of the class interval 5.5–6.5 MPa. The latter has a cumulative frequency of 111, and the frequency of the interval within which the median is located is 78. We write

$$111 \times w + 78 \times x = 135w.$$

Hence,

$$x = \tfrac{24}{78}w = 0.307 \times 1 = 0.307 \text{ MPa}$$

to the right of 6.5 MPa. Therefore,

$$\text{median} = 6.5 + 0.31 = 6.81 \text{ MPa}.$$

Because the median is a positional value (in contrast to the arithmetic character of the mean), it is less affected by extreme values within the group than the mean. This property of the median makes it in some cases a useful measure of central tendency. For example, the median of 2, 3, 6, 8, 9, 9, 12 is 8. If the extreme values change so that the set is now 3, 3, 6, 8, 9, 9, 18, the median is still 8 but the mean has increased from 7 to 8.

We can now find the median value for the data on the solids content of water, given previously. Arranging the results in ascending order, we have 4490, 4500, 4500, 4520, 4520, 4520, 4520, 4540, 4570, 4570, 4590, and the median value is 4520 ppm.

MODE

Mode is the value of the observation that occurs most frequently if the variable is discrete or the class interval (often quoted as a class midpoint) that has the highest frequency if the variable is continuous. The mode thus represents a peak value in a frequency distribution. Like the median, the mode is less affected by extreme values than the mean.

In the example concerning the solids content of water, the value of 4520 has the highest frequency, namely 4, and is, therefore, the modal value. We have thus a mode and a median of 4520, and a mean of 4531 ppm. The mode for the data on the transverse strength of 270 bricks is, from Table 3.2, equal to 6.00 MPa, since this is the midpoint of the class interval that has the highest frequency of 81.

Some distributions have more than one mode, but in experimental work this is rare, although bimodal distribution is encountered in microscope counts and particle-size gradings. In many other cases, the appearance of a bimodal distribution means that the data contain values from two different distributions. For example, if two machines manufacturing an item are set at different averages sufficiently far apart and all the items are pooled, the resulting frequency distribution will be bimodal. If the distribution is multimodal, knowing the modes tells us little about the central tendency of the distribution of the data.

SKEWNESS

We can now view the three measures of central tendency, mean, median, and mode, on a general frequency distribution curve, shown in Fig. 3.1. The mode is the value corresponding to the highest point on the curve; the median divides the area under the curve into two halves; and the mean passes through the centroid of the area. (The latter arises from the fact that the sum of deviations of all observations from the mean is zero.) The median usually lies between, or coincides with, the mean and the mode.

When the three averages do not coincide, the frequency distribution curve is said to be *skew* or *skewed*. It is skewed to the right when the median is to the right of the mode, that is, when the tail to the right (the direction of increasing

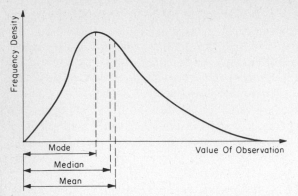

Figure 3.1   Mean, median, and mode in a distribution skewed to the right.

values) is longer than the tail to the left. Such a curve is also said to be *positively skewed*.

As an example, let us determine the direction of skewness of the data on the transverse strength of 270 bricks, given in Table 2.1. For the grouped data, it was found that the mean = 6.92 MPa; median = 6.81 MPa; and mode = 6.00 MPa. Since the median is to the right of the mode, the frequency distribution of the data on the 270 bricks is said to be skewed to the right.

There is no accepted method of measuring skewness. To compare the skewness of different distributions the ratio

$$\frac{\text{mean} - \text{mode}}{\text{standard deviation}}$$

may be used. The term in the denominator, standard deviation (considered in Chapter 4) makes a comparison of distributions with different widths of scatter possible.

For moderately skewed distributions there is an approximate relation between the various averages:

$$\text{mean} - \text{mode} = 3(\text{mean} - \text{median}). \tag{3.4}$$

It is interesting to note that in skew distributions that are sharply peaked, the median is often a particularly useful measure of central tendency. For example, if we are interested in the distribution of periods of time at which atoms of a radioactive element have disintegrated, the median represents the time at which half the atoms have disintegrated, and is a common measure of radioactivity.

Skewness arises usually from natural causes and is characteristic of many distributions, such as those dealt with in Chapters 8 and 9, and also of some continuous distributions. For example, the frequency of the occurrence of a very large defect in a material (e.g., a blowhole) is smaller than that of a very small defect. Thus the frequency curve for defects of various sizes is skewed to the left. However, skewness can also be caused by selection. For instance, in testing concrete specimens the very poorly made ones may well be discarded prior to testing, with the result that a frequency curve for the strength of the concrete specimens would be skewed to the right. This behavior has, in fact, been observed in some tests.

A great many observations are, of course, distributed symmetrically, that is, the departure of observations from the mean by any given amount occurs with a sensibly equal frequency in the up and down directions. Such a distribution is simply said to be *symmetrical*, and the mean, mode, and median all coincide.

USE OF MEAN, MEDIAN, AND MODE

We have mentioned earlier that the arithmetic mean is usually the most important and reliable measure of the central tendency of data. The reason for this is that the arithmetic mean uses the information about every item in the data and not only differences among the individual values of the data. However, in cases when the distribution is markedly skewed the mean may not be a very appropriate measure. This would be the case, for instance, if we wanted to describe the central tendency of family income in a country where great disparities exist between the incomes of a large part and of a small part of the population. Evidently, in such a case we need to use the median as a measure of central tendency since it is unaffected by the relatively few extreme values in the tails of the distribution; the same applies to the mode. Let us give an example.

Tests have shown that the life of vacuum tubes under normal operating conditions is not symmetrical. As a result, the mean life is not located in the cluster of the distribution since it is influenced by the few tubes that last particularly long before failure. On the other hand, the median lies in the cluster of the distribution as it is not influenced by extreme values as is the case with the mean.

As already mentioned, the mean uses more of the raw data, taking account of the differences among all values in the data, rather than merely considering their relative frequencies (as does the mode) or their rank order (as does the median).

The median is easier to calculate than the mean, but the latter has the advantage, as will be shown on page 111, in that the sample mean is always an unbiased estimate of the population mean.

QUANTILES

In a manner similar to that of the median, which divides a set of observations so that 50 percent of them fall above and 50 percent below the median, we can introduce other points, which divide the observations into a number of equal parts, known as *quantiles*. An example of commonly used quantiles are *quartiles*, which divide the set into four equal parts; for example, the upper quartile is the value above which 25 percent of the set falls. The *interquartile range* contains the middle 50 percent of the set, with 25 percent falling above and 25 percent below the range, and is sometimes used as a measure of dispersion. A *decile* divides the set of observations into 10 groups, the lowest decile, for example, being a value below which 10 percent of the set falls. Other quantiles are described as *percentiles*, for example, a 5th percentile.

GEOMETRIC MEAN

There is another type of average that is of interest in engineering calculations. This is the *geometric mean*, defined as the nth root of the product of n observations. Thus the geometric mean $\bar{x}_g$, of n observations $x_1, x_2, \ldots, x_n$ is

$$\bar{x}_g = \sqrt[n]{x_1 \times x_2 \times \cdots \times x_n}. \tag{3.5}$$

This average is used when dealing with observations each of which bears an approximately constant ratio to the preceding one, for example, in averaging rates of growth (increase or decrease), as illustrated in the following example.

EXAMPLE

The number of degrees *cum laude* awarded at a university during six consecutive years is given in Table 3.3. What is the average percentage increase in the number of such degrees per annum?

To find the answer, we calculate the geometric mean of the ratios given in the last column. This is

$$\sqrt[5]{1.2 \times 1.5 \times 1.67 \times 2.0 \times 1.67} = 1.585$$

that is an average increase per year of 58.5 percent.

It might be asked why an arithmetic mean cannot be used. This is $\frac{1}{5}(1.2 + 1.5 + 1.67 + 2.0 + 1.67) = 1.61$ or an increase of 61 percent, which is higher than that given by the geometric mean; the arithmetic mean is always higher than the geometric mean. The bias in the answer given by the arithmetic mean arises from the influence of the absolute magnitude of the ratios. For example, doubling a value represents a ratio of 2, while halving means a ratio of $\frac{1}{2}$. Thus if we consider a value of 100 which falls to 50 and subsequently rises to 100, the ratios are $\frac{1}{2}$ and 2, respectively. The geometric mean is $\sqrt{\frac{1}{2} \times 2} = 1$, and this is the average rate of increase. This answer is intuitively correct as the overall change is zero. However,

TABLE 3.3

Year	Number of degrees	Ratio to previous year's value
1959	5	—
1960	6	1.20
1961	9	1.50
1962	15	1.67
1963	30	2.00
1964	50	1.67

the arithmetic mean of the ratios is $\frac{1}{2}(\frac{1}{2} + 2) = 1.25$. If the ratios were 3 and $\frac{1}{3}$, the geometric mean would still be 1 but the arithmetic mean would be $1\frac{2}{3}$. ■ ■

The use of the geometric mean can be avoided by transforming the original variable x into $\log x$: the antilog of the arithmetic mean of the new variable will then give the right answer, since from Eq. (3.5),

$$\log \bar{x}_g = \frac{\sum(\log x_i)}{n}.$$

HARMONIC MEAN

The harmonic mean, also of interest in engineering, $\bar{x}_h$ of a set of n observations $x_1, x_2, x_3, \ldots, x_n$ is the reciprocal of the arithmetic mean of the reciprocals of the numbers. Thus

$$\frac{1}{\bar{x}_h} = \frac{\sum\limits_{i=1}^{n} \frac{1}{x_i}}{n} = \frac{1}{n} \sum_{i=1}^{n} \frac{1}{x_i}. \tag{3.6}$$

For grouped data, where $x_1, x_2, x_3, \ldots$ represent the class midpoints with class frequencies $f_1, f_2, f_3, \ldots$, respectively, the harmonic mean is given by

$$\bar{x}_h = \frac{1}{n}\left(\frac{f_1}{x_1} + \frac{f_2}{x_2} + \cdots\right) = \frac{1}{n} \sum_{k=1}^{k} \frac{f_k}{x_k}$$

where $n = f_1 + f_2 + \cdots = \sum\limits_{k=1}^{k} f_k$, k being the number of class intervals.

For a set of positive numbers $x_1, x_2, \ldots$, the geometric mean is less than or equal to the arithmetic mean but is greater than or equal to the harmonic mean. We can write thus

$$\bar{x}_h \leqslant \bar{x}_g \leqslant \bar{x}. \tag{3.7}$$

SOLVED PROBLEMS

3-1. Three hundred and three tensile pieces of a certain new brittle lacquer (used for experimental stress analysis) gave the tensile strengths in Table 3.4 at the age of 7 days.
   a. Complete the frequency table.
   b. Draw the histogram and frequency polygon.
   c. Draw the cumulative frequency diagram.
   d. Calculate the mean tensile strength and indicate this on the histogram.

   Solution
   a. In view of the form in which the data are presented, we shall adopt a class width of 30 kN/m^2, with the first class midpoint at 215 kN/m^2 (see Table 3.5).
   b. The histogram and frequency polygon are shown in Fig. 3.2.

TABLE 3.4

Strength interval (kN/m²)	200–230	230–260	260–290	290–320	320–350	350–380	380–410	410–440	440–470	470–500
Number of test pieces	7	30	50	77	53	40	35	6	3	2

TABLE 3.5

Class interval	Class midpoint	Class frequency, f_i	Cumulative frequency, F	Deviation from origin in terms of class width, X_i'	f_iX_i'	$f_iX_i'^2$
200–230	215	7	7	0	0	0
230–260	245	30	37	1	30	30
260–290	275	50	87	2	100	200
290–320	305	77	164	3	231	693
320–350	335	53	217	4	212	848
350–380	365	40	257	5	200	1000
380–410	395	35	292	6	210	1260
410–440	425	6	298	7	42	294
440–470	455	3	301	8	24	192
470–500	485	2	303	9	18	162
Totals					$\sum f_iX_i' = 1067$	$\sum f_iX_i'^2 = 4679$

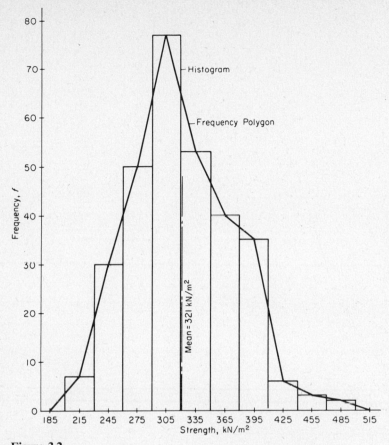

Figure 3.2

 c. The cumulative frequency diagram is shown in Fig. 3.3.
 d. From the table in (a),

$$\text{mean from first class midpoint in terms of class width} = \tfrac{1067}{303} = 3.52$$

$$\therefore \text{mean} = 215 + 3.52 \times 30 = 321 \text{ kN/m}^2.$$

The mean tensile strength of the brittle lacquer test pieces is marked in Fig. 3.2.

 3-2. Midblock passenger-car spot speeds under urban conditions were found to be as listed in Table 3.6.
 a. Complete the frequency table.
 b. Draw the cumulative frequency diagram.
 c. Find the mode, median, and the mean speed.
 d. If the 85th and 98th percentiles are employed in speed regulation and design, respectively, calculate the speed limit and the design speed for the locality.

Solution
 a. Take the origin at the first class midpoint, that is, at 12 km/h. With a class width $w = 8$ km/h, we tabulate the data in Table 3.7.

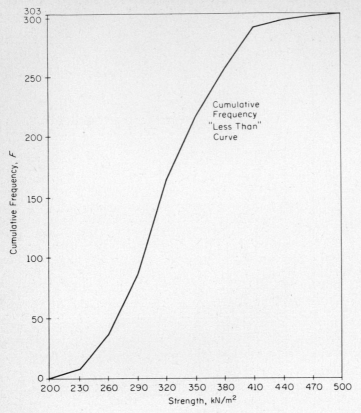

Figure 3.3

b. The cumulative frequency diagram is shown in Fig. 3.4.

c. By inspection of Table 3.7, the mode = 44 km/h. The median divides the histogram into two equal areas.

Now, one-half the area of the histogram

$$= \frac{w \times 541}{2} = 270.5 \times w.$$

The median will fall to the right of the class interval with the highest cumulative frequency below 270.5, that is to the right of the 32 to 40 km/h class interval. Hence,

$$181 \times w + 178 \times x = \frac{541 \times w}{2}$$

or

$$x = \frac{89.5}{178} \times w = \frac{89.5}{178} \times 8$$

that is,

$$x = 4.02 \text{ km/h to the right of 40 km/h.}$$

TABLE 3.6

Speed interval (km/h)	8–16	16–24	24–32	32–40	40–48	48–56	56–64	64–72	72–80	80–88	88–96
Number of vehicles	0	1	34	146	178	130	31	16	3	2	0

Source: Data from T. M. Matson, W. S. Smith, and F. W. Hurd, *Traffic Engineering* (New York: McGraw-Hill Book Company, 1941), p. 50. The original data were in mph units.

TABLE 3.7

Class interval	Class midpoint	Class frequency, f_i	Cumulative frequency, F	Deviation from origin in terms of class width, X_i	$f_i X_i$	$f_i X_i^2$
8–16	12	0	0	0	0	0
16–24	20	1	1	1	1	1
24–32	28	34	35	2	68	136
32–40	36	146	181	3	438	1314
40–48	44	178	359	4	712	2848
48–56	52	130	489	5	650	3250
56–64	60	31	520	6	186	1116
64–72	68	16	536	7	112	784
72–80	76	3	539	8	24	192
80–88	84	2	541	9	18	162
88–96	92	0	541	10	0	0
Totals		$\sum f_i = 541$			$\sum f_i X_i = 2209$	$\sum f_i X_i^2 = 9803$

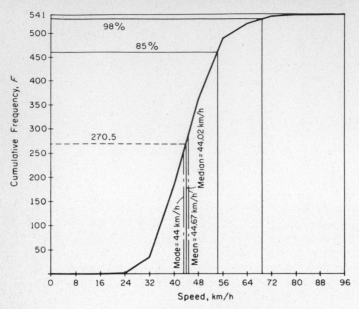

Figure 3.4

Therefore,

$$\text{median} = 40 + 4.02 = 44.02 \text{ km/h}$$
$$\text{mean} = 12 + \tfrac{2209}{541} \times 8 = 44.67 \text{ km/h}.$$

d. 98 percent of 541 cars = 530 cars, and 85 percent of 541 cars = 460 cars.

From the cumulative frequency diagram the speed not exceeded by 530 cars is 67 to 69 km/h; that is, the design speed is, say, 68 km/h. For 460 cars the corresponding speed is 54 km/h, that is, the speed limit for the locality is 54 km/h.

3-3. Bacteria are known to exhibit exponential growth. In a laboratory experiment, the number of bacteria (coded) at the end of four consecutive equal periods of time was estimated to be

$$250 \quad 480 \quad 850 \quad 1650.$$

Calculate the average number of bacteria over the whole period of time considered.

Solution. Since the results are exponential, we use the geometric mean to calculate the average. Thus, from Eq. (3.5),

$$\bar{x}_g = \sqrt{250 \times 480 \times 850 \times 1650}$$
$$= 640.$$

[NB. Using Eq. (3.1) for the arithmetic mean, $\bar{x} = 807$, which is an overestimate.]

PROBLEMS

3-1. The following was the number of vehicles passing a certain point on different days:

$$1310 \quad 1207 \quad 760 \quad 983 \quad 260 \quad 618 \quad 1262 \quad 1152 \quad 598 \quad 1218 \quad 1391.$$

Determine the mean, median, and mode for the above values.

TABLE 3.8

0.529	0.538	0.532	0.529	0.535
0.536	0.534	0.542	0.537	0.530
0.538	0.536	0.536	0.536	0.526
0.525	0.524	0.543	0.530	0.539
0.542	0.528	0.546	0.532	0.534
0.535	0.539	0.527	0.544	0.527
0.535	0.534	0.540	0.540	0.536
0.532	0.535	0.535	0.535	0.528
0.541	0.531	0.540	0.532	0.535
0.533	0.535	0.537	0.537	0.545

3-2. The diameters in centimeters of a sample of 50 ball bearings manufactured by one company are as shown in Table 3.8.

   a. Prepare a frequency table. (HINT: Take a class width of 0.002 cm, with the first class interval as 0.524 to 0.526.)

   b. Draw a histogram, a frequency polygon, and a cumulative frequency diagram.

   c. Calculate the mean diameter from the grouped data in the frequency table and indicate the mean on the histogram.

3-3. Calculate the mean of data for the annual precipitation given in Problem 2-1 from

   a. the ungrouped data;

   b. the frequency table.

Calculate and then comment on the percentage error between the values of the mean found from (a) and (b) above.

3-4. The number of students entering engineering increased in 5 years from 3000 to 4880. Calculate the average annual rate of increase.

3-5. For the data of Problem 2-3 find the mean, mode, and median. Also find the mean using a grouped frequency table.

3-6. The distribution for times between failures of electronic components is shown in Table 3.9.

   a. Draw a histogram, a frequency polygon, and a cumulative frequency diagram.

   b. Calculate the mean, median, and mode of failure time.

3-7. Find the mean, mode, and median for the number of defective bolts in Problem 2-4.

TABLE 3.9

Time (h)	0–100	100–200	200–300	300–400	400–500	500–600	600–700	700–800	800–900	900–1000	1000–1100	1100–1200	1200–1300
Number of failures	280	200	170	100	75	45	10	8	6	4	4	2	1

Chapter 4

Characteristics of Distributions: Dispersion

In the preceding chapter we considered the central tendency of sets of observations and the calculation of averages. The average is a single value that typifies the whole group but does not generally give adequate information about the distribution of observations within the group. To choose a simple example, the mean of 99.9 cm, 100.0 cm, and 100.1 cm is 100.0 cm while the mean of 99.0 cm, 100.0 cm, and 101.0 cm is also 100.0 cm, but it is clear that the two sets of observations (each set being assumed to constitute a population) differ appreciably in the scatter of the values about their mean. This scatter is of considerable importance. Let us assume, for example, that tests show the mean strength of a structural material to be 30 MPa, but it is only the knowledge of scatter of the results that will tell us the proportion of specimens whose strength is, say, below 20 MPa, the latter value being critical for safety.

There are several measures of scatter or dispersion, which will now be considered.

VARIANCE

If our set of values (a *finite population*) consists of n observations x_i, whose mean is μ, we can write for each observation the *deviation* $(x_i - \mu)$, known also as the *residual*. The mean square deviation is known as variance, which is given by

$$\sigma^2 = \frac{\sum_{i=1}^{n} (x_i - \mu)^2}{n}. \tag{4.1}$$

By writing $\sum_{i=1}^{n=1} (x_i - \mu)^2$ as $\sum_{i=1}^{n} (x_i)^2 - n\mu^2$, Eq. (4.1) can also be written as

$$\sigma^2 = \frac{1}{n} \sum_{i=1}^{n} (x_i)^2 - \mu^2. \tag{4.1a}$$

For reasons to be discussed in the next section, it is important to remember that the deviations must be calculated from the true mean of the set of values.

   If, on the other hand, we have a *sample* of n observations x_i, with a sample mean $\bar{x}$, and we are interested in the variance of the actual sample *only,* we can still use Eq. (4.1) provided we substitute $\bar{x}$ for μ. Thus, in this case

$$\text{variance of sample} = \frac{\sum_{i=1}^{n} (x_i - \bar{x})^2}{n} \tag{4.2}$$

where $\bar{x} = \text{mean of } n \text{ observations} = \dfrac{\sum_{i=1}^{n} x_i}{n}.$

We can note that the variance of a sample is rarely of interest.

   Equation (4.1) is applicable when we are interested in the mean of a set of n items (specimens or observations), all of which have been determined; μ is then the true mean. In many cases, however, we actually test only a limited number of specimens out of a *population* (or a *universe*, the two terms being synonymous) of all those that could be tested. The same applies to taking a limited number of observations (e.g., temperature at intervals of time) when we are really interested in all the observations that could be made (in this case, an infinite number of determinations of temperature during the given time interval). Under such circumstances, the true or population mean μ is unknown, and we have only the mean of the actual observations $\bar{x}$, that is the sample mean. We calculate the deviations from $\bar{x}$ and not from μ, and in consequence put $(n - 1)$ instead of n in the denominator of the expression for the estimate of σ^2; the estimate is denoted by s^2 to distinguish it from the true variance σ^2. The reason for this correction of $n/(n - 1)$, known as *Bessel's correction*, is that the sum of squares of deviations has a minimum value when taken about the sample mean $\bar{x}$, and is therefore smaller than it would be if taken about the population mean (which is presumably different from $\bar{x}$). Thus, the estimate of σ^2 is

$$s^2 = \frac{\sum_{i=1}^{n} (x_i - \bar{x})^2}{n - 1}. \tag{4.3}$$

Appendix A gives a proof of the above equation. Bessel's correction can, of course, be neglected when n is large.

   It is important to appreciate the difference between Eq. (4.1) and Eq. (4.3), and to use the correct one, depending on whether we are interested in the variance of the observations in hand (considered as a finite population) or in an estimate of the variance of the population.

From Eq. (4.3), we can see that if only one observation is made, nothing can be said about its precision. Assume that the observation is x_1. Then the best estimate of the population mean is given by $\bar{x} = x_1$. Hence,

$$s^2 = \frac{(\bar{x} - x_1)^2}{n - 1} = \frac{0}{0}$$

and the estimate of the population variance is, therefore, indeterminate.

STANDARD DEVIATION

While variance is a fundamental measure of dispersion, it is not a convenient practical measure as its units are the square of the units of the variate.[1] Furthermore, many numerical characteristics of distributions are expressed directly in terms of the square root of variance. It is, therefore, preferable to give this square root the name standard deviation σ. Standard deviation is thus the root-mean-square (rms) deviation and is always positive. Its units are the same as those of the variate. The standard deviation of the population is thus

$$\sigma = \sqrt{\frac{\sum_{i=1}^{n}(x_i - \mu)^2}{n}}. \tag{4.4}$$

Similarly, the standard deviation of a sample is, from Eq. (4.2),

$$\text{standard deviation of sample} = \sqrt{\frac{\sum_{i=1}^{n}(x_i - \bar{x})^2}{n}}. \tag{4.5}$$

For the simple case of the groups of observations given at the beginning of this chapter (each group being a finite population), the values of the standard deviation in the two cases are [from Eq. (4.4)], respectively,

$$\sigma_1 = \sqrt{\frac{(0.1)^2 + (0.1)^2}{3}} = \sqrt{0.0067} = 0.08 \text{ cm}$$

and

$$\sigma_2 = \sqrt{\frac{1^2 + 1^2}{3}} = \sqrt{\frac{2}{3}} = 0.8 \text{ cm}.$$

Similarly to the case of variance, if μ is not known, an unbiased estimate of the standard deviation of the population σ, denoted by s, is derived from Eq. (4.3) as

$$s = \sqrt{\frac{\sum_{i=1}^{n}(x_i - \bar{x})^2}{n - 1}}. \tag{4.6}$$

---

[1] The quantity that varies and is being studied.

The calculation of the standard deviation by Eqs. (4.4) and (4.6) is laborious, especially when the mean involves more significant places than the variate and thus introduces fractional values.

For a sample of n observations from a population whose mean μ is unknown, it is more convenient to use another form of Eq. (4.6), namely,

$$s = \sqrt{\frac{\sum x_i^2 - n\bar{x}^2}{n-1}} = \sqrt{\frac{\sum x_i^2 - (\sum x_i)^2/n}{n-1}}. \qquad (4.7)$$

It may be noted that we have now omitted the symbols indicating that the summation proceeds from $i = 1$ to $i = n$, as such a notation is cumbersome. We must remember, however, that these are the limits of our summation unless otherwise indicated. Equation (4.7) arises from the algebraic identity (which we now apply to a sample with a mean $\bar{x}$):

$$\sum(x_i - \bar{x})^2 = \sum x_i^2 - 2\bar{x}\sum x_i + n\bar{x}^2.$$

But
$$\bar{x} = \frac{\sum x_i}{n} \quad \text{(by definition)}.$$

Therefore,
$$2\bar{x}\sum x_i = 2\bar{x}n\bar{x} = 2n\bar{x}^2.$$

Hence,
$$\sum(x_i - \bar{x})^2 = \sum x_i^2 - n\bar{x}^2$$

or
$$\sum(x_i - \bar{x})^2 = \sum x_i^2 - \frac{(\sum x_i)^2}{n}.$$

The advantage of Eq. (4.7) is that we do not need to find the deviations $(x_i - \bar{x})$. The squares of the variate x_i^2 can be obtained rapidly from tables or by means of a calculator. The fundamental difference between $\sum x_i^2$ and $(\sum x_i)^2$ must not be overlooked.

DEGREES OF FREEDOM

At this stage it may be convenient to introduce the concept of the number of degrees of freedom, which plays an important role in statistical methods, and its meaning must, therefore, be understood. A degree of freedom is defined as a comparison between the data, *independent* of the other comparisons in the analysis. For example, if we are comparing each observation x_i (in a random sample of size n) with the sample mean $\bar{x}$ by calculating the residuals $(x_i - \bar{x})$, then the number of degrees of freedom is the number of *independent* residuals, viz. $(n - 1)$. The value of 1 has to be subtracted from n because there exists one constraint between all the values of x_i and $\bar{x}$, as given by Eq. (3.1).

In the case where an estimate s^2 [see Eq. (4.3)] is made of the population variance σ^2, the true population mean μ is not known. Thus, when the observations are compared with the sample mean $\bar{x}$, there is a constraint on the values of $(x_i - \bar{x})$ imposed by the fact that the sum of the deviations about the sample mean $\bar{x}$ is zero, that is,

$$\sum_{i=1}^{n} (x_i - \bar{x}) = 0. \qquad [3.1]$$

Hence, one degree of freedom is lost, leaving $(n - 1)$ comparisons or degrees of freedom. Therefore, to obtain an estimate of the variance, that is, the mean square of deviations, we divide the sum of the squares of deviations by the number of comparisons, that is, degrees of freedom $(n - 1)$:

$$s^2 = \frac{\sum(x_i - \bar{x})^2}{n - 1}.$$

We can see then that the term degrees of freedom represents a measure of the number of observations in the sample that can be used to estimate the variance of the parent population.

In the case when the true mean μ is known and we want to compare it to n observations of a sample, each of the n observations can be compared independently with μ: hence, when we calculate the mean square deviation, σ^2, we divide the term $\sum(x_i - \mu)^2$ by n, the degrees of freedom in this case [see Eq. (4.1)].

The concept of degrees of freedom can also be illustrated by referring to a point that can move freely in three-dimensional space. The point can be located in space by three variable coordinates x, y, and z. If we constrain the point to move in a plane, such as $ax + by + cz = d$, it can move in two dimensions and has 2 degrees of freedom. Alternatively, those 2 degrees of freedom can be deduced as the number of independent variables (x, y, and z, i.e., 3) minus the number of constraints (1 for the equation $ax + by + cz = d$). In general, the degrees of freedom are the number of independent variables minus the number of constraints. If we were dealing with, say, n independent variables related by m equations (restrictions), then the number of degrees of freedom would be $(n - m)$.

The analogy between this geometric concept and the degrees of freedom in statistical language is quite clear. For example, for a sample of size n from a population whose mean μ is unknown, the term $\sum_{i=1}^{n} (x_i - \bar{x})^2$ will have $(n - 1)$ degrees of freedom. This is obtained from the number of variables n minus the one constraint imposed, viz.

$$\sum_{i=1}^{n} (x_i - \bar{x}) = 0. \qquad [3.1]$$

In other words, when we use the sample to determine $\bar{x}$ as representing the population mean μ, we force a certain degree of agreement among the variables, for example, the quantity

$$\sum_{i=1}^{n} (x_i - \bar{x})^2.$$

However, if μ is known, then the degrees of freedom will be simply n, since there is no longer a constraint.

In Chapter 1, we mentioned that a statistic derived from the sample is used to estimate the corresponding population parameter; such an estimate tends to be relatively accurate when it is based on a large number of independent observations (degrees of freedom), in contrast to the situation when the observations tend to be dependent on each other; in the latter case, the chances of an error increase and the estimate will be less accurate. Thus, in general, as the number of degrees of freedom of a sample statistic increases, the estimated population parameter becomes more accurate.

We shall see that the distributions of some statistics depend on the number of degrees of freedom, such as χ^2 (Chapter 14), t (Chapter 15), and F (Chapter 16). The concept of degrees of freedom will be illustrated further in Chapters 13–17, 19, and 23.

SIMPLIFIED COMPUTATION OF STANDARD DEVIATION

Computations can be simplified without any loss in accuracy by a suitable reduction of data (or coding). Two rules are useful:

a. If a constant number is added to or subtracted from a set of numerical values, their mean will increase or decrease by the same constant number, the standard deviation remaining unaffected.
b. If a set of numerical values is multiplied or divided by a constant number, their mean and standard deviation are multiplied or divided by the same constant number.

EXAMPLE
Let us consider the data on the strength of bricks, given in Table 2.2. To compute the standard deviation by Eq. (4.6), we first require the mean; this was quoted previously to be $\bar{x} = 6.89$ MPa. We now compute the deviations $(x_i - \bar{x})$ and find their squares; a tabular form is convenient (Table 4.1). Thus, from Eq. (4.6),

$$s = \sqrt{\frac{518.9963}{269}} = 1.39 \text{ MPa.}$$

Let us now find the solution using Eq. (4.7) (see Table 4.2).

Thus
$$\sum x_i = 1861.30$$
$$\left(\sum x_i\right)^2 = 3{,}464{,}437.69$$

and
$$\sum x_i^2 = 13{,}351.7562.$$

Hence,
$$s = \sqrt{\frac{13{,}351.7562 - (3{,}464{,}437.69/270)}{269}}$$

$$= 1.39 \text{ MPa, \quad as before.}$$

TABLE 4.1

Observation	x_i	$|x_i - \bar{x}|$*	$(x_i - \bar{x})^2$
1	1.86	5.03	25.3009
2	3.17	3.72	13.8384
3	3.93	2.96	8.7616
⋮	⋮	⋮	⋮
269	11.24	4.35	18.9225
270	13.86	6.97	48.5809
$n = 270$			$\sum(x_i - \bar{x})^2 = 518.9963$

* The absolute value of the deviation is entered, since its sign is immaterial.

TABLE 4.2

Observation	x_i	x_i^2
1	1.86	3.4596
2	3.17	10.0489
3	3.93	15.4449
⋮	⋮	⋮
269	11.24	126.3376
270	13.86	192.0996
$n = 270$	$\sum x_i = 1861.30$	$\sum x_i^2 = 13351.7562$

TABLE 4.3

Observation	$X_i' = (x_i \times 100) - 186$	$X_i'^2$
1	0	0
2	131	17 161
3	207	42 849
⋮	⋮	⋮
269	938	879 844
270	1200	1440 000
$n = 270$	$\sum X_i' = 135\,910$	$\sum X_i'^2 = 73\,618\,121$

We can now use the simplifications of rules (a) and (b). Since all values have two decimal places, we can easily multiply them by 100. To reduce the numerical values further, we can subtract 186 from all the values. (It is generally preferable to avoid negative values, such as would result from subtracting, say, 700, but there is nothing incorrect in doing so.) We can tabulate the computation as shown in Table 4.3.

Thus $(\sum X_i')^2 = 18,471,528,100$. Hence, in terms of X',

$$s_{X'} = \sqrt{\frac{73,618,121 - (18,471,528,100/270)}{269}}$$

$$= 139.$$

To allow for the multiplication by 100 we have to divide $s_{x'}$ by 100; hence

$$s = \frac{139}{100}$$

$$= 1.39 \text{ MPa}, \quad \text{as before.}$$

The decision on the amount of simplification is a matter for individual preference, but the advantage of Eq. (4.7) over Eq. (4.6) is great, especially when a calculator is used. ■ ■

With data in a grouped-frequency form, a shorter, though approximate, computation of the estimate of the standard deviation of the population can be made. We assume that each observation is replaced by an observation at the class midpoint so that

$$s = \sqrt{\frac{\sum f_i(x_i' - \bar{x})^2}{n - 1}} \tag{4.8}$$

where f_i = the frequency in the class interval, and

x_i' = the class midpoint.

Following Eq. (4.7), the expression becomes

$$s = \sqrt{\frac{\sum f_i x_i'^2 - \left[\dfrac{(\sum f_i x_i')^2}{n}\right]}{n - 1}}. \tag{4.9}$$

We can further replace x_i' by X_i' = deviation from an arbitrary origin, measured in terms of class width w. Then

$$s = w \sqrt{\frac{\sum f_i X_i'^2 - \left[\dfrac{(\sum f_i X_i')^2}{n}\right]}{n - 1}}. \tag{4.10}$$

As an example, let us apply this method of calculation of the standard deviation to the data of Table 3.2. Then

$$s = w \sqrt{\frac{7079 - \left[\dfrac{(1329)^2}{270}\right]}{269}} = 1.41w.$$

Since the class width w is 1.00,

$$s = 1.41 \times 1.00 = 1.41 \text{ MPa.}$$

The difference between this value and the accurate value of σ from Eq. (4.7) is small and for most purposes not significant.

MEAN DEVIATION

In some cases, instead of standard deviation, mean (absolute) deviation d_m is used; this is the mean of the absolute values of deviations:

$$d_m = \frac{\sum |x_i - \bar{x}|}{n}. \tag{4.11}$$

The use of absolute values is necessary because the algebraic sum of deviations from the mean is, by definition of the mean, always equal to zero.

The usefulness of the mean deviation in statistical calculations is small, and practically no statistical methods of analysis involve its use. However, in the case of normal distribution there is a simple relation between the mean deviation and standard deviation; this is discussed in Chapter 11.

COEFFICIENT OF VARIATION

As mentioned before, the standard deviation is expressed in the same units as the original variate x_i, but for many purposes it is convenient to express the dispersion of results on a percentage basis, that is, in relative rather than absolute terms. To achieve this, we take the ratio of the standard deviation, σ, to the mean, μ, and define the coefficient of variation of the population, V, as

$$V = \frac{\sigma}{\mu} \times 100. \tag{4.12}$$

It is a dimensionless quantity.

An estimate for the coefficient of variation of the population, whose μ and σ are unknown, but are estimated from a sample, is given by

$$V = \frac{s}{\bar{x}} \times 100. \tag{4.13}$$

For the observations on the strength of bricks used in the preceding example, the estimate of the coefficient of variation is

$$V = \frac{1.39}{6.89} \times 100 = 20.17 \text{ percent.}$$

While the coefficient of variation is extremely useful in giving a value that is independent of the units employed, it may sometimes be meaningless. This is the case when the origin of measurement is not uniquely fixed; for example, if we measure temperature and find the mean to be 10°C and the standard deviation 1°C, we could report the coefficient of variation as $\frac{1}{10} \times 100 = 10$ percent. If however, the measurements were converted to degrees Fahrenheit, we would have a mean of 50°F and a standard deviation of 1.8°F. One could thus report a coefficient of variation of

$$\frac{1.8}{50} \times 100 = 3.6 \text{ percent.}$$

The absurdity of these calculations is obvious, and we would have done well to have reported our results in terms of standard deviation.

RANGE

Range is a simple measure of dispersion, very rapid to compute as it is merely the difference between the highest and the lowest observations. However, because of this dependence on two values only, range is a rather crude measure of dispersion, and is an efficient statistic[2] when we deal with small samples only.

It is important to note that the larger the number of observations in a sample the more likely it is that values remote from the mean will be encountered. Thus, range increases with the sample size. If this is not remembered and the ranges of samples of different sizes are compared indiscriminately, misleading results are obtained.

The range and the standard deviation are related to one another so that for any given number of observations n, an estimate of the standard deviation s of the underlying population can be obtained from the mean value of sample range $\bar{R}$:

$$s = \bar{R} \times d. \tag{4.14}$$

This expression is valid when the variate is normally distributed,[3] and the estimate s becomes less accurate the more the distribution departs from normality.

The values of d are given in Table A.1. It may be observed that for n between 3 and 12, d varies approximately as $1/\sqrt{n}$.

We must remember that the estimate of the standard deviation given by Eq. (4.14) is no more than an approximation and should be used only when the average range $\bar{R}$ is obtained from a reasonably large number of samples (say, not less than 10) all of the same size. For the same total number of observations the estimate is considerably more accurate when the samples are many and small, rather than few and large.

If a large number of observations has been made without subdivision into samples, a breakdown of the observations into equal subgroups can be achieved by random sampling. The range R of each subgroup is then calculated, and, hence, the mean value of range $\bar{R}$ is found. This is then multiplied by the coefficient d from Table A.1, corresponding to the number of

[2] A value that characterizes the data.
[3] A definition of the normal distribution is given in Chapter 10.

TABLE 4.4

Subgroup	Observations, MPa	Range, R
1	3.90—4.00—4.03—3.74	0.29
2	3.62—4.05—3.93—3.96	0.43
3	4.09—4.19—4.50—3.76	0.74
4	4.02—4.01—3.45—4.05	0.60
5	4.27—4.13—3.96—3.99	0.31
6	4.71—4.32—4.14—4.43	0.57
7	4.07—3.96—4.52—4.08	0.56
8	4.50—4.32—3.99—4.05	0.51
9	4.09—4.12—3.64—4.14	0.50
10	3.96—4.05—4.07—3.90	0.17
11	3.95—3.94—4.05—3.83	0.22
12	4.16—3.92—4.25—3.95	0.33
13	4.36—4.01—4.10—3.98	0.38
Total		$\sum R = 5.61$

Source: K. E. C. Nielsen, "Calculation of Statistical Data," *Beton-Teknik* (Copenhagen), vol. 3, no. 24, 1958, p. 170. The original data were in psi units.

observations in a subgroup, and hence an estimate of the standard deviation is obtained. This procedure is illustrated by the following example.

EXAMPLE

The modulus of rupture was determined on 52 concrete test beams. By random selection, the observations were arranged in 13 subgroups, as shown in Table 4.4.

The value of range for each subgroup is shown in the right-hand column. Hence the mean value of range is

$$\bar{R} = \frac{5.61}{13} = 0.4315.$$

For $n = 4$, Table A.1 gives $d = 0.4857$. Using Eq. (4.14), we estimate the standard deviation to be

$$s = 0.4315 \times 0.4857 = 0.21 \text{ MPa.}$$

A direct calculation of s using Eq. (4.6) gives $s = 0.23$ MPa. The difference may for some purposes not be important, while the saving in computational effort is considerable.

A comparison of experimental results with the theoretical relation between range and standard deviation is shown in Fig. 4.1 for tests on the compressive strength of concrete. (It has been shown that the compressive strength of concrete sensibly follows a normal distribution.[4]) ■ ■

[4] A. M. Neville, "Some Aspects of the Strength of Concrete," *Civil Engineering* (London), vol. 54, Oct.–Dec. 1959.

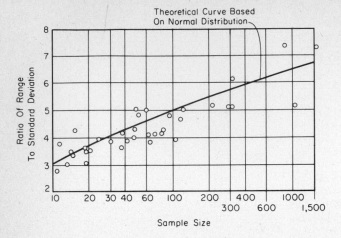

Figure 4.1 Ratio of range to standard deviation for samples of different sizes; tests on concrete compression cubes. (From P. J. F. Wright, "Variations in the Strength of Portland Cement," *Magazine of Concrete Research*, vol. 10, no. 30, Nov. 1958, pp. 123–132.)

SOLVED PROBLEMS

4-1. To obtain the shrinkage limit of a particular clay, the moisture content in percent of dry weight was determined on 20 specimens with the following results:

15.2 16.7 15.8 14.6 18.1 17.2 18.0 15.9 16.1 16.9

14.8 17.6 18.2 16.9 17.3 16.5 15.6 16.7 15.8 18.2.

a. Calculate the mean, $\bar{x}$, and standard deviation, s, by the long method.
b. Calculate the mean and standard deviation using an arbitrary origin.

Solution

a. mean $= \bar{x} = \dfrac{\sum x}{n}$

$$= \frac{15.2 + 16.7 + \cdots + 16.9 + 14.8 + 17.6 + \cdots + 18.2}{20}$$

$$= \frac{332.1}{20}$$

$$= 16.605.$$

The estimate of the standard deviation of the population of clay samples is given by Eq. (4.7):

$$s = \sqrt{\frac{\sum x^2 - \left[\dfrac{(\sum x)^2}{n}\right]}{n-1}}.$$

TABLE 4.5

x_i	Deviation from arbitrary origin, X'_i		X'^2_i
	Negative	Positive	
15.2	0.8		0.64
16.7		0.7	0.49
15.8	0.2		0.04
14.6	1.4		1.96
18.1		2.1	4.41
17.2		1.2	1.44
18.0		2.0	4.00
15.9	0.1		0.01
16.1		0.1	0.01
16.9		0.9	0.81
14.8	1.2		1.44
17.6		1.6	2.56
18.2		2.2	4.84
16.9		0.9	0.81
17.3		1.3	1.69
16.5		0.5	0.25
15.6	0.4		0.16
16.7		0.7	0.49
15.8	0.2		0.04
18.2		2.2	4.84
Totals	$\sum X'_i = -4.3$ +	$16.4 = 12.1$	$\sum X'^2_i = 30.93$

Now

$$\sum x^2 = 15.2^2 + 16.7^2 + \cdots + 18.2^2 = 5538.13$$

and

$$(\sum x)^2 = (332.1)^2 = 110{,}290.41.$$

Hence,

$$s = \sqrt{\frac{5538.13 - \left[\dfrac{110{,}290.41}{20}\right]}{19}}$$

$$= \sqrt{\frac{23.61}{19}}$$

$$= 1.11.$$

b. Let the arbitrary origin = 16. Then, we can write the data as shown in Table 4.5. Therefore,

$$\text{mean} = \bar{x} = 16 + \frac{\sum X'_i}{n}$$

$$= 16 + \frac{12.1}{20}$$

$$= 16.605$$

and $\qquad$ standard deviation $= s = \sqrt{\dfrac{\sum X'^2 - \left[\dfrac{(\sum X')^2}{n}\right]}{n-1}}$

$$= \sqrt{\dfrac{30.93 - \left[\dfrac{(12.1)^2}{20}\right]}{19}}$$

$$= \sqrt{1.243}$$

$$s = 1.11.$$

4-2. Calculate the range, R, and the standard deviation, s, for the data given in Solved Problem 3-1. If the permissible tensile strength allowed in design is equal to the mean less 2.33 times the standard deviation, calculate this allowable strength and indicate whether any of the 303 brittle lacquer test pieces fell below this stength. If this criterion for allowable strength is used, show that, when the estimated coefficient of variation of the population $V = 10$ percent, the maximum allowable design tensile strength $= 0.77 \times$ mean strength.

Solution. Range $= R = 500 - 200 = 300 \text{ kN/m}^2$. For grouped data, and from Eq. (4.10),

$$s = w\sqrt{\dfrac{\sum f_i X_i'^2 - \left[\dfrac{(\sum f_i X_i')^2}{n}\right]}{n-1}}.$$

From the values in Table 3.5, we have

$$s = w\sqrt{\dfrac{4679 - \left[\dfrac{(1067)^2}{303}\right]}{302}} = 1.75 \times \text{class width}$$

$$= 1.75 \times 30 = 52.5 \text{ kN/m}^2.$$

Allowable tensile strength in design $= 321 - 2.33 \times 52.5 = 199 \text{ kN/m}^2$. According to Table 3.5, no brittle lacquer test piece had a tensile strength below 199 kN/m^2.

Now the maximum allowable design tensile strength $= \bar{x} - 2.33s$. But, from Eq. (4.13),

$$V = \dfrac{s}{\bar{x}}.$$

Thus $\qquad\qquad\qquad\qquad\qquad s = V\bar{x}.$

Hence, maximum allowable design tensile strength

$$= \bar{x} - 2.33V\bar{x}$$
$$= (1 - 2.33 \times 0.10)\bar{x}$$
$$= 0.77\bar{x} \text{ (approximately)}, \qquad \text{for} \quad V = 0.10.$$

TABLE 4.6

	1	2	3	4	5	6	7	8
A	49.7	52.2	55.9	57.4	59.5	56.5	55.4	55.2
B	52.0	56.2	56.2	56.8	54.8	55.6	53.5	51.2
C	58.1	52.3	55.4	49.6	51.2	50.6	51.0	50.9
D	53.8	56.6	54.1	55.7	54.2	53.4	50.9	54.6
E	53.0	54.6	55.3	54.3	56.8	50.6	55.7	55.2
F	57.7	55.6	52.7	53.8	53.7	56.4	53.5	52.3
G	52.4	55.2	51.4	49.4	50.5	56.3	52.4	55.2
H	54.9	52.3	53.9	55.4	51.6	57.1	52.4	59.4

PROBLEMS

4-1. The following measurements (in Newtons) were obtained from a test on the tensile strength of rubber samples.

$$1419 \quad 1410 \quad 1410$$
$$1403 \quad 1396 \quad 1389$$
$$1400 \quad 1380 \quad 1422.$$

Calculate the mean, $\bar{x}$, and the estimated standard deviation, s, of the tensile strength of the rubber from which the samples were drawn. What is the range?

4-2. Determine the variance, standard deviation, and coefficient of variation of the distribution in Problem 3-1. Can you estimate the standard deviation from the range in this case? State the reason.

4-3. Determine the range of the data in Problem 3-2. Also find the standard deviation of the diameters of the ball bearings from:
a. the ungrouped data;
b. the frequency table.
What is the coefficient of variation in each case?
By random selection, arrange the data in 10 subgroups, and hence estimate the standard deviation from the mean range. Compare this value with the values obtained in (a) and (b).

4-4. Calculate the estimate of the standard deviation of the population of television components in Problem 2-2. Determine the variance and the coefficient of variation of the tubes.

4-5. In order to determine the hardness of concrete in a shell roof the roof area was divided into 64 equal parts.[5] The average of 10 measurements of hardness (sclerometer readings) in each part is given in Table 4.6 for all 64 parts. The individual values of hardness readings in eight parts were as given in Table 4.7:
a. Find the root-mean-square value of the standard deviation in the eight parts. Hence, estimate the testing error (the rms value divided by the square root of

[5] "Détermination de la Dispersion des Valeurs de la Résistance du Béton en Place au Moyen du Scléromètre," *Bulletin du Ciment*, no. 10 (Switzerland), Oct. 1962.

TABLE 4.7

Point	Individual values of hardness										Mean value	Standard deviation
A1	48	52	50	45	45	44	49	54	55	55	49.7	4.21
B1	56	54	52	51	52	52	52	50	50	51	52.0	1.82
C1	55	61	61	57	56	56	57	60	60	58	58.1	2.23
D1	54	56	57	58	55	54	52	50	50	52	53.8	2.78
E1	52	50	48	57	50	53	59	58	49	54	53.0	3.92
F1	61	59	56	57	57	57	55	58	58	59	57.7	1.70
G1	55	53	56	51	52	53	51	50	55	48	52.4	2.50
H1	52	56	52	58	59	60	54	55	51	52	54.9	3.25

the number of values, namely, eight). (HINT: The individual readings need not be used.)

b. Find the standard deviation of the hardness readings for the entire roof, exclusive of the testing error (the square root of the difference between the variance of the 64 average values and the square of the testing error).

TABLE 4.8

Cube number	Strength, MPa	Cube number	Strength, MPa
1	22.3	26	22.8
2	18.2	27	22.1
3	24.8	28	21.2
4	23.5	29	23.4
5	19.8	30	18.1
6	27.0	31	23.4
7	25.9	32	23.0
8	29.2	33	23.6
9	24.1	34	25.4
10	24.3	35	22.2
11	21.7	36	17.8
12	23.4	37	28.0
13	23.3	38	28.8
14	28.3	39	22.1
15	23.4	40	20.1
16	20.0	41	20.8
17	26.1	42	23.0
18	15.2	43	28.2
19	20.0	44	23.0
20	22.8	45	30.4
21	32.0	46	25.1
22	25.6	47	24.8
23	20.8	48	19.9
24	23.2	49	18.2
25	26.9	50	25.1

Source: Cement and Concrete Association: *Technical Memorandum,* No. 8 (London), April 1960. The original data were in psi units.

TABLE 4.9

Test number	28-day strength, MPa		Test number	28-day strength, MPa	
	Cylinder number 1	Cylinder number 2		Cylinder number 1	Cylinder number 2
1	24.8	22.0	24	23.5	24.1
2	24.5	24.5	25	19.2	21.9
3	23.6	25.3	26	21.3	22.8
4	20.1	22.8	27	22.1	22.8
5	23.0	22.0	28	24.1	22.8
6	25.9	23.4	29	19.9	21.0
7	27.8	27.0	30	26.3	24.1
8	27.6	24.4	31	26.4	26.2
9	25.4	25.2	32	31.6	30.1
10	19.5	21.5	33	24.8	25.5
11	20.3	23.8	34	24.2	22.5
12	21.0	22.1	35	23.1	26.5
13	22.1	20.0	36	20.8	24.0
14	26.3	22.0	37	21.7	20.3
15	27.2	25.7	38	17.3	19.4
16	21.7	20.4	39	23.2	24.8
17	20.2	18.6	40	29.0	26.6
18	24.9	22.1	41	26.2	22.1
19	30.6	27.6	42	20.7	21.0
20	26.7	26.0	43	24.3	23.0
21	30.3	24.8	44	27.2	22.4
22	24.5	26.1	45	24.8	23.7
23	21.0	23.4	46	27.0	25.9

Source: "Evaluation of Compression Test Results of Field Concrete," *Journal of American Concrete Institute*, vol. 52, Nov. 1955, p. 255. The original data were in psi units.

4-6. On a construction job it was required to make concrete with a specified minimum compressive strength of 17 MPa. The minimum was understood to be a value exceeded by not less than 95 percent of test results. The values of strength of 50 test cubes are given in Table 4.8.

Calculate the mean strength, range, mean deviation, standard deviation, and coefficient of variation. Find whether the specification requirements are satisfied.

4-7. The strengths of concrete specimens, made two at a time over a period of 2 months on a construction site, are given in Table 4.9.

Find the mean strength, standard deviation, and coefficient of variation, working in terms of mean test values; for example, the first mean value = $\frac{1}{2}(24.8 + 22.0) = 23.4$ MPa, and the second mean value = 24.5 MPa, and so on.

4-8. For the data of Problem 4-7, estimate the standard deviation from the mean range. (HINT: Group the 46 mean values into nine subgroups, each containing 5 values, with the ninth subgroup having 6 values.)

4-9. For the data of Problem 4-7, determine the value of strength exceeded by 90 percent of tests (a "test" is the average of two specimens).

TABLE 4.10

Temperature, °C	1000	1025	1050	1075	1100	1125	1150
Number of readings	1	10	14	20	10	8	2

4-10. Readings on a filament temperature were taken by several persons using an optical pyrometer. The results are given in Table 4.10.

    a. Calculate the "best" representative value for the filament temperature.

    b. Estimate the variance and standard deviation of the optical pyrometer. (Assume there is no reading error due to personnel.) What is the coefficient of variation?

Chapter 5

Probability, Probability Distributions, and Expectation

PROBABILITY

In Chapter 1, we discussed the relation between statistics and probability. We noted that in statistical problems we estimate parameters of a distribution from sample data, whereas in probability problems the parameters of the mathematical model of the system are known, and it is the behavior of parts of the system, or samples, that is deduced. Thus, broadly speaking, the two approaches are the inverse of one another.

We also noted that the decisions which we make are affected by the unavoidable random behavior of natural processes and phenomena. In consequence, these decisions cannot be made with complete confidence but only under conditions of uncertainty involving risks. To *quantify* such uncertainty and to assess the associated risk we use the principles of probability. We can define *probability* as a measure of what is expected to happen on the average if a given observation or measurement is repeated a large number of times under identical conditions.

Let us illustrate, by a simple example, how we use probability to make inferences or decisions. Two types of can openers, A and B, were to be compared; it was assumed before the experiment[1] that type A was better. Twenty homemakers, selected at random,[2] tested the can openers and 18 of them concluded that type B was the better gadget. Now, if our original assumption that type

---

[1] Any activity or process that yields an outcome or observation, for example, flipping a coin and observing heads or tails.

[2] Since the homemakers were selected at random, it can be assumed that they are representative of a population of all the homemakers in the town who may use the can openers.

A is better was true, then we would have expected that at least 50 percent of the homemakers would have indicated so. However, only 2 of the 20 homemakers preferred type *A*, a result that is highly improbable *if* our original assumption was correct. Thus, since the result of the experiment is so improbable, we conclude that our original assumption was not correct.

In general, we would want to know how improbable a particular result is. We do this by calculating the probability of observing a result at least as extreme[3] as we have found, given that the original assumption is true. Depending on the magnitude of such a probability, we can then say whether the assumption is reasonable or whether it should be rejected as untrue. Thus, probability provides us with the necessary means for making decisions about the population on the basis of information from a sample.

The origin of probability theory dates back to the seventeenth century when certain mathematicians such as Pascal and Fermat were interested in the games of chance. Using this field, let us imagine flipping a coin a large number of times and recording the number of times that a head shows up. If the coin were perfectly true (unbiased) we would expect the *proportion* of heads observed to converge closer and closer to $\frac{1}{2}$ as more and more tosses are completed; this is so because the outcome of the experiment is governed solely by chance.[4] In fact, if the observed proportion of heads did not stabilize very closely to $\frac{1}{2}$ as the number of flips becomes large, we would suspect that the coin is biased. Figure 5.1 shows a coin-tossing experiment simulated by a digital computer. The rapid stabilization near the value of $\frac{1}{2}$ is evident. We can therefore say that the probability of an event which can occur as a result of a specified random process can be defined as the number that represents the proportion of occurrence of the event in an unlimited number of repetitions of the experiment.

Let us denote the occurrence of a certain event as success and its nonoccurrence as failure. If we consider all the possible (imaginable) arrangements (or trials), and also the arrangements corresponding to success, then the ratio of the latter to the former defines the probability of success. All the arrangements considered must be mutually exclusive and equally likely, and exhaustive.[5] If there are *n* possible arrangements, and success occurs in *m* cases, the probability of success is m/n, and the probability of failure is $1 - (m/n)$. Probability is thus

---

[3] If we assume that an extreme result is improbable then it follows that all the results which are even more extreme are clearly even more improbable. Therefore, in probability considerations we look at *all* the results to one side of the result in question, that is, the results *at least* as extreme.

[4] W. A. Shewhart explained, by means of the following example, the meaning of *chance* in *Economic Control of Quality of Manufactured Product* (Van Nostrand, New York, 1931, p. 5). Someone is asked to write the letter *a* on the blackboard and then try to copy it exactly several times. His letters *a* will look much alike, but there will be small and unavoidable differences which are due to *chance causes*. Now, someone else is asked to repeat the experiment; his letters *a* will again differ from one another by chance. But the two sets of *a* will differ not only due to chance causes but also due to what we call *assignable causes* because of the differences in handwriting between the two people.

[5] Two outcomes are mutually exclusive if, when one occurs, the other cannot do so. A mutually exclusive and exhaustive set is one in which the outcomes are such that one of the outcomes constituting the set must occur, but only one can occur in a single trial.

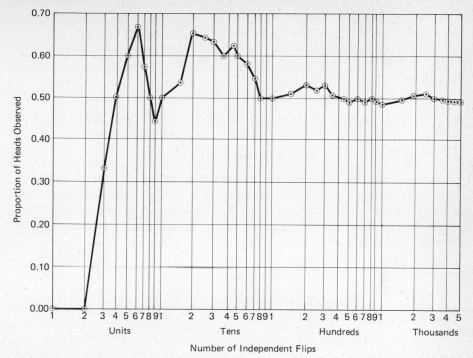

Figure 5.1

expressed as a number not greater than 1. A value of unity denotes a certainty of success, and a value of zero means an impossibility of success.

Strictly speaking, we should distinguish two types of probability. In the first, the probability of an event is established solely by the definition of the system, for example, the probability of obtaining a given number on rolling a die is $\frac{1}{6}$. This is an *a priori* probability since we apply reasoning to arrive at the answer. In many practical problems, we define probability by *relative frequency;* this concept was already demonstrated in Fig. 5.1.

In many other cases, we are concerned with an *empirical* probability, which is based solely on experimental data, for example, on the past records of deaths, accidents, and so on.

There is also *subjective* probability where a probability value is assigned to an event on the basis of a person's *degree of belief* in the occurrence of the event. Engineering statistics are frequently concerned with a combination of the above types of probabilities.

PROBABILITY RULES

There are two rules of probability that are of fundamental importance:

a. The probability of occurrence of several of a number of mutually exclusive events is the sum of the probabilities of the separate events. Events are said to be *mutually exclusive* if only one of them can occur at a time (e.g., in a hurricane, a suspension bridge collapses or does not collapse; a person passes or fails a particular test; a die shows a 1 or a 6, but not both).

For example, in tossing a die, the probability of throwing a 3 *or* 6 is equal to the probability of throwing 3 plus the probability of throwing 6, that is, it is equal to

$$\tfrac{1}{6} + \tfrac{1}{6} = \tfrac{1}{3}.$$

We may note that the sum of the probabilities of *all* the possible events is always 1; for example, the probability of not throwing a 3 or 6 is $\tfrac{2}{3}$, and hence the sum of the probabilities of all possible outcomes is $\tfrac{1}{3} + \tfrac{2}{3} = 1$.

Proof of the Addition Rule. Let there be n equally likely cases such that event A occurs in r of them and event B occurs in s of them. Since the occurrence of A does not coincide with that of B (they are mutually exclusive), there is no overlapping between the $(r + s)$ cases; that is, the event A or B occurs in only the $(r + s)$ cases. Hence,

$$P(A \text{ or } B) = P(A + B) = \frac{r + s}{n} = \frac{r}{n} + \frac{s}{n} = P(A) + P(B). \tag{5.1}$$

This rule can be readily generalized to several mutually exclusive events, $A, B, C, \ldots$; thus, we can write

$$P(A \text{ or } B \text{ or } C \text{ or } \cdots) = P(A) + P(B) + P(C) + \cdots$$

or $\qquad\qquad P(A + B + C + \cdots) = P(A) + P(B) + P(C) + \cdots. \tag{5.2}$

b. The probability of a *simultaneous* occurrence of a number of *independent* events is the product of the separate probabilities. An event is considered independent if its occurrence does not affect the probability of the occurrence of other events.

For example, in tossing two dice, the probability of throwing a double 6 is equal to the probability of throwing a six times the probability of throwing a six; that is, it is equal to $\tfrac{1}{6} \times \tfrac{1}{6} = \tfrac{1}{36}$.

Proof of the Multiplication Rule. Let us assume that there are m favorable cases for event A in a total of n cases, and M favorable cases for event B in a total of N cases; the events A and B are assumed independent. Then $P(A) = m/n$ and $P(B) = M/N$. When we consider the joint event "A and B," we have altogether nN possible cases all equally likely, since A and B are independent. Each favorable case for A combines with each favorable case for B to yield a favorable case for the joint event A and B. Thus there are mM favorable cases for the event A and B; hence,

$$P(A \text{ and } B) = P(AB) = \frac{mM}{nN} = \frac{m}{n} \times \frac{M}{N} = P(A)\, P(B). \tag{5.3}$$

We can readily generalize this rule to the situation where there are several independent events $A, B, C, \ldots$; thus

$$P(A \text{ and } B \text{ and } C \text{ and } \cdots) = P(A)\, P(B)\, P(C) \cdots$$

or $\qquad\qquad P(ABC \cdots) = P(A)\, P(B)\, P(C) \cdots. \tag{5.4}$

EXAMPLE

Thirty high-strength bolts became mixed by mistake with 25 ordinary bolts and it was not possible to tell them apart from appearance. If two bolts are drawn in succession, what is the probability that one of them is of the high-strength type and the other one is ordinary?

In this problem, the mutually exclusive events are:

a. Drawing a high-strength bolt on the first trial and an ordinary one on the second.

b. Drawing an ordinary bolt on the first trial and a high-strength one on the second.

Now the probability of (a) is

$$\tfrac{30}{55} \times \tfrac{25}{54} = \tfrac{25}{99}$$

and the probability of (b) is

$$\tfrac{25}{55} \times \tfrac{30}{54} = \tfrac{25}{99}.$$

The probability of either (a) or (b) is the sum of the two probabilities:

$$\tfrac{25}{99} + \tfrac{25}{99} = \tfrac{50}{99}. \qquad\blacksquare\ \blacksquare$$

Earlier, we considered events that are mutually exclusive, but this, of course, need not always be the case. For instance, if we are interested in the proportion of people who are left-handed or myopic, we find in addition to those who have either of these attributes also those who have both. Suppose that the probability of being left-handed is $P(A)$ and the probability of being myopic is $P(B)$. Then the probability of being either left-handed or myopic, $P(A + B)$, is given by an addition expression which has to recognize that the group with both attributes must not be counted twice. Thus

$$P(A + B) = P(A) + P(B) - P(AB) \qquad (5.5)$$

where $P(AB)$ is the probability of being both left-handed and myopic. A graphical representation of this situation is given in Fig. 5.2.

EXAMPLE

If one card is selected at random from a deck of 52 cards, what is the probability that the card is a club or a face card or both? (Count an ace as a face card.)

The probability of a club, $P(A)$, is $\tfrac{13}{52}$. The probability of a face card, $P(B)$, is $\tfrac{16}{52}$. Since four of the clubs are also face cards, then $P(AB)$ is $\tfrac{4}{52}$.

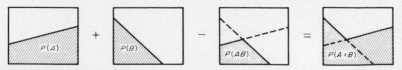

Figure 5.2 Probability of occurrence of either or both of two independent events.

Thus, the required probability is

$$P(A + B) = P(A) + P(B) - P(AB) = \tfrac{13}{52} + \tfrac{16}{52} - \tfrac{4}{52} = \tfrac{25}{52}. \qquad \blacksquare \ \blacksquare$$

We should further recognize that events which are not mutually exclusive may be independent or *dependent*. In the latter case, the occurrence of an event affects the probability of other events. For instance, drawing a card from a pack (e.g., an ace) affects the probability of drawing any other given card (e.g., a queen) unless the first card is returned before the second draw. We are dealing, therefore, with *conditional probability*, which is the probability of an event A, given that the event B has occurred; such a conditional probability can be written as $P(A|B)$. Thus, in our notation,

$$P(A|B) = \frac{P(AB)}{P(B)}. \tag{5.6}$$

We see thus that the conditional probability eliminates all the elements of event A that are not also elements of event B; hence the fraction $P(AB)/P(B)$.

A diagrammatic representation of the classification of various types of events, shown in Fig. 5.3, may be helpful.

We can use the definition of conditional probability to deduce the definition of independence; thus, two events A and B are said to be independent if and only if

$$P(A|B) = P(A) \quad \text{or} \quad P(B|A) = P(B). \tag{5.7}$$

Intuitively, if two events are unrelated, then the probability of one event's occurring is unaltered if the other event has occurred.

Equation 5.6 can also be written as

$$P(AB) = P(A|B)\, P(B)$$

and similarly,

$$P(AB) = P(B|A)\, P(A).$$

Thus, if A and B are independent, then, by Eq. (5.7),

$$P(AB) = P(A)\, P(B) \tag{5.3}$$

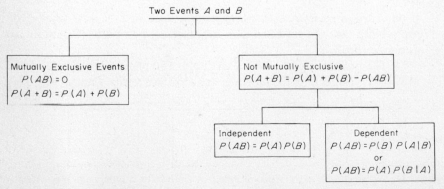

Figure 5.3

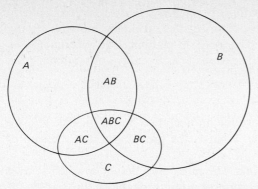

Figure 5.4 Events that are not mutually exclusive but are independent.

as before. It should be noted that if A and B are mutually exclusive events, then

$$P(A|B) = 0.$$

For three not mutually exclusive and dependent events, A, B, and C (see Fig. 5.4) we have, by inspection,

$$P(A + B + C) = P(A) + P(B) + P(C) - P(AB)$$
$$- P(BC) - P(AC) + P(ABC) \qquad (5.8)$$

and $$P(ABC) = P(A|BC)\,P(B|C)\,P(C) \qquad (5.9)$$

where $$P(A|BC) = \frac{P(ABC)}{P(BC)} \qquad (5.10)$$

and $$P(B|C) = \frac{P(BC)}{P(C)}. \qquad [5.6]$$

If the events are independent, then $P(A|BC) = P(A)$, $P(B|C) = P(B)$, and hence Eq. (5.9) becomes

$$P(ABC) = P(A)\,P(B)\,P(C). \qquad [5.4]$$

It is worthwhile observing that if events are independent then their complements[6] are also independent. Thus,

$$P(\bar{A}\bar{B}\bar{C}) = P(\bar{A})\,P(\bar{B})\,P(\bar{C}) \qquad (5.11)$$

where $\bar{A}$, $\bar{B}$, $\bar{C}$ denote the complements of A, B, C, respectively.

Furthermore, we can note that the probability rules of addition and multiplication apply also to conditional probabilities. For example,

$$P[(A + B)|C] = P(A|C) + P(B|C) - P(AB|C) \qquad (5.12)$$

and $$P(AB|C) = P[(A|B)|C]\,P(B|C). \qquad (5.13)$$

It should be emphasized that consideration of *dependent events* generally complicates statistical analyses. The reasons for this are: (i) it is difficult to define

---

[6] The complement of A is a value $\bar{A}$ such that $A + \bar{A} = 1$.

the exact nature of the dependence; and, (ii) even if the nature of the dependence is known, the resulting analytical equations become complex enough to cause algebraic and inference difficulties. Therefore, in planning our experiments we should ensure the *independence* of the various tests by means of randomization techniques (considered in Chapter 23).

EXAMPLE

A roll of two fair dice has shown the number 4 on one of the dice. We are not told what the other die is. What is the probability that the sum of numbers on both dice is 9?

There are 36 sample points. The number of points in which at least one 4 turns up is 11; thus the corresponding probability, $P(B)$, is $\frac{11}{36}$. Of the four points that result in the sum of 9, $[(6, 3), (5, 4), (4, 5), \text{and } (3, 6)]$, there are two in which 4 appears. Therefore, $P(AB)$ is $\frac{2}{36}$.

Hence, the required probability, $P(A|B)$, is

$$P(A|B) = \frac{P(AB)}{P(B)} = \frac{\frac{2}{36}}{\frac{11}{36}} = \frac{2}{11}.$$ ■ ■

EXAMPLE

A milk delivery company operating a fleet of vans driven both by gasoline and by electric motors maintained annual records on motor overhauls. In Table 5.1 is listed the number of kilometers before an overhaul is necessary for each type of van.

    a. What is the probability that a motor (of whatever type) will exceed 40,000 kilometers?

    b. What influence does the motor type have on this probability?

We find

    a. The probability of exceeding 40,000 kilometers before an overhaul is necessary is $\frac{30}{180}$ or $\frac{1}{6}$.

    b. Here we deal with conditional probability, since we wish to find the probability that a motor will exceed 40,000 kilometers prior to overhaul, given that the motor is either gasoline or electric.

TABLE 5.1

Kilometers	Vans with		Total
	Gasoline motor	Electric motor	
40,001 and over	10	20	30
20,001–40,000	60	50	110
0–20,000	30	10	40
Total	100	80	180

For gasoline motors, the required value of probability is

$$P = \frac{\frac{10}{180}}{\frac{100}{180}} = 0.1.$$

For electric motors, the value is

$$P = \frac{\frac{20}{180}}{\frac{80}{180}} = 0.25.$$ ■ ■

EXAMPLE

A shopping complex is to be designed to accommodate firms with different needs for hot and cold water. The engineer is to design these utilities in such a manner that the provisions should not greatly exceed the actual demand; nor should the capacities be inadequate.

There are four classifications: for hot water either 10 or 20 units, namely, H_{10} and H_{20}; and for cold water 2 or 4 units, namely, W_2 and W_4. The owner of the complex, based on previous experience, has given the engineer the following estimates of the probability of encountering the four classifications (see Table 5.2).

Find the probability of

a. The cold water demand being 4 units.
b. The hot water demand being 20 units.
c. Either the cold water demand being 4 units or the hot water demand being 20 units.
d. A firm known to have a hot water demand of 10 units, also having a cold water demand of 4 units.

We find

a. Probability $= P[H_{10}W_4] + P[H_{20}W_4] = 0.2 + 0.5 = 0.7.$
b. Probability $= P[H_{20}W_2] + P[H_{20}W_4] = 0.2 + 0.5 = 0.7.$
c. Probability $= (a) + (b) - P[H_{20}W_4] = 0.7 + 0.7 - 0.5 = 0.9.$
d. $P[W_4|H_{10}] = P[H_{10}W_4]/P[H_{10}] = 0.2/0.3 = 0.66$, which is the conditional probability that W_4 will occur, given the knowledge that H_{10} has occurred. ■ ■

TABLE 5.2

Event	Probability
$H_{10}W_2$	0.1
$H_{10}W_4$	0.2
$H_{20}W_2$	0.2
$H_{20}W_4$	0.5

TABLE 5.3

	(B)	($\bar{B}$)	Total
(A)	0.10	0.30	0.40
($\bar{A}$)	0.15	0.45	0.60
Total	0.25	0.75	1.00

EXAMPLE

A system S consists of components A and B. It functions 0.10 of the time; component A fails 0.15 of the time and component B fails 0.30 of the time. Check whether components A and B function independently of each other.

Let us denote the functioning of component A as (A) and its non-functioning as $(\bar{A})$, and similarly for component B. See Table 5.3.

Now,

$$P(A) = P(AB) + P(A\bar{B}) = 0.10 + 0.30 = 0.40$$

and

$$P(B) = P(AB) + P(\bar{A}B) = 0.10 + 0.15 = 0.25.$$

Thus,

$$P(A) \cdot P(B) = (0.40)(0.25) = 0.10$$

which is equal to the value given for $P(AB)$. Therefore, the two components A and B function independently.

Also, from the definition of independence, we have

$$P(A|B) = \frac{P(AB)}{P(B)} = \frac{0.10}{0.25} = 0.40$$

which is equal to $P(A)$, and

$$P(B|A) = \frac{P(AB)}{P(A)} = \frac{0.10}{0.40} = 0.25$$

which is equal to $P(B)$, thus satisfying Eq. (5.7).   ■ ■

EXAMPLE

For the pin-jointed truss shown in Fig. 5.5, under the external loads shown, the probabilities of failure of members A, B, and C are 0.04, 0.03, and 0.08, respectively. From statistics we know that the failure of any member or members leads to the collapse of the entire truss. Assuming that failures of the individual members are statistically independent, calculate the probability of failure of the truss.

We have:

$$P(A) = 0.04, \qquad P(B) = 0.03, \qquad P(C) = 0.08.$$

From the condition of statistical independence,

$$P(AB) = P(A)\,P(B) = 0.0012; \qquad P(AC) = P(A)\,P(C) = 0.0032;$$
$$P(BC) = P(B)\,P(C) = 0.0024; \qquad P(ABC) = P(A)\,P(B)\,P(C) = 0.000096.$$

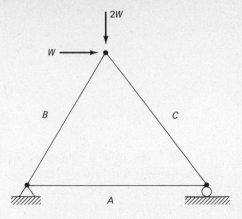

Figure 5.5 Axially loaded truss.

Referring to Fig. 5.8, the probability of any one or more members failing (and hence the failure of the truss) is

$$P(A + B + C) = P(A) + P(B) + P(C) - P(AB) - P(BC) - P(AC)$$
$$+ P(ABC)$$
$$= 0.04 + 0.03 + 0.08 - 0.0012 - 0.0024 - 0.0032$$
$$+ 0.000096$$
$$= 0.143296 \simeq 0.14.$$

By another method,

$$P(A + B + C) = 1 - P(\bar{A}\bar{B}\bar{C})$$
$$= 1 - P(\bar{A})\, P(\bar{B})\, P(\bar{C})$$

where

$$P(\bar{A}) = 1 - P(A) = 0.96; \qquad P(\bar{B}) = 0.97, \qquad P(\bar{C}) = 0.92.$$

Therefore,

$$P(A + B + C) = 1 - (0.96 \times 0.97 \times 0.92)$$
$$= 0.143296, \qquad \text{as before.} \qquad \blacksquare\ \blacksquare$$

EXAMPLE

The soil in a certain locality is likely to settle when subjected to a concentrated load; from past experience, the estimated probability that one of the two footings of a rigid structure shown in Fig. 5.6 will settle is 0.1 while the probability that a footing will settle given that the other one has settled is 0.7. Determine the probability of:

a. settlement;
b. differential settlement.

For (a), if we refer to the settlement of the two footings as A and B, then the possible events regarding settlement of the two footings are: both A

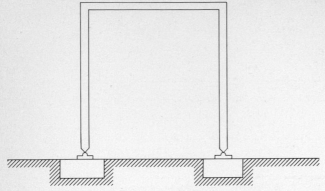

Figure 5.6   Rigid frame with settlement problem.

and B settle (AB); A does not settle but B settles $(\bar{A}B)$; A settles while B does not settle $(A\bar{B})$; neither A nor B settles $(\bar{A}\bar{B})$. Thus,

$$P(A + B) = P(A) + P(B) - P(AB)$$
$$= 0.1 + 0.1 - P(A|B)\, P(B)$$
$$= 0.1 + 0.1 - (0.7 \times 0.1)$$
$$= 0.13.$$

For (b), the event of differential settlement is a compound event, that is, event $(\bar{A}B)$ and event $(A\bar{B})$. Both these events are mutually exclusive. Therefore,

$$\text{the required probability} = P(\bar{A}B) + P(A\bar{B})$$
$$= P(\bar{A}|B)\, P(B) + P(\bar{B}|A)\, P(A)$$
$$= [1 - P(A|B)]\, P(B) + [1 - P(B|A)]\, P(A)$$
$$= (1 - 0.7) \times 0.1 + (1 - 0.7) \times 0.1$$
$$= 0.06. \qquad \blacksquare\ \blacksquare$$

EXAMPLE

A reinforced-earth retaining wall, Fig. 5.7, can fail by either sliding (S) or by rupturing of the steel ties (R). Assuming that: (i) probability of failure by sliding is twice as great as that of rupturing the steel ties, that is, $P(S) = 2P(R)$; (ii) probability that the retaining wall also fails by sliding given that it has failed by the rupture of the ties is $P(S|R) = 0.5$; and (iii) probability of failure of the wall $= 0.001$;

a. Calculate the probability that sliding will occur.
b. Calculate $P(SR)$.

For (a),

$$P(S + R) = P(S) + P(R) - P(SR) = 0.001.$$

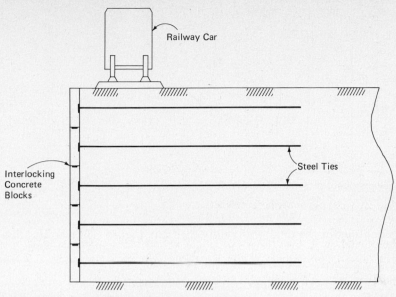

Figure 5.7 Reinforced-earth retaining wall.

Also, $$P(S|R) = \frac{P(SR)}{P(R)}.$$

Therefore,

$$P(S + R) = 0.001 = 2P(R) + P(R) - P(R)\,P(S|R)$$
$$= P(R)[2 + 1 - 0.5]$$
$$= 2.5P(R).$$

Hence, $$P(R) = 0.0004.$$

Thus, $$P(S) = 2P(R) - 0.0008$$

For (b),

$$P(SR) + P(R)\,P(S|R) = 0.0004 \times 0.5 = 0.0002. \qquad \blacksquare\ \blacksquare$$

TOTAL PROBABILITY THEOREM

Frequently, the probability of an event A cannot be found directly. However, if its occurrence is accompanied by the happening of other mutually exclusive events, $B_i\ (i = 1, 2, \ldots, n)$, then the probability of A can be found from

$$P(A) = P(A|B_1)\,P(B_1) + P(A|B_2)\,P(B_2) + \cdots + P(A|B_n)\,P(B_n)$$

which can be written as

$$P(A) = \sum_{j=1}^{n} P(A|B_j)\,P(B_j). \qquad (5.14)$$

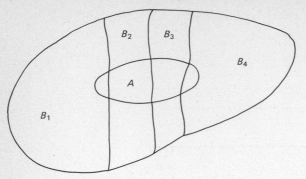

Figure 5.8   Dependence of event A on events $B_1, \ldots, B_4$.

This is the equation for the total probability theorem. Figure 5.8 illustrates this for B_i $(i = 1, \ldots, 4)$.

BAYES' RULE

Sometimes, we may ask what is the probability that a particular event B_i has occurred if an event A has been or will be observed.

We know from Eq. (5.6) that

$$P(B_i \mid A) = \frac{P(B_iA)}{P(A)} = \frac{P(A \mid B_i)\, P(B_i)}{P(A)}.$$

Using Eq. (5.14) for $P(A)$, we have

$$P(B_i \mid A) = \frac{P(A \mid B_i)\, P(B_i)}{\displaystyle\sum_{j=1}^{n} P(A \mid B_j)\, P(B_j)}. \tag{5.15}$$

Equation (5.15) describes Bayes' rule. Its importance lies in the fact that we can incorporate new information into prior probability assessments so as to yield new values of probability, that is, *posterior probability*. In a sense, Bayes' rule updates or revises the prior probability $P(B)$ by incorporating the observed information contained within event A into the model.

EXAMPLE

A van-manufacturing plant purchases its electronic relays from two manufacturers, I and II. Past records show that suppliers I and II have shipped relays containing 5 percent and 10 percent defectives, respectively. Assuming that 60 percent of the current relays in the plant are from supplier I, if a defective relay is selected at random from the current relays, calculate the probability that it came from supplier I.

Let B_i be the event that a relay is from supplier I, where $i = 1, 2$ since in this case there are only two suppliers. Also, let A be the event that the selected relay is defective. Then, from Eq. (5.15),

$$P(B_1|A) = \frac{P(A|B_1)\,P(B_1)}{P(A|B_1)\,P(B_1) + P(A|B_2)\,P(B_2)}$$

$$= \frac{0.05 \times 0.60}{0.05 \times 0.60 + 0.10 \times 0.40}$$

$$\simeq 0.43.$$

This shows that there is a smaller chance that supplier I will be the one whose current relays are defective than supplier II. ■ ■

EXAMPLE
The ultimate design load for a pile group supporting a pier of a bridge is 3500 kN. Based on previous pilot tests and field experience with similar pile foundations, the soil engineer estimated a probability of 0.75 that any pile group can support a 3500 kN load. However, he also noted that, of the pile groups with an ultimate capacity of less than 3500 kN, 50 percent failed at loads less than 3000 kN. In order to update his estimated probability, the engineer wishes to carry out a site test on one pile group. If the load carried exceeds 3000 kN, what would be his new estimate of the probability that a pile group can carry an ultimate load of up to 3500 kN?

Let

A = event that capacity of pile group will equal or exceed 3500 kN,

and

B = event that capacity of pile goup will equal or exceed 3000 kN.

We are given $P(\bar{B}|\bar{A}) = 0.5$. Hence, $P(B|\bar{A}) = 1 - 0.5 = 0.5$. Now, $P(A) = 0.75$; hence, $P(\bar{A}) = 1 - P(A) = 0.25$. Also, $P(B|A) = 1.0$. From Bayes' rule, Eq. (5.15),

$$P(A|B) = \frac{P(B|A)\,P(A)}{P(B|A)\,P(A) + P(B|\bar{A})\,P(\bar{A})}$$

$$= \frac{1.0 \times 0.75}{1.0 \times 0.75 + 0.5 \times 0.25}$$

$$= \frac{0.75}{0.75 + 0.125} = 0.857 \simeq 0.86.$$

Thus, if the site test load is equal to at least 3000 kN, the soil engineer can increase the probability of a pile group supporting 3500 kN from 0.75 to 0.86. ■ ■

It should be mentioned that the concept of updating information is very useful and sometimes necessary in scientific and engineering planning and design. This is the subject of Bayesian statistics but is outside the scope of this book.

PROBABILITY DISTRIBUTIONS

In Chapter 1, we introduced the concept of a random variable but it is useful to discuss it in more detail for the purpose of considering probability distributions.

A random variable X is a numerically valued function whose values correspond to the various outcomes of an experiment; alternatively, it is a function that assumes numerical values governed by chance so that a particular value cannot be predicted in advance. Random variables can be discrete or continuous, as well as quantitative or qualitative, as defined in Chapter 1. A notation sometimes used for random variables is an uppercase letter such as X, Y, or Z while lowercase letters are used for particular values taken on by the random variable; for example, if the random variable X has 10 values, then we refer to them as x_1, $x_2, \ldots, x_{10}$. However, in this book, unless there is ambiguity, we shall use lowercase letters to represent random variables as well as the numerical values which they take on; the content of the paragraph should enable the reader to distinguish between the use of, say, lowercase x as a random variable and a particular value, x_i, taken by a random variable.

Let us consider the sample of the twenty homemakers testing the two types of can opener, A and B. The number of homemakers showing a preference for type A opener is a random variable x corresponding to a particular experimental outcome. In the experiment we select a random sample of 20 homemakers and observe how many prefer type A openers. We should note that the value of x cannot be predicted with certainty prior to the experiment, that is, the particular value taken by x is governed solely by chance, and therefore x is a random event. If we can *imagine* repeating this experiment a very large number of times, the measured results would form a population of the random variable x and the probability of each x defines the *probability distribution* of the population of x. Of course, we never actually measure each member of the population, but use a random sample[7] representing the population, to describe and make inferences about the population. In order to do this, we need to have the knowledge of the probability associated with each value of the random variable, that is, we require the probability model of the random variable which represents the theoretical relative frequency for the population of numerical measurements. We shall see in the next section how the theory of probability provides the means for calculating the probabilities for some random variables, as well as for making inferences.

Before proceeding further, it is useful to repeat some of the relevant definitions made in earlier chapters. A variable is continuous if it can theoretically assume any value between two given limits; otherwise, it is a discrete variable. In Chapter 2, we dealt with frequency distributions of data from *samples*. Now we shall deal with probability distributions of *populations*. We should remember that a random sample is one that is chosen in such a manner that every individual in the population has an equal chance of being chosen for the sample.

---

[7] The terms sampling and random sample are explained in Chapter 6.

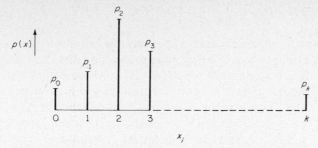

Figure 5.9 Probability distribution of a discrete random variable x.

DISCRETE PROBABILITY DISTRIBUTIONS

If a random variable x can assume discrete values $x_0, x_1, x_2, \ldots, x_k$ with respective probabilities $p_0, p_1, p_2, \ldots, p_k$, where $p_i \geq 0$ for all i, and

$$\sum_{i=0}^{i=k} p_i = 1 \tag{5.16}$$

then probability $(x = x_i)$, or simply $p(x_i) = p_i$, characterizes a discrete probability distribution for the variable x (see Fig. 5.9). Thus, we can say that a probability distribution for a discrete random variable can be represented by a formula, table, or graph providing the probability associated with each value of the random variable.

EXAMPLE

An experiment was conducted on tossing 3 coins. Let the random variable x be the number of heads observed. Determine the probability for x.

Let H = event of a head showing, and T = event of no head (tail) showing. Then the various compound events are: HHH, HHT, THH, HTH, HTT, THT, TTH, TTT. Thus, the number of possible events is $n = 8$. In tabular form, we have:

Event	Frequency, f	Probability, $f/\sum f$
Zero head	1	$\frac{1}{8}$
One head	3	$\frac{3}{8}$
Two heads	3	$\frac{3}{8}$
Three heads	1	$\frac{1}{8}$
	$\sum f = 8$	

The probability distribution is shown in Fig. 5.10. ■ ■

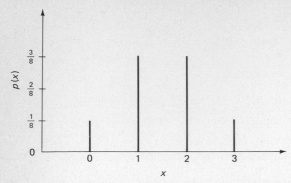

Figure 5.10 Probability distribution of the number of heads in tossing 3 coins.

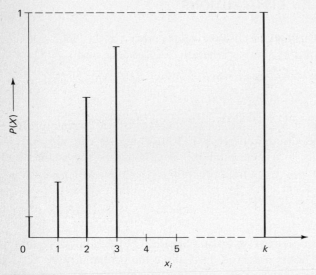

Figure 5.11 Cummulative distribution function (cdf) of a discrete random variable x.

The cumulative distribution function of a discrete random variable is defined as

$$P(X) = \sum_{x_1 \leq X} p_i. \tag{5.17}$$

This function is a step function that is constant over every interval not containing any of the points x_i, as shown in Fig. 5.11.

It is interesting to note that $p(x)$ and $P(X)$ represent probabilities and cumulative probabilities, respectively, for a large parent *population* in contrast to f and F, which represent frequency and cumulative frequency, respectively (as discussed in Chapter 2), in a *sample* of grouped data.

Thus, we can associate probability distributions with *population* whereas the relative frequency distributions (considered in Chapter 2) are distributions for *samples* drawn from this population; in other words, we can regard a probability distribution as a relative frequency distribution for an indefinitely *large sample* (population).

EXAMPLE

Draw the probability distribution and cumulative probability distribution for a random variable x, defined as the sum of the upturned faces of two fair dice.

Now, x can take the values 2, 3, 4, 5, ... 11, 12.

Probability of obtaining the sum of 2 is $(\frac{1}{6})(\frac{1}{6}) = \frac{1}{36} = p(2)$

Probability of obtaining the sum of 3 is $(\frac{1}{6})(\frac{1}{6}) + (\frac{1}{6})(\frac{1}{6}) = \frac{2}{36} = p(3)$

Probability of obtaining the sum of 4 is $(\frac{1}{6})(\frac{1}{6}) + (\frac{1}{6})(\frac{1}{6}) + (\frac{1}{6})(\frac{1}{6})$
$= \frac{3}{36} = p(4)$

Probability of obtaining the sum of 5 is $4(\frac{1}{6})(\frac{1}{6}) = \frac{4}{36} = p(5)$

Probability of obtaining the sum of 6 is $5(\frac{1}{6})(\frac{1}{6}) = \frac{5}{36} = p(6)$

Probability of obtaining the sum of 7 is $6(\frac{1}{6})(\frac{1}{6}) = \frac{6}{36} = p(7)$

Probability of obtaining the sum of 8 is $5(\frac{1}{6})(\frac{1}{6}) = \frac{5}{36} = p(8)$
$$\vdots$$

Probability of obtaining the sum of 12 is $(\frac{1}{6})(\frac{1}{6}) = \frac{1}{36} = p(12)$.

These probabilities are plotted in Fig. 5.12.

The cumulative probability distribution is as follows:

The cumulative probability of obtaining the sum of 2 or less is
$p(2) = \frac{1}{36}$.

The cumulative probability of obtaining the sum of 3 or less is
$$p(2) + p(3) = \frac{1}{36} + \frac{2}{36} = \frac{3}{36}$$
$$\vdots$$

The cumulative probability of obtaining the sum of 12 or less is
$$p(2) + p(3) + p(4) + \cdots + p(12) = \frac{36}{36} = 1.$$

A plot of the cumulative probability is shown in Fig. 5.13 (see also Table 5.4). Note that
$$\sum_{x=2}^{x=12} p(x) = 1.$$

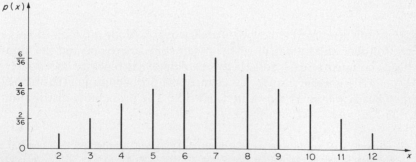

Figure 5.12   Probability distribution of the sum of the upturned faces of two fair dice.

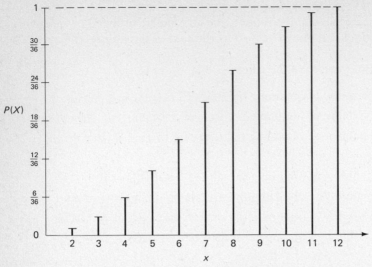

Figure 5.13 Cumulative distribution function of the sum of the upturned faces of two fair dice.

TABLE 5.4

x	2	3	4	5	6	7	8	9	10	11	12
$p(x)$	$\frac{1}{36}$	$\frac{2}{36}$	$\frac{3}{36}$	$\frac{4}{36}$	$\frac{5}{36}$	$\frac{6}{36}$	$\frac{5}{36}$	$\frac{4}{36}$	$\frac{3}{36}$	$\frac{2}{36}$	$\frac{1}{36}$
$P(X)$	$\frac{1}{36}$	$\frac{3}{36}$	$\frac{6}{36}$	$\frac{10}{36}$	$\frac{15}{36}$	$\frac{21}{36}$	$\frac{26}{36}$	$\frac{30}{36}$	$\frac{33}{36}$	$\frac{35}{36}$	$\frac{36}{36}$ $(=1)$

Now, if the two dice are "fair" the actual outcomes of the random variable in question should follow the laws of probability in the long run; in this case, the probability is known *a priori*. However, in most statistical problems, the probability distribution of the random variable is not known and, therefore, we must use the outcomes of the random variable from a sample to make decisions about the unknown probability distribution of the population. The binomial distribution and Poisson's distribution discussed in Chapters 8 and 9 are examples of discrete distributions.   ■ ■

Let us now demonstrate how probability distributions are used to make inference. Consider an experiment where 20 fair coins are tossed and the number of heads counted at each toss. If this experiment is repeated indefinitely, with the outcome governed solely by chance, the probability for the various numbers of heads will be as shown in Table 5.5.[8] The probability distribution is shown in Fig. 5.14.

[8] These results can be deduced readily from the binomial distribution (considered in Chapter 8), using the probability of a head in one toss of a fair coin, $p_0 = \frac{1}{2}$.

TABLE 5.5

Number of heads, x[a]	0	1	2	3	4	5	6	7	8	9	10
Probability	0	0	0	0.001	0.005	0.015	0.037	0.074	0.120	0.160	0.176

Number of heads, x	11	12	13	14	15	16	17	18	19	20
Probability	0.160	0.120	0.074	0.037	0.015	0.005	0.001	0	0	0

[a] Rounded to 3 significant figures.

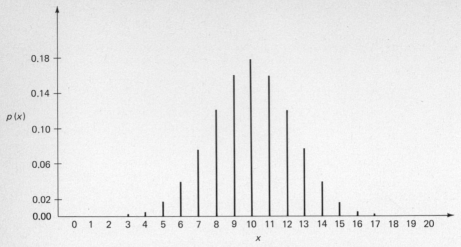

Figure 5.14   Probability distribution of the number of heads for 20 coins.

Suppose that an experiment was actually carried out on tossing 20 coins, on the assumption that they are fair coins ($p = \frac{1}{2}$), and it was found that only four coins showed heads, that is, $x = 4$. We can conclude that this result is highly improbable since, from Table 5.5, the probability of 4 heads = 0.005, a small number indeed. Therefore, we can infer that our assumption of $p = \frac{1}{2}$ for the set of 20 coins used in this experiment cannot be true, and we conclude that not all the coins are fair.

CONTINUOUS PROBABILITY DISTRIBUTIONS

In Chapter 2, we explained how data describing a continuous variable can be plotted as a histogram and then as a frequency polygon. We also mentioned that, if the total number of observations is increased indefinitely and the class width correspondingly approaches zero, the histogram as well as the frequency polygon will approach a continuous curve, namely, a frequency distribution curve (or a relative frequency distribution curve), as shown in Fig. 5.15.

If the height of the frequency curve A is standardized so that the area under curve A is made equal to unity, then a continuous probability distribution is determined as shown in Fig. 5.16, where $p(x)$ is the probability density function such that

$$\int_{-\infty}^{+\infty} p(x)\,dx = 1. \qquad (5.18)$$

The function $p(x)$ models mathematically the relative frequency histogram of the population.

The area under the curve and between lines $x = x_1$, and $x = x_2$ (the shaded area in Fig. 5.17) is the probability that x lies between x_1 and x_2, or

$$\text{probability}\,(x_1 < x < x_2) = \int_{x=x_1}^{x=x_2} p(x)\,dx. \qquad (5.19)$$

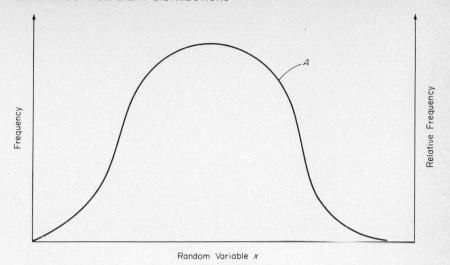

Figure 5.15 Frequency curve and relative frequency curve of a random variable x.

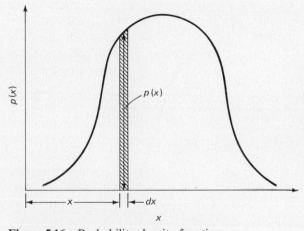

Figure 5.16 Probability density function.

It is essential to understand that the probability of observing a specific value such as $x = x_3$ is zero, since the calculation of a probability entails the calculation of an area under the curve; in this case, dx for a continuous variable is equal to zero, and hence the corresponding probability will also be zero. This is expressed mathematically as

$$\int_{x=x_3}^{x=x_3} p(x)\,dx = 0.$$

Thus, the proper definition of $p(x)$ is that for a small interval dx, $p(x)\,dx$ is the probability of observing a value between x and $x + dx$; that is, it is the shaded area in Fig. 5.16.

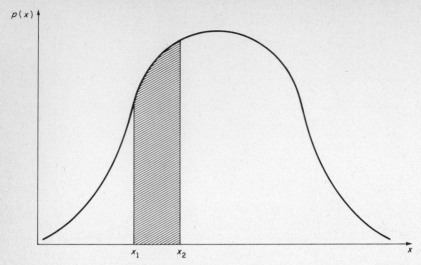

Figure 5.17   Probability density function.

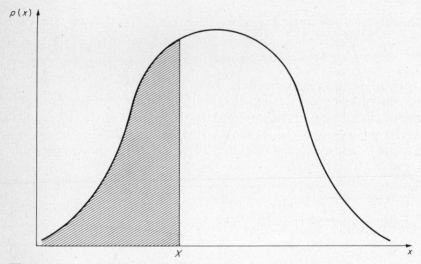

Figure 5.18   Probability density function.

The cumulative distribution function, $P(x)$, for a random variable x is defined as the probability of observing a value less than or equal to X, that is, the shaded area in Fig. 5.18. Thus,

$$P(X) = \int_{-\infty}^{X} p(x)\,dx. \tag{5.20}$$

The probability that x lies between x_1 and x_2 (Fig. 5.17) can now be written as

$$\text{probability } (x_1 < x < x_2) = \int_{x_1}^{x_2} p(x)\,dx = P(x_2) - P(x_1). \tag{5.21}$$

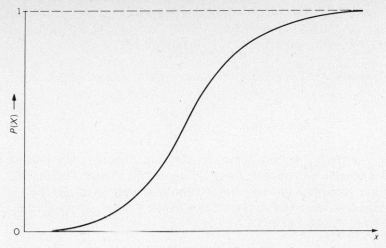

Figure 5.19 The cumulative distribution function of a continuous random variable.

The cumulative distribution function must increase from zero to one, since we have

$$P(-\infty) = 0 \quad \text{and} \quad P(\infty) = 1$$

and it is often an S-shaped curve, as shown in Fig. 5.19.

The probability density function $p(x)$ provides a mathematical model for the population relative frequency histogram that exists in reality. The choice of the model depends on the nature of the phenomenon studied and on the corresponding data collected, and we shall now list some of the more useful probability models.

SOME IMPORTANT PROBABILITY DISTRIBUTIONS

The following are some of the important probability distributions that are used in practice to model results from engineering and scientific experiments. These distributions, which are fully discussed later on in the book, are classified as discrete and continuous distributions.

A. Discrete Probability Distributions (Point Probability Functions)

A(i) Binomial Distribution X is a discrete random variable with range 0, 1, 2, . . . , n (n being a fixed integer), such that its probability function is given by

$$p(x_r) = P(X = x_r) = \frac{n!}{r! \, (n-r)!} \, p^r (1-p)^{n-r} \tag{5.22}$$

for $r = 1, 2, \ldots, n$.[9] The parameters of this distribution are n and p; its mean and variance are np and $np(1 - p)$, respectively. In Chapter 8, where we discuss this distribution, we write, for simplicity, P_r instead of $P(X = x_r)$.

A(ii) Poisson Distribution X is a discrete random variable with range $0, 1, 2, \ldots,$ such that

$$p(x_r) = P(X = x_r) = \frac{e^{-\mu}\mu^r}{r!} \tag{5.23}$$

for $r = 1, 2, \ldots$. Here, μ, the only parameter of this distribution, is a positive constant, and is equal to both the mean and variance of the Poisson distribution. This distribution becomes a good approximation to the binomial distribution with $\mu = np$, when n is large and p is small. In Chapter 9, where we use this distribution, we write P_r instead of $P(X = x_r)$.

B. Continuous Probability Distributions
(Probability Density Functions)

B(i) Normal Distribution   A random variable X is said to be normally distributed if its probability density function is given by

$$p(x) = \frac{1}{\sigma\sqrt{2\pi}} e^{-(x-\mu)^2/2\sigma^2} \tag{5.24}$$

with $-\infty < x < +\infty$, and where μ and σ are, respectively, the mean and variance as well as the two parameters of the distribution. Any normal distribution can be transformed into a standard form, $f(z)$, by putting $z = (x - \mu)/\sigma$. Hence,

$$f(z) = \frac{1}{\sqrt{2\pi}} e^{-z^2/2}. \tag{5.25}$$

The normal distribution is the best-known and most widely used distribution in statistics.

B(ii) Lognormal Distribution   A random variable X has a lognormal probability distribution if $\log_e X$ is normally distributed. The density function of the lognormal distribution is given by

$$p(x) = \frac{1}{\zeta x\sqrt{2\pi}} e^{-(\log_e x - \lambda)^2/2\zeta^2} \tag{5.26}$$

where $x > 0$, $\zeta > 0$, mean $= \mu = e^{(\lambda + \zeta^2/2)}$, variance $= \sigma^2 = (e^{\zeta^2} - 1)e^{(2\lambda + \zeta^2)}$, and λ and ζ are the parameters of the distribution.

---

[9] See page 136.

B(iii) Weibull Distribution The probability density function for the Weibull distribution is given by

$$p(x) = m\gamma x^{m-1} e^{-\gamma x^m} \tag{5.27}$$

with $x \geq 0$, $\gamma > 0$, and $m > 1$. The parameters of this distribution are m and γ, as explained in Chapter 13.

B(iv) Exponential Distribution When $m = 1$ and $\gamma = 1/\lambda$, Eq. (5.27) reduces to the following probability density function of the exponential distribution

$$p(x) = \frac{1}{\lambda} e^{-x/\lambda} \tag{5.28}$$

with $0 \leq x \leq \infty$. The parameter of this distribution is λ, which is also equal to the mean μ. The variance is given by $\sigma^2 = \lambda^2$.

Among other widely known distributions are the chi-squared (χ^2) distribution, the F distribution, and the t distribution. These are extremely important in statistical analyses and shall be described in the context of sampling and sampling distributions in Chapter 6.

It should be emphasized that, as we have seen above, the parameters of a distribution are not necessarily its mean and variance.

We can calculate means, variances, and other parameters of a population from its probability distribution similarly to the calculation of sample statistics from a frequency distribution (discussed in Chapters 3 and 4). This leads us to the subject of expectation.

EXPECTATION

We sometimes find that it is not necessary to deal with the entire probability distribution but only with representative values; one such value is the mean, average, or *expected value* of the random variable of the probability distribution; in fact, the expected value of the random variable is the centroid of the probability mass. We can, therefore, think of expectation simply as the theoretical or long-run average of the quantity in question; alternatively, expectation is the average value of a statistic if it were calculated from an infinite number of equal-sized samples from a given population.

Consider a random variable x. If x is discrete with a probability distribution p, then the *expected value* of x (or mean of x) is defined as

$$E(x) = \sum_i p_i x_i \tag{5.29}$$

where x_i is the value of the ith event and p_i is the probability of the ith event.

Now, if x is continuous with $p(x)$, the probability density function, then

$$E(x) = \int_{-\infty}^{+\infty} x p(x) \, dx \tag{5.30}$$

or, we can write

$$\mu = E(x)$$

where μ is the mean of the probability distribution.

EXAMPLE

Find the mean μ for the example on the upturned faces of two fair dice. Using Eq. (5.29), we obtain

$$E(x) = \mu = 2(\tfrac{1}{36}) + 3(\tfrac{2}{36}) + 4(\tfrac{3}{36}) + 5(\tfrac{4}{36}) + 6(\tfrac{5}{36}) + 7(\tfrac{6}{36}) + 8(\tfrac{5}{36})$$
$$+ 9(\tfrac{4}{36}) + 10(\tfrac{3}{36}) + 11(\tfrac{2}{36}) + 12(\tfrac{1}{36}) = \tfrac{252}{36} = 7. \quad \blacksquare\blacksquare$$

EXAMPLE

The probability density function, $p(x)$, of the life of electric light bulbs, random variable x, is given as

$$p(x) = 0 \quad \text{for} \quad x < 0$$

and

$$p(x) = \frac{1}{800} e^{(-x/800)} \quad \text{for} \quad x \geqslant 0$$

as shown in Fig. 5.20. Using Eq. (5.30), we obtain

$$E(x) = \mu = \int_{-\infty}^{+\infty} xp(x)\,dx = \int_{0}^{+\infty} \frac{x}{800} e^{(-x/800)}\,dx$$

$$= 800 \text{ h}.$$

(This definite integral can be solved by the use of standard integral tables or by integration by parts.) $\quad \blacksquare\blacksquare$

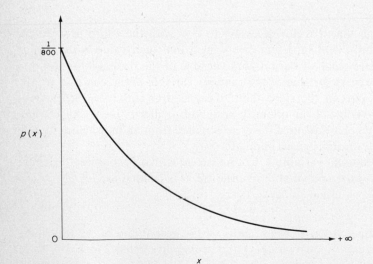

Figure 5.20

Another important constant is that which measures the spread of the probability distribution about its mean, μ, that is, the variance of the random variable x.

The variance σ^2 of x is the *expected* value of the squared deviation from the population mean. Thus,

$$\text{Var}(x) = \sigma^2 = E[(x - \mu)^2]$$

$$= \sum_i p_i(x_i - \mu)^2 \qquad \text{if } x \text{ is discrete,} \qquad (5.31)$$

and $\qquad \text{Var}(x) = \sigma^2 = E(x - \mu)^2$

$$= \int_{-\infty}^{+\infty} (x - \mu)^2 p(x)\,dx \qquad \text{if } x \text{ is continuous.} \qquad (5.32)$$

It should be noted that the expressions for $E(x)$ and $E(x - \mu)^2$ are, respectively, the first moment of the probability distribution about the origin and the second moment about the mean.

In fact, the mean and variance of the random variable are the same as the mean and variance of the population. In the limiting case of zero variance, the random variable takes on a single value with a probability equal to one, that is, it is deterministic.

The usefulness of the concept of expectation is that it corresponds to our intuitive ideal of average. Since the concept will be found to be helpful in subsequent chapters, we shall now list, without proof, some rules governing mathematical expectations. Each result follows from our definition of expected value. The derivation is left as an exercise for the reader.

Rule 1: $E(C) = C$, where C is a constant.
Rule 2: $\text{Var}(C) = 0$.
Rule 3: $E(Cx) = CE(x)$.
Rule 4: $\text{Var}(Cx) = C^2\,\text{Var}(x)$.
Rule 5: $E(x \pm y) = E(x) \pm E(y)$.

If x and y are independent random variables, then:

Rule 6: $E(x \times y) = E(x) \times E(y)$.
Rule 7: $\text{Var}(x \pm y) = \text{Var}(x) + \text{Var}(y)$.

EXAMPLE

Determine the expectation and variance of the random variable, $y = a + bx$, where a and b are constants.

$$E(y) = E(a + bx) = E(a) + E(bx)$$
$$= a + bE(x), \qquad \text{by Rules 1 and 3.}$$
$$\text{Var}(y) = \text{Var}(a + bx) = \text{Var}(a) + \text{Var}(bx)$$
$$= 0 + b^2\,\text{Var}(x) = b^2\,\text{Var}(x), \qquad \text{by Rules 2 and 4.} \qquad \blacksquare\ \blacksquare$$

EXAMPLE

Determine the expectation and variance of the random variable $z = (x - \mu)/\sigma$.

$$E(z) = E\left(\frac{x - \mu}{\sigma}\right) = \frac{1}{\sigma} E(x - \mu) = \frac{1}{\sigma} [E(x) - E(\mu)]$$

$$= \frac{1}{\sigma} [\mu - \mu], \qquad \text{by Rule 1 and by definition of expected value.}$$

Therefore, $E(z) = 0$.

$$\text{Var}(z) = \text{Var}\left(\frac{x - \mu}{\sigma}\right) = \frac{1}{\sigma^2} [\text{Var}(x) - \text{Var}(\mu)]$$

$$= \frac{1}{\sigma^2} [\sigma^2 - 0], \qquad \text{by Rule 2 and by definition of Var}(x).$$

Therefore, $\text{Var}(z) = 1$.   ■ ■

Another measure of variation which is useful is the covariance of two random variables, x and y, $\text{Cov}(x, y)$; this is a measure of how the two variables vary together, that is, how they co-vary. It is defined as

$$\text{Cov}(x, y) = E[(x - \mu_x)(y - \mu_y)] \tag{5.33}$$

where $\mu_x = E(x)$ and $\mu_y = E(y)$. The covariance is the analog of the product of inertia. Thus,

$$\text{Cov}(x, y) = E[xy - \mu_x y - \mu_y x + \mu_x \mu_y]$$
$$= E(xy) - \mu_x E(y) - \mu_y E(x) + \mu_x \mu_y$$

or $$\text{Cov}(x, y) = E(xy) - \mu_x \mu_y - \mu_y \mu_x + \mu_x \mu_y.$$

Therefore, $$\text{Cov}(x, y) = E(xy) - \mu_x \mu_y. \tag{5.34}$$

It can be noted that variance is a special case of covariance of a random variable with itself, that is,

$$\text{Cov}(x, x) = E(xx) - \mu_x \mu_x = E(x^2) - \mu_x^2,$$

or, dropping the subscript x,

$$\text{Cov}(x, x) = E(x^2) - \mu^2 = \text{Var}(x).$$

This can be illustrated by the following example. Determine the expectation of the random variable x^2. By definition,

$$\text{Var}(x) = \sigma^2 = E(x - \mu)^2$$
$$= E(x^2 - 2x + \mu^2) = E(x^2) - 2E(x) + E(\mu^2)$$

or $$\text{Var}(x) = E(x^2 - 2\mu\mu + \mu^2) = E(x^2) - \mu^2,$$

a result which proves that $\text{Cov}(x, x) = \text{Var}(x)$. This result also shows that

$$E(x^2) = \sigma^2 + \mu^2, \tag{5.35}$$

an expression which is used in subsequent chapters. The expectation of more complicated analytic functions can be derived by expanding them in a Taylor series and then taking a termwise expectation. This will be discussed under the heading of propagation of errors in Chapter 16.

EXAMPLE

Determine $E(\bar{x})$, $Var(\bar{x})$, and $E(s^2)$, where $\bar{x}$ is the mean of a random sample,

$$E(\bar{x}) = E\left(\frac{\sum x}{n}\right) = \frac{1}{n}\sum E(x)$$

$$= \frac{1}{n}\sum \mu = \frac{1}{n} n\mu = \mu. \tag{5.36}$$

$$Var(\bar{x}) = Var\left(\frac{\sum x}{n}\right) = \frac{1}{n^2} Var(\sum x)$$

$$= \frac{1}{n^2}\sum Var(x) = \frac{1}{n^2} n\sigma^2 = \frac{\sigma^2}{n}. \tag{5.37}$$

$$E(s^2) = E\left[\frac{\sum(x - \bar{x})^2}{n - 1}\right] = \frac{1}{n - 1} E[\sum(x^2 - 2x\bar{x} + \bar{x}^2)]$$

$$= \frac{1}{n - 1} E[\sum x^2 - n\bar{x}^2]$$

$$= \frac{1}{n - 1} \{\sum [E(x^2)] - nE(\bar{x}^2)\}$$

$$= \frac{1}{n - 1} \left\{\sum(\sigma^2 + \mu^2) - n\left(\frac{\sigma^2}{n} + \mu^2\right)\right\},$$

that is, $$E(s^2) = \frac{1}{n - 1} [n\sigma^2 + n\mu^2 - \sigma^2 - n\mu^2]$$

$$= \frac{(n - 1)\sigma^2}{n - 1} = \sigma^2. \tag{5.38}$$

■ ■

TCHEBYSHEFF'S THEOREM

Tchebysheff derived an equality which relates the mean and the standard deviation of probability distributions whose density function need not be known. The theorem states: if x is a random variable with mean μ and variance σ^2, then, for any positive value c,

$$P(|x - \mu| \leqslant c\sigma) \geqslant 1 - \frac{1}{c^2}. \tag{5.39}$$

This can be rewritten as

$$P(\mu - c\sigma \leqslant x \leqslant \mu + c\sigma) \geqslant 1 - \frac{1}{c^2}.$$

For example, when $c = 2.5$, then the interval $\mu - 2.5$ to $\mu + 2.5$ will contain

$$\text{probability area} = 1 - \frac{1}{c^2} = 1 - \frac{1}{(2.5)^2} = 0.84.$$

In design problems, the constant c is related to the safety of a particular design by establishing bounds for the safety region. Although these bounds are invariably conservative, the Tchebysheff's inequality remains quite popular due to its simplicity and generality.

PERMUTATIONS

Many problems in probability reduce to that of counting the elements which make up the events. Counting such elements is often simplified by using the rules for permutations and combinations so that probabilities in some complicated problems can be readily handled. Although the topics of permutations and combinations are undoubtedly familiar to the majority of readers, for the sake of presenting a complete picture, brief notes are given below.

The number of permutations of n different items is the number of different arrangements in which these items can be placed. We can take all n items every time, or r ($r < n$) items at a time. Not only their identity, but also the order in which the items are arranged is significant.

We write the number of permutations as $_nP_r$, n being the number of items available and r the number chosen at a time. Thus, if all items are chosen every time, the number of permutations is $_nP_n$.

In the general case, we have r places to fill with n items to choose from so that

> the first place can be filled in n ways,
>
> the second place can be filled in $n - 1$ ways,
>
> the third place can be filled in $n - 2$ ways,
>
> $\vdots$
>
> the rth place can be filled in $n - r + 1$ ways.

We now apply a fundamental principle which states that if one selection can be made in p ways and if, after this selection has been made, the second selection can be made in q ways, the two selections together can be made in pq ways. Using this principle in succession, the number of permutations is

$$_nP_r = n(n - 1)(n - 2) \cdots (n - r + 1)$$

$$= \frac{n!}{(n - r)!} \tag{5.40}$$

in which $n!$ is the symbol for factorial $n = 1 \times 2 \times 3 \times \cdots (n-1)n$.
When $r = n$,

$$_nP_n = n! \tag{5.41}$$

since by definition $0! = 1$.

EXAMPLE

How many three-digit numbers can be formed from the numbers 1, 2, 3, ' and 5 if each number can be repeated?

The first place can be filled in five ways; the second place can also be filled in five ways; and so can the third place. Hence, we can form

$$5 \times 5 \times 5 = 125 \text{ different numbers.} \quad \blacksquare \blacksquare$$

EXAMPLE

How many four-digit numbers can be formed from the numbers 1 to 9? There is no provision for repeating any number within any four-digit number. We can thus use the standard expression with $n = 9$ and $r = 4$:

$$_nP_r = \frac{n!}{(n-r)!} = \frac{9!}{5!} = 9 \times 8 \times 7 \times 6 = 3024 \text{ numbers.} \quad \blacksquare \blacksquare$$

EXAMPLE

A product is coded by three letters and two numbers, the letters preceding the numbers. Only the letters A and B and the numbers 1 to 6 can be used. How many different code "numbers" are possible?

Consider the letters:

each can appear as A or B, i.e., in 2 ways.

Therefore,

3 letters can be arranged in $2 \times 2 \times 2 = 8$ ways.

Consider the numbers:

each can appear as 1 or 2 or $\cdots$ or 6, i.e., in 6 ways.

Therefore,

2 numbers can be arranged in $6 \times 6 = 36$ ways.

Thus the total number of code "numbers" is $8 \times 36 = 288$.

Consider now the permutation of n items taken all at a time, when the n items consist of r_1 alike, r_2 alike, ..., r_k alike, so that

$$r_1 + r_2 + \cdots + r_k = n.$$

The number of permutations is then

$$P = \frac{n!}{r_1! r_2! \cdots r_k!}. \tag{5.42} \quad \blacksquare \blacksquare$$

EXAMPLE

How many different patterns (in a single row) can be made with 3 yellow tabs, 2 red ones, and 7 green ones?

We have

$$n = 3 + 2 + 7 = 12.$$

From Eq. (5.42),

$$P = \frac{12!}{3! \times 2! \times 7!} = 7920. \qquad \blacksquare \ \blacksquare$$

COMBINATIONS

The number of combinations of n different items is the number of different selections of r items each, without reference to the order or arrangement of the items in the group. This disregard of arrangement distinguishes combinations from permutations.

The reason that r items can be arranged in $r!$ ways is that:

the first place can be filled in r ways,

the second place can be filled in $r - 1$ ways,

the third place can be filled in $r - 2$ ways,

$$\vdots$$

the last can be filled in 1 way,

so that r places can be filled in $r(r - 1)(r - 2) \cdots 1 = r!$ ways.

Thus the number of combinations of r items from n items, denoted by

$$_nC_r \quad \text{or} \quad \binom{n}{r}$$

is $r!$ times smaller than the number of permutations. Hence,

$$_nC_r = \frac{_nP_r}{r!} = \frac{n!}{(n - r)!r!}. \tag{5.43}$$

It follows from symmetry that

$$_nC_r = {_nC_{n-r}}. \tag{5.44}$$

The use of this identity may save time in computations.

EXAMPLE

In how many ways can a team of 9 be selected from 12 people? This is evidently a problem of selection and not of arrangement, as the assignment of positions is not considered. We use, therefore, Eq. (5.43) with $n = 12$ and $r = 9$

$$_nC_r = \frac{n!}{r!(n - r)!} = \frac{12!}{9! \times 3!} = \frac{12 \times 11 \times 10}{2 \times 3} = 220. \qquad \blacksquare \ \blacksquare$$

EXAMPLE

From 5 men and 4 women, in how many ways can we select a group of 3 men and 2 women?

a. We can select 3 men from 5 men in $_5C_3$ ways.
b. We can select 2 women from 4 women in $_4C_2$ ways.

By the fundamental principle of selections we can do (a) and (b) in $_5C_3 \times {}_4C_2$ ways. Thus the number of possible selections is

$$\frac{5 \times 4}{2} \times \frac{4 \times 3}{2} = 60. \qquad \blacksquare\ \blacksquare$$

EXAMPLE

From 6 men and 5 women, how many committees of 8 members can be formed when each committee is to contain at least 3 women?

The conditions of the problem are satisfied if a committee contains

5 men and 3 women	selected in $_6C_5 \times {}_5C_3$ ways
4 men and 4 women	selected in $_6C_4 \times {}_5C_4$ ways
3 men and 5 women	selected in $_6C_3 \times {}_5C_5$ ways.

The number of possible committees is thus:

$$_6C_5 \times {}_5C_3 + {}_6C_4 \times {}_5C_4 + {}_6C_3 \times {}_5C_5 = 155. \qquad \blacksquare\ \blacksquare$$

It frequently happens that a problem involves both a selection and an arrangement with a limitation upon either or both. A safe procedure is to deal first with the selections (combinations) and then with the arrangements (permutations).

EXAMPLE

How many lineups are possible in choosing a hockey team composed of 4 seniors and 2 juniors from 8 seniors and 7 juniors if any man can be used in any position?

4 seniors can be selected in $_8C_4$ ways

2 juniors can be selected in $_7C_2$ ways.

Hence, a team of players can be selected in $_8C_4 \times {}_7C_2$ ways. Any one set of 6 men can be arranged in 6! ways. Thus the total number of possible lineups is $_8C_4 \times {}_7C_2 \times 6! = 1,058,400.$ $\qquad \blacksquare\ \blacksquare$

EXAMPLE

Suppose that in the last example any chosen team had to include a certain senior player for center and a certain junior player as a goal keeper. How many lineups are then possible?

When a particular senior player is always included in a team, the problem is to find the number of combinations of 3 seniors from the remaining 7 seniors, and with regard to juniors, to find the number of combinations of 1 junior from the remaining 6 juniors. Thus

$$3 \text{ seniors can be selected in } _7C_3 \text{ ways}$$
$$1 \text{ junior can be selected in } _6C_1 \text{ ways.}$$

Hence, a team of players can be selected in $_7C_3 \times {}_6C_1$ ways.

Since the positions of goal and center are already assigned, the remaining four positions in any one team can be filled in 4! ways. Thus the total number of possible lineups is $_7C_3 \times {}_6C_1 \times 4! = 5040.$ ■ ■

It is important to observe that $_nC_r$ is the coefficient of the $(r + 1)$th term in the binomial expression $(a + b)^n$, whose expansion is

$$(a + b)^n = a^n + na^{n-1}b + \frac{n(n - 1)}{2!} a^{n-2}b^2 + \cdots$$

$$+ \frac{n(n - 1) \cdots (n - r + 1)}{r!} a^{n-r}b^r + \cdots + b^n \qquad (5.45)$$

and can be conveniently written as:

$$(a + b)^n = a^n + {}_nC_1 a^{n-1}b + {}_nC_2 a^{n-2}b^2 + \cdots + {}_nC_r a^{n-r}b^r + \cdots + b^n$$

or
$$(a + b)^n = \sum_{r=0}^{n} {}_nC_r a^{n-r}b^r \qquad (5.46)$$

provided that we define $_nC_0 = 1$.

The use of binomial coefficients is considered again in Chapter 8.

SOLVED PROBLEMS

5-1. A machine contains a component A that is vital to its operation. The reliability of component A is 80 percent. To improve the reliability of the machine, a similar component is used in parallel to form system S, as shown in Fig. 5.21. The machine will work, provided that one of these components functions correctly. Calculate the reliability of the system S.

Solution. Denote the probability of success of A as $P(A)$ and the probability of its failure as $P(\bar{A})$. Given $P(A) = 0.8$, we have $P(\bar{A}) = 0.2$. The probability of both components A failing simultaneously is $P(\bar{A}) \cdot P(\bar{A}) = 0.04$. Therefore, the probability of at least one component A functioning properly is $1 - 0.04 = 0.96$, which is the reliability of the system S.

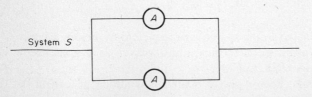

Figure 5.21

5-2. An experimental fighter aircraft is estimated to have a probability of 0.85 for a successful first flight. In case of failure there is a 0.05 probability of a catastrophic explosion, in which case the abort system cannot be used. The abort system has a reliability of 0.95. Calculate the probability of every possible outcome of the initial flight.

Solution. Let us define the events: flight success as A; flight failure as $\bar{A}$; non-catastrophic failure as B; catastrophic failure as $\bar{B}$; successful abort as C; abort failure as $\bar{C}$; pilot survives as D; pilot is killed as $\bar{D}$.

From the nature of the problem, we note that A is mutually exclusive with B, $\bar{B}$, C, $\bar{C}$, and $\bar{D}$, since a successful flight cannot be associated with catastrophic or noncatastrophic failure, abort success or failure, or with the pilot's being killed. Similarly, $\bar{B}$ is mutually exclusive with C, $\bar{C}$, and D. Also, C is mutually exclusive with $\bar{D}$.

Now $P(A) = 0.85$ and hence $P(\bar{A}) = 1 - 0.85 = 0.15$, since events A and $\bar{A}$ are complementary.

$$P(\bar{A}\bar{B}) = P(\bar{A})\,P(\bar{B}\,|\,\bar{A}).$$

But a catastrophic failure ($\bar{B}$) can only occur if a flight failure ($\bar{A}$) occurs. Thus we can write

$$\begin{aligned}
P(\bar{B}) = P(\bar{A}\bar{B}) &= P(\bar{A})\,P(\bar{B}\,|\,\bar{A}) \\
&= (0.15)(0.05) \\
&= 0.0075.
\end{aligned}$$

Similarly,
$$\begin{aligned}
P(B) = P(\bar{A}B) &= P(\bar{A})\,P(B\,|\,\bar{A}) \\
&= (0.15)(0.95) \\
&= 0.1425
\end{aligned}$$

$$\begin{aligned}
P(C) = P(CB) &= P(B)\,P(C\,|\,B) \\
&= (0.1425)(0.95) \\
&= 0.1354
\end{aligned}$$

$$\begin{aligned}
P(D) &= P(A) + P(C) \\
&= 0.85 + 0.1354 \\
&= 0.9854
\end{aligned}$$

$$P(\bar{D}) = 1 - P(D) = 0.0146$$

(since events D and D are complementary)

$$\begin{aligned}
P(\bar{C}) = P(\bar{C}B) &= P(B)\,P(\bar{C}\,|\,B) \\
&= (0.1425)(0.05) \\
&= 0.007125.
\end{aligned}$$

To check our solution, we see that

$$P(\bar{D}) = P(\bar{B}) + P(\bar{C})$$

$$0.0146 = 0.0075 + 0.0071.$$

5-3. A traffic study is to be conducted at an intersection. The study consists of observing the movement of pairs of vehicles entering the intersection; each vehicle can turn right, left or continue straight ahead.

    a. Determine the simple events and their probabilities, if all possible outcomes are equally likely.

b. Find the probability: that both vehicles turn left; that at least one vehicle makes a turn; that at least one vehicle turns right.

c. Find the probability that at least one of the two vehicles turns right, given that at least one of the two vehicles turns.

Solution

a. A simple event here is an ordered pair made up of the first and the second vehicles. Thus, if we denote a vehicle turning right by R, left by L, and continuing straight ahead by S, then the simple events are: $RR, RL, RS, LR, LL, LS, SR, SL, SS$. Since there are 9 possible outcomes, all equally likely, the probability of each is $\frac{1}{9}$.

b. Probability that both vehicles turn left $= P(LL) = \frac{1}{9}$.

Probability that at least one vehicle makes a turn $= 1 - P(SS) = 1 - \frac{1}{9} = \frac{8}{9}$.

Probability that at least one vehicle turns right $= P(RR, RL, RS, LR, SR) = \frac{5}{9}$.

c. Define the following events:

$$A = \text{at least one of the two vehicles turns right}$$
$$B = \text{at least one of the two vehicles turns.}$$

Thus,

$$P(A|B) = \frac{P(AB)}{P(B)} = \frac{P(A)}{P(B)} = \frac{\frac{5}{9}}{\frac{8}{9}} = \frac{5}{8}.$$

5-4. The probability distribution for the number of defects (X) in a random sample is as follows:

x	0	1	2	3	4
$P(x)$	0.35	0.40	0.20	0.04	0.01

Calculate the expected value, variance, and standard deviation for the random variable X.[10]

Solution. From Eq. (5.29), and writing x for X:

$$E(x) = \mu = \sum p_i x_i$$
$$= (0) \times (0.35) + (1) \times (0.40) + (2) \times (0.20)$$
$$+ (3) \times (0.04) + (4) \times (0.01)$$
$$= 0.96.$$

From Eq. (5.31),

$$\text{Var}(x) = \sigma^2 = \sum p_i (x_i - \mu)^2$$
$$= (0.35) \times (0 - 0.96)^2 + (0.40) \times (1 - 0.96)^2$$
$$+ (0.20) \times (2 - 0.96)^2 + (0.04) \times (3 - 0.96)^2$$
$$+ (0.01) \times (4 - 0.96)^2$$
$$= 0.80.$$

$$\text{Standard deviation of } X = \sqrt{\text{Var}(x)}$$
$$= \sqrt{\sigma^2}$$
$$= 0.89.$$

---

[10] As mentioned on page 78, X refers to a random variable, whereas x refers to the particular sample values taken on by the random variable.

5-5. Given that $E(x) = 4$ and $E[x(x - 1)] = 30$, calculate
a. $E(x^2)$, and
b. $\text{Var}(x)$.

Solution
a. Expanding $E[x(x - 1)]$, we have:

$$E[x(x - 1)] = E(x^2 - x) = E(x^2) - E(x).$$

Hence,

$$E(x^2) = 30 + 4 = 34.$$

b. From Eq. (5.35),

$$E(x^2) = \sigma^2 + \mu^2.$$

Since $E(x) = \mu$, $\mu^2 = 16$. Therefore,

$$\text{Var}(x) = \sigma^2 = E(x^2) - \mu^2$$
$$= 34 - 16$$
$$= 18.$$

5-6. Industrial and automobile exhausts contribute to the air pollution of the environment. In the next decade, the chances of successfully controlling these two sources of pollution are, respectively, 85 percent and 70 percent. It is assumed that, if only one of the two sources is successfully controlled, the probability of reducing the pollution below an acceptable level is 0.85.
a. What is the probability of successfully controlling air pollution in the next decade?
b. If, in the next decade, the pollution level is not sufficiently controlled, what is the probability that this is due to the failure to control automobile exhaust?

Solution. Let I and A denote, respectively, the events of controlling industrial and automobile exhausts. There are 4 events, namely: AI, $A\bar{I}$, $\bar{A}I$, $\bar{A}\bar{I}$. Their probabilities are

$$P(AI) = (0.70) \times (0.85) = 0.595$$
$$P(A\bar{I}) = (0.70) \times (0.15) = 0.105$$
$$P(\bar{A}I) = (0.30) \times (0.85) = 0.255$$
$$P(\bar{A}\bar{I}) = (0.30) \times (0.15) = 0.045.$$

Let us denote the event of controlling air pollution by C. Then
a. $P(C) = (1.0) \times (0.595) + (0.85) \times (0.105) + (0.85) \times (0.255)$
$\qquad + (0) \times (0.045)$
$\qquad = 0.91.$

b. $P(\bar{A}I|\bar{C}) = \dfrac{P(\bar{C}|\bar{A}I)\, P(\bar{A}I)}{P(\bar{C})}$

$\qquad = \dfrac{(1 - 0.85) \times 0.255}{0.09}$

$\qquad = 0.42.$

5-7. How many straight lines are determined by 10 points, no 3 of which are in the same straight line?

Solution. The number of combinations of 2 points for a straight line from 10 points is

$$_{10}C_2 = \frac{10!}{2!8!} = \frac{10 \times 9}{2} = 45 \text{ lines.}$$

5-8.

a. In how many ways can 6 soldiers stand in a line so that two soldiers in particular will not be next to one another?

b. Show that

$$(1) \quad _nC_r + {}_nC_{r-1} = {}_{n+1}C_r$$

and

$$(2) \quad _{n+2}C_{r+1} = {}_nC_{r+1} + 2{}_nC_r + {}_nC_{r-1}.$$

c. A university senate is composed of 50 staff members of whom 6 are engineers. In how many ways can a committee of 10 be chosen so as to contain at least 4 engineers?

Solution

a. Let us consider 5 soldiers. These can be arranged in $n! = 5!$ ways. For each arrangement of these 5 soldiers, the sixth one can stand in four different locations without being adjacent to the particular soldier in question (see Fig. 5.22). Therefore,

$$\text{total number of ways} = 4 \times 5! = 480.$$

b. (1) Expanding the left-hand side, we have

$$_nC_r + {}_nC_{r-1} = \frac{n!}{r!(n-r)!} + \frac{n!}{(r-1)!(n-r+1)!}$$

$$= \frac{n!(n-r+1)}{r!(n-r+1)!} + \frac{n!r}{r!(n-r+1)!}$$

$$= \frac{n!(n+1)}{r!(n-r+1)!}.$$

Therefore, $$_nC_r + {}_nC_{r-1} = \frac{(n+1)!}{r!(n-r+1)!}.$$

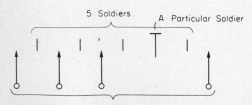

Figure 5.22

But
$$_{n+1}C_r = \frac{(n + 1)!}{r!(n + 1 - r)!},$$

Thus,
$$_nC_r + {}_nC_{r-1} = {}_{n+1}C_r.$$

(2) Expanding the right-hand side of the given identity, we have

$$_nC_{r+1} + 2{}_nC_r + {}_nC_{r-1}$$

$$= \frac{n!}{(r + 1)!(n - r - 1)!}$$

$$+ \frac{2n!}{r!(n - r)!} + \frac{n!}{(r - 1)!(n - r + 1)!}$$

$$= \frac{n![(n - r)(n - r + 1) + 2(r + 1)(n - r + 1) + r(r + 1)]}{(r + 1)!(n - r + 1)!}$$

$$= \frac{n!(n + 1)(n + 2)}{(r + 1)!(n - r + 1)!}$$

$$= \frac{(n + 2)!}{(r + 1)!(n - r + 1)!}.$$

But
$$_{n+2}C_{r+1} = \frac{(n + 2)!}{(r + 1)!(n + 2 - r - 1)!} = \frac{(n + 2)!}{(r + 1)!(n - r + 1)!}.$$

Thus the two sides of the identity are equivalent.

c. A committee of 10 can be chosen so that there are either 4, 5, or 6 engineers on it. Hence, the number of possible selections is

$$(_6C_4 \times {}_{44}C_6) + (_6C_5 \times {}_{44}C_5) + (_6C_6 \times {}_{44}C_4)$$

$$= \frac{6!}{4!2!} \times \frac{44!}{6!38!} + \frac{6!}{5!1!} \times \frac{44!}{5!39!} + \frac{6!}{6!0!} \times \frac{44!}{4!40!}$$

$$= 112{,}537{,}579 \text{ ways (an adequate number even for academics).}$$

PROBLEMS

5-1. From a box containing 20 balls, one-half of them white, one-half black, four balls are drawn at random. What is the probability of obtaining: **(a)** all of them of the same color; **(b)** all of them black; **(c)** all of them black if each ball is replaced before the next one is drawn?

5-2. In dealing a pack of 52 cards to four players, what is the probability of one of them obtaining 13 cards of a given suit?

5-3. If one-quarter of the dancers are eliminated after each dance, the elimination being random, what is the mathematical probability of successfully completing 5 consecutive dances?

5-4. A fair die is tossed twice. Find **(a)** the probability of a 3 turning up at least once, **(b)** the probability of getting a 3, 4, or 5 on the first toss and 1, 2, 3, or 6 on the second toss.

Figure 5.23

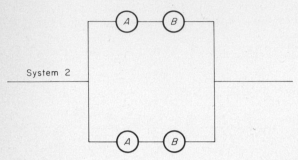

Figure 5.24

5-5. In a classroom it was required to seat 7 men students and 6 women students in a row so that the women occupy the even places. How many such arrangements are possible?

5-6. In the "football pools" operated in England one has to predict the result of 14 matches, there being three possible results of each match (home win, away win, and draw). How many entries would you have to submit in order to make sure that the winning entry is included?

5-7. A system has two components, A and B. If the probability of A's failing is 0.7 and the probability of B's failing is 0.8, what is the probability of: **(a)** the system's remaining sound; **(b)** both components failing; **(c)** either component's failing?

5-8. Two machines have components A and B arranged in the systems shown in Figs. 5.23 and 5.24. The reliabilities of correct functioning of components A and B, are 0.7 and 0.8, respectively. Assuming that A and B function independently of each other, determine the reliability of each system if:
    a. Both components must function correctly for system 1 to function correctly (see Fig. 5.23).
    b. The components are connected in parallel in such a way that, if either link $A-B$ functions correctly, system 2 functions correctly (see Fig. 5.24).

5-9. The probability that a missile propulsion system will function is 0.90 and the probability that its guidance system will work is 0.80. What is the probability of a successful mission?

5-10. The chance that a certain old bridge will fail is 0.002. A new bridge will cost $50,000. If losses for the bridge failure will amount to $5 million, determine whether the new bridge should be built.

5-11. A system consists of components A and B; it functions 0.06 of the time. Experience has shown that component A fails 0.14 of the time and component B fails 0.24 of the time. Determine whether components A and B perform independently of each other.

5-12. A loaded die was tossed. The toss values 1, 2, 3, 4, 5, and 6 occurred with probabilities $\frac{1}{4}$, $\frac{1}{3}$, $\frac{1}{12}$, $\frac{1}{12}$, p, and $\frac{1}{6}$, respectively.

    a. Calculate the value p.

    b. Find probability $(2 \leqslant x < 5)$.

    c. Compute the cumulative distribution function.

5-13. A machine produces daily either 0, 1, 2, or 3 defective items with probabilities $\frac{1}{6}$, $\frac{1}{2}$, $\frac{1}{6}$, $\frac{1}{6}$, respectively. Calculate the mean value and the variance of the defective items turned out.

5-14. A probability distribution that approximates the number of defective rivets in an airplane is given by:

$$\text{probability } (x = c) = \frac{2^c e^{-2}}{c!} \quad \text{for} \quad c = 0, 1, 2, 3, \ldots$$

Calculate the probability that the number of defective rivets is less than or equal to 3. (Note that $0! = 1$.)

5-15. A certain tube has a life (in hours) with a probability density $p(x) = c/x^3$ where $x \geqslant 600$, and $p(x) = 0$, where $x < 600$. Find an expression for the cumulative distribution function of the tube life. Calculate the probability that a tube will last at least 1000 h. Calculate the mean of the tube life in hours.

5-16. The probability distributions for the number of vehicles X arriving at a certain intersection during a particular one-hour period is as follows:

x	0	1	2	3	4
$p(x)$	0.37	0.39	0.19	0.04	0.01

Calculate the expected value, variance, and standard deviation of the random variable X.

5-17. The cost in dollars of replacing two components A and B, jointly operating an electronic system, is given by

$$C = 100 + 3A + 5B.$$

Find:

    a. $E(C)$, and

    b. $\text{Var}(C)$.

5-18. The production of automobile transmissions at a certain plant has averaged 400 per day with a standard deviation of 40. Using Tchebysheff's Theorem:

    a. Find the fraction of days which will have a production output between 460 and 340.

    b. What is the shortest interval that will contain at least 95 percent of the daily production output?

5-19. Equal numbers of automobile transmissions are made in two different plants but are stored in the same warehouse. Transmissions from the warehouse are sampled and tested on a regular basis; from past experience it is known that 1.0 percent and 1.5 percent of the transmissions from plant A and B, respectively, are defective.

If a transmission is selected at random from the warehouse and is found to be defective, find the probability that it was made in plant B.

5-20. The switch system shown in Fig. 5.25 is an electric circuit with three relays. Components A and B are connected in series while components C and D are in parallel.

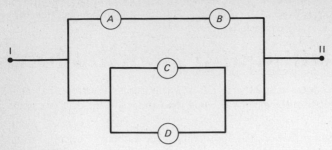

Figure 5.25

Each component operates independently of the others, and closes properly (i.e., it works) with a probability = 0.9.

    a. Find the probability that the current will flow from station I to station II when the relays are switched to the closed position.

    b. Find the probability that relay D is closed properly, given that current is flowing from station I to station II.

Chapter 6

Sampling Distributions

We have indicated earlier that probability theory is used to deal with problems of uncertainty. In this chapter, we link this theory to that objective of statistics which is to reach decisions about population parameters on the basis of information from the statistics computed from random samples drawn from the population studied. This is accomplished by: (i) taking a random sample from the population of interest; in so doing we let chance ensure randomness; (ii) calculating appropriate sample statistics, for example, mean $\bar{x}$ and variance s^2, (discussed in Chapters 3 and 4); (iii) on the basis of the data in hand and of the nature of the problem, choosing sampling distribution(s) of our sample statistics in order to make inferences about the unknown population parameters (various sampling distributions are described in this chapter); and (iv) stating the confidence in the inferences and conclusions made. The procedure of statistical inference is described in detail in Chapter 7.

SAMPLING

We shall now consider more fully some of the properties of samples. It is obvious that a complete knowledge of our population would be had if we could easily and economically measure or test *every* element of the population. However, testing the entire population is rarely practicable, especially in destructive tests or in tests involving a large expense or effort, and sampling is therefore resorted to. It is useful to note that, in most practical situations, sufficiently accurate and precise results describing the population can be obtained more quickly and economically by testing a sample from the population.

It is essential, however, that the sample be representative of the population from which it is drawn and it must, therefore, be drawn in a random manner—which means that every member of the population has an equal chance of being drawn in every trial.[1] How this is done in practice depends on the problem in hand.

Although we gave a simple definition of a random sample in Chapter 1, a more formal statement may be useful. A random sample has to satisfy two conditions: all sample values are independent, and the underlying population from which the successive samples are drawn remains the same. In shorthand, they may be said to be independent and identically distributed. These conditions of independence and identical distribution are met if any sample that can be drawn has an equal probability of being selected and if sampling is performed with replacement or from an infinite population. Moreover, when sampling is done without replacement from a finite population of size N such that $N \gg n$, where n is the sample size, then these conditions are approximately satisfied. In most practical problems and with proper procedures, we can assume that we are dealing with a random sample.

The need to have a random sample needs emphasizing. It arises from the fact that we wish to make inferences about a population on the basis of only a small sample selected from that population. The sample must be random to ensure that the probability theory (based on laws of chance) used in conjunction with the sample data provides a basis for correct inference. A random method of choosing a sampling will ensure that such a sample is representative of the population and is not biased in favor of a certain portion or proportion of the population.

We use the word *sample* in a very broad sense, meaning the observations (of any type) that have been made, while the term *population* refers to all the observations that could be made. Samples are tested for the purpose of making inferences about properties of the population, and the investigator must be clear as to what population he is interested in; for example, a particular batch of concrete, or all concrete placed in a given day, or all concrete in a given structure.

Tests on a sample can give results that are beyond doubt only so far as the sample itself is concerned. With respect to the underlying population a sampling investigation can give results only in terms of probability, and the confidence that we can have in our answers depends on the size of the sample.

There are two kinds of sampling—with and without replacement. In studying a particular property of a population, we may choose several items for measurement. If each item is chosen, measured, and then returned to the population, the sampling is said to be *with replacement*, since after each mea-

---

[1] The qualification "in every trial" precludes the use of methods such as choosing randomly a name in a list, and then taking every tenth name thereafter. The latter method would, for instance, in Scotland, result in a fixed proportion of people whose name begins with Mac being definitely included rather than being likely to be included.

surement the population remains the same as before and an item that has already been measured might be selected again. If each item is chosen one by one to form the sample and then measured, the sampling is said to be *without replacement*. Sampling with replacement is quite frequent; however, sampling without replacement is sometimes necessary, since the chosen items are destroyed in the process of measurement, for example, the testing of a concrete cylinder for strength. In deriving the equations in this chapter, it is assumed that sampling is without replacement.

DEFINITION OF SAMPLING DISTRIBUTION

A sampling distribution is a probability distribution of a sample statistic computed from all possible samples of size n randomly chosen from some population. In Chapters 3 and 4, we calculated sample statistics such as $\bar{x}$ and s. Let us consider further the sample mean, $\bar{x}$. If repeated random samples of the same size are drawn from a population being studied and the mean of each sample is calculated, we can construct a frequency distribution of $\bar{x}$. Now, imagine performing this experiment indefinitely; this will lead to a sampling frequency distribution of $\bar{x}$ from which the corresponding sampling probability distribution (or simply the sampling distribution) of $\bar{x}$ can be deduced by making the area under the frequency curve equal to unity.

Statistical inference is based on models of sampling distributions. In many practical situations, only *one* random sample is selected from the population in order to test a hypothesis or to estimate the value of a parameter. Indeed, the actual process of generating a sampling distribution by selecting an indefinite number of random samples from the population is virtually never carried out in practice. Sometimes, we could not do this even if we wanted to, because the exact population may not be known.

We shall see in succeeding sections that the sample mean, $\bar{x}$, and its variance $\sigma_{\bar{x}}^2$ are related to the mean and the variance of the population. It is these two sample statistics that enable us to assess the precision of our estimates of the parameters of the population based on only one random sample. It is important to remember that it is the sampling distribution which provides the underlying theoretical basis for the above statement. We should note that any sampling distributions of $\bar{x}$ and $\sigma_{\bar{x}}^2$ always refer to a particular population that is being sampled, in terms of a specific random sample size: if either the population or the sample size is changed, we obtain a new sampling distribution.

It may be worth emphasizing that conclusions about a population drawn from information about a sample are always subject to error. This sampling error is the difference between the value of a sample statistic and the corresponding population parameter, and can never be completely eliminated. There is always the possibility that the conclusion from an experiment is really due to a sampling error and not to a relation between the independent and dependent variables.

SAMPLING DISTRIBUTION OF THE SAMPLE MEAN, $\bar{x}$

In Chapter 4, we showed how an estimate of the population variance can be made from the sample variance; we shall now consider the determination of the population mean from the sample mean.

A problem that sometimes arises in the collection of data in practice is to decide how many observations to make. Specifically, if we are taking measurements of what is presumed to be the same unique quantity, and if we are satisfied to take the mean of the observations as the appropriate single measure, how is the accuracy increased, if at all, as the number of observations is increased? For example, suppose that a certain length has been measured by four people who have found it to be: 30.45 m, 30.20 m, 30.45 m, and 30.10 m. The mean is 30.30 m. Suppose that five more measurements are made by equally skilled people: 30.25 m, 30.15 m, 30.20 m, 30.40 m, and 30.05 m. The mean of all 9 measurements is 30.25 m instead of 30.30 m for the first four measurements. We can now ask: is 30.25 m a more accurate result than 30.30 m? If so, how much more accurate can we expect it to be?

We should intuitively expect a larger sample to yield a more accurate result, but in order to have a quantitative appreciation, we have to determine how the representative nature of a sample improves with the sample size.

Suppose that we have a population of N observations from which we draw samples, each of n observations. We find the mean of each sample:

$$\bar{x} = \frac{x_1 + x_2 + \cdots + x_n}{n}.$$

The number of different samples that can be drawn is the number of combinations of n elements from a population of N, that is,

$$_NC_n = \frac{N!}{n!(N-n)!}.$$

We shall now show that the mean of the means of all the samples is equal to the mean of the original population. Now, since there are $N!/[n!(N-n)!]$ samples, the mean of the means of all the samples is

$$\bar{\bar{x}} = \frac{\bar{x}_1 + \bar{x}_2 + \bar{x}_3 + \cdots}{\dfrac{N!}{n!(N-n)!}}.$$

That is,

$$\bar{\bar{x}} = \frac{\dfrac{(x_1 + x_2 + \cdots)}{n} + \dfrac{(x_1 + x_3 + \cdots)}{n} + \dfrac{(x_2 + x_3 + \cdots)}{n} + \cdots}{\dfrac{N!}{n!(N-n)!}}. \tag{6.1}$$

Consider all samples containing x_1. We obtain these by removing x_1 from the original N observations and selecting $n - 1$ observations out of the remaining $N - 1$. There are $(N-1)!/[(n-1)!(N-n)!]$ ways of doing this, and this will be the number of samples that contain x_1. Collecting all the terms of Eq. (6.1) containing x_1, we obtain the coefficient of x_1:

$$\frac{(N-1)!/[(n-1)!(N-n)!] \times 1/n}{N!/[n!(N-n)!]} = \frac{1}{N}.$$

Similarly, the coefficient of $x_2 = 1/N$, and the coefficient of $x_3 = 1/N$, and so on. Hence, the mean of all the means is

$$\bar{\bar{x}} = \frac{x_1}{N} + \frac{x_2}{N} + \frac{x_3}{N} + \cdots + \frac{x_N}{N}$$

$$= \frac{x_1 + x_2 + x_3 + \cdots + x_N}{N}$$

or, $\qquad\qquad \bar{\bar{x}} = \text{mean of the original population} - \mu.$ $\qquad\qquad$ (6.2)

This relation is also true for sampling with replacement. In this case, the number of samples would be N^n.

EXAMPLE

Consider observations: 1, 3, 4, 5, 12. Then $N = 5$. Take samples of 2 (i.e., $n = 2$) and verify that the mean of all the sample means = mean of the population (see Table 6.1).

$$\text{Number of different samples} = \frac{N!}{n!(N-n)!} = \frac{5!}{2!3!} = 10.$$

Mean of all sample means =

$$\bar{\bar{x}} = (2 + 2.5 + 3 + 6.5 + 3.5 + 4 + 7.5 + 4.5 + 8 + 8.5) \times \frac{1}{10} = 5.$$

$$\text{Mean of original population} = \mu = (1 + 3 + 4 + 5 + 12) \times \frac{1}{5} = 5.$$

Thus, $\bar{\bar{x}} = \mu$; that is, mean of all sample means = mean of original population. ■ ■

TABLE 6.1

Sample	Mean of sample	Number of samples
1, 3	2	
1, 4	2.5	
1, 5	3	$N - 1 = 4$
1, 12	6.5	
3, 4	3.5	
3, 5	4	$N - 2 = 3$
3, 12	7.5	
4, 5	4.5	
4, 12	8	$N - 3 = 2$
5, 12	8.5	$N - 4 = 1$
Total		10

This result can be found also by the use of rules governing expectations. If we put $\bar{\bar{x}} = \mu_{\bar{x}}$, we can use Eq. (5.36):

$$E(\bar{x}) = \text{mean of all sample means}, \mu_{\bar{x}} = \mu,$$

and hence Eq. (6.2).

By inspection of Table 6.1, we observe that the frequency for each sample mean is unity; if we plot the value of the sample mean, $\bar{x}$, as an observation against the frequency, the resulting plot is the sampling frequency distribution of $\bar{x}$.

So far we have established the value of the mean of all the sample means, but we still know nothing about how these sample means vary one from the other. We shall, therefore, now consider the distribution of the sample means, and also the relation between the standard deviation of the means and the standard deviation of the original population.

As before, we describe the population mean and standard deviation by μ and σ, respectively. The number of different samples was shown to be

$$\frac{N!}{n!(N-n)!}.$$

Therefore, using Eq. (4.1), the variance of the means of samples of size n drawn from a population of N is

$$\sigma_{\bar{x}}^2 = \frac{\sum(\bar{x} - \mu)^2}{N!/[n!(N-n)!]} \tag{6.3}$$

or, using the form of Eq. (4.1a),

$$\sigma_{\bar{x}}^2 = \frac{\sum \bar{x}^2}{N!/[n!(N-n)!]} - \mu^2. \tag{6.4}$$

In each case the summation extends over all, that is, $N!/[n!(N-n)!]$ samples. Now, the sum of squares of the sample means is

$$\sum \bar{x}^2 = \left(\frac{x_1 + x_2 + \cdots}{n}\right)^2 + \left(\frac{x_1 + x_3 + \cdots}{n}\right)^2 + \left(\frac{x_2 + x_3 + \cdots}{n}\right)^2 + \cdots.$$

Expanding the right-hand side.

$$\sum \bar{x}^2 = A(x_1^2 + x_2^2 + \cdots + x_N^2) + B(x_1 x_2 + x_1 x_3 + x_2 x_3 + \cdots). \tag{6.5}$$

To obtain A, we have to determine the coefficient of x_1^2. The number of samples containing x_1 was shown to be $(N-1)!/[(n-1)!(N-n)!]$, and the number of samples containing x_1^2 is the same. Therefore, the coefficient of x_1^2 is

$$A = \frac{1}{n^2} \times \frac{(N-1)!}{(n-1)!(N-n)!} = \frac{(N-1)!}{n(n!)(N-n)!}.$$

To obtain B in Eq. (6.5), we find the coefficient of $x_1 x_2$. The number of samples containing x_1 and x_2 is $(N-2)!/[(n-2)!(N-n)!]$. Hence the coefficient of $x_1 x_2$ is

$$B = \frac{2}{n^2} \times \frac{(N-2)!}{(n-2)!(N-n)!} = \frac{2(n-1)(N-2)!}{n(n!)(N-n)!}.$$

Therefore, the sum of the squares of sample means is

$$\sum \bar{x}^2 = \frac{(N-1)!}{n(n!)(N-n)!}(x_1^2 + x_2^2 + \cdots + x_N^2)$$

$$+ \frac{2(n-1)(N-2)!}{n(n!)(N-n)!}(x_1 x_2 + x_1 x_3 + x_2 x_3 + \cdots).$$

Also, $\mu^2 = \left(\dfrac{x_1 + x_2 + \cdots + x_N}{N}\right)^2$

$$= \frac{x_1^2 + x_2^2 + \cdots + x_N^2}{N^2} + \frac{2}{N^2}(x_1 x_2 + x_1 x_3 + x_2 x_3 + \cdots).$$

Substituting in Eq. (6.4), we have

$$\sigma_{\bar{x}}^2 = (x_1^2 + x_2^2 + \cdots + x_N^2)\left(\frac{1}{Nn} - \frac{1}{N^2}\right)$$

$$+ (x_1 x_2 + x_1 x_3 + \cdots)\left(\frac{2(n-1)}{nN(N-1)} - \frac{2}{N^2}\right)$$

or $\sigma_{\bar{x}}^2 = (x_1^2 + x_2^2 + \cdots + x_N^2)\left(\dfrac{N-n}{N^2 n}\right)$

$$- 2(x_1 x_2 + x_1 x_3 + \cdots)\left(\frac{N-n}{nN^2(N-1)}\right). \qquad (6.6)$$

We may remember that our intention is to compare the variance of the sample means with the variance of the original population. Using Eq. (4.1a), the latter variance can be written

$$\sigma^2 = \frac{x_1^2 + x_2^2 + \cdots + x_N^2}{N} - \frac{(x_1 + x_2 + \cdots + x_N)^2}{N^2}$$

or $\sigma^2 = \dfrac{N-1}{N^2}(x_1^2 + x_2^2 + \cdots + x_N^2) - \dfrac{2}{N^2}(x_1 x_2 + x_1 x_3 + \cdots). \qquad (6.7)$

STANDARD DEVIATION OF THE SAMPLE MEAN

Comparing Eqs. (6.6) and (6.7), we obtain

$$\sigma_{\bar{x}}^2 = \frac{N-n}{n(N-1)}\sigma^2. \qquad (6.8)$$

This equation is valid for sampling without replacement for any ratio n/N.

If, as is usually the case, N is very large (i.e., $N \gg n$), then

$$\frac{N - n}{N - 1} \to 1.$$

Thus Eq. (6.8) becomes

$$\sigma_{\bar{x}}^2 = \frac{\sigma^2}{n} \tag{6.9}$$

or, in terms of standard deviations,

$$\sigma_{\bar{x}} = \frac{\sigma}{\sqrt{n}}. \tag{6.10}$$

This equation is of considerable importance.[2] It should be noted that Eq. (6.10) applies also to sampling *with replacement* for both finite and infinite populations, since sampling from a finite population with replacement is equivalent to sampling from an infinite population. The result expressed in Eq. (6.9) can be derived by the use of the rules of expectation, as was shown by Eq. (5.37):

$$\text{Var}(\bar{x}) = \sigma_{\bar{x}}^2 = \frac{\sigma^2}{n}$$

and hence Eq. (6.10).

The role of Eq. (6.8) [or Eq. (6.9)] is important since the equation measures the extent to which a sample mean varies due to chance. Furthermore, the results expressed by Eqs. (6.2) and (6.8) are extremely important in statistics since they are *independent* of the type of distribution describing the parent population, that is, these equations apply regardless of whether the parent population has a normal, Poisson, binomial, or any other distribution. Thus, *one* sample selected at random will provide information about the distribution of all possible values of the sample mean without actually calculating them; this is indeed a remarkable characteristic of simple random sampling.

In many cases, σ is not known but is estimated from the sample. Such an estimate is denoted by s and is more precise the larger the sample. Using this estimate, we can estimate the standard deviation of the mean to be

$$s_{\bar{x}} = \frac{s}{\sqrt{n}}. \tag{6.11}$$

Equation (6.10) shows that the standard deviation of the sampling distribution of the random variable $\bar{x}$ varies inversely as the square root of the sample size. Since the standard deviation of the mean is a measure of the scatter of the sample means, it affords a measure of the precision that we can expect of a

---

[2] It may be relevant to note that, for a normal random variable, the standard deviation of the median is $1.25\sigma/\sqrt{n}$. Thus we can see that, for the same precision of the estimate, the sample size in the case of an estimate of the median has to be $(1.25)^2$ times greater than in the case of the mean. We can say, therefore, that, for normally distributed variables, the median is less efficient than the mean as a measure of central tendency.

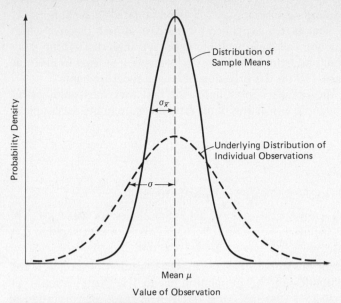

Figure 6.1   Probability distribution of sample means compared with the underlying distribution; sample size = 4.

mean of one sample. For this reason, σ_x is often called the *standard error of the mean*. We may observe that a sample of 16 observations is only twice as precise as a sample of 4 so that the gain in precision is small relative to the effort in taking the additional 12 observations. The argument cannot, however, be used too far because a sample of 2 is only $\sqrt{2}/2$ as precise as a sample of 4; here a doubling of the sample size may be well worthwhile.

It is further obvious that a sample of one tells us nothing about the precision of the estimated mean, as s in Eq. (6.11) cannot be estimated.[3] With a number of samples of unit size, the standard deviation could be estimated, but $s_{\bar{x}}$ would be no smaller than the standard deviation of the underlying distribution.

Figure 6.1 shows a comparison between the (probability) distribution of individual observations and the (probability) distribution of means of samples drawn from this underlying distribution. The considerably narrower distribution of the sample means is apparent; this indicates that the mean is an efficient measure of central tendency.[4] The higher peak of the curve for the means is due to the fact that the areas under the two curves are equal to one another and to unity, as each represents the sum of all probabilities.

It can be shown that, if the underlying population of x has a normal distribution, then the sampling distribution of $\bar{x}$ will be normal, too. When the distribution of the population is not normal, what is the nature of the sampling distribution of $\bar{x}$? It is important to note that for almost all types of population

[3] The calculation of s [Eq. (4.6)] involves $n - 1$ in the denominator.
[4] The median is less efficient (see footnote 2).

distributions, the sampling distribution of $\bar{x}$ is approximately normal for sufficiently large samples. This fact is explained by the *central limit theorem* which is a very important theorem of statistical inference. We shall discuss the theorem in the next section, but, before doing so, let us answer, at least in part, the question posed on page 110 on the precision of length measurements.

Let us refer to the sample consisting of the first four measurements as sample 1, and to the sample consisting of all nine measurements as sample 2.

We thus have

$$\bar{x}_1 = 30.30 \text{ m} \quad \text{and} \quad \bar{x}_2 = 30.25 \text{ m}.$$

We calculate

$$s_1 = 0.178 \text{ m} \qquad s_2 = 0.150 \text{ m}.$$

From Eq. (6.11),

$$s_{\bar{x}1} = 0.089 \text{ m} \qquad s_{x2} = 0.050 \text{ m}.$$

The standard error of sample 2 is thus smaller than that of sample 1, and we can write our estimates of the population mean (i.e. "true" length) as: 30.30 ± 0.089 m and 30.25 ± 0.050 m, respectively. The exact interpretation of statements of this type is discussed in Chapter 11.

EXAMPLE

To verify Eq. (6.8) for a population of observations: 2, 4, 6. Here $N = 3$ and $\mu = 4$. Thus

$$\sigma^2 = \frac{2^2 + 0^2 + 2^2}{3} = \frac{8}{3}.$$

Consider $n = 2$. The samples are then 2, 4; 2, 6; and 4, 6. The sample means are 3, 4, and 5.

$$\text{Mean of sample means} = \frac{3 + 4 + 5}{3}$$

$$= 4$$

(which checks with the population mean) and

$$\text{variance of sample means} = \frac{1^2 + 0^2 + 1^2}{3} = \frac{2}{3}.$$

Substituting in Eq. (6.8), we find that

$$\sigma_{\bar{x}}^2 = \frac{N - n}{n(N - 1)} \sigma^2$$

$$= \frac{1}{2 \times 2} \times \frac{8}{3} = \frac{2}{3}$$

which checks with the value calculated directly from the sample means. ∎ ∎

EXAMPLE

If we consider the results of strength tests on 270 bricks, given in Table 2.2, as a sample of the population consisting of all the bricks made by the given works during the sampling period, then we can say that the standard deviation of the sample mean (calculated in Chapter 3 to be 6.89 MN/m^2) is, from Eq. (6.11):

$$s_{\bar{x}} = \frac{s}{\sqrt{n}} = \frac{1.39}{\sqrt{270}} = 0.0846 \text{ MN/m}^2$$

[1.39 is the value of the *sample* standard deviation (found in Chapter 4), but because n is large, the error involved in ignoring Bessel's correction is negligible.]

The interpretation of the standard deviation of the mean in relation to the precision of the calculated mean is considered on page 209. ■ ■

CENTRAL LIMIT THEOREM

We shall now consider certain properties of sampling distributions which logically belong to the present chapter. However, the reader would be well advised to study this material again after he has become familiar with Chapters 8 to 10 and 14 to 16.

The importance of the normal distribution lies not only in the fact that numerous variables are actually nearly normally distributed, but also in the large body of statistical methods and tables derived for the normal distribution and often applicable approximately even to distributions departing from normal. In particular, numerous statistical techniques concerned with sampling involve the use of normal distribution. Indeed, we mentioned earlier that sample means follow approximately normal distribution even if the underlying distribution is not normal, and we shall now present this more formally as the central limit theorem.[5]

If we have $x_1, x_2, \ldots, x_n$ identically distributed independent random variables, each with mean μ and finite variance σ^2, then the variable $\bar{x}$, given by

$$\bar{x} = \frac{1}{n} \sum_{i=1}^{n} x_i$$

will have a distribution

$$z = \frac{\bar{x} - \mu}{\sigma/\sqrt{n}}$$

which approaches a normal distribution with mean 0 and variance 1 as n becomes indefinitely large. We note from the above that the mean of n identically

---

[5] Proof of this theorem can be found in H. Cramer, *Mathematical Methods of Statistics* (Princeton, N.J.: Princeton University Press, 1946).

distributed independent random variables will be approximately normally distributed, *regardless* of the underlying distribution of the individual variables. Thus, we can state that if we draw samples of size n from a population with a mean μ and a finite variance σ^2, with an increase in n the distribution of sample means approaches a normal distribution with a mean μ and variance σ^2/n. We can see that virtually the only limitation on the underlying distribution is that the variance be finite, and this is satisfied in nearly all engineering and scientific problems.

For example, in Chapter 16 (page 345) we deal with errors of measurements and we assume that such errors are normally distributed. This is quite valid by the central limit theorem, since these errors are usually composed of the sum of many small independent components. For instance, errors in estimating wind loads on suspension bridges or the reliability of a nuclear plant are a result of the *additive* effect of many random variables, none of which dominates the total. It is by virtue of the central limit theorem (CLT) that the normal distribution provides a "good fit" to our experimental results (see also page 174). In fact, the basic underlying reason for the importance of the normal distribution in engineering and science is the central limit theorem.

How good the approximation is for a given sample size depends on the shape of the underlying distribution. We can look at the problem another way and say that the further the underlying distribution is removed from normal the larger the samples need to be for their mean to be nearly normally distributed. Even if the underlying distribution is rectangular or triangular, the means of samples of four items or more are approximately normally distributed. The approximation is least accurate near the tails, and care is necessary when that part of the distribution is of importance. Figure 6.2 illustrates the strength of the central limit theorem for three different parent populations as the sample size n increases.

We can ensure that the CLT applies to practical problems if the following rules of thumb are used: (i) for a well-behaved symmetric distribution, not radically different from the normal distribution, the sample size n can be as small as 4; (ii) for a fairly behaved distribution with no prominent mode, the sample size n should not be less than 12; and (iii) for an ill-behaved distribution, with most of its density in the tails, such as those shown in Fig. 6.3, it is difficult to establish a satisfactory value of n. However, in engineering and scientific applications, it has been found that the necessary sample size n should be at least 100.

Thus, we can see how the use of normal distribution is extended by the central limit theorem. Furthermore, many statistical tests that have been derived for normal distribution (such as tests of significance and analysis of variance, dealt with in Chapters 15 and 20) remain valid when applied to sample means of distributions which depart from normality. This is extremely important since most of the procedures for estimating parameters or testing of hypotheses are dependent upon the sample mean, $\bar{x}$. We should also note that the presence of normality is required in the derivation of other sampling distributions such as t, χ^2, and F, as shown later in this chapter.

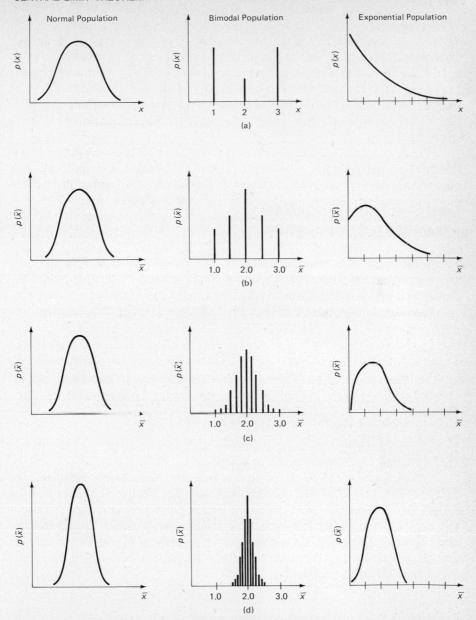

Figure 6.2 Distribution of: (a) parent population; (b) sample means, $\bar{x}$, sample size $n = 2$; (c) sample means, $\bar{x}$, sample size $n = 5$; (d) sample means, $\bar{x}$, sample size $n = 30$. (Vertical scale varies from one row of diagrams to another.)

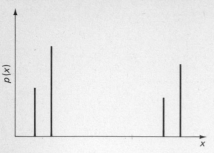
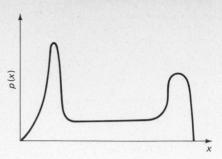

Figure 6.3

SAMPLING FROM A NORMALLY DISTRIBUTED POPULATION

If $\bar{x}$ is the mean of a random sample of size n drawn from a normally distributed population with a mean μ and a finite variance σ^2, then the sampling distribution of $\bar{x}$ is normally distributed with mean μ and variance σ^2/n. Since the parameters μ and σ are constant, the statistic z, given by the fraction

$$z = \frac{\bar{x} - \mu}{\sigma/\sqrt{n}} \tag{6.12}$$

has a sampling distribution which is normal with parameters of zero mean and variance of unity. The same applies to the standardized normal variate

$$z = \frac{x - \mu}{\sigma} \tag{6.13}$$

where x is any observation in the population.

When a *non-normally* distributed population is randomly sampled, the sampling distribution of the sample mean does not depart markedly from a normal distribution, provided the underlying population is not highly skewed and does not have long tails; this was demonstrated earlier by the central limit theorem. Therefore, the same result as expressed by Eq. (6.11) will be applicable here, too, provided the size of the sample n is adequate to meet the rules of thumb mentioned earlier.

SAMPLING DISTRIBUTION OF ESTIMATED VARIANCE s^2

If repeated random samples of size n are drawn from a normally distributed population with variance σ^2, the estimated variance from the sample, s^2, will vary from sample to sample; its sampling distribution, in standardized form $(n - 1)s^2/\sigma^2$, is described by the statistic χ^2 given by

$$\chi^2 = \frac{(n - 1)s^2}{\sigma^2} = \frac{(x_1 - \bar{x})^2 + \cdots + (x_n - \bar{x})^2}{\sigma^2}. \tag{6.14}$$

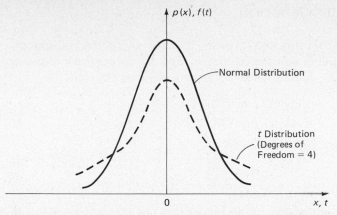

Figure 6.4   Comparison between the normal and *t* distributions.

The statistic χ^2 can be calculated also as $\sum_{i=1}^{n} z_i^2$ where z is the standardized normal variate given by Eq. (6.13); the substitution of $\bar{x}$ for μ is justified since we have already shown by Eqs. (6.2) and (6.8) that the sample mean $\bar{x}$ provides a good estimate of μ. The statistic χ^2 is used rather than χ to emphasize that the statistic *cannot* be negative.

The χ^2 distribution is considered in Chapter 14. It is interesting to note that, for small sample size, n, the distribution of s^2 is highly skewed with the bulk of the area close to the origin. However, as the sample size increases, it becomes more nearly symmetrical and in fact approaches a normal distribution with a mean equal to σ^2; this phenomenon is explained by the central limit theorem.

SAMPLING THE *t* DISTRIBUTION

The statistic z in Eq. (6.13) is calculated on the basis of a known σ. Usually, σ is not known but is estimated from the sample by the statistic s,[6] whose distribution is far from normal when n is small. Even though sampling is from a normally distributed population, the fraction $[(\bar{x} - \mu)/(s/\sqrt{n})]$ will *not* be normally distributed. It was found by W. S. Gosset that the random variable

$$t = \frac{\bar{x} - \mu}{s/\sqrt{n}} \tag{6.15}$$

follows another distribution, called the *t* distribution. The statistic *t* has a mean of zero and variance > 1, which causes the distribution to be less peaked at the center and higher in the tails than the normal distribution (see Fig. 6.4). Of course, when n becomes large, the *t* distribution approaches the normal distribution. The uses of the *t* distribution are considered in Chapter 15.

---

[6] We have shown in Chapter 5 in the example on page 93, that $E(s^2) = \sigma^2$.

SAMPLING THE *F* DISTRIBUTION

If we wish to compare the estimated variances s_1^2 and s_2^2, computed, respectively, from independent random samples of size n_1 and n_2 drawn from normally distributed populations with variances σ_1^2 and σ_2^2, we form the ratio

$$\left(\frac{s_1^2/\sigma_1^2}{s_2^2/\sigma_2^2}\right).$$

R. A. Fisher established that the statistic

$$F = \frac{s_1^2/\sigma_1^2}{s_2^2/\sigma_2^2} \tag{6.16}$$

follows an F distribution. Using Eq. (6.14), we can put Eq. (6.16) in terms of χ^2 as

$$F = \frac{\chi_1^2/(n_1 - 1)}{\chi_2^2/(n_2 - 1)}. \tag{6.17}$$

A discussion of the F distribution is found in Chapter 16.

It is interesting to note that the random variables χ^2 (or s^2), t, and F are all related to the standardized normal variate z; for example, we note that the variable χ^2 (or s^2) is a function of z^2; the variable t is a function of z as well as of s; and the variable F is a function of χ^2 or s^2. These relationships are presented more formally in the next section.

RELATION BETWEEN THE NORMAL, χ^2, *t*, AND *F* DISTRIBUTIONS

We recall that the *normal* distribution is that associated with a random variable $x\,(-\infty < x < \infty)$ whose density function is given by

$$p(x) = \frac{1}{\sqrt{2\pi}\sigma}\, e^{-(x-\mu)^2/2\sigma^2} \tag{5.24}$$

where μ and σ, respectively, are the mean and the standard deviation of the random variable x. In terms of the standardized normal variate

$$z = \frac{x - \mu}{\sigma} \tag{6.13}$$

the density function can be written as

$$f(z) = \frac{1}{\sqrt{2\pi}}\, e^{-z^2/2}. \tag{5.25}$$

As mentioned previously, when the distribution of the underlying random variable is normal, the sample mean, $\bar{x}$, is also normally distributed. However, the distribution of other random variables that are functions of normally distributed variables is *not* necessarily normal. For example, the random variable x^2 is not normally distributed, even though x or z is.

Consider a set of random variables $z_1, z_2, \ldots, z_v$, which are independent and normally distributed, each with a zero mean and a unit variance. Then the sum of the squares of z, denoted by χ^2, must also be a random variable, since it is a function of random variables. The quantity

$$\chi_v^2 = \sum_{i=1}^{i=v} z_i^2$$

is said to have a chi-squared distribution with v degrees of freedom.

It is obvious that the range of all possible values of χ^2 is between zero and $+\infty$, since χ^2 is a sum of squares. The distribution is always skewed to the right but for a large number of degrees of freedom the distribution tends toward normal.

Let us further consider z, which is a random variable, normally distributed with a zero mean and a unit variance. Assume that we have another random variable χ_1^2, independent of z, with v degrees of freedom. Then the statistic t, given by

$$t = \frac{z}{\sqrt{\chi_1^2/v}}$$

has a t distribution with v degrees of freedom. This distribution is symmetrical about zero (as is the case with the normal distribution) and its range extends from $-\infty$ to ∞, since the values of z lie in this interval and the values of χ_1^2 are non-negative. With an increase in the number of degrees of freedom, the t distribution approaches the normal distribution. In fact, the two distributions will coincide when $v = \infty$.

Let us consider now two random variables χ_1^2 and χ_2^2, independent of each other. If χ_1^2 has v_1 degrees of freedom and χ_2^2 has v_2 degrees of freedom, then the ratio

$$F_{v_1,v_2} = \frac{\chi_1^2/v_1}{\chi_2^2/v_2}$$

is said to have an F distribution with v_1 and v_2 degrees of freedom. The range of all possible values of the random variable F is given by the interval zero to $+\infty$, since the values of χ_1^2 and χ_2^2 are all non-negative. By comparing the F distribution with the χ^2 and t distributions, it can readily be deduced that the density function of the F distribution approaches that of the χ^2 distribution as v_2 increases; also, for $v_1 = 1$,

$$F_{1,v,\alpha} = t_{v,\alpha}^2$$

where α = level of significance.

It can be shown also that

$$F_{v_1,v_2,\alpha} = \frac{1}{F_{v_2,v_1,1-\alpha}}$$

The above sampling distributions are the means by which statistical inferences are made. The subject of statistical inference, which includes estimation of parameters and hypotheses testing, is introduced in the next chapter.

We have seen in this chapter that the sampling distribution of sample means can be well described by the normal distribution on the basis of the central limit theorem. While other statistics, such as the number or proportion of occurrences of an event, have their own sampling distributions, it is frequently far simpler to use the normal distribution for inference purposes, provided of course the conditions of the central limit theorem are met. The various sampling distributions will be discussed as appropriate in connection with statistical inference; for example, in Chapter 15, we shall evaluate the precision with which the sample mean estimates the population mean when there is no information about the population other than that provided by the sample.

PROBLEMS

6-1. Calculate the standard deviation of the mean of Problem 3-2.

6-2. Calculate the standard error of the mean tensile strength of rubber of Problem 4-1. By what factor would this standard error be changed if we took 18 measurements? Assume that the estimated standard deviation is the same in both cases.

6-3. The coded length of specimens of a certain type was found to be: 17, 17, 12, 15, and 20. By considering all possible samples of size two, drawn with replacement from the above population, find: **(a)** the population mean, **(b)** the population standard deviation, **(c)** the mean of the sample means, and **(d)** the standard deviation of the sample means.

Check (c) and (d) from (a) and (b), respectively, by using the appropriate formulas.

6-4. Determine the standard error of the mean precipitation found in Problem 3-3.

6-5. Samples of 4 building blocks were taken, and the mean range of their mass was found to be 0.09 kg. Estimate the standard deviation of mass of the blocks. Estimate also the standard deviation of the mean mass.

6-6. The vibration time of a member was measured 13 times, the following values in seconds being obtained:

59.6, 60.4, 60.2, 60.7, 60.1, 59.8, 59.8, 60.3, 60.0, 59.9, 59.5, 60.2, 60.3.

Find the mean and standard deviation for these values. Find also the standard deviation of the mean, mean deviation, and coefficient of variation.

6-7. The wavelength of a spectral line was measured and the results were as follows: 3452, 3458, 3457, 3451, 3455, 3458, 3454. Using coding to simplify the data, calculate the **(a)** mean wavelength, **(b)** standard deviation, **(c)** coefficient of variation, **(d)** estimate of the standard deviation of the mean wavelength, and **(e)** the standard error in the wavelength.

6-8. The independent, normally distributed random variables $x_1, x_2, \ldots, x_n$ have a mean of μ_x and variance σ_x^2. Also, $y_1, y_2, \ldots, y_m$ are independent, normally distributed random variables with mean of μ_y and variance σ_y^2. Assuming that the values of x and of y are independent of each other, determine whether the following random variables are normally distributed, t distributed, χ^2 distributed, F distributed, or none of the above.

a. $\dfrac{(x_2 - \mu_x)}{\sigma_x}$;

b. $\dfrac{(y_1 - \mu_y)}{s_y}$;

c. $\dfrac{\bar{x} - \bar{y}}{\left(\sqrt{\dfrac{\sigma_x^2}{n} + \dfrac{\sigma_y^2}{m}} \right)}$;

d. $\dfrac{s_y^2}{s_x^2}$;

e. $\displaystyle\sum_{i=1}^{n} \dfrac{x_i^2}{\sigma_x^2}$;

f. $\dfrac{(n-1)s_x^2}{\sigma_x^2} + \dfrac{\displaystyle\sum_{i=1}^{m} (y_i - \bar{y})^2}{\sigma_y^2}$;

g. $\dfrac{\bar{x}\sqrt{n}}{s_x}$;

h. $\dfrac{\bar{y}}{\bar{x}}$;

i. $\dfrac{(\bar{x} - \mu_x)\sqrt{n}}{s_x}$.

Chapter 7

Statistical Inference

In Chapter 1, we pointed out that one of the main aims of statistical analysis is to estimate the properties of a population from tests on samples drawn from that population. Since we *infer* from the data obtained experimentally the unknown properties of the population, the process is known as statistical inference. Our results are frequently presented in terms of estimates of values of the population parameters, and hence we are engaged in *estimation*. The parameters of greatest interest in engineering and science include: (i) mean μ; (ii) variance σ^2 or standard deviation σ; proportion p; the difference between means of two populations $(\mu_1 - \mu_2)$; and difference between proportions in two populations $(p_1 - p_2)$. The inference process involves making a hypothesis about the parameter of interest and the hypothesis is then tested for acceptance or rejection. The result of this test is expressed in terms of a certain probability of being correct.

The method of estimation of a parameter, generally in the form of an equation, is called an *estimator;* any particular value based on information from a sample is called an *estimate*. This is similar to the distinction between a function and a particular value which it assumes. We should note that the estimate cannot, except fortuitously, give the true value of the parameter exactly. Indeed, the estimate is a function of the observations (which are random variables) and is therefore itself a random variable.

Care must be taken to identify the population as clearly as possible, and it is also important that the sample be homogeneous, that is, that it is drawn from only one population. This point was illustrated on page 33.

All statistical inference should be followed by a decision. This could be a decision to do something (which was investigated with the aid of a test) or not to do it, or maybe to do more testing. The inference itself is in terms of probability statements about the estimate of a parameter or about the hypothesis made. Now, knowledge of the subject matter investigated is necessary in the formulation of a proper probabilistic model to represent the behavior of the population, and this is why an engineer or a scientist must himself have some knowledge of statistics rather than leave it all to a "pure" statistician.

POINT ESTIMATORS AND INTERVAL ESTIMATORS

There are two general approaches to making inferences about parameters. In one, we consider a single-valued estimate and express the probability of its having a certain value. This is called a point estimate. We calculate the standard error of the estimate so as to know the possible error. Chapter 11 develops this topic.

The alternative approach is to calculate interval estimators rather than point estimators. An interval estimate gives the range of values between which the parameter is expected to lie with a given probability. Imagine, for example, that an experiment was repeated using a large number of samples and that an interval estimate was calculated for each sample. Then a good interval estimate would contain within it the parameter in a large proportion of cases. This proportion is called the *confidence coefficient* of the estimator and the interval estimator is called the *confidence interval*. The confidence coefficient frequently used is 95 percent.

We can note that an interval estimate combines the information given by a point estimate with the measure of its variability.

PROPERTIES OF ESTIMATORS

The usual notation is as follows. Suppose that the parameter of interest has an unknown value θ_0. The estimate would then be denoted by $\hat{\theta}$, although in some common cases different notation is used; for instance, in the case of the mean the symbols for the parameter and the estimate are, respectively, μ and $\bar{x}$, and in the case of standard deviation, σ and s.

How can we tell whether an estimator is good? Its quality is judged by the distribution of estimates which it yields, that is, by the properties of its sampling distribution. The first of these is that the estimator should be *unbiased*. This means that it has no tendency to be regularly above or below the parameter so that the estimate is distributed in an unbiased manner about the true value of the parameters. Formally, this has the consequence that the mean of the estimated values is equal to the parameter. Figure 7.1 illustrates the distribution of an unbiased and of a biased estimator.

The second property of a good estimator is that the spread of its distribution be as small as possible. A visual indication of the variability of an estimator is shown in Fig. 7.2.

As the sample size increases, the scatter of possible values of the sample mean $\hat{\theta}$ about its mean decreases so that the probability that a given value

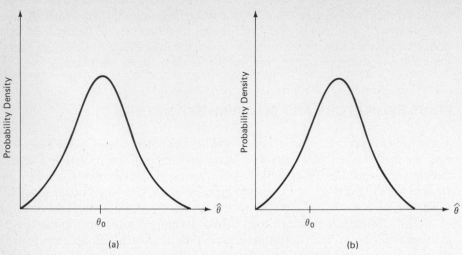

Figure 7.1   Distribution of estimators: (a) unbiased, (b) biased.

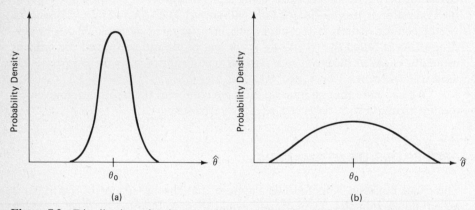

Figure 7.2   Distribution of estimators: (a) more accurate, (b) less accurate.

of $\hat{\theta}$ differs by more than a fixed amount from the mean θ_0 decreases. We can therefore say that the accuracy (see page 20) of the estimator increases as the sample size increases; in other words, the variance of the sampling distribution of $\hat{\theta}$ is inversely proportional to sample size.

This property of increasing accuracy with sample size is obviously desirable and an estimator which has that property is said to be *consistent*. Mathematically, this means that the probability that the estimate differs from the parameter by less than an arbitrary small error approaches unity as the sample size increases to infinity. This property is analogous to convergence in the mathematical sense. For example, the sample mean $\bar{x}$ is a consistent estimator of the population mean μ since

$$\sigma_{\bar{x}} = \frac{\sigma}{\sqrt{n}} \qquad\qquad [6.10]$$

becomes smaller as n increases.

The property of consistency is concerned with the behavior of an estimator as the sample size increases to infinity. We should note that a consistent
estimator is not necessarily unbiased. Likewise, an unbiased estimator is not
necessarily consistent. However, the estimators with which we are concerned
in this book are both unbiased and consistent. In this connection, we can note
that, whatever the probability distribution of observations, the sample mean is
always an unbiased estimate of the population mean. However, the variance
of a set of observations is a biased estimate of the population variance, and this
is why Bessel's correction was introduced in Chapter 4.

The sample mean is the most important property of a sample. If the
sample is large, its mean has an approximately normal distribution even if the
parent population is not normal (see central limit theorem, page 117). It is for
this reason that so much attention is paid to the normal distribution, and not
simply because much in nature is normally distributed.

To assess the significance of an experimental mean we require information
both about the mean and the unbiased estimate of the population variance,
s^2. In assessing s^2 as an estimator of the population variance σ^2, we should
note that $(n-1)s^2/\sigma^2$ has a χ^2 distribution with $(n-1)$ degrees of freedom.
This is considered in Chapter 16.

It is important to remember that any distribution is described by one or
more parameters. However, the form of distribution must be known or assumed
by the investigator. This makes it possible to evaluate the probability distribution of the estimate.

NULL HYPOTHESIS

We are often interested to know whether an observed distribution differs *significantly* from an assumed model of a particular distribution. To answer this
question we proceed as follows. We postulate that there is no significant difference between the observed and model distributions being compared. This
is known as a *null hypothesis*. We measure the probability of a difference at
least as large as found occurring due to chance alone, and if this probability is
very small, we reject the null hypothesis and infer that a real difference exists.
The same procedure is also applied to a test of significance of an estimate of a
parameter of a population, given that the probability model of the population
is known.

We must emphasize that we can never formally prove the null hypothesis
to be correct. This may seem an unsatisfactory state of affairs, but statistical
inference is not an end in itself; it is only a tool that enables us to fit a hypothesis to observed physical facts or, alternatively, makes us reject it and seek
another pattern.

The null hypothesis approach may, at first sight, seem to be too indirect.
Typically, an experiment is performed because there *are* reasons to believe that
varying an independent variable will influence the dependent variable. Thus,
the *rejection* of the null hypothesis is a significant finding. Conversely, as a

general rule, the retention of a null hypothesis is not a very conclusive finding and leads to further tests. We should emphasize that a nonsignificant result does not prove that the null hypothesis is correct, merely that it is tenable, that is, we do not have adequate grounds for rejecting it. We should therefore not talk about accepting the hypothesis but rather about retaining it. We must remember, of course, that the hypothesis is concerned with population parameters, which are always unknown.

The approach to hypothesis testing is as follows:

1. A null hypothesis, denoted by H_0, is stated in terms of a specified parameter and the level of significance, α, is specified.
2. The sampling distribution of the parameter is chosen. (The more commonly used distributions were briefly described in Chapter 6.)
3. A random sample is drawn and the sample statistic corresponding to the parameter is calculated.
4. The statistic is compared with the sampling distribution.

If the probability that the statistic was drawn from the population represented by the sampling distribution is less than α (i.e., the statistic falls into the rejection region), the hypothesis is rejected.

ALTERNATIVE HYPOTHESIS

Before testing the null hypothesis, we should also postulate a clear alternative hypothesis, which we shall denote by H_a. For instance, let us consider the case when the population parameter is θ_0 and we have obtained a sample mean θ_a. We can postulate the null hypothesis $H_0 : \theta_a = \theta_0$. Then, if H_0 is rejected, H_a can be either $\theta_a \neq \theta_0$, or $\theta_a > \theta_0$, or $\theta_a < \theta_0$. The choice of the alternative determines whether we apply a one-tailed (or one-sided) or a two-tailed (or two-sided) test. The use of the word "tail" refers to the tails of the distribution.

How to decide which test to use? Sometimes, the investigator knows enough about the circumstances of an experiment to be sure that, if a certain difference is not zero, then it is positive. For instance, using a shorter lap length in a joint can make it weaker or may not affect its strength, but cannot make the joint stronger. In this case, the test is one tailed. At other times, the investigator is interested only in a difference in a certain direction, for example, does a new and more expensive way of making a joint make it stronger? If it makes it weaker, it is of no interest. Here again the test is one tailed. The choice of a one- or two-tailed test must be made in the light of practical consequences of a wrong decision. These could be financial or physical or may have safety implications. Sometimes, of course, a difference in either sense is of interest, and we then apply a two-tailed test. This is, for instance, the case when we have a choice of two automobiles of the same price and quality, and we want to know which one has a lower gasoline consumption.

It cannot be emphasized too strongly that the choice between a one-tailed and two-tailed test must be made *a priori* and not after the test results have become available so as to achieve, or not achieve, a significant result and "prove" what pleases the investigator. It will be shown in Chapter 15 that, for the same level of significance, a one-tailed test is more likely to lead to the rejection of the null hypothesis.

A comment on the relation between a two-tailed test and the confidence interval of an estimate may be in order. A simple relation exists between a 5 percent two-tailed test of the null hypothesis that the value of the estimate θ_a is equal to the parameter θ_0 and the 95 percent confidence interval for θ_a. Assuming that the rejection areas are symmetrically located about θ_a, if the test fails to reject the null hypothesis at the 5 percent level, then θ_0 lies inside the 95 percent confidence interval for θ_a, and vice versa. Also, if the test rejects the null hypothesis, then θ_0 lies outside the 95 percent confidence interval, and vice versa. Assuming that the population variance σ^2 is known and that a value of θ_a is estimated from the mean of a sample size n, if θ_0 lies in the confidence interval, then

$$\theta_a - 1.96 \frac{\sigma}{\sqrt{n}} < \theta_0 < \theta_a + 1.96 \frac{\sigma}{\sqrt{n}}.$$

From the left-hand part of the inequality,

$$\theta_a - \theta_0 < \frac{1.96}{\sqrt{n}} \sigma$$

which gives $z < 1.96$ (see page 303). Likewise, from the right-hand part of the inequality, we obtain $z > -1.96$ so that we do not reject the hypothesis at the 5 percent level. If $|z| > 1.96$, θ_0 lies outside the 95 percent interval for θ_a and we reject the null hypothesis.

However, the two techniques serve different purposes. The confidence interval answers the question: how accurately do we know θ_0? The null hypothesis test is concerned with the question: could θ_a have the value θ_0?

TYPE I AND TYPE II ERRORS

We must realize that the rejection of a null hypothesis does not prove that it is false because there is the possibility that the null hypothesis is indeed true. Likewise, the failure to reject the null hypothesis does not prove that it is true as there is a possibility that it is false. In other words, both the rejection and the nonrejection of a null hypothesis are associated with risks of being in error. Rejection of a true null hypothesis is called a Type I error, and the probability of committing a Type I error is denoted by α, which is also referred to as the *level of significance*. The value of α must be determined *before* the experiment on the basis of research experience, risks involved, and consequences of an erroneous conclusion. The level of significance α is also defined as the probability of obtaining a value of the test statistic under study as extreme as, or more extreme than, that actually observed when the null hypothesis is true. In fact, α determines the rejection region of the null hypothesis, which is those values of the statistic for which the null hypothesis is rejected.

To summarize then: there is *always* a risk of making an incorrect decision as shown below.

| Decision | Null hypothesis, H_0 | |
	True	False
Reject H_0	Type I error	Correct decision
Retain H_0	Correct decision	Type II error

The probability of making a Type I error is called the significance level of the statistical test. This description reflects the weight of evidence supporting the rejection of the null hypothesis. Sometimes, a test result is significant at the 5 percent level but not at the 1 percent level. The investigator has to decide how to react to this situation in the light of possible consequences of failing to reject the null hypothesis.

The goodness of a statistical test of a hypothesis is represented by the probability of making a Type I or Type II error, denoted by α and β, respectively. The two errors are not independent. Specifically, for a given sample size, since α is the probability that the test statistic will wrongly fall in the rejection region, an increase in α will increase the size of the rejection region and, at the same time, decrease β. Conversely, still for a given sample size, reducing α will decrease the size of the rejection region and increase β. If the sample size is increased, both α and β will decrease because more test information is available. An example on page 328 shows that when $n = 50$ and $\alpha = 0.01$, $\beta = 0.11$. With the same α, when $n = 62$, β becomes 0.05.

The probability of making a Type II error depends on the difference between the true value of the parameter and the hypothesized value. A plot of this probability of making a Type II error, β, as a function of the true value of the parameter is called the operating characteristic curve. A plot of $(1 - \beta)$, that is, the probability of rejecting a hypothesis, against the same abscissa gives the power curve. The latter name arises from the fact that the curve represents the power of discerning a Type II error. This topic is considered on page 294.

When he has a considerable freedom of choice, the investigator would make up his mind about the magnitude of the probability of committing Type I and Type II errors (α and β, respectively) which he is prepared to tolerate. He will know what deviation from the hypothesized value of the parameter is of *practical* importance. This will determine the acceptable magnitude of the Type I error. The operating characteristic curves for various sample sizes will then enable him to choose that sample size which corresponds to a given Type II error.

Let us consider an example where the parameter investigated is θ. We have an estimator $\hat{\theta}$ and let the null hypothesis be that $\theta = \theta_0$, where θ_0 is the true value of the parameter, with the alternative hypothesis that $\theta > \theta_0$, that is,

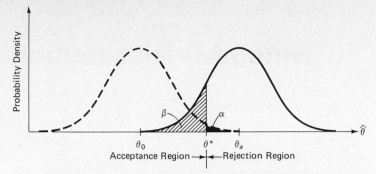

Figure 7.3 Distribution of estimator $\hat{\theta}$ when the null hypothesis $\theta = \theta_0$ is false and, in fact, $\theta = \theta_a$.

we have a one-tailed test. Imagine that the null hypothesis is false and that, in fact, $\theta = \theta_a$ where $\theta_a > \theta_0$. The test statistic $\hat{\theta}$ is then distributed, say, normally, about a mean θ_a, as shown by the right-hand curve in Fig. 7.3. The hypothesized distribution of $\hat{\theta}$ is shown by the dotted left-hand curve. The critical value of $\hat{\theta}$ for rejection is θ^* such that the area under the left-hand curve to the right of θ^* is α percent of the total area under the same curve. The area corresponding to the Type II error, β, that is, the probability of accepting the hypothesis when it is in fact false, is the area under the right-hand distribution curve which falls over the acceptance region, that is, to the left of θ^*.

If the test results lead to a rejection of the null hypothesis, the probability of an erroneous conclusion, α, is known because the value of α was chosen *a priori* in establishing the rejection region. On the other hand, if we do not reject the null hypothesis, it does not follow that the hypothesis is valid: we simply have inadequate evidence to reject it. Ideally, a value of the estimator significant in practical terms could have been selected in advance and the sample size chosen so as to make the probability of committing a Type II error sufficiently small. Alas, all too frequently this is not, or cannot be, done: a sample size is determined and the statistical analysis has to cope with the available test results.

This chapter, on its own, does not enable the reader to apply inference testing. The objective of presenting the material at this stage has been to explain the methods and purposes of inference testing. Specific applications and examples will be given, as appropriate, in later chapters. Following their study, the rereading of this chapter may be of value in consolidating the subject matter.

Chapter 8

Binomial Distribution

In some cases, a population consists of only two classes of individuals, for example, alive or dead, even or odd, heads or tails, or simply possessing or not possessing a certain attribute (e.g., a defect). When one trial is made, for example, one ball is drawn at random from a collection containing a proportion p of black balls, the probability of the ball being black is p. For sampling with replacement, the probability per trial is thus fixed. When a random sample of size n is drawn from the population (i.e., by making n trials), the distribution of the two classes of individuals (black balls and others) is, of course, discrete and is of the binomial type.

The name of the distribution arises from an equality between the distribution of the probabilities of obtaining 0, 1, 2, . . . items considered as a success in a sample of size n and the successive terms of the binomial expansion $(q + p)^n$, where p denotes the probability of success in a simple trial, and q (such that $p + q = 1$) the probability of failure.

In general terms, it is usual to call the occurrence of some event, as specified, a success; its nonoccurrence—that is, the occurrence of any other event—is called a failure. The classification of one of the two possible outcomes as a "success" is a holdover from the times when probability theory was applied mainly to games of chance, but "success" may in practice mean an undesirable outcome such as a defective part.

In order to understand better the binomial distribution, let us consider an experiment which has two complementary outcomes, namely a success and a failure; this is known as a Bernoulli trial.[1] Coin tossing is an example. Here,

---

[1] See footnote 3 (page 150) for a definition of a Bernoulli variable.

either one coin is tossed n times, or n coins are tossed once, the observation "heads" or "tails" being recorded for each toss. In real life, there are many experiments of this type in many fields of endeavor. For example, a hydrologist wants to determine the design flood from the annual maximum flow of the river over a sequence of n years (i.e., n trials) relative to a specified flood level. There are only two possible outcomes in each trial, namely, the occurrence or non-occurrence of an event: the river does or does not exceed the specified flood level.

Problems of the type described above may be modeled by the binomial probability distribution (binomial distribution, for short) provided the following conditions are met:

1. The experiment consists of n identical trials: the outcome of any specific trial is determined by chance.
2. Each trial has only two possible outcomes: the occurrence (i.e., success) and nonoccurrence (i.e., failure) of a discrete event.
3. Trials are independent: the outcome of any given trial or sequence of trials does not affect the outcome of subsequent trials.
4. The probability of success on a single trial, p, remains constant from trial to trial. The probability of failure is equal to $(1 - p)$.

In the manufacturing industry, where the binomial distribution is used extensively in quality control, these conditions are satisfied from the practical point of view; specifically, batches are so large that the proportion of defectives in the batch is virtually unaffected by the drawing of a small sample. (Very small batches may be 100 percent inspected!) Furthermore, samples are considered independent, provided, of course, the method of manufacturing does not change. For example, from past experience, it is known that a particular machine produces 30 percent defective microprocessors of the early type of manufacture. The probability, p, of drawing a defective microprocessor from a batch (finite population) of 300 microprocessors is $\frac{3}{10}$; assuming no replacement, the probability of a defective microprocessor on the second draw will be equal to $\frac{89}{299}$ or $\frac{90}{299}$, depending on whether the first draw was a defective or nondefective microprocessor. The last value is close to $\frac{3}{10}$ and this would continue to be the case for the third, fourth, and nth draw (trial) as long as n is not too large. Hence, the probability of a defective microprocessor, p, remains approximately $\frac{3}{10}$ from trial to trial, and, for all practical purposes, the trials (or outcomes) can be regarded as independent.

On the other hand, if the batch (finite population) contains only 10 microprocessors, then the probability of a defective on the first draw is still $\frac{3}{10}$, but the probability of a defective on the second draw is either $\frac{2}{9}$ or $\frac{3}{9}$, depending on whether a defective was or was not drawn on the first trial; these two probabilities are quite different from $\frac{3}{10}$. Therefore, for small populations and sampling without replacement, the probability of a defective will vary appreciably from trial to trial, independence will not exist, and the resulting experiment cannot be described by a binomial distribution.

DERIVATION

Consider n trials in each of which the probability of success is p. Then the probability of failure is $1 - p = q$. To find the probability of r successes, we observe that:

> the probability of 1 success in 1 try is p,
>
> the probability of 2 successes in 2 tries is $p \times p$ or p^2,
>
> the probability of 3 successes in 3 tries is $p \times p \times p$ or p^3,
>
> $\vdots$

the probability of r successes in r tries is p^r, and the probability of subsequent $(n - r)$ failures in $(n - r)$ tries is $(1 - p)^{n-r} = q^{n-r}$. From the rule given in Chapter 5, it follows that the probability of r successes followed by $(n - r)$ failures is $p^r(1 - p)^{n-r}$. Here, we have considered only one particular group or combination of r events, that is, we have started with r successes and finished with $(n - r)$ failures. Every other possible ordering of r successes and $(n - r)$ failures will also have the same probability.

The number of possible combinations or the number of selections of r successes and $(n - r)$ failures in n trials is

$$\frac{n!}{[r!(n - r)!]} \quad \text{[see Eq. (5.43)]}.$$

Therefore, the probability P_r of an event succeeding r times is

$$P_r = \frac{n!}{r!(n - r)!} \, p^r(1 - p)^{n-r} \tag{8.1}$$

or
$$P_r = {}_nC_r p^r q^{n-r}. \tag{8.1a}$$

It may be observed that this term is similar to the rth term of the binomial expansion $(q + p)^n$ [see Eq. (5.45) or Eq. (5.46)], which can be written

$$(q + p)^n = \sum_{r=0}^{n} {}_nC_r p^r q^{n-r}. \tag{8.2}$$

The successive terms of the expansion give the probability P_r of an event succeeding r times in n trials for values of r varying in steps of one from 0 to n.

Since q is not independent but is equal to $(1 - p)$, we can see that the binomial distribution can be expressed in terms of two parameters, n and p.

In many cases, we are interested not in the probability of an event succeeding exactly r times but in the probability of its succeeding *at least* r times in n trials. This is given by the *theorem of repeated trials* as $P_r + P_{r+1} + \cdots + P_n$.

It should be emphasized again that, for the binomial distribution to be applicable, the probability of success must be constant from trial to trial and all the trials must be independent events. Thus the conditions (e.g., the method of manufacture) must not change while the samples are being taken and the sampling must be done in a random manner, each selection being independent. In industrial work where the binomial distribution is used in lot-by-lot acceptance inspection, these conditions are satisfied from a practical point of view, since the lot size is usually very large compared to the sample size.

The binomial distribution gives the probability of obtaining a specified number of successes in sampling from an *infinite* population. In cases where there is only a finite number of objects, the situation of an infinite population is simulated by sampling with replacement. For example, let us imagine that there are 10 voltmeters of a particular type in an electronics shop. A technician picks a voltmeter at random and returns it at the end of his day. The voltmeter selected the following day is taken at random from the replenished supply. In such a case, the population can be considered to be infinite because the process may be continued indefinitely.

Let us now consider several simple examples of binomial distribution.

EXAMPLE

Two coins are tossed (i.e., we take samples of two from an infinite population of coins). There are three possibilities for each toss or observation:

$$\text{no heads} \qquad \text{one head} \qquad \text{two heads.}$$

Two coins can fall in $2^2 = 4$ ways, all of which we regard as equally likely. They give us no heads in only one case (when they both fall tails) so that the probability of no heads is $\frac{1}{4}$. For there to be one head, there are two possible arrangements: a head on the first coin or a head on the second coin; hence, the probability of one head is $\frac{2}{4}$. Finally, for there to be two heads, both coins have to fall heads, and thus the probability of two heads is $\frac{1}{4}$. We can, therefore, write the probabilities:

$$\text{no heads} \qquad \text{one head} \qquad \text{two heads}$$
$$\frac{1}{4} \qquad\qquad \frac{1}{2} \qquad\qquad \frac{1}{4}.$$

Denoting the probability of success (heads) in one trial as p and the probability of failure (no heads) as q, we can write the binomial expansion for two tosses:

$$(q + p)^2 = q^2 + 2qp + p^2.$$

Since $p = q = \frac{1}{2}$, the expansion gives the probabilities for the three possible cases, respectively:

$$(q + p)^2 \quad = \quad (\tfrac{1}{2})^2 \quad + \quad 2(\tfrac{1}{2})(\tfrac{1}{2})^2 + \quad (\tfrac{1}{2})^2$$

with a
probability of   no heads   one head   two heads.   ■ ■

EXAMPLE

If four coins are tossed, what are the probabilities of obtaining various numbers of heads?

We may treat a toss as a Bernoulli trial and assume that the four coins are fair (unbiased).

The number of possible ways in which 4 coins can be tossed is $2^4 = 16$.

For no heads, the number of favorable events is 1 (probability $= \frac{1}{16}$), since, in order to get no heads, all four coins have to be tails.

For one head, the number of favorable events is 4 (probability $= \frac{4}{16}$), since

the 1st coin could be tossed as a head, or

the 2nd coin could be tossed as a head, or

the 3rd coin could be tossed as a head, or

the 4th coin could be tossed as a head.

For two heads, the number of favorable events is the number of ways in which one can select 2 items out of 4, that is,

$$_4C_2 = \frac{4 \times 3}{2} = 6.$$

(This represents a probability $= \frac{6}{16}$.)

For three heads, the number of favorable events is $_4C_3 = 4$ (probability $= \frac{4}{16}$).

For four heads, the number of favorable events is $_4C_4 = 1$ (probability $= \frac{1}{16}$).

Compare these values with the binomial expansion of

$$\left(\frac{1}{2} + \frac{1}{2}\right)^4 = \left(\frac{1}{2}\right)^4 + 4\left(\frac{1}{2}\right)^3\left(\frac{1}{2}\right) + \frac{4 \times 3}{2}\left(\frac{1}{2}\right)^2\left(\frac{1}{2}\right)^2$$

$$= \frac{1}{16} + \frac{4}{16} + \frac{6}{16}$$

with a probability of	no heads	1 head	2 heads

$$+ \frac{4 \times 3 \times 2}{2 \times 3}\left(\frac{1}{2}\right)\left(\frac{1}{2}\right)^3 + \left(\frac{1}{2}\right)^4$$

$$+ \frac{4}{16} + \frac{1}{16}$$

3 heads	4 heads.

This distribution is shown in the frequency diagram of Fig. 8.1, and it can be seen that when $p = q$ the distribution of the probabilities is (as expected) symmetrical. ■ ■

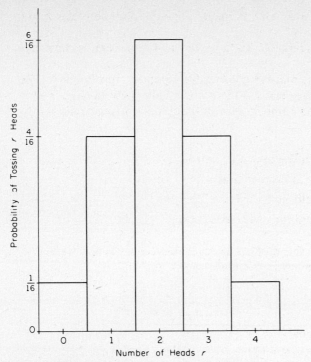

Figure 8.1 Probability distribution for throwing various numbers of heads in tossing four coins.

Nonsymmetrical distribution is illustrated by the following case.

EXAMPLE

Consider a population consisting of equal numbers of balls of three different colors from which we draw four balls at a time, replacing the balls every time. What is the probability of obtaining in our sample $0, 1, \ldots,$ 4 balls of a given color, say black?

For each ball drawn, the probability of success (black ball) is $p = \frac{1}{3}$; the probability of failure is $q = \frac{2}{3}$. Using binomial distribution, we have

$$\left(\frac{2}{3} + \frac{1}{3}\right)^4 = \frac{16}{3^4} + \frac{32}{3^4} + \frac{24}{3^4} + \frac{8}{3^4} + \frac{1}{3^4}$$

$$= 0.1975 \quad 0.3951 \quad 0.2963 \quad 0.0988 \quad 0.0123$$

| for the probability of: | no black balls | 1 black ball | 2 black balls | 3 black balls | 4 black balls. |

The probability distribution (plotted in Fig. 8.2) is nonsymmetrical. ∎ ∎

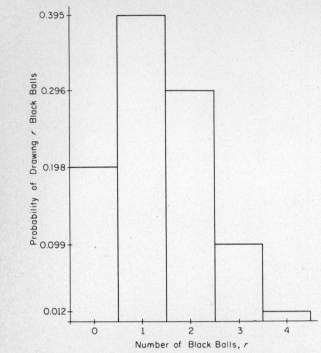

Figure 8.2 Probability distribution for drawing different numbers of black balls in a sample of 4 balls drawn from a population of balls of 3 colors in equal proportions.

EXAMPLE

Seven races are to be held, the same six dogs taking part in each race. What are the probabilities of one particular dog's winning 1, 2, . . . , 7 races, assuming that all dogs are "equally good"?[2]

In any one race our dog has a $\frac{1}{6}$ chance of winning (probability of success $= p = \frac{1}{6}$) and a $\frac{5}{6}$ chance of not winning (probability of failure $= q = \frac{5}{6}$). Binomial expansion gives

$$\left(\frac{5}{6}+\frac{1}{6}\right)^7 \;=\; \left(\frac{5}{6}\right)^7 \;+\; 7\left(\frac{5}{6}\right)^6\left(\frac{1}{6}\right) \;+\; \frac{7\times 6}{2}\left(\frac{5}{6}\right)^5\left(\frac{1}{6}\right)^2$$

with a
probability of   no wins   1 win   2 wins

$$+\;\frac{7\times 6\times 5}{2\times 3}\left(\frac{5}{6}\right)^4\left(\frac{1}{6}\right)^3 \;+\cdots+\; \left(\frac{1}{6}\right)^7$$

3 wins   7 wins.

■ ■

[2] An assumption of doubtful validity.

CUMULATIVE TERMS FOR BINOMIAL DISTRIBUTION

From what was said about the theorem of repeated trials (page 136), it can be seen that it is often advantageous to find *directly* the probability of an event succeeding at least r times in n trials. The relevant data can be presented in tabular form, their derivation being as follows.

The probability P_r of an event succeeding *exactly* r times in n trials is given by Eq. (8.1a),

$$P_r = {}_nC_r p^r q^{n-r}.$$

The probability of an event succeeding *at least* r' times in n trials is given by

$$\sum_{r=r'}^{r=n} P_r = \sum_{r=r'}^{r=n} {}_nC_r p^r q^{n-r}. \tag{8.3}$$

The values of the summation of Eq. (8.3) are given in Table A.2 for p ranging from 0.05 to 0.50, with n between 2 and 20, and r' between 1 and 20.

For $p > 0.5$, we can utilize the fact that the probability is

$$P = 1 - \sum_{r=n-r'+1}^{r=n} {}_nC_r q^r p^{n-r}. \tag{8.4}$$

EXAMPLE

For a probability of success $p = 0.75$ and 4 trials, what is the probability of at least 3 successes? We look up the value in Table A.2 for $n = 4$, $r' = 2$ (from $r = n - r' + 1$, i.e., $3 = 4 - r' + 1$), and $q = 0.25$ (q interchanges with p in the same table) and find 0.2617. Therefore, the answer is $1 - 0.2617 = 0.7383$. Clearly, this is the same as the probability of at most one failure.

■ ■

PASCAL'S TRIANGLE

The binomial coefficients can be obtained from Pascal's triangle; this is constructed so that each term is the sum of the two terms immediately above and to either side, as shown in Fig. 8.3. The second term of each line corresponds to the value of n in $(q + p)^n$, and the sum of coefficients in any line is equal to 2^n.

The coefficients of the binomial expansion can, of course, be computed quite rapidly using tables of factorial values. If, however, appropriate factorial values are not available and n is large, Stirling's formula can be used. This gives the factorial

$$n! \simeq e^{-n} n^n \sqrt{2\pi n}. \tag{8.5}$$

The error involved is less than 0.1 percent for n greater than 100 and less than 1 percent for n greater than 10.

```
                                    1
                                1       1
                            1       2       1
                        1       3       3       1
                    1       4       6       4       1
                1       5       10      10      5       1
            1       6       15      20      15      6       1
        1       7       21      35      35      21      7       1
    1       8       28      56      70      56      28      8       1
1       9       36      84      126     126     84      36      9       1
1   10      45      120     210     252     210     120     45      10      1
1   11      55      165     330     462     462     330     165     55      11      1
1   12      66      220     495     792     924     792     495     220     66      12      1
```

Figure 8.3   Pascal's triangle.

The binomial distribution is used extensively in quality testing; a very simple illustration follows.

EXAMPLE

In the production of wire connections consisting of 4 wires in parallel, it was found that on the average 1 wire in 10 was not tightened. If the strength of each wire is 250 newtons, find the proportion of connections that can withstand 750 newtons.

We assume that a wire which has not been tightened carries no load.

$$\text{probability of a good wire} = p = 0.9$$
$$\text{probability of a defective wire} = q = 0.1$$

Using the binomial distribution, we obtain

$$(0.1 + 0.9)^4 = (0.1)^4 + 4(0.1)^3(0.9) + \frac{4 \times 3(0.1)^2(0.9)^2}{2}$$

$$= 0.0001 \qquad 0.0036 \qquad\qquad 0.0486$$

| with a probability of | all defective | 3 defective, 1 good | 2 defective, 2 good |

$$+ \frac{4 \times 3 \times 2(0.1)(0.9)^3}{2 \times 3} + (0.9)^4$$

$$0.2916 \qquad\qquad 0.6561$$

1 defective,   all good.
3 good

We can say, therefore, that of all connections made:

65.61 percent will have a strength of $4 \times 250 = 1000$ N

$65.61 + 29.16 = 94.77$ percent will have a strength of 3×250

$$= 750 \text{ N or more}$$

$$94.77 + \quad 4.86 = 99.63 \text{ percent will have a strength of } 2 \times 250$$
$$= 500 \text{ N or more}$$

$$99.63 + \quad 0.36 = 99.99 \text{ percent will have a strength of } 1 \times 250$$
$$= 250 \text{ N or more}$$

0.01 percent will have no strength.

We can readily obtain the above results from Table A.2. Thus, for all four connections being good, $r = 4$ and $r' = 1$ (from $r = n - r' + 1$, n being equal to 4). Entering Table A.2 and using $q = 0.1$ (instead of p, since $p = 0.9 > 0.5$) we find the value of 0.3439; the required probability is then calculated by Eq. (8.4) to be $1 - 0.3439 = 0.6561$; that is, 65.61 percent of all connections made will have a strength of 1000 N. For at least three connections being good, $r = 3$ with $r' = 2$, and the value from the table is 0.0523. The corresponding probability is $(1 - 0.0523)$, that is, 94.77 percent will have a strength of 750 N or more. The other values can be obtained in a similar manner. ■ ■

EXAMPLE
Wireless sets are manufactured with 25 soldered joints each. On the average, 1 joint in 500 is defective. How many sets can be expected to be free from defective joints in a consignment of 10,000 sets?

Let the probability of a defective joint ("success") be $p = 0.002$. Then $q = 0.998$. Using the binomial expansion,

$$(0.998 + 0.002)^{25} = \quad (0.998)^{25} \quad + 25 \times (0.998)^{24} \times 0.002 + \cdots$$

$$\begin{array}{cc} \text{no defective} & \text{1 joint} \\ \text{joints} & \text{defective} \end{array}$$

Thus the proportion of sets with no defective joints is $(0.998)^{25} = 0.95118$ so that in 10,000 sets, 9512 would be expected to be free from defective joints. It is clear that some sets would have more than one defective joint. ■ ■

MEAN AND STANDARD DEVIATION

Let us now consider further the properties of the binomial distribution. If p is the proportion of successes in the population, then the mean number of successes in n trials is

$$\mu = np. \tag{8.6}$$

This is obvious, as the mean number of successes in n trials is equal to the probability of success in one trial times the number of trials.

The standard deviation of a binomial frequency distribution is

$$\sigma = \sqrt{npq}. \tag{8.7}$$

Equations (8.6) and (8.7) will now be derived using the definition of expectation for the mean and variance introduced in Chapter 5. Thus, from Eq. (5.29),

$$E(r) = \mu = \sum_{r=0}^{n} rP_r = \sum_{r=0}^{n} r \frac{n!}{r!(n-r)!} p^r(1-p)^{n-r}$$

$$= np \sum_{r=1}^{n} \frac{(n-1)!}{(r-1)!(n-r)!} p^{r-1}(1-p)^{n-r}$$

$$= np[p+q]^{n-1}$$

or $$\mu = np. \tag{8.6}$$

For the variance σ^2 we use Eq. (5.31):

$$E(r-\mu)^2 = \sigma^2 = \sum_{r=0}^{n} (r-\mu)^2 P_r$$

$$= \sum_{r=0}^{n} r^2 P_r - 2\mu \sum_{r=0}^{n} rP_r + \mu^2 \sum_{r=0}^{n} P_r$$

$$= \sum_{r=0}^{n} r^2 P_r - 2\mu(\mu) + \mu^2$$

since $$\sum_{r=0}^{n} P_r = 1 \quad \text{and} \quad \sum_{r=0}^{n} rP_r = \mu = np.$$

Thus, $$\sigma^2 = \sum_{r=0}^{n} r^2 P_r - (np)^2$$

$$= \sum_{r=0}^{n} [r(r-1)+r]P_r - (np)^2$$

$$= \sum_{r=2}^{n} r(r-1) \frac{n!}{r!(n-r)!} p^r(1-p)^{n-r} + \sum_{r=0}^{n} rP_r - (np)^2$$

$$= n(n-1)p^2 \sum_{r=2}^{n} \frac{(n-2)!}{(r-2)!(n-r)!} p^{r-2}(1-p)^{n-r} + np - (np)^2$$

$$= n(n-1)p^2[p+q]^{n-2} + np - (np)^2$$

or $$\sigma^2 = n(n-1)p^2 + np - (np)^2 = np(1-p) = npq.$$

Hence, $$\sigma = \sqrt{npq}. \tag{8.7}$$

An illustration of the use of Eqs. (8.6) and (8.7) is afforded by the following example.

TABLE 8.1

Number of heads, x_i	Theoretical frequency, f_i	$f_i x_i$	$f_i x_i^2$
0	2	0	0
1	8	8	8
2	12	24	48
3	8	24	72
4	2	8	32
Totals	$\sum f_i = 32$	$\sum f_i x_i = 64$	$\sum f_i x_i^2 = 160$

EXAMPLE

Consider 32 trials, each consisting of tossing four coins. The frequencies from the binomial distribution are given by $32(\frac{1}{2} + \frac{1}{2})^4$, as shown in Table 8.1. Using the general expressions for mean and standard deviation [Eqs. (3.2) and (4.9)], we have

$$\text{mean} = \mu = \frac{\sum f_i x_i}{\sum f_i} = \frac{64}{32} = 2$$

(as, indeed, expected) and, from the relationship

$$\sigma = s\sqrt{\frac{n-1}{n}},$$

$$\text{population standard deviation} = \sigma = \sqrt{\frac{\sum f_i x_i^2 - [(\sum f_i x_i)^2 / \sum f_i]}{\sum f_i}}$$

$$= \sqrt{\frac{160 - [(64)^2 / 32]}{32}} = 1.$$

We can now check these results against Eqs. (8.6) and (8.7): $n = 4$, $p = \frac{1}{2}$, and $q = \frac{1}{2}$. Then,

$$\mu = np = 4 \times \tfrac{1}{2} = 2$$

and
$$\sigma = \sqrt{npq} = \sqrt{4 \times \tfrac{1}{2} \times \tfrac{1}{2}} = 1. \qquad \blacksquare\blacksquare$$

COMPARISON OF EXPERIMENTAL AND BINOMIAL DISTRIBUTIONS

All the preceding examples in this chapter were problems in probability rather than in statistics: the composition of the binomial population, characterized by p, that is, the probability of success in a single trial, was assumed *known* and we were interested in calculating the probability of certain numerical events. We shall see in the following discussion of acceptance tests how the information

TABLE 8.2

Number of heads, x_i	Observed frequency, f_i	$f_i x_i$	$f_i x_i^2$
0	0	0	0
1	8	8	8
2	15	30	60
3	6	18	54
4	3	12	48
Totals	$\sum f_i = 32$	$\sum f_i x_i = 68$	$\sum f_i x_i^2 = 170$

contained in the sample (representing a population) is used to infer the characteristics of the population.

Let us consider an actual experiment in which the results in Table 8.2 were obtained. Here,

$$\bar{x} = \frac{68}{32} = 2.12$$

and

$$s = \sqrt{\frac{170 - \left[\dfrac{(68)^2}{32}\right]}{31}} = 0.91.$$

A comparison of the observed distribution with the preceding binomial distribution is shown in Fig. 8.4.

We should note that if the comparison is made in terms of frequencies rather than of probabilities, the expected frequency can have noninteger values and therefore it has a mathematical and not a strictly physical meaning, as fractions of, say, heads are not possible.

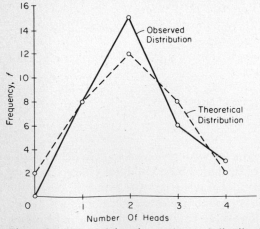

Figure 8.4 Binomial and experimental distribution for 32 throws of 4 coins.

A practical problem of comparison arises in acceptance tests which involve the concept of hypothesis testing discussed in Chapter 7. In such tests, the following procedure is used:

1. We consider the conditions pertaining to the binomial distribution and decide whether this distribution is the correct model representing the variable under investigation.
2. If all the conditions for the binomial distribution are met, we adopt this distribution to describe the behavior of the random variable being studied and use a null hypothesis (considered in Chapter 7) about the parameter p, that is, $H_0: p = p_0$, with an alternative hypothesis $H_a: p \geqslant p_0$.
3. We calculate the probability of obtaining at least the number of defectives found in the sample data.
4. If that probability is very small, we recommend nonacceptance of the null hypothesis that the number of rejects in the sample is due to chance; we therefore conclude that the actual number of rejects is due to other causes, perhaps poor quality merchandise. Thus we make a *decision* to reject the consignment; the risk of erroneously rejecting the null hypothesis is, in fact, the probability calculated.

As an example, let us imagine that a manufacturer delivers a product on the understanding that no more than 10 percent of the items are defective. We take a sample of 4 items and find 2 of them defective. Are we justified in rejecting the entire consignment? Use a significance level $\alpha = 0.10$.

We shall answer this question by considering the binomial distribution according to the procedure given above. Let us assume that the conditions for adopting the binomial model are met, that is, the binomial distribution is the one to represent the number of defective items in the merchandise (population), with the null hypothesis $H_0: p \leqslant 0.1$. We *hypothesize* now that $p = 0.1$ also applies to our sample of 4 items ($n = 4$) extracted from the merchandise produced. More formally, $H_0: p = 0.1$, and $H_a: p > 0.1$. Note that we have replaced the original null hypothesis, $p \leqslant 0.1$, by the simpler claim that $p = 0.1$, since, if this is rejected, the original H_0 would also be rejected.

Now, we have to calculate the probability P of obtaining at least 2 defective items in a sample of 4; the reason for "at least 2 defective items" is that a sample (of merchandise) which contains 3 or 4 defective items is at least as bad as that with two defective items. Therefore, all these possibilities have to be considered. Thus, with $n = 4$, $p = 0.1$, and $q = 0.9$,

$$P = P_2 + P_3 + P_4$$
$$= {}_4C_2(0.1)^2(0.9)^2 + {}_4C_3(0.1)^3(0.9) + {}_4C_4(0.1)^4$$
$$= 0.0523.$$

Thus, there is a small probability of only 0.0523 (or approximately 1 in 20) of drawing at least 2 defectives in a sample of 4; this probability is smaller than the level of significance $\alpha = 0.10$. Therefore, we would be far from unreasonable if we rejected the consignment. This answer can also be directly obtained from Table A.2: with $n = 4$, $r = r' = 2$, $p = 0.1$, we read the required probability as 0.0523.

We can say more generally that sometimes the appropriate inference is in terms of a certain number or fewer (or more) occurrences and not of the exact number alone. For instance, if obtaining "one" 10 times in 12 throws of a die leads us to infer that the die is biased, our reasoning should recognize that 11 and 12 occurrences of "one" are an even stronger evidence of bias. We should therefore consider the probability of obtaining *at least* 10 "ones." In other words, all possible results of a test should be divided into those more favorable to the truth of the hypothesis than the actual observation and those at least as unfavorable as the actual value.

The following is a rule of thumb telling us when the probability P can be considered small so as to reject the null hypothesis H_0.

If $P > 0.1$, there is no reason to reject the null hypothesis.

If $0.1 > P > 0.01$, there is good reason to reject the null hypothesis.

If $P < 0.01$, there is strong reason to reject the null hypothesis.

The above limits might vary from problem to problem depending on the risk which we are prepared to take through making the *wrong* decision.

In the example on page 147 we may want to find the probability of accepting the hypothesis that $p = 0.1$ when actually $p = 0.2$; that is, the probability β of making a Type II error (see Chapter 7). This is calculated as follows:

$$\beta = 1 - \left[_4C_2(0.2)^2(0.8)^2 + {}_4C_3(0.2)^3(0.8) + {}_4C_4(0.2)^4 \right]$$
$$= 1 - [0.1536 + 0.0256 + 0.0016]$$
$$= 0.8192.$$

Thus, even when $p = 0.2$ so that the null hypothesis is false, such a departure from H_0 will *not* be detected in about 82 percent of cases. In other words, there is a large chance (82 percent) of accepting $H_0 : p = 0.1$ when actually $p = 0.2$.

It should be stressed that an intuitive approach to problems of this type can often be misleading. For example, what answer would the reader expect to the following problem?

Lottery tickets are sold, it being advertised that every fourth ticket carries a prize. If we buy 4 tickets, this being a random sample, what is the probability that we get at least one winning ticket?

The probability of having at least one winning ticket is

$$P = 1 - P_0$$

where P_0 is the probability of having no winning ticket in a sample of 4, and the term 1 represents all the possible cases. We have $p = 0.25$ and $n = 4$. Thus

$$P = 1 - {}_4C_0(0.25)^0(0.75)^4$$
$$= 0.684$$

that is, there is a 68.4 percent probability of having at least one winning ticket. This may interest those who did not get a winning ticket under similar circumstances and ended up by suspecting the promoters.

The answer to our problem could also be obtained by adding the probabilities of drawing 1, 2, 3, and 4 winning tickets, but the method used here involves less effort. Of course, Table A.2 gives the answer at once with $p = 0.25$, $n = 4$, and $r = r' = 1$.

Another comparison between an experimental distribution and the binomial distribution may be of interest.

EXAMPLE

Ten tosses of a suspected die gave the results 1, 1, 1, 6, 1, 1, 3, 1, 1, 4. What is the probability of at least this many aces (ones) if the die is true?

The event "at least 7 aces" can materialize in four mutually exclusive ways: 7 aces, 8 aces, 9 aces, and 10 aces.

The probability of throwing at least 7 aces, P, is the sum of the probabilities for 7, 8, 9, and 10 aces, that is,

$$P = P_7 + P_8 + P_9 + P_{10}.$$

We have $n = 10$, and the probability of throwing an ace in any throw is $p = \frac{1}{6}$. In this case, we shall adopt the null hypothesis $H_0 : p = \frac{1}{6}$ against the alternative hypothesis $H_a : p \neq \frac{1}{6}$. In other words, we are assuming that the die is unbiased and, in consequence, the outcome of each trial (toss) is governed solely by chance. Therefore,

$$P = {}_{10}C_7\left(\frac{1}{6}\right)^7\left(\frac{5}{6}\right)^3 + {}_{10}C_8\left(\frac{1}{6}\right)^8\left(\frac{5}{6}\right)^2 + {}_{10}C_9\left(\frac{1}{6}\right)^9\left(\frac{5}{6}\right) + {}_{10}C_{10}\left(\frac{1}{6}\right)^{10}$$

$$= 0.00027.$$

This probability is so small that it is most unlikely that the observed 7 aces in 10 throws could be obtained with $p = \frac{1}{6}$. We conclude, therefore, that the null hypothesis $p = \frac{1}{6}$ should be rejected, that is, the die is biased or "loaded." ■ ■

We can, of course, test the agreement between the two distributions quantitatively in terms of probability; the appropriate methods are dealt with in Chapter 14.

Before concluding this chapter we should point out a very useful property of the binomial distribution. As we observed before, if the parameter p is less than 0.5, then the binomial distribution will be skewed to the right as shown in Fig. 8.5; on the other hand, if p exceeds 0.5, the distribution will be skewed to

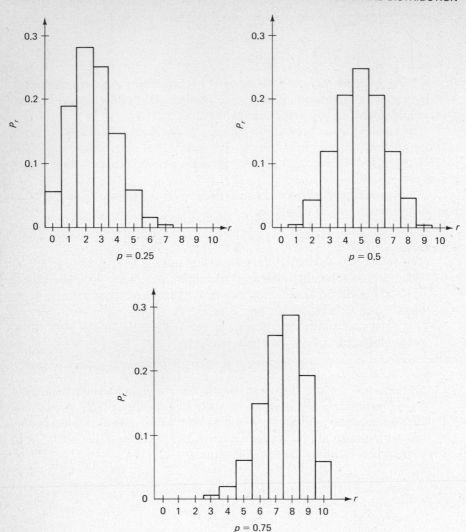

Figure 8.5   Binomial distribution for sample size $n = 10$ and various values of p.

the left. Now, if p is held constant and the sample size, n, increases, the sum of the Bernoulli variables[3] increases, and the binomial distribution becomes more and more symmetrical by virtue of the central limit theorem (page 117); this is illustrated in Fig. 8.6 in which p is held constant at 0.25 and $n = 5$, 10, 20, and 40. We shall see in Chapter 11 that, for a large n, the binomial distribution in fact approaches a normal distribution; this property is very useful from the standpoint of sampling theory and practice.

---

[3] A Bernoulli variable is any random variable whose only possible values are 0 and 1. For example, 0 can signify the nonexistence of an event and 1 its existence. (See page 134 for a definition of a Bernoulli trial.)

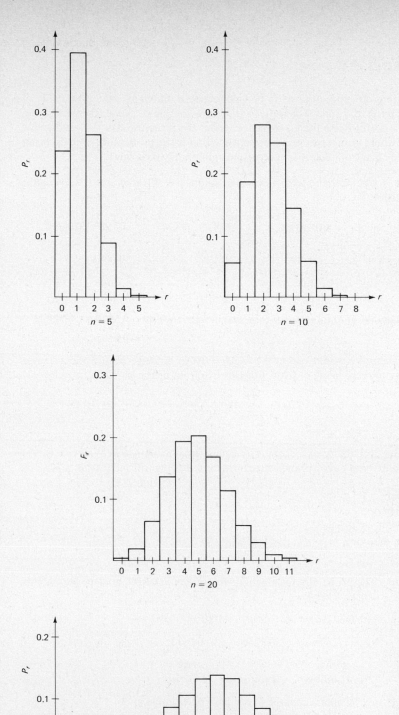

Figure 8.6 Binomial distribution for $p = 0.25$ and various values of sample size n.

SOLVED PROBLEMS

8-1. If the probability of a weld's being defective is 0.1, what is the probability of obtaining exactly 0, 1, 2, and 3 defective welds in a sample of 5 welds? What is the probability of obtaining less than 2 defective welds? If a structure has 100 welds, how many of them would you expect to be defective? What is the probability of there being at least 90 welds free from defect in a structure containing 100 welds?

Solution.   The probability of a defective weld is $p = 0.1$, then $q = 0.9$. Using the binomial expansion, we obtain

$$(0.9 + 0.1)^5 = (0.9)^5 + 5(0.9)^4(0.1) + \frac{5 \times 4}{2!}(0.9)^3(0.1)^2 + \frac{5 \times 4 \times 3}{3!}(0.9)^2(0.1)^3 + \cdots$$

	0.59049	0.32805	0.0729	0.0081
with a probability of	all good	one defective	two defectives	three defectives

Hence, probability of obtaining less than two defective welds = 0.59049 + 0.32805

$$= 0.91854.$$

Of 100 welds we would expect $0.1 \times 100 = 10$ to be defective (on the average). The probability of there being at least 90 welds free from defect is

$$\sum_{r=90}^{100} P_r$$

where $P_r = {}_{100}C_r(0.1)^{100-r}(0.9)^r$.

8-2. If the probability of a structure's collapsing after 30 years of service is 0.01 find the probability that out of 10 such structures the following will collapse after 30 years of service.
  a. None.
  b. Exactly one.
  c. Not more than one.
  d. More than one.
  e. At least one.

Solution.   The probability of a sound structure is $p = 0.99$, and the probability of a collapse is $q = 0.01$. Therefore,

$$(0.99 + 0.01)^{10} = (0.99)^{10} + 10(0.99)^9(0.01) + \cdots$$

	= 0.9036	0.0913
with a probability of	no collapse	one collapse

Logarithms are used to obtain the above results. For example, put

$$(0.99)^{10} = y.$$

Then $$\log y = 10 \log 0.99 = \bar{1}.9956 \times 10$$

$$= \overline{10} + 9.956$$

$$= \bar{1}.9560.$$

Hence $y = 0.9036$. Thus the probabilities are
- **a.** 0.9036
- **b.** 0.0913
- **c.** $0.9036 + 0.0913 = 0.9949$
- **d.** $1 - 0.9949 = 0.0051$
- **e.** $1 - 0.9036 = 0.0964$.

PROBLEMS

8-1. On checking assembly lines, it was found that 1 of the 10 lines produced defective items. The products of all the lines were mixed by then, and the defectives could not be easily separated out. If a random sample of 10 items is taken, what is the probability of its containing the following number of defective items?
- **a.** No defective items.
- **b.** One defective item.
- **c.** Not more than two defective items.
- **d.** More than one defective item.

8-2. If the probability of a child's being male is 0.55, what is the probability of having three daughters in succession?

8-3. A product is supposed to contain 5 percent of defective items. We take a sample of 10 items and find it to contain 2 defectives. Are we justified in suspecting that the consignment is not up to specification? Use $\alpha = 0.05$.

8-4. A manufacturing process is intended to produce precast units with no more than 2 percent defective. It is checked every day by testing 10 units selected at random from the day's production. If one or more of the 10 fails, the process is halted and carefully examined. If, in fact, its probability of producing a defective unit is 0.01:
- **a.** What is the probability of obtaining one or more defective units?
- **b.** What is the probability of obtaining no defectives in a given test?
- **c.** Find the mean and the standard deviation of the number of defective units in a sample of 10 units.

8-5. The foreman of a casting section in a certain factory finds that on the average 1 in every 5 castings made is defective. If the section makes 8 castings a day, what is the chance that 2 of these will be defective? What is the chance that 5 or more defective castings are made in one day?

8-6. Samples of 6 items are drawn at random from a supply source that contains 9 percent defectives. Draw a histogram showing the probabilities of having $0, 1, \ldots, 6$ defectives in the sample.

8-7. In a game of Russian roulette one chamber of a six-chamber gun is loaded. The cylinder is spun around, and the trigger is pulled. Three men are playing the "roulette," taking 3 turns each at pulling the trigger. What is the probability that:
- **a.** A particular man will survive the game?
- **b.** One of the three men will survive the game?
- **c.** All the men will survive?

8-8. From seven different concrete mixes a number of compression test specimens of two sizes were made. The results are given in Table 8.3. Test the hypothesis that there is no difference between the strength of specimens of 10-cm and 20-cm size. Use

TABLE 8.3

| Mix | 10-cm specimens | | 20-cm specimens | |
	Sample size	Mean strength, MPa	Sample size	Mean strength, MPa
A	6	13.8	6	11.3
B	27	23.2	21	21.4
C	15	28.3	12	27.0
D	6	36.0	9	31.8
E	12	44.3	7	42.6
F	18	58.0	6	50.7
G	11	72.5	9	63.4

Source: A. M. Neville, "Some Aspects of the Strength of Concrete," Part II, *Civil Engineering and Public Works Review,* vol. 54, no. 640. Nov. 1959, pp. 1308–1310. The original data were in kg/cm^2 units.

$\alpha = 0.05$. (HINT: Calculate the probability of obtaining the observed number of differences of the same sign if positive and negative differences occur equally often in the parent population.)

8-9. From previous experience it is known that the probability of a specific structure failing under load is 1 in 500. Strengthening of the structure would cost $15,000. If total losses due to failure are estimated at $10,000,000, should the present structure be strengthened?

8-10. A car-manufacturing company has detected that 5 percent of its new model cars have an idling problem. To solve this problem a new nozzle was introduced in a pilot lot of 100 cars.

  a. How many cars would one expect to have the idling problem if the new nozzle has no effect?
  b. Would you conclude that the new nozzle has solved the problem if it was found that only 2 cars in the pilot lot are now experiencing the idling problem? Use $\alpha = 0.05$. (HINT: Find the probability of getting 2 or fewer defectives in a sample size of 100, assuming that the new nozzle has no effect.)

Chapter 9

Poisson Distribution

The Poisson distribution represents the probability of an isolated event occurring a specified number of times in a given interval of time (or space) when the rate of occurrence in a continuum of time (or space) is fixed. The occurrence of events must be affected by chance alone, and the Poisson distribution, therefore, is such that information about the position of one event is of no help in predicting the position of any other specific event; furthermore, data on one small interval of time (or space) are of no help in predicting how many events will occur in any other interval.

A characteristic feature of the Poisson distribution is the fact that only the occurrence of an event can be counted; its nonoccurrence cannot because it has no physical meaning. Thus the total number of events n cannot be measured, and, in consequence, the binomial distribution is not precisely applicable. The Poisson distribution is a chance distribution which can predict the occurrence of *discrete events* (e.g., defects). It is, therefore, a discrete distribution, like the binomial distribution, but with an infinitely large number of possible outcomes.

Examples of phenomena which follow the Poisson distribution are: flaws in castings, and in general defects observed in various types of surfaces or objects; cosmic-ray counts from a Geiger counter; number of telephone calls; number of traffic accidents; number of accidents in a factory; bacterial densities; number of cars passing a particular station on a highway; the number of deaths in the celebrated case of cavalrymen killed by a horse kick (discussed later in this chapter). All these illustrations have the following in common: the given occurrences can be described in terms of a discrete random variable which takes on values of 0, 1, 2, ...; for instance, the number of defects or flaws can be counted as 0, 1, 2, ..., and so on, in a specified area of an aluminum rolled sheet. The Poisson distribution is used in manufacturing and experimental work where certain occurrences happen by chance, sometimes in profusion, and sometimes hardly at all! For example, fatigue cracks can occur anywhere along a continuous weld; or an earthquake can occur at any time and anywhere in a region prone to earth tremors.

The Poisson distribution is based on the following assumptions:

i. The probability of an occurrence of a discrete event in a small subinterval of time (or space) is very small (see probability p in example on page 164; this probability is constant. The discrete event occurs at random and at any time (or space).

ii. The probability of more than one occurrence in each subinterval is so small that it may be considered negligible.

iii. The occurrences (or nonoccurrences) must be independent. (Examples of dependent events are: the situation when defects are more likely in some environment than in others; or a Geiger counter which has been briefly desensitized for some reason.)

Let us now apply these assumptions to the number of flaws found in producing aluminum rolled sheets. From past experience, it is known that the aluminum sheets produced have a certain rate of flaws per interval, say, one per 50-m length. Suppose that the entire length of a rolled sheet is subdivided into very small subintervals, say, of 1 mm each. Then:

i. The probability that exactly one flaw occurs in this subinterval of 1 mm is very small ($p = \frac{1}{50,000}$), and is constant for each such interval. The number of flaws which occur in an interval of 1 mm does not depend on where the subinterval is located.

ii. The probability of one or more flaws in a subinterval is so small that it is negligible.

iii. The number of flaws which occur in a subinterval does not depend on the number of flaws detected in any other nonoverlapping interval.

It should be mentioned that there are events which seem to have random occurrences but which, in fact, are affected by other factors. For example, the number of static bursts per hour on a radio receiver could be a random phenomenon but might also be influenced by local television viewing or by rush-hour traffic.

TERMS OF THE POISSON DISTRIBUTION

The Poisson distribution is made up of a series of terms,

$$e^{-\mu}, \quad e^{-\mu}\mu, \quad e^{-\mu}\frac{\mu^2}{2!}, \quad e^{-\mu}\frac{\mu^3}{3!}, \quad e^{-\mu}\frac{\mu^4}{4!}, \cdots$$

representing, respectively, the probability of the occurrence of 0, 1, 2, 3, 4, and so on, events, where e is the base of natural logarithms and μ is the mean frequency of occurrence. The sum of all terms of the series is unity, as must be the case with a sum of all probabilities.

If r is the number of occurrences whose probability we require, we can write the general term of the series

$$P_r = \frac{e^{-\mu}\mu^r}{r!}. \tag{9.1}$$

The values of $e^{-\mu}$ for values of μ between 0.01 and 5 are given in Table A.3, but such a computation is tiresome, and the use of tabulated (see Table A.4) or plotted (see Fig. 9.1) values is preferable. Clearly, a calculator can also be used.

It is important to note from Eq. (9.1) that the Poisson distribution is characterized by only *one parameter* μ. The distribution is always skewed to the right (since r cannot be lower than zero and may be any positive integer); however, the distribution becomes more symmetrical when the mean $\mu \geqslant 6$. The relation between the mode and the mean μ is such that the mode is

at 0 occurrence when $\mu < 1$,

at 1 occurrence when $1 \leqslant \mu < 2$,

at 2 occurrences when $2 \leqslant \mu < 3$, and so on.

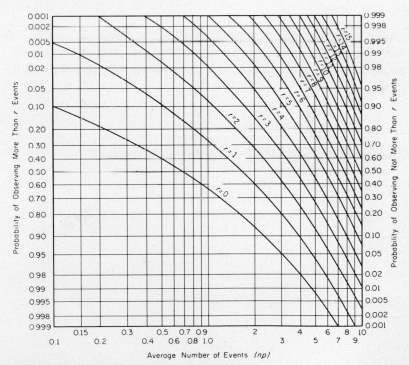

Figure 9.1 Cumulative Poisson distribution.

The terms of the Poisson distribution [Eq. (9.1)] are derived from a Poisson process in Appendix B. A Poisson process is a random physical mechanism in which events occur randomly on a time scale (or distance scale), the conditions being laid down on page 156. For example, the time of occurrence of accidents at a specific road junction follows a Poisson process. It should be remembered that we cannot predict exactly how many accidents will take place in a particular time interval, but we can predict the *pattern* of accidents in a large number of such time intervals.

We have mentioned that the Poisson distribution can be derived from a Poisson process and thus can be used in its own right. As shown later in the chapter, the Poisson distribution can also be deduced from a limiting form of the binomial distribution and can thus be used to approximate the binomial probabilities. It should be pointed out that the Poisson process is a memoryless one, which means that future behavior is independent of present or past behavior; this makes it possible to choose any arbitrary time origin for the Poisson process.

SOME PRACTICAL POISSON DISTRIBUTIONS

It may be useful to consider several practical cases of Poisson distributions.

EXAMPLE

It is assumed that cosmic-ray counts from Geiger counters are completely random and follow a Poisson distribution. Check whether this is true for the following data on counts recorded in 50 consecutive periods of 60 s.

1, 0, 2, 4, 1, 1, 2, 1, 3, 0, 0, 2, 1, 0, 2, 3, 3,

0, 4, 1, 2, 0, 2, 1, 1, 4, 2, 1, 1, 3, 1, 1, 4, 2,

0, 0, 3, 2, 1, 2, 3, 1, 0, 2, 3, 1, 0, 1, 0, 3.

The data are arranged in tabular form in Table 9.1.

TABLE 9.1

Count in 60-s interval, r	0	1	2	3	4	>4	Total
Observed number of 60-s intervals with r counts, f	11	16	11	8	4	0	50
Probability P_r by Poisson distribution [Eq. (9.1)]	0.21	0.33	0.26	0.13	0.05	0.02	1.0
Expected numbers of intervals $P_r \times \sum f$	10.5	16.5	13.0	6.5	2.5	1.0	50.0

As was shown in Chapter 6, we can use the sample mean $\bar{x}$ as a point estimate of the population mean μ. Thus, from the table,

$$\mu = x = \frac{\sum fr}{\sum f} = \frac{0 \times 11 + 1 \times 16 + 2 \times 11 + 3 \times 8 + 4 \times 4}{50} = \frac{78}{50} = 1.56.$$

This is the average number of counts per 60-second interval.

Substituting $\mu = 1.56$ in Eq. (9.1), we have

$$P_r = \frac{e^{-1.56}(1.56)^r}{r!} \quad \text{for} \quad r = 0, 1, 2, 3, 4.$$

The values of P_r are calculated and the expected number of 60-s intervals is obtained from $P_r \times \sum f$. The results are shown in Table 9.1. A comparison between the observed and expected values indicates good agreement. (The question of how good this agreement is can be answered rigorously by the χ^2 test, considered in Chapter 14.) This conclusion is of interest because it tells us that our observed data are the result of chance happenings. A non-Poisson distribution of cosmic-ray counts would suggest that randomness or chance of the counts changed during the test or that some malfunction of the counter occurred; this would then initiate action to correct the situation. ■ ■

As was mentioned earlier in this chapter, the Poisson distribution is used extensively in traffic studies. What makes the distribution suitable in this situation is that in freely flowing traffic the following conditions, necessary for "randomness," exist.

1. Each driver positions his vehicle independently of others except when his headway is very small, that is, his position at any time is independent of all other vehicles.
2. At any given volume of traffic, the number of vehicles passing a particular point in a given interval of time is independent of the number passing in any other equal interval of time.

Thus, if

P_r = probability of arrival of r vehicles at a particular point during a given interval of time,

μ = mean number of vehicles arriving in a given interval of time = $\dfrac{tv}{3600}$, in which t = given length of time gap between vehicles (in seconds), and v = volume of traffic (in vehicles per hour),

then Eq. (9.1) applies. Solved Problem 9-1 illustrates the use of the Poisson distribution in traffic studies.

EXAMPLE

The traffic signal at a single highway intersection has a cycle of 50 s; one approach road has 180 vehicles per hour turning left. The design layout of the intersection allows two left-turning vehicles per cycle without delay whereas 3 or more left-turning vehicles cause delays to other traffic. Find: (a) in what percentage of the cycles would such delays occur? (b) if a left-turn phase is provided, determine the percentage of cycles in which the new design would be unnecessary because there are no left-turning vehicles. Assume a Poisson process.

a. μ = average number of left turns per cycle

$$= \frac{180}{3600} \times 50 = 2.5.$$

Then, the probability P is

$$P_{r \geqslant 3} = 1 - \sum_{r=0}^{r=2} \frac{e^{-2.5} \times 2.5^r}{r!}$$

$$= 1 - \left(1 + 2.5 + \frac{6.25}{2}\right) \times e^{-2.5}$$

$$= 1 - 0.55$$

$$= 0.45.$$

Thus, delays can be expected in 45 percent of the cycles.

b. Here we need to find the probability of no left turns:

$$P_{r=0} = \frac{e^{-2.5} \times 2.5^0}{0!} = 0.082.$$

In other words, the new design would not be required in about 1 out of every 12 cycles. ■ ■

The same procedure is applied in business analysis such as queuing theory or waiting-line theory. Here, it is of interest to study customer waiting times at service facilities, service time, downtime, or the probability that the service facilities will be overtaxed, in order to determine whether an additional service facility should be added, a current one dropped, or adjustments made in the current service facilities. For example, using probabilities calculated from the Poisson distribution, decisions are made about the number of checkout counters in a store to be open during a specific period in the day.

EXAMPLE

It has been found that on long weekends, the Department of Customs and Immigration at a road border crossing between two countries can expect an average of three arrivals per minute at an officer's gate. If an officer can handle a maximum of 2 motorists per minute, what is the probability that during any given minute during a long weekend, an officer will be "swamped"? Assume that arriving motorists follow a Poisson distribution.

The probability that an officer will be "swamped" is the probability that the number of motorists during any given minute, R, exceeds 2. Since R is a Poisson random variable with the mean number of arrivals per minute $\mu = 3$,

$$P_{r>2} = \sum_{r=3}^{\infty} p(r) = 1 - [p(0) + p(1) + p(2)]$$

$$= 1 - \left[\frac{e^{-3}3^0}{0!} + \frac{e^{-3}3^1}{1!} + \frac{e^{-3}3^2}{2!} \right]$$

$$= 0.575.$$

Therefore, the chances are about 1 in 2 that during any given minute during a long weekend, the immigration officer will not be able to handle the arriving motorists adequately. ■ ■

To illustrate the application of the Poisson distribution to the problem of traffic accidents, let us consider the following situation. Accident histories of a number of drivers, selected at random, were collected for a 5-year period. The average number of accidents for this period was calculated to be $\mu = 0.25$ accidents. If we wish to know whether a driver having 3 accidents in a 5-year period is an accident-prone driver, we calculate P_r for $r = 3$ and $\mu = 0.25$.

$$P_r = \frac{e^{-\mu}\mu^r}{r!} = \frac{e^{-0.25}(0.25)^3}{3!} = 0.002.$$

This means that the chances are 500 to 1 against an *average* driver's having 3 accidents. Therefore, we conclude that a driver who has this many accidents is a bad risk.

DERIVATION FROM BINOMIAL DISTRIBUTION

The Poisson distribution can also be deduced from the binomial distribution, provided that n is large ($\rightarrow \infty$), p is very small ($\rightarrow 0$), and np is finite and equal to μ. It was shown earlier [Eq. (8.1)] that in n trials the probability of an event succeeding r times is

$$P_r = \frac{n!}{r!(n-r)!} p^r q^{n-r}. \tag{9.2}$$

When n is large compared with r,

$$\frac{n!}{(n-r)!} = n(n-1)(n-2)\cdots(n-r+1)$$

$$\eqsim n^r.$$

Therefore, the probability of r successes becomes

$$P_r = \frac{n^r}{r!} p^r q^{n-r}. \tag{9.3}$$

Now, if p is very small and r is not large,

$$q^r = (1 - p)^r \simeq 1$$

and

$$q^{n-r} \simeq q^n = (1 - p)^n.$$

Hence,

$$P_r = \frac{(np)^r}{r!} (1 - p)^n$$

$$= \frac{(np)^r}{r!} \left(1 - \frac{np}{n}\right)^n.$$

From introductory calculus, we know that as $n \to \infty$,

$$\left(1 + \frac{c}{n}\right)^n \to e^c.$$

Hence,

$$\left(1 - \frac{np}{n}\right)^n \to e^{-np}.$$

Thus,

$$P_r \simeq \frac{(np)^r}{r!} e^{-np}. \tag{9.4}$$

This, then, is the probability of r successes in n trials. When the experiment is run indefinitely, the mean $\mu = np$, and therefore Eq. (9.4) becomes identical to Eq. (9.1).

It is important to note again that the Poisson distribution contains only one parameter, μ, the mean occurrence of an event. The Poisson distribution gives us the probabilities for the number of times an event occurs but not for the number of times an event does not occur. Thus, we do not know the value of n. On the other hand, in the binomial distribution we know the number of times an event occurs and the number of times an event does not occur.

MEAN AND STANDARD DEVIATION

The mean number of occurrences of an event per unit of time (or space) is

$$\mu = np \tag{9.5}$$

and the standard deviation of the numbers of events is

$$\sigma = \sqrt{np}. \tag{9.6}$$

Thus the mean and variance are equal to one another:

$$\mu = \sigma^2 = np. \tag{9.7}$$

Equation (9.7) can also be used to check whether experimental data follow the Poisson distribution.

Equations (9.5) and (9.7) will now be derived using Eqs. (5.29) and (5.31). From Eq. (5.29),

$$\text{mean} = E(r) = \sum_{r=0}^{\infty} r P_r = \sum_{r=0}^{\infty} \frac{r e^{-\mu} \mu^r}{r!}$$

$$= 0 + \mu e^{-\mu} + 2 \frac{\mu^2 e^{-\mu}}{2!} + 3 \frac{\mu^3 e^{-\mu}}{3!} + \cdots$$

$$= \mu e^{-\mu} \left[1 + \mu + \frac{\mu^2}{2!} + \frac{\mu^3}{3!} + \cdots \right]$$

$$= \mu e^{-\mu} e^{\mu} = \mu. \qquad [9.5]$$

The variance σ^2 is given by Eq. (5.31):

$$\sigma^2 = E(r - \mu)^2 = \sum_{r=0}^{\infty} (r - \mu)^2 P_r$$

$$\sigma^2 = \sum_{r=0}^{\infty} r^2 P_r - 2\mu \sum_{r=0}^{\infty} r P_r + \mu^2 \sum_{r=0}^{\infty} P_r.$$

Now,

$$-2\mu \sum_{r=0}^{\infty} r P_r = -2\mu(\mu) = -2\mu^2,$$

$$\mu^2 \sum_{r=0}^{\infty} P_r = \mu^2(1) = \mu^2,$$

and

$$\sum_{r=0}^{\infty} r^2 P_r = \sum_{r=0}^{\infty} [r(r - 1) + r] P_r$$

$$= \sum_{r=0}^{\infty} r(r - 1) P_r + \mu$$

$$= \left[0 + 0 + 2 \frac{\mu^2 e^{-\mu}}{2!} + 6 \frac{\mu^3 e^{-\mu}}{3!} + \cdots \right] + \mu$$

$$= \mu^2 e^{-\mu} \left[1 + \mu + \frac{\mu^2}{2!} + \cdots \right] + \mu$$

$$= \mu^2 e^{-\mu} (e^{\mu}) + \mu = \mu^2 + \mu.$$

Thus, collecting the terms, we have

$$\sigma^2 = \mu^2 + \mu - 2\mu^2 + \mu^2$$

or

$$\sigma^2 = \mu. \qquad [9.7]$$

It may be observed that Eq. (9.5) is identical with Eq. (8.6), derived for the binomial distribution. Likewise, Eqs. (9.6) and (8.7) are identical, provided that we remember that the Poisson distribution was derived for $q \simeq 1$.

POISSON DISTRIBUTION AS AN
APPROXIMATION TO BINOMIAL DISTRIBUTION

The Poisson distribution can be used as an approximation to the binomial distribution when the sample size n is large and the probability of success p is small (the same applies when q is small, p and q being of course interchangeable), that is, when the binomial distribution is highly skewed. As a guide, we can say that a good approximation is obtained when $n \geqslant 20$ and $p \leqslant 0.05$, and the approximation improves with a decrease in p.

As an exercise, the reader might like to compare the probabilities from the binomial distribution [Eq. (8.1)] with those approximated by the Poisson distribution [Eq. (9.4)] for $n = 20$ and $p = 0.05$, taking $r = 0, 1, 2,$ and 3.

EXAMPLE

In making glass, undissolved particles called "stones" sometimes occur. Let us assume that there is an average of 1 stone per kilogram of glass made. If there are 100,000 "particles" in 1 kg of glass, then the probability of a stone is

$$p = 10^{-5}.$$

If we are making glass lenses of $\frac{1}{10}$ kg mass each, then there will be, on the average, 1 stone in every 10 lenses. Thus $np = 0.1$.

What is the proportion of lenses free from stones? The probability P_r of finding r stones in a lens is given by Eq. (9.4):

$$P_r = \frac{(np)^r}{r!} e^{-np}$$

and is tabulated as follows (see also Table A.4):

Number of stones in a lens, r	0	1	2	3	4
Probability, P_r	0.9048	0.09048	0.004524	—	—

Therefore,

90.48 percent of all lenses made will be free from stones,

9.05 percent of all lenses made will contain 1 stone,

0.45 percent of all lenses made will contain 2 stones,

and so on.

If each lens had a mass of 1 kg, then we would have $np = 1$, and hence the following values of probability of obtaining a lens containing *r* stones:

Number of stones in a lens, r	0	1	2	3	4	5
Probability, P_r	0.367	0.367	0.183	0.061	0.015	—

Therefore,

  36.7 percent of all lenses made will be free from stones,

  36.7 percent of all lenses made will contain 1 stone,

  18.3 percent of all lenses made will contain 2 stones,

  6.1 percent of all lenses made will contain 3 stones,

  1.5 percent of all lenses made will contain 4 stones,

and so on.   ■ ■

The Poisson distribution (instead of binomial expansion) is particularly useful when *n* is extremely large and *p* very small, as it then becomes virtually impossible to compute the binomial terms. For example, assume that we have *n* radioactive nuclei such that the probability of one of these decaying in a time interval *t* is *p*. We want to calculate the probability of *r* of these undergoing decay in time *t*.

In terms of binomial distribution, the required probability is [from Eq. (8.1a)]:

$$P_r = {}_nC_r p^r (1 - p)^{n-r}.$$

If $n = 10^{23}$ and $p = 10^{-22}$, the probability becomes

$$P_r = \frac{(10^{23})!}{(10^{23} - r)! r!} p^r (1 - p)^{10^{23} - r}$$

which is difficult to evaluate. We prefer, therefore, to work in terms of $np = 10$ and use the Poisson approximation [Eq. (9.4)]:

$$P_r = \frac{10^r}{r!} e^{-10}.$$

USEFULNESS OF POISSON DISTRIBUTION

Sometimes, we may suspect that a set of occurrences is completely random in nature, and we may want to determine whether this is so. We proceed to compare the experimental distribution with an assumed Poisson distribution; if the agreement is good, we conclude that the distribution of occurrences is influenced by chance alone. If the agreement is not good, we suspect that some definite influences may exist. We then have to study the data further, for example, by examining the periods of tests and seeking a correlation between these and some other, possibly intermittent, influence.

TABLE 9.2

Number of deaths per corps per annum, r	0	1	2	3	4	5
Probability of an army corps with r deaths, P_r	$e^{-0.61}$ $= 0.543$	$0.61e^{-0.61}$ $= 0.331$	$\dfrac{(0.61)^2 e^{-0.61}}{2}$ $= 0.101$	$\dfrac{(0.61)^3 e^{-0.61}}{2 \times 3}$ $= 0.021$	$\dfrac{(0.61)^4 e^{-0.61}}{2 \times 3 \times 4}$ $= 0.003$	...
Calculated number of army corps per annum with r deaths $= 200P_r$	109	66	20	4	$0.6 \simeq 1$	...
Observed number of army corps per annum with r deaths	109	65	22	3	1	0

The goodness of fit of the observed distribution to the assumed Poisson distribution may be tested by the χ^2 test, discussed in Chapter 14. At this stage, we shall make only a simple comparison.

EXAMPLE

Records of deaths due to horse kicks were kept in 10 army corps over a period of 20 years:[1]

Number of deaths per corps per annum, r	0	1	2	3	4	5 or more
Number of corps per annum with r deaths, f	109	65	22	3	1	0

Compare these values with a Poisson distribution derived from the observed mean frequency of death.

We take an army corps per annum as a unit. We have thus $20 \times 10 = 200$ observations.

The mean number of deaths per corps per annum is

$$\mu = \bar{x} = \frac{\sum fr}{\sum f} = \frac{0 \times 109 + 1 \times 65 + 2 \times 22 + 3 \times 3 + 4 \times 1 + 5 \times 0}{200}$$

$$= \frac{122}{200}$$

$$= 0.61.$$

Substituting in Eq. (9.4), we obtain the data in Table 9.2.

[1] Obtained by Bortkewitch and quoted in R. A. Fisher, *Statistical Methods for Research Workers* (New York: Hafner Publishing Co., 1958), p. 55.

As shown by the two last lines of Table 9.2, the agreement is extremely close, and we conclude that the distribution of deaths is due to chance alone and not to such factors as the locality where different corps are stationed or the personality of the general commanding. ■ ■

The following example illustrates the use of the Poisson distribution in the testing of a hypothesis.

EXAMPLE

The long-run average of traffic accidents per year at a busy intersection in a city has been 5. In an attempt to reduce the number of accidents, the intersection was redesigned; in the 12-month period following the redesign, the number of accidents was 3. On the basis that the number of traffic accidents per unit of time follows a Poisson process, determine whether the redesign has achieved greater safety. Assume a level of significance of 0.05.

The null hypothesis is that safety is the same after redesign as before, that is, we maintain that the average number of accidents per year is *still* 5. Thus,

$$H_0: \mu = 5 \text{ versus } H_a: \mu < 5.$$

The observed number of accidents (3) is a particular case of $\mu < 5$. We calculate the probability of obtaining 3 accidents or fewer as a result of the redesign:

$$P_{r \leqslant 3} = \sum_{r=0}^{r=3} \frac{\mu^r e^{-\mu}}{r!} = \sum_{r=0}^{r=3} \frac{(5)^r e^{-5}}{r!}$$

$$= 0.007 + 0.034 + 0.085 + 0.140$$

$$= 0.266.$$

This is greater than the level of significance, 0.05. We conclude, therefore, that there is no evidence to reject the null hypothesis, that is, the observed result is consistent (at a significance level $-$ 0.05) with the hypothesis that the given year (immediately following the redesign) is like past years. Thus, further improvements in the redesign of the intersection may be required to achieve our objective. ■ ■

We may want to calculate the probability of committing a Type II error, that is, of accepting the hypothesis that $\mu = 5$ when actually $\mu = 3$, say. With $\mu = 3$, we have

$$\beta = 1 - \sum_{r=0}^{r=3} \frac{(3)^r e^{-3}}{r!}$$

$$= 1 - 0.65$$

$$= 0.35.$$

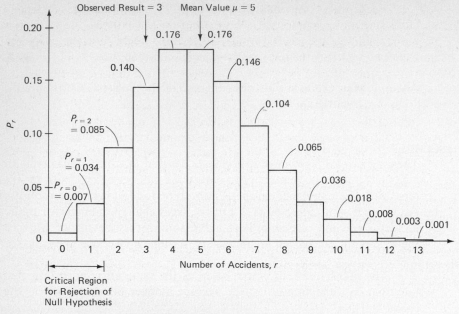

Figure 9.2 Poisson distribution for the example on page 167.

$$\left[p(r) = \frac{\mu^r e^{-\mu}}{r!} \text{ with } \mu = 5 \right].$$

Thus there is a 35 percent probability of incorrectly rejecting the claim that improvement has been effected.

We can also apply another procedure to test the hypothesis. Figure 9.2 shows a graph of the Poisson distribution with a mean $\mu = 5$; the probabilities for various values of r are shown. Since the Poisson distribution is discrete, the significance level is not 0.05 precisely. In fact, the critical region for rejecting the hypothesis is defined by $P(R \leqslant 1)$ and is equal to 0.041 from adding $P(0)$ and $P(1)$; we cannot include $P(2)$ within the critical region since $P(2) = 0.085$ and hence $P(R \leqslant 2) > 0.05$. Now, since the observed result, $r = 3$, does not lie in the critical region, the null hypothesis cannot be rejected.

POISSON PROBABILITY PAPER

A graph paper ruled so that the abscissae represent, to a logarithmic scale, the expected average number of events and the ordinates give the probability of occurrence to a Poisson probability scale is called a Poisson probability paper. Lines can be drawn showing the probability of an event occurring not more than r times for values of $r = 0, 1, 2, 3, \ldots 15$, as shown in Fig. 9.1.

If we require the probability of an event's occurring exactly a certain number of times, we have to use differences. For example, if the average number of events is 1, and we require the probability of an event's occurring 3 times, we find from Fig. 9.1 that the probability of its occurring not more than 3 times is 0.981. The probability of its occurring not more than 2 times is 0.920. Hence, the probability of its occurring 3 times is $0.981 - 0.920 = 0.061$.

Poisson probability paper can also be used to check whether an actual distribution agrees closely with the Poisson distribution, and, if so, what is the expected number of occurrences. From the experimental data we calculate the frequency and (by dividing by the total frequency) the probability of an event's occurring not more than 1, 2, 3, etc., times. For a Poisson distribution the points corresponding to a calculated probability and the average number of events would lie on a vertical line; the proximity of the actual points to such a line indicates the agreement with a Poisson distribution, and the abscissa of the line gives the expected (average) number of events.

The paper is generally valuable when we can use the Poisson distribution as an approximation to the binomial distribution, that is, when the latter is highly skewed.

SOLVED PROBLEMS

9-1. The number of cars passing over a toll bridge during the time interval 10 to 11 A.M. is 1200. The cars pass individually and collectively at random following a Poisson distribution. Write an expression for the probability that not more than 4 cars will pass during the 1-min interval 10:45 to 10:46. Derive an expression for the probability that 5 or more cars will pass during the same interval.

Solution

$$\text{Number of cars in 60 min} = 1200.$$

$$\text{Mean number of cars in 1-min interval} = \tfrac{1200}{60} = 20 = \mu.$$

Using Eq. (9.1),

probability of not more than 4 cars passing in that given interval

= sum of probabilities of 0 cars to and including 4 cars

$$= \sum_{r=0}^{r=4} \frac{\mu^r e^{-\mu}}{r!} = \left[\frac{(20)^0}{0!} + \frac{(20)^1}{1!} + \frac{(20)^2}{2!} + \frac{(20)^3}{3!} + \frac{(20)^4}{4!} \right] e^{-20}.$$

Hence,

$$\text{probability of 5 or more cars} = 1 - \sum_{r=0}^{4} \frac{(20)^r e^{-20}}{r!}.$$

9-2. If the probability of a concrete beam failing in compression is 0.05, use the Poisson approximation to obtain the probability that from a sample of 50 beams:
   a. at least 3 will fail in compression;
   b. no beam will fail in compression.

Solution. Here, $p = 0.05$. Mean number of failures in compression $= np = 0.05 \times 50 = 2.5$. Using Eq. (9.4):

a. The probability of at least 3 beams failing

$$= 1 - \sum_{r=0}^{2} \frac{(np)^r e^{-np}}{r!}$$

$$= 1 - \left[\frac{(2.5)^0 e^{-2.5}}{0!} + \frac{(2.5)^1 e^{-2.5}}{1!} + \frac{(2.5)^2 e^{-2.5}}{2!} \right]$$

$$= 1 - e^{-2.5}[1 + 2.5 + 3.125]$$

$$= 1 - 0.082 \times 6.625 = 0.4575.$$

b. The probability of no beam failing in compression

$$= \frac{(2.5)^0 e^{-2.5}}{0!} = 0.082.$$

Alternatively, we can use Poisson probability paper (see Fig. 9.1). For $np = 2.5$, the probability of at least 3 beams failing $= 1 -$ the probability of not more than 2 beams failing. For $r = 2$, probability $= 0.54$. Therefore, the required probability of at least 3 beams failing is $1 - 0.54 = 0.46$. This can be found directly from the vertical scale on the left in Fig. 9.1. (It is also possible to find this probability from Table A.4.)

For $r = 2$, probability $= 0.46$. Also, from Fig. 9.1, the probability of no failure, for $np = 2.5$ and $r = 0$, is 0.08.

9-3. If the probability of a Bailey bridge collapsing after 10 years of service without maintenance is 0.02, find the probability that out of 30 such bridges (having 10 years of service) the following will collapse.

a. None.
b. Exactly two.
c. Not more than one.
d. More than two.
e. At least one.

Solution. Since the probability of success (bridge collapsing) $p < 0.05$ and the sample size $n > 20$, we can conveniently use the Poisson distribution as a good approximation to the binomial distribution. We have $p = 0.02$ and $n = 30$. Therefore,

$$np = 0.6.$$

Using the cumulative Poisson probability graph of Fig. 9.1 or, alternatively, Table A.4, with $np = 0.6$ and the appropriate r, we obtain:

a. For $r = 0$, probability $= 0.54$ or 54 percent.
b. For $r = 2$, probability $= 0.975 - 0.875 = 0.10$ or 10 percent.
c. For $r \not> 1$, probability $= 0.875$ or 87.5 percent.
d. For $r > 2$, probability $= 0.025$ or 2.5 percent.
e. For $r \geqslant 1$, read off for $r > 0$ (i.e., left-hand ordinate), probability $= 0.44$ or 44 percent.

9-4. Past observations show that certain bacteria occur in water of a particular mountain lake at the rate of 1 bacterium per litre. From past experience, it is known that the number of bacteria in a sample has a Poisson distribution. If a sample of 4 litres is taken, determine the probability of obtaining not more than 3 bacteria.

Solution. Let

$$R = \text{number of bacteria (random variable.)}$$

Now, mean number of bacteria in a sample of 4 litres,

$$\mu = 1 \times 4 = 4.$$

From Eq. (9.1),

$$P_{r \leqslant 3} = \sum_{r=0}^{r=3} \frac{(4)^r e^{-4}}{r!}$$

$$= 0.43, \text{ using Fig. 9.1.}$$

Probability of finding more than 3 bacteria $= 1 - 0.43 = 0.57$, a result which should be given careful attention.

PROBLEMS

9-1. The numbers of road accidents per day reported in a given city on 100 consecutive days are as follows:

Number of accidents	0	1	2	3	4	5	6
Number of days	19	26	26	15	9	4	1

Check whether the distribution of accidents can be considered to be a Poisson distribution.

9-2. The probability for people of a certain age of dying within a year of their birthday is 0.0038. If there are 1000 people of this age in a certain town, what is the probability of 10 of them dying during the year?

9-3. Cosmic ray counts are believed to follow a Poisson distribution. Is this true of the following data?

Number of counts in 1 min, r	0	1	2	3	4	5	6	7
Number of minutes having r counts	40	70	41	20	13	0	1	0

9-4. If a product is supposed to contain 2 percent of defective items, would we be justified in rejecting a consignment if, after testing 50 items, we find it to contain 5 defectives? Use $\alpha = 0.05$.

9-5. If the proportion of defective bearings manufactured is $\frac{1}{25}$, approximate by means of a Poisson distribution the probability that a random sample of 75 bearings will contain 3 or fewer defectives.

9-6. The number of failures of telephones connected to a private exchange is shown in Table 9.3. Test the assumption that the failures follow a Poisson distribution.

TABLE 9.3

Number of failures reported in a day, r	Number of days with r failures
0	101
1	60
2	31
3	8
4	0
5	1
6	0

TABLE 9.4

Number of vacant one-hour parking spaces per observation period	0	1	2	3	4	5	$\geqslant 6$
Observed frequency	30	45	20	15	7	3	0

9-7. A study of four block faces containing 52 one-hour parking spaces was carried out and the results are given in Table 9.4. Assuming that the data follow a Poisson distribution, determine the:

a. mean number of vacant parking spaces,

b. standard deviation, and

c. probability of finding one or more vacant one-hour parking spaces.

9-8. A large batch of piston rings manufactured by a certain machine is examined by taking samples of 6 rings. It is found that the numbers of samples containing 0, 1, 2, 3, 4, 5, defective rings are 60, 36, 15, 7, 2, 0, respectively. Do these data follow a Poisson distribution?

Chapter 10

Normal Distribution

Chapters 8 and 9 dealt with distributions of occurrences of distinct events, that is, with discrete variables. We shall now return to the consideration of quantities that vary continuously, and, specifically, to the properties of populations (and of samples drawn from such populations) whose individual members vary due to what is commonly referred to as errors. One of the most important continuous chance distributions that describe the occurrence of continuous variables is the normal distribution. It is important because:

    i. It represents the distribution of random errors in many kinds of measurements.

   ii. Even if individual observed errors in the data do not follow the normal distribution, the *mean* of these errors follows the normal distribution (by virtue of the central limit theorem, page 117).

  iii. Many sets of experimental results in practice turn out to follow the normal distribution.

GAUSS FUNCTION

In Chapter 2, we introduced the classification of errors into two broad types: *systematic* errors and *random* errors. The former arise from causes that act consistently under the given circumstances; for example, a rule calibrated at one temperature will read systematically incorrectly at another, and the same applies in the simpler case of a false zero through the end of the rule having been cut off. Such an error can and should be avoided by suitable experimental techniques.

But even when all systematic errors have been eliminated, there still remain accidental or random errors, which consist of a large number of very small effects, such as imprecision in an estimate of a fraction of a division on a scale, or a small, natural (random) variation in temperature from the standard at which the equipment has been calibrated (but not a seasonal variation that would introduce a systematic error and should be allowed for). Some of these effects are positive, others negative—that is, they affect the value of the observation being made in a positive or negative direction with an equal probability. Thus the probability p of the occurrence of a positive error is $\frac{1}{2}$, and the probability q of its nonoccurrence (i.e., occurrence of a negative error) is also $\frac{1}{2}$. This fact is of fundamental importance and will be used in deriving the equation for the normal distribution from the binomial distribution.

It is convenient to assume that all the small contributory errors are of equal absolute magnitude $|E|$, and in any particular case there are $2n$ of them. Thus the total error will range from $-2nE$ (when all the contributory errors are negative) to $+2nE$ (when they are all positive). In any intermediate case, there will be a surplus (or a deficiency) of positive errors equal in number to $2r$, so that the resultant positive error is $2rE = X$. It is this error that causes variation between observations even under most carefully controlled conditions.

The behavior of such errors was of interest to scholars in the sixteenth and seventeenth centuries in connection with contests such as darts and archery games. From their observations, they concluded that:

1. Small errors occur more often than large errors; in fact, the latter occur very seldom.
2. Positive errors (errors to the right) are about as frequent as negative errors (errors to the left).

We now know that the distribution of these errors can be derived from mathematical considerations, and is given by the so-called Gauss function (Fig. 10.1):

$$y(X) = Ce^{-h^2X^2} \tag{10.1}$$

where $X =$ the error (i.e., deviation from the mean or "true" value);
  $y(X) =$ probability density of the occurrence of this error[1];
  $e =$ base of natural logarithms;
  $C =$ constant that determines, as will be shown later, the maximum height of the curve; this is done by making the area under the curve equal to unity[2]; and
  $h =$ constant that determines the spread of the curve, that is, expresses the precision of the measurement, and is known as the *precision constant*.

---

[1] Since $y(X) = y(x)$, we shall henceforth write the probability density simply as y.

[2] If the variable is discrete and the total number of observations is N, we make the area under the curve equal to N. Then, $y(X)$ represents the probability (see Fig. 10.3).

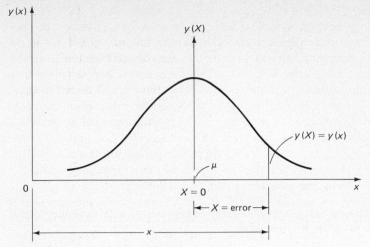

Figure 10.1   The Gauss function.

The Gauss function, given by Eq. (10.1), can also be viewed from another standpoint, namely, as an empirical (approximate) formula for the distribution of many physical quantities that have a continuously variable magnitude. These twin *raisons d'être* of the Gauss function make it particularly important in statistical work. We may note in passing that the function was first derived, as a limiting form of the binomial distribution, by DeMoivre, some 200 years ago, and later, directly and independently, by both Gauss and Laplace.

The distribution described by the Gauss function [Eq. (10.1)] is commonly known as the *normal* distribution, but the name should not be construed to mean that the distribution is any more normal than other distributions. The name normal came to be applied because attempts were made during the eighteenth and nineteenth centuries to use the distribution as the underlying probability law for *all* continuous variables. This assumption of generality is not correct: for instance, measurements of life of electronic components do not follow the normal law, since they are influenced by "extreme" and not average behavior in that, for example, a capacitor may fail because of one extremely low voltage input rather than in consequence of the average effect of many small inputs.

DERIVATION OF THE FUNCTION

A general mathematical derivation of the Gauss function is not considered appropriate in this book, but a derivation from the binomial distribution should be of engineering interest.

Let us consider the binomial distribution $(q + p)^n$ with $p = q = \frac{1}{2}$. The mean is then $\mu = np = \frac{1}{2}n$. The frequency polygon for this distribution with $n = 8$ is shown in Fig. 10.2. As n increases indefinitely, the frequency polygon

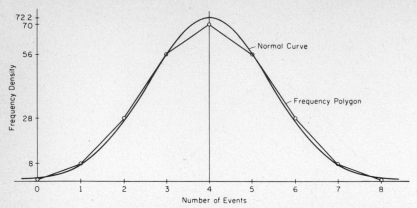

Figure 10.2 Frequency polygon for binomial distribution $(\frac{1}{2} + \frac{1}{2})^8$ and the normal distribution curve, drawn to the same scale.

will approach a smooth curve, symmetrical about a vertical line through the mean, and we can consider the normal curve to be the limit of the binomial expansion $(\frac{1}{2} + \frac{1}{2})^n$ as $n \to \infty$. The normal curve is plotted in Fig. 10.2 to the same scale as the frequency polygon; that is, the area under each is the same.

Let us consider the expansion

$$(\tfrac{1}{2} + \tfrac{1}{2})^{2n} = 2^{-2n}(1 + {}_{2n}C_1 + {}_{2n}C_2 + \cdots + {}_{2n}C_{n+r} + \cdots + 1). \qquad (10.2)$$

The successive terms in brackets of the right-hand side are plotted in Fig. 10.3 as ordinates at intervals Δx, beginning with the first term at the origin $x = 0$; each term represents the frequency, which is equal to $2^{2n} \times$ probability. The maximum term in Eq. (10.2) is $2^{-2n} \times {}_{2n}C_n$, and this is the ordinate at the mean μ. It is convenient to transfer the origin to the mean, so that

$$\left. \begin{array}{c} X = x - \mu \\ \Delta X = \Delta x \end{array} \right\} \qquad (10.3)$$

The y coordinate remains unaltered.

Consider points U and V in Fig. 10.3. Their ordinates are:

$$y_U = {}_{2n}C_{n+r} \quad \text{and} \quad y_V = y_U + \Delta y = {}_{2n}C_{n+r+1}.$$

But

$${}_{2n}C_{n+r+1} = \frac{{}_{2n}C_{n+r}(n - r)}{n + r + 1}$$

(see footnote[3]). Therefore,

$$\begin{aligned} \Delta y &= y_V - y_U \\ &= {}_{2n}C_{n+r+1} - {}_{2n}C_{n+r} \\ &= {}_{2n}C_{n+r}\left(\frac{n - r}{n + r + 1} - 1 \right) \end{aligned}$$

---

[3] Since ${}_mC_{k+1} = \dfrac{m!}{(m - k - 1)!(k + 1)!} = \dfrac{m!}{(m - k)!k!} \times \dfrac{(m - k)}{(k + 1)} = {}_mC_k \times \dfrac{(m - k)}{(k + 1)}.$

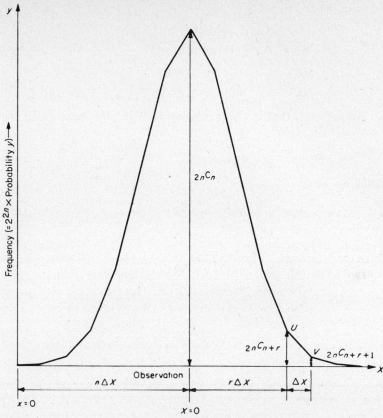

Figure 10.3 Frequency polygon for binomial distribution $(\frac{1}{2} + \frac{1}{2})^{2n}$.

or

$$\Delta y = {}_{2n}C_{n+r} \times \frac{n - r - n - r - 1}{n + r + 1}$$

$$= {}_{2n}C_{n+r} \times \left(\frac{-2r - 1}{n + r + 1} \right)$$

$$= y \times \left(\frac{-2r - 1}{n + r + 1} \right).$$

Hence,

$$\frac{\Delta y}{\Delta X} = \frac{y}{\Delta X} \left(\frac{-2r - 1}{n + r + 1} \right). \tag{10.4}$$

The abscissa of point U is

$$X = r\,\Delta X.$$

Hence,

$$r = \frac{X}{\Delta X}.$$

Substituting in Eq. (10.4),

$$\frac{\Delta y}{\Delta X} = \frac{y}{\Delta X}\left(\frac{-(2X/\Delta X) - 1}{n + (X/\Delta X) + 1}\right)$$

or

$$\frac{\Delta y}{\Delta X} = \frac{y}{\Delta X}\left(\frac{-2(X + \Delta X)}{n\,\Delta X + X + \Delta X}\right). \tag{10.5}$$

It is shown in Appendix C that in the expansion $(\frac{1}{2} + \frac{1}{2})^{2n}$ the mean of all the terms is

$$\mu = n\,\Delta x = n\,\Delta X \tag{10.6}$$

and the variance is

$$\sigma^2 = \frac{n}{2}(\Delta x)^2 = \frac{n}{2}(\Delta X)^2. \tag{10.7}$$

Substituting in Eq. (10.5), we obtain

$$\frac{\Delta y}{\Delta X} = \frac{-y(2X + \Delta X)}{2\sigma^2 + X\,\Delta X + (\Delta X)^2}.$$

As $n \to \infty$,

$$\Delta X \to 0 \quad \text{and} \quad \frac{\Delta y}{\Delta X} \to \frac{dy}{dX}.$$

Therefore,

$$\frac{dy}{dX} = -y\frac{X}{\sigma^2}$$

or

$$\frac{dy}{y} = -\frac{X\,dX}{\sigma^2}.$$

Integrating,

$$y = Ce^{-(X^2/2\sigma^2)}. \tag{10.8}$$

Putting

$$h = \frac{1}{\sqrt{2}\sigma} \tag{10.9}$$

(h being the precision constant of the Gauss function), we can write Eq. (10.8) as

$$y = Ce^{-h^2X^2}$$

which is Eq. (10.1).

THE NORMAL CURVE

The equation to the normal distribution curve can be written in several different forms. If we require the normal *frequency distribution* curve, the equation must satisfy the condition that the area under the curve is equal to the total number of observations N. Thus

$$\int_{-\infty}^{+\infty} y\,dX = N. \tag{10.10}$$

The integration extends between $-\infty$ and $+\infty$ because, when we postulated in our derivation that $n \to \infty$, we extended the curve to infinity in either direction from the mean μ.

Such a curve can be directly compared with a histogram because the area under the histogram is also equal to the total number of observations.

Substituting in Eq. (10.10) from Eq. (10.8), we have

$$C \int_{-\infty}^{+\infty} e^{-X^2/2\sigma^2} dX = N. \tag{10.11}$$

It is shown in Appendix D that

$$\int_{-\infty}^{+\infty} e^{-X^2/2\sigma^2} dX = \sigma\sqrt{2\pi}. \tag{10.12}$$

Hence, the maximum height of the curve is

$$C = \frac{N}{\sigma\sqrt{2\pi}} \tag{10.13}$$

and the equation to the normal frequency distribution curve can be written:

$$y = \frac{N}{\sigma\sqrt{2\pi}} e^{-X^2/2\sigma^2}. \tag{10.14}$$

As previously defined, σ is the standard deviation of the population.

If we operate in terms of actual observations x (rather than deviations from the mean X), we can substitute from Eq. (10.14):

$$y = \frac{N}{\sigma\sqrt{2\pi}} e^{-(x-\mu)^2/2\sigma^2}. \tag{10.15}$$

For many purposes it is preferable to deal with probability rather than frequency distribution. Since the sum of all probabilities is unity, the area under the normal *probability distribution* curve must be equal to unity. Such a curve is said to be *normalized*, and is given by

$$p(x) = \frac{1}{\sigma\sqrt{2\pi}} e^{-(x-\mu)^2/2\sigma^2} \tag{10.16}$$

where $p(x)$ is the *probability density* for the deviation $(x - \mu)$ and represents the rate of change of probability with x.

Since the mean μ is constant for any one distribution, the effect of μ is to move the position of the normal curve along the x-axis but not to change the spread of the curve, which depends on the value of standard deviation σ only. Thus σ determines the horizontal spread, and it is for many purposes convenient to use σ as a unit of deviation from the mean. We put

$$z = \frac{x - \mu}{\sigma} = \frac{X}{\sigma}. \tag{10.17}$$

Hence, $$dz = \frac{1}{\sigma} dX = \frac{1}{\sigma} dx.$$

Now, from our definitions of probability density and probability distribution of a continuous variable (see Fig. 5.15), changing the variable from x to z does not alter the probability sought; that is, the probability that a value x_1 will occur in the interval between x and $x + \Delta x$ is equal to the probability that z_1 will occur in the interval between z and $z + \Delta z$. Thus we can deduce by means of calculus that

$$p(x)\,dx = f(z)\,dz$$

or
$$f(z) = p(x)\frac{dx}{dz}$$

where $p(x)$ and $f(z)$ are the probability densities in terms of the variables x and z, respectively. Thus from Eqs. (10.16) and (10.17) we have

$$f(z) = p(x)\frac{dx}{dz} = \frac{1}{\sigma\sqrt{2\pi}}\,e^{-z^2/2}\,\sigma.$$

Hence,
$$f(z) = \frac{1}{\sqrt{2\pi}}\,e^{-z^2/2}. \qquad (10.18)$$

It should be noted that the random variable z has a mean of zero with a standard deviation of unity. Using the results derived from the definition of expectation in Chapter 5, we have

$$E(z) = E\left(\frac{x-\mu}{\sigma}\right) = \frac{1}{\sigma}\left[E(z) - E(\mu)\right]$$

$$= \frac{1}{\sigma}\left[\mu - \mu\right]$$

$$= 0 \qquad \text{(since } \mu \text{ is constant).}$$

$$\text{Var}(z) = E[z - E(z)]^2 = E(z^2)$$

$$= E\left[\frac{x-\mu}{\sigma}\right]^2 = \frac{1}{\sigma^2}E(x-\mu)^2$$

$$= \frac{\sigma^2}{\sigma^2}$$

$$= 1.$$

Equation (10.18) for a normal probability distribution is said to be in a standard form,[4] and it is for this form that most statistical tables have been prepared. Table A.5 gives the values of $f(z)$. [To standardize a variate, we transform it, using Eq. (10.17); that is, we subtract the mean from all values and divide the results by the standard deviation.]

From the above argument it is clear that μ and σ are the parameters of the normal distribution. All normal distributions have the same bell-shaped

[4] It applies to x when $\mu = 0$ and $\sigma = 1$.

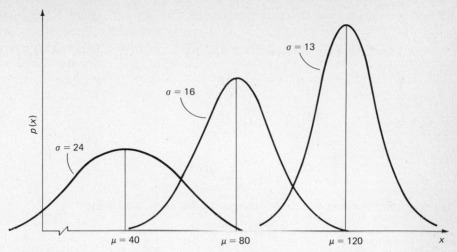

Figure 10.4 Normal distribution curves for various values of μ and σ. (Each curve continues from $-\infty$ to $+\infty$.)

curve. The mean, μ, determines the location of the distribution, while the standard deviation, σ, determines the spread of the distribution. We need know *only* the mean and the standard deviation to be able to compute the entire distribution. Thus, Eq. (10.16) represents a family of distributions, of which each specific member is determined by particular values of μ and σ (see Fig. 10.4).

The mean and variance of the normal distribution will now be derived using the notion of expectation and Eqs. (5.30) and (5.32). From Eq. (5.30),

$$E(x) = \int_{-\infty}^{+\infty} xp(x)\,dx = \int_{-\infty}^{+\infty} \frac{x}{\sigma\sqrt{2\pi}} e^{-(x-\mu)^2/2\sigma^2}\,dx.$$

If we put $z = (x - \mu)/\sigma$, then

$$E(x) = \int_{-\infty}^{+\infty} \frac{1}{\sqrt{2\pi}} (\mu + \sigma z)e^{-z^2/2}\,dz$$

$$= \mu \int_{-\infty}^{+\infty} \frac{1}{\sqrt{2\pi}} e^{-z^2/2}\,dz + \sigma \int_{-\infty}^{+\infty} \frac{1}{\sqrt{2\pi}} ze^{-z^2/2}\,dz.$$

The value of the first integral is 1, since

$$\int_{-\infty}^{+\infty} \frac{1}{\sqrt{2\pi}} e^{-z^2/2}\,dz = \int_{-\infty}^{+\infty} f(z)\,dz = \int_{-\infty}^{+\infty} p(x)\,dx = 1$$

[see Eqs. (10.18) and (5.18)]. The second integral,

$$\int_{-\infty}^{+\infty} \frac{1}{\sqrt{2\pi}} ze^{-z^2/2}\,dz = -\frac{1}{\sqrt{2\pi}} [e^{-z^2/2}]_{-\infty}^{+\infty} = 0.$$

Thus, $$E(x) = \mu(1) + \sigma(0) = \mu.$$

To find the variance we evaluate, by using Eq. (5.32),

$$E(x - \mu)^2 = \int_{-\infty}^{+\infty} (x - \mu)^2 p(x) \, dx$$

$$= \int_{-\infty}^{+\infty} (x - \mu)^2 \frac{1}{\sigma \sqrt{2\pi}} e^{-(x-\mu)^2/2\sigma^2} \, dx$$

$$= \int_{-\infty}^{+\infty} \sigma^2 z^2 \frac{1}{\sqrt{2\pi}} e^{-z^2/2} \, dz$$

$$= \sigma^2 \int_{-\infty}^{+\infty} \frac{z^2}{\sqrt{2\pi}} e^{-z^2/2} \, dz.$$

Transforming the variable z and integrating by parts, we obtain

$$\text{Var}(x) = E(x - \mu)^2 = \sigma^2 \left\{ \left| \frac{-ze^{-z^2/2}}{\sqrt{2\pi}} \right|_{-\infty}^{+\infty} + \int_{-\infty}^{+\infty} \frac{1}{\sqrt{2\pi}} e^{-z^2/2} \, dz \right\}$$

$$= \sigma^2 \{0 + 1\}.$$

Thus, $\text{Var}(x) = \sigma^2.$

GRAPHICAL REPRESENTATION OF
STANDARD DEVIATION

Consider Eq. (10.16), using $X = x - \mu$. In order to find the point at which the curvature of this curve changes sign, we equate the second differential coefficient of the equation to zero. Thus

$$\frac{d^2 p(X)}{dX^2} = \frac{-1}{\sigma^3 \sqrt{2\pi}} \left(e^{-X^2/2\sigma^2} - \frac{X^2}{\sigma^2} e^{-X^2/2\sigma^2} \right) = 0$$

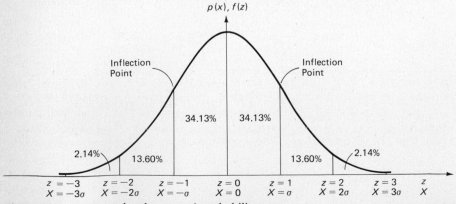

Figure 10.5   Areas under the normal probability curve.

TABLE 10.1 AREAS UNDER THE NORMAL CURVE [SEE EQ. (10.19)]

z	$F(z)$	$2 \times F(z)$
0	0.0000	0.0000
0.25	0.0987	0.1974
0.50	0.1915	0.3830
0.67	0.2486	0.4972
0.6745	0.2500	0.5000
0.68	0.2518	0.5035
1.00	0.3413	0.6826
1.96	0.4750	0.9500
2.00	0.4772	0.9544
2.50	0.4938	0.9876
2.576	0.4950	0.9900
3.00	0.4987	0.9974

whence

$$1 - \frac{X^2}{\sigma^2} = 0$$

or

$$X = \pm\sigma.$$

In other words, the point of inflection occurs on either side of the mean at a distance equal to the standard deviation, that is, $z = 1$. This establishes a physical significance of the standard deviation and should be remembered when sketching the normal curve (see Fig. 10.5).

AREA UNDER THE NORMAL CURVE

The area under the *normal probability* curve between the mean ($z = 0$) and $z = z$ is

$$F(z) = \int_0^z f(z)\,dz.$$

(see footnote[5]). Thus, from Eq. (10.18),

$$F(z) = \frac{1}{\sqrt{2\pi}} \int_0^z e^{-z^2/2}\,dz. \tag{10.19}$$

Figure 10.5 shows the normal probability curve, the abscissae being marked in terms of both X and z. The areas under the curve $F(z)$ corresponding to deviations in steps of one standard deviation are written on the figure. It may be noted that Eq. (10.19) cannot be integrated directly and $F(z)$ must be obtained by numerical methods (see Appendix D). The full range of values of $F(z)$ is given in Table A.6. A selection of values of $F(z)$ is given in Table 10.1,

---

[5] As one can observe from the limits of integration, $z = 0$ to $z = z$, $F(z)$ is *not* the cumulative distribution function of the normal distribution.

together with areas for the range $(\mu - z\sigma, \mu + z\sigma)$, that is, corresponding to a deviation from the mean not exceeding $\pm z\sigma$. The latter areas are equal to $2 \times F(z)$ and give the probability of a given deviation in *either* direction not being exceeded, while $F(z)$ gives values for a positive (or negative) deviation not being exceeded. The distinction is obvious, but it is important to remember it at all times.

The probability of a deviation's lying between two values of z is given by the area under the normal curve between these limits. Thus, in order to find the probability that a deviation or an error z will fall between z_1 and z_2 we calculate the area under the standardized normal probability curve between the limits $z = z_1$ and $z = z_2$. Assuming $z_2 > z_1$,

$$\text{required probability} = \int_0^{z_2} f(z)\, dz - \int_0^{z_1} f(z)\, dz$$

$$= \int_0^{z_1} \frac{1}{\sqrt{2\pi}} e^{-z^2/2}\, dz - \int_0^{z_2} \frac{1}{\sqrt{2\pi}} e^{-z^2/2}\, dz.$$

These areas are given in Table A.6. Since, by definition of $F(z)$ this table gives the values of $F(z)$ with the lower limit of $z = 0$, we have to use differences. For example, the probability of a deviation z such that $1 \leqslant z \leqslant 2$ is obtained by subtraction of $F(z)$ for $z = 1$ from $F(z)$ for $z = 2$, namely, $0.4772 - 0.3413 = 0.1359$. Thus, the probability of an observation's having a deviation from the mean not smaller than σ and not greater than 2σ is 0.1359.

EXAMPLE

Find the probabilities of a set of observations, believed to be normally distributed, having values that fall outside the range specified in column 1 of Table 10.2. Hence, find the number per 1000 outside the specified range.

To obtain column 2, we find $F(z)$ from Table A.6. For example, in order to find the probability for the range $-\frac{1}{4}\sigma$ to $+\frac{1}{4}\sigma$, we observe that the area under the normal curve between $z = 0$ and $z = \frac{1}{4}$ is 0.0987. Since the curve is symmetrical, the probability for the range $-\frac{1}{4}\sigma$ to $+\frac{1}{4}\sigma$ is

TABLE 10.2

(1) Range	(2) Probability of falling inside the range	(3) Number of observations per 1000 outside the specified range
$-\frac{1}{4}\sigma, +\frac{1}{4}\sigma$	0.1974	803
$-1\frac{1}{2}\sigma, +\frac{1}{2}\sigma$	0.6247	375
$-\frac{1}{2}\sigma, +1\frac{1}{2}\sigma$	0.6247	375
$-\frac{1}{2}\sigma, +3\sigma$	0.6902	310
$+2\sigma, +4\sigma$	0.0228	977

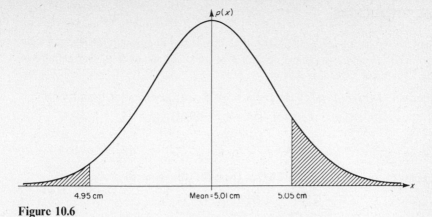

Figure 10.6

$2 \times 0.0987 = 0.1974$. To obtain column 3, we multiply the probability of falling inside the range by 1000 and subtract the result from 1000.

To find the probability for the range $-1\frac{1}{2}\sigma$ to $+\frac{1}{2}\sigma$, we have to find $F(z)$ for 0 to $\frac{1}{2}\sigma$ (0.1915), and $F(z)$ for 0 to $1\frac{1}{2}\sigma$ (0.4332) and add the two results (obtaining 0.6247). We utilize the fact that $F(z)$ for 0 to $-1\frac{1}{2}\sigma$ is the same as $F(z)$ for 0 to $+1\frac{1}{2}\sigma$. For the same reason, we can write the probability for the range $\frac{1}{2}\sigma$ to $1\frac{1}{2}\sigma$ without further calculations.

For the probability for the range $+2\sigma$ to $+4\sigma$, we have to subtract $F(z)$ for 0 to 2σ (0.4772) from $F(z)$ for 0 to 4σ (0.49997); the answer is 0.02277.

■ ■

PHYSICAL "DEMONSTRATION" OF
NORMAL DISTRIBUTION

An amusing "demonstration" of the normal distribution curve, that is, of the bell-shaped form, was given by Galton.[6] In his experiment, a large number of steel balls or lead shot are made to pass through a hole in a vertical "plane" vessel (one ball diameter thick). Each ball hits a pin in its vertical path and rebounds to left or right with equal probability. Two pins are placed on a horizontal line lower down so that the ball must hit one of them; again it rebounds to left or right. Beneath each of these pins, there are two pins and so on. Thus the balls proceed downward and end up in narrow slots (to prevent sideways shift). If the face of the vessel is transparent it will be seen that the distribution of the balls closely approximates the normal distribution shape (see Fig. 10.8).

[6] Francis Galton, *Natural Inheritance*, 1889, described by H. M. Cundy and A. P. Rollett in *Mathematical Models* (Oxford: Clarendon Press, 1972). The book proves the validity of the experiment on the basis of probability of each ball moving sequentially to the left or to the right, which can be represented by binomial distribution.

SOLVED PROBLEMS

10-1. The finished inside diameter of a piston ring is normally distributed with a mean of 4.50 cm and a standard deviation of 0.005 cm. What is the probability of obtaining a diameter exceeding 4.51 cm?

Solution.   Given $\mu = 4.50$ cm and $\sigma = 0.005$ cm. The deviation from the mean is

$$x - \mu = 4.51 - 4.50 = 0.01.$$

Hence,
$$z = \frac{x - \mu}{\sigma} = \frac{0.01}{0.005} = 2.0.$$

From Table A.6 for $z = 2.0$, $F(z) = 0.4772$. Therefore, the required probability

$$= 0.5000 - 0.4772$$
$$= 0.0228$$
$$= 2.28 \text{ percent (a chance of 1 in 44)}.$$

10-2. The resistance of a foil strain gauge is normally distributed with a mean of 120.0 ohms and a standard deviation of 0.4 ohm. The specification limits are 120.0 ± 0.5 ohms. What percentage of gauges will be defective?

Solution.   Given $\mu = 120.0$ ohms and $\sigma = 0.4$ ohm. The allowable deviation from the mean is

$$x - \mu = \pm 0.5 \text{ ohm.}$$

Hence,
$$z = \frac{x - \mu}{\sigma} = \frac{0.5}{0.4} = 1.25.$$

From Table A.6, for $z = 1.25$, $F(z) = 0.3944$. Therefore, the probability of a defective gauge

$$= 1 - 2 \times 0.3944$$
$$= 1 - 0.7888$$
$$= 0.2112$$
$$= 21.12 \text{ percent.}$$

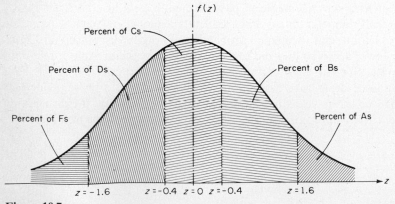

Figure 10.7

10-3. The measurement of the inside diameter of a cast-iron pipe is normally distributed with a mean of 5.01 cm and standard deviation of 0.03 cm. The specification limits are 5.00 ± 0.05 cm. What percentage of pipes is not acceptable?

Solution.   Refer to Fig. 10.6. For the upper range,

$$z = \frac{5.05 - 5.01}{0.03} = 1.33.$$

From Table A.6 for $z = 1.33$, $F(z_1) = 0.4082$. For the lower range,

$$z = \frac{5.01 - 4.95}{0.03} = \frac{0.06}{0.03} = 2.0.$$

The corresponding $F(z_2) = 0.4772$. The probability of falling within the specified limits

$$= F(z_1) + F(z_2)$$
$$= 0.4082 + 0.4772$$
$$= 0.8852.$$

Probability of falling outside the limits

$$= \text{percentage of unacceptable pipes}$$
$$= 1 - 0.8852 = 0.1148$$
$$= 11.48 \text{ percent.}$$

10-4. A teacher of a large class assigns grades using a system commonly known as "grading on the curve" in the following manner:
   a. If the mark $> \bar{x} + 1.6\sigma$ the grade is A.
   b. If $\bar{x} + 0.4\sigma \leqslant \text{mark} \leqslant \bar{x} + 1.6\sigma$ the grade is B.
   c. If $\bar{x} - 0.4\sigma \leqslant \text{mark} \leqslant \bar{x} + 0.4\sigma$ the grade is C.
   d. If $\bar{x} - 1.6\sigma \leqslant \text{mark} \leqslant \bar{x} - 0.4\sigma$ the grade is D.
   e. If mark $< \bar{x} - 1.6\sigma$ the grade is F.
   Assuming that the marks are normally distributed with mean $\bar{x}$ and standard deviation σ (valid, since class size is large), what is the percentage of each grade given by the teacher?

Solution.   Referring to Fig. 10.7 and using Table A.6, we find that:
   a. Percent of As: For $z = 1.6$, $F(z) = 0.4452$.

$$\text{area required} = 0.5 - 0.4452$$
$$= 0.0548.$$

Therefore, the percent of As is approximately 5.5 percent.
   b. Percent of Bs: For $z = 1.6$, $F(z) = 0.4452$; for $z = 0.4$, $F(z) = 0.1554$.

$$\text{required area} = 0.4452 - 0.1554 = 0.2898.$$

Therefore, the percent of Bs is approximately 29 percent.
   c. Percent of Cs: For $z = 0.4$, $F(z) = 0.1554$. Therefore, the area between limits $z = 0.4$ to $z = -0.4$

$$= 2 \times F(0.4) = 0.3108.$$

Therefore, the percent of Cs is 31 percent.

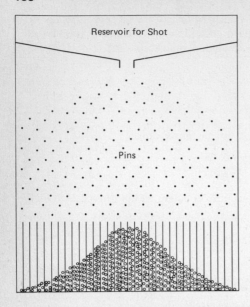

Figure 10.8

d. Percent of Ds: For $z = -1.6$, $F(z) = 0.4452$; for $z = -0.4$, $F(z) = 0.1554$.

$$\text{required area} = 0.4452 - 0.1554 = 0.2898.$$

Therefore, the percent of Ds is approximately 29 percent.

e. Percent of Fs: For $z = -1.6$, $F(z) = 0.4452$.

$$\text{required area} = \tfrac{1}{2} - F(z) = 0.0548.$$

Therefore, the percent of Fs is approximately 5.5 percent.

PROBLEMS

10-1. If μ is the mean and σ is the standard deviation of the diameters of ball bearings, which follow a normal distribution, what percentage of ball bearings would have the following diameters?

    a. Within the range $(\mu \pm 2\sigma)$.

    b. Outside the range $(\mu \pm 0.9\sigma)$.

    c. Greater than $(\mu - 1.5\sigma)$.

10-2. The strength of a plastic produced by a certain method is known to be normally distributed. If 10 percent of the results exceed 8000 N and 70 percent exceed 6000 N, what are the mean and the standard deviation?

10-3. If x is normally distributed with a mean of 100 and a standard deviation of 18, find the probability of a random observation falling between **(a)** 115 and 140; **(b)** 90 and 120.

10-4. If the I.Q. scores of recruits are normally distributed with a mean of 100 and a standard deviation of 13, find:

    a. The fraction who have an I.Q. greater than 133.

    b. The fraction who have an I.Q. greater than 90.

    c. The I.Q. exceeded by the upper quartile of recruits.

10-5. The navy uses stockings that have a mean life of 50 days with a variance of 64 (days)^2. Assuming that the life of such stockings is normally distributed, of 150,000 pairs issued how many would be expected to need replacement after 42 days? After 63 days?

10-6. Electric bulbs bought for lighting an outdoor rink have a mean life of 3000 h with a coefficient of variation of 11.3 percent. If it is more economical to replace all the bulbs when 20 percent of them have burned out than to change them as needed, after how many hours should the bulbs be changed? It can be assumed that the life of electric bulbs is normally distributed.

Assuming that the lamps have not been changed, find the period after which an additional 20 percent of the lamps will have burned out.

10-7. A standard 5000-ohm resistor is measured a large number of times using an ohmmeter. It is found that one-half of all readings lie outside the range 4750 to 5250 ohms. Estimate the precision constant h of the ohmmeter assuming that the normal distribution applies.

10-8. An automatic parachute has been equipped with a new altitude detector which has a precision constant h of 0.004 m^{-1}. It is known that parachutes opening less than 30 m from the ground will smash and damage their payload. Of the 200 dropped parachutes with detectors set to open them at 300 m, how many will damage their payload? Assume a normal distribution.

Chapter 11

Use of Normal Distribution

Two comments on normal distribution may now be in order. First, we should recall that in a mathematical derivation of the normal distribution curve, x (or X) is assumed to be a continuous variable. For this reason the probability of x having *exactly* a particular value is zero, and we consider only the probability of x, when chosen at random, falling between x and $(x + \Delta x)$; this is given by the area $p(x)\,\Delta x$. In the limit, this area becomes $p(x)\,dx$. As mentioned before, $p(x)$ represents the probability density (see also Chapter 5).

LIMITS OF PRACTICAL DISTRIBUTIONS

The second comment concerns the limits of the normal distribution curve. Equation (10.11) shows these as $-\infty$ and $+\infty$, and yet in many cases the observed values cannot extend so far from the mean; furthermore, negative values of x may sometimes have no physical meaning. To explain this anomaly, we should remember that we use the normal distribution as an approximation to physical observations, the mathematical equation being valid only between finite limits. The approximation is, however, very good as 99.9936 percent of the area under the normal curve lies within a range of plus or minus four standard deviations from the mean; for plus or minus three standard deviations, the area contained is 99.740 percent (see Table A.6). We are, therefore, justified in the majority of cases in ignoring the *tails* of the distribution beyond $z = 4$, or some other appropriate value.

SOME IMPORTANT PROBABILITIES

Several values of area under the normal probability curve are of especial interest and are shown diagrammatically in Fig. 11.1. Figure 11.1(a) illustrates the fact that one-half of the area under the curve lies within $\pm 0.6745\sigma$ from the mean. Thus, a single observation has an equal chance of falling within or without this range. For this reason, such a deviation has in the past been called the *probable error*, but the term is not often used nowadays.[1]

Figure 11.1(b) shows that within a range of $\pm\sigma$ from the mean there are contained 68.26 percent of all observations. A deviation of $\pm\sigma$ is referred to as a *standard error* and is often quoted as a measure of precision. Thus, if a mean value of a quantity is given, for example, as 27.05 ± 0.042, we interpret

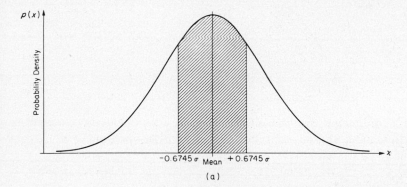

(a)

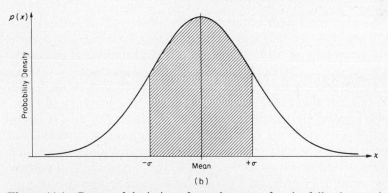

(b)

Figure 11.1   Range of deviations from the mean for the following probabilities of an observation falling within the range: (a) 50 percent; (b) 68.26 percent; overleaf (c) 95 percent; and (d) 99 percent.

[1] The probable error of the mean $\bar{x}$ is a value ϵ such that there is a 50 percent probability that $\bar{x}$ does not differ from μ by more than ϵ.

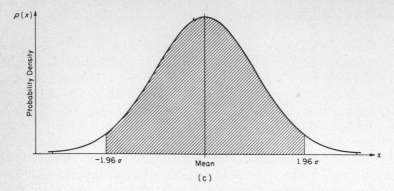

(c)

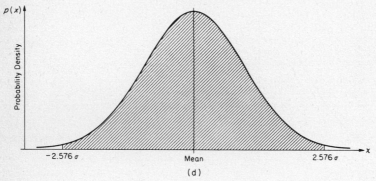

(d)

Figure 11.1   (Continued)

this to mean that the "true" value of the mean lies between $(27.05 - 0.042)$ and $(27.05 + 0.042)$, and there is a 68.26 percent probability of our being correct. In other words, if we present results in this form on a large number of occasions, we shall be correct in our statements in 68.26 percent of all cases.

Figures 11.1(c) and (d) are of particular interest as they show the values of a deviation, positive or negative, exceeded by chance in 5 percent and 1 percent of all cases, respectively, these percentages being extensively used in statistical treatment of data. If we are interested in a deviation of a specified sign only, say positive, the probability would be given by the area under the normal curve from the specified deviation to $+\infty$. Thus, the magnitude of a positive deviation that would be exceeded in 1 percent of all cases is given by

$$0.5 + F(z) = 0.99.$$

Hence, $$F(z) = 0.49.$$

From Table A.6,

$$z = 2.33$$

that is, a deviation of $+2.33\sigma$ is exceeded by chance in 1 percent of all cases.

FITTING A NORMAL CURVE

In experimental work, we frequently obtain a set of observations that we consider as members of a population, but we may have no assurance that the data follow a normal distribution, or any other standard distribution. We may, however, suspect on the basis of past experience that certain observations conform to a given distribution, and it is one of the more important applications of statistics to the problems of measurement to investigate whether the data in hand fit an assumed distribution.

We shall now consider fitting a normal curve by following a numerical example. Before proceeding, however, we should recall two assumptions made in our derivation of the normal frequency curve:

a. The mean and the standard deviation of the normal frequency distribution are equal, respectively, to the mean and standard deviation of the actual observations.
b. The area under the normal frequency distribution curve is equal to the total number of observations, i.e. to the area under the histogram.

EXAMPLE

Let us fit the normal curve to the theoretical frequency distribution of heads when 8 coins are tossed.

In Fig. 10.2 the binomial expansion of $(\frac{1}{2} + \frac{1}{2})^8$ was shown to have the following values:

Number of successes, r	0	1	2	3	4	5	6	7	8
Frequency, $p(r) \times 2^{2 \times 8}$	1	8	28	56	70	56	28	8	1

Thus, the total number of observations is $N = \sum$ frequency $= 256$. It should be noted that N is equal to the area under the histogram $= w \sum$ frequency, where w is the class width. In this case w is unity and hence $N = \sum$ frequency.

$$\text{Mean} = \mu = np = \tfrac{1}{2} \times 8 = 4$$

and

$$\sigma = \sqrt{npq} = \sqrt{8 \times \tfrac{1}{2} \times \tfrac{1}{2}} = \sqrt{2}.$$

Substituting in Eq. (10.15) for the normal frequency distribution,

$$y = \frac{N}{\sigma\sqrt{2\pi}} e^{-(x-\mu)^2/2\sigma^2} \tag{11.1}$$

that is,

$$y = \frac{128}{\sqrt{\pi}} e^{-(x-4)^2/4}. \tag{11.2}$$

We can now plot y for various values of x and draw a smooth curve through the points. This has been done in Fig. 11.2, which shows also the

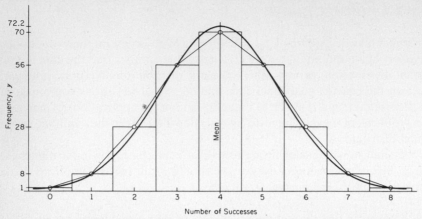

Figure 11.2   Histogram, polygon, and fitted normal curve for the example on page 193.

frequency polygon and histogram for the binomial distribution. Since we are dealing with an ideal distribution, the agreement between the curves is, of course, good, the discrepancy being due solely to the discontinuous character of the binomial distribution.

In practice, instead of calculating the values from Eq. (11.2), we use tabulated values of the ordinate of the normal curve. Table A.5 gives the ordinates for the normal curve in the standard form [Eq. (10.18)], that is,

$$f(z) = \frac{1}{\sqrt{2\pi}} e^{-z^2/2}.$$

In our case, the tabulated ordinates would have to be multiplied by

$$\frac{N}{\sigma} = \frac{256}{\sqrt{2}}. \qquad \blacksquare \blacksquare$$

Let us now consider an example based on experimental results, as distinct from a theoretical distribution.

EXAMPLE

Two hundred and fifty-five lengths of wire were roughly cut to a length of 100.060 m each. When measured, they were found to range between 100.005 m and 100.125 m. The measured lengths in excess of 100 m were recorded for intervals of 0.5 to 1.5 cm, 1.5 to 2.5 cm, . . . , 11.5 to 12.5 cm, with the following observed frequency distribution:

Class midpoint (cm), x_i	1	2	3	4	5	6	7	8	9	10	11	12
Frequency, f_i	2	10	19	25	40	44	41	28	25	15	5	1

TABLE 11.1

x_i	f_i	Deviation from fictitious mean, X_i'	$f_i X_i'$	$f_i X_i'^2$
1	2	-5	-10	50
2	10	-4	-40	160
3	19	-3	-57	171
4	25	-2	-50	100
5	40	-1	-40	40
6	44	0	0	0
7	41	1	41	41
8	28	2	56	112
9	25	3	75	225
10	15	4	60	240
11	5	5	25	125
12	1	6	6	36
Totals	$\sum f_i = 255$		$\sum f_i X_i' = -197 + 263$ $= 66$	$\sum f_i X_i'^2 = 1300$

In order to fit the normal curve to this distribution, we have to estimate the mean and the standard deviation of the normal distribution from the observed data. It is convenient to assume a fictitious mean $\bar{X}_0 = 6$ cm. We can then use a new variable $X_i' = x_i - \bar{X}_0$ and tabulate the results as shown in Table 11.1. Hence, we estimate μ by

$$\bar{X} = \bar{X}_0 + \frac{\sum f_i X_i'}{\sum f_i} = 6 + \frac{66}{255} = 6.26 \text{ cm}$$

and estimate σ by

$$s = \sqrt{\frac{\sum f_i X_i'^2 - (\sum f_i X_i')^2/n}{n - 1}} = \sqrt{\frac{1300 - (66^2/255)}{254}} = 2.25 \text{ cm.}$$

Substituting in Eq. (10.14), we obtain

$$y = \frac{255}{2.25\sqrt{2\pi}} e^{-X^2/2(2.25)^2}$$

$$= 45.21 e^{-0.0986 X^2}$$

where $$X = x - \mu$$

and $$\mu \simeq \bar{X}.$$

It should be noted that $N = n = 255$, since the class width of the histogram is unity.

For the purpose of plotting the curve, we multiply the values of the ordinate of the normal curve in the standard form $f(z)$ (Table A.5) by

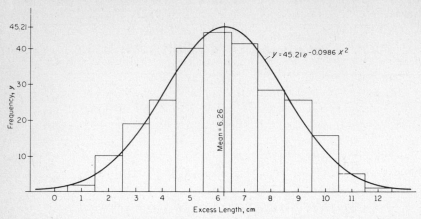

Figure 11.3 Histogram and fitted normal curve for the example on page 194; the lengths plotted are those in excess of 100 m.

$N/\sigma = 255/2.25$ and obtain:

$z = X/\sigma$	0	± 0.5	± 1.0	± 1.5	± 2.0	± 2.5	± 3.0
$f(z)$	0.3989	0.3521	0.2420	0.1295	0.0540	0.0175	0.0044
$y = f(z)(N/\sigma)$	45.21	39.90	27.43				
X	0	1.12	2.25				
x	6.26	5.14	4.01				
		7.38	8.51	9.63	10.76	11.88	13.01

Figure 11.3 shows the plot of $y = (N/\sigma)f(z)$ against x.

It is important to note that the ordinates of the normal curve have been calculated for deviations of X from the mean, while the histogram is plotted for the arbitrary intervals of 1 cm, 2 cm, 3 cm, and so on. The height of the histogram blocks is obtained by dividing each class frequency by the class width; the histogram will then be plotted to the same scale as the normal curve. Since in our case the class width is unity, the heights are numerically equal to frequencies. Finally, we must not forget that the lengths plotted are those in excess of 100 m. ■ ■

PROBABILITY PAPER

We may recall the cumulative frequency curve, mentioned in Chapter 2. When a variate follows a normal distribution, the cumulative frequency plots as an S-shaped curve. A curve of such shape is not convenient to use, and it is preferable to rectify it. This is achieved by the use of probability paper.

The construction of this paper is based on the fact that the cumulative frequency represents the area under the normal probability curve between $-\infty$

and the value of the variate up to which the cumulative frequency is required. Hence, we make the increments in the ordinates (labeled as the cumulative area under the normal curve) equal for equal increments in the abscissae (representing the variate). On commercial probability paper, the ordinates are marked off for probabilities of 0.01, 0.02, ..., 0.1, 0.2, ..., 1.0, 1.2, ..., 2, 3, ..., 20, 22, ..., 50, and on to 100 percent. Since the normal distribution is symmetrical, the spacing is symmetrical about the ordinate of 50 percent. The abscissae represent the variate to a linear scale. The normal probability paper is shown in Fig. 11.4.

We may note that the areas used in constructing the probability paper are the tail areas, while the area $F(z)$ given in Table A.6 is reckoned from the

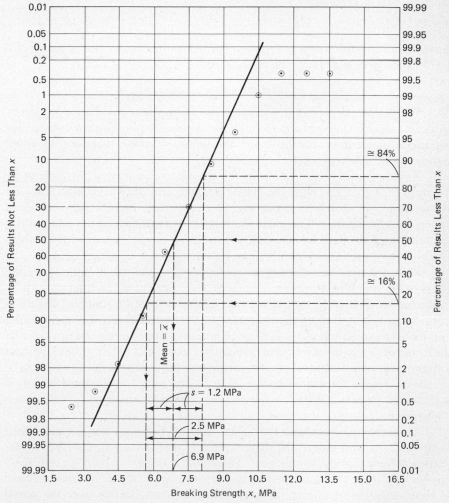

Figure 11.4 Cumulative percentage frequency for the data of Table 2.3; abscissae show the upper class boundaries.

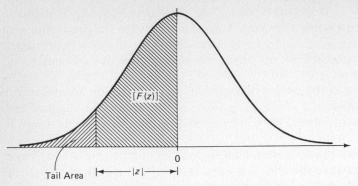

Figure 11.5 Diagrammatic representation of tail area used in construction of probability paper and $F(z)$ of Table A.6.

mean, that is, from the axis of symmetry of the normal curve; this is shown diagrammatically in Fig. 11.5. The relation between the two is simply

$$\text{tail area} = 0.5 - F(z).$$

When normal probability paper is used, a normal cumulative frequency plots as a straight line passing through the centroidal point (mean value of the variate, 50 percent probability), and the paper is useful, therefore, in visual testing of normality of a set of observations.

As an example, Fig. 11.4 shows the cumulative frequency distribution for the data of Table 2.3, with the "best" straight line drawn by eye. Since we are interested in strengths lower than a given value, the abscissae represent upper class boundaries. The mean is found as the abscissa of the point corresponding to a 50 percent cumulative frequency, in our case 6.9 MPa, which agrees closely with the value obtained by calculation following Eq. (3.3).

Since the area under a normal curve between the mean and a deviation equal to the standard deviation is equal to 34.13 percent of the total area under the curve (see Fig. 10.5), we can read off an estimate of the standard deviation from our graph by finding the difference in abscissae between the mean and a point whose ordinate is $50 - 34.13 \simeq 16$ percent. Alternatively, we can say that the values of $(\bar{x} \pm s)$ correspond to cumulative frequencies of (50 ± 34.13) percent (or approximately 16 and 84 percent) and hence the standard deviation s can be estimated. This is illustrated in Fig. 11.4. In our case, the standard deviation is estimated to be 1.2 MPa, compared with 1.39 MPa obtained by calculation following Eq. (4.10).

The agreement between the values read off Fig. 11.4 and the calculated values is good, and indeed the diagram shows that the actual distribution departs only very slightly from normal. We should note that in drawing the "best" line we pay more attention to points *near the center* of the distribution than to those near the extremes. Tails are bound to show scatter since the actual number of observations in that region is usually very small; for example, the normal distribution may require 0.4 percent of observations to have a strength

less than 3.50 MPa. This would correspond to $0.4 \times 10^{-2} \times 270 = 1.08$ observations. The actual number must be an integer—if 1, it is too low; if 2, it is too
high.

To offer general guidance, we can say that a line which, even though
straight, does not pass through the centroidal point (i.e., a point whose coordinates are the true sample mean and the 50 percent probability) signifies a
skewed distribution.

If the points are so distributed that those corresponding to probabilities
somewhat below 50 percent "less than" lie below a straight line through the
centroidal point, and those corresponding to probabilities above 50 percent
"less than" lie above the straight line, the distribution is more peaked than
normal. If the deviations are in the opposite direction, the distribution is less
peaked than normal. However, to establish the significance for departures from
normality not less than about 500 observations are needed.

MEAN DEVIATION IN NORMAL DISTRIBUTION

The use of mean deviation d_m was discouraged in Chapter 4, but in the case
of the normal distribution, d_m may be of use when only a very approximate
value of standard deviation σ is required. It can be shown that, when the variate
is normally distributed,

$$\sigma = \sqrt{\frac{\pi}{2}}\, d_m$$

that is, $\sigma \simeq 1.25\, d_m.$

The mean deviation d_m has the advantage, of course, of being obtained very
rapidly from Eq. (4.11).

BINOMIAL APPROXIMATION

Although we have fitted different distributions to different types of sets of data,
it is important to be aware of the relation between the various distributions. In
Chapter 9, we saw how a markedly asymmetrical binomial distribution can be
approximated by a Poisson distribution. Later, we used a symmetrical binomial
distribution to obtain a normal distribution. The agreement between the terms
of an expansion of $(q + p)^n$ (where $p = q = \frac{1}{2}$) and a normal distribution is
better the larger the value of n. It is interesting to note that when n is very
large, the approximation of the binomial distribution by the normal distribution is good, even if p differs considerably from q, as the binomial distribution
loses a great deal of its skewness. For example, for $q = 0.8$, $p = 0.2$, and $n =$
50 the binomial distribution approximates closely to normal. The greater the
difference between p and q the larger n has to be for a given closeness of
approximation.

CONTINUITY CORRECTION

This correction is applied when we approximate a discrete distribution by a continuous one. Figure 11.6 shows a discrete probability distribution of the variable r, together with the continuous normal probability distribution. The probability that r will fall in the range $r_1 \leqslant r \leqslant r_2$ is the total area of the four rectangles marked A, B, C, and D. The approximation to this area afforded by the normal distribution, *without correction*, is the shaded portion. However, it can be readily observed that an improvement to this approximation can be made if the integration of the area under the normal probability curve is carried out from $r_1 - \frac{1}{2}$ to $r_2 + \frac{1}{2}$ instead of from r_1 to r_2, that is, from the lower boundary of rectangle A to the upper boundary of rectangle D. Thus, it can be seen that in the case of a discrete distribution, where the values of r differ by unity, the continuity correction consists of adding $\frac{1}{2}$ to the upper middle point (to form the upper limit of integration), and subtracting $\frac{1}{2}$ from the lower middle point (to form the lower limit of integration). If the discrete values of the statistic r differ by γ, then the corresponding continuity corrections will be $\pm \gamma/2$ to the integration limits.

EXAMPLE

Find the probability of obtaining between 4 and 7 heads in 10 throws of a coin, using the binomial expansion and approximating by the normal distribution.

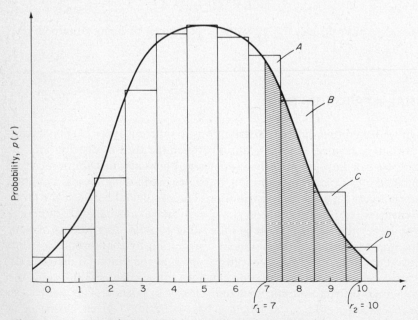

Figure 11.6 Normal approximation to discrete distribution.

Using the binomial distribution, we write by virtue of the theorem of repeated trials, and from Eq. (8.1a),

$$P = \sum_{i=4}^{7} {}_{10}C_i \left(\frac{1}{2}\right)^{10}$$

$$= \frac{210 + 252 + 210 + 120}{1024}$$

$$= 0.7734,$$

that is, the probability of obtaining the required number of heads is 77.34 percent.

In the approximation based on the normal distribution, we obtain a more accurate result if we recognize that the extreme values (4 and 7 heads) represent class midpoints; the actual class intervals extend to the (rather theoretical) values of $3\frac{1}{2}$ and $7\frac{1}{2}$, respectively (Fig. 11.7). Thus, the area under the histogram, which is to be equaled by the fitted normal curve, should be taken to these extremes. We have

$$p = q = \frac{1}{2}$$

$$\mu = np = 5$$
$$\sigma = \sqrt{npq} = 1.58$$
$$X_1 = 3.5 - 5 = -1.5$$
$$X_2 = 7.5 - 5 = +2.5.$$

Therefore,
$$z_1 = \frac{-1.5}{1.58} = -0.95$$

and
$$z_2 = \frac{2.5}{1.58} = 1.58.$$

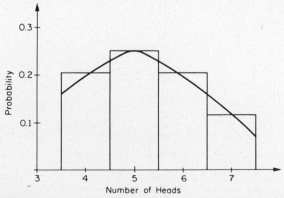

Figure 11.7 Probability distribution for the example on page 200.

The areas under the normal curve between these values of z and the mean are found from Table A.6 to be $0.3289 + 0.4430 = 0.7719$. The approximation is thus very close.   ■ ■

TRANSFORMATION TO A NORMALLY DISTRIBUTED VARIATE

So far, we have dealt with actual distributions thought to be normal. If, however, a distribution is known not to be normal and its shape is known, it would be foolish to disregard this knowledge. But even then, it may be possible to transform the data to a form that is normally distributed. For example, in fatigue tests, the variation in the number of cycles which metal members survive before failing is such that logarithms of these life values are normally distributed.

The log transformation is applicable in many other cases, especially when the range of observations covers several orders of magnitude. The measurement of acidity by pH and of noise intensity by decibels are examples of such a transformation in ordinary scientific work.

Transformation of the observed variable x other than by logarithms may be required to achieve a normal distribution relation; the more common transforms are $1/x$, $\sqrt{x}$, $\sqrt[3]{x}$, and so on.

The need for transformation may arise from the method of measurement used. For example, assume that spherical components are manufactured and their size (diameter) is known to be normally distributed. If we measure the components by weight, we shall find that the weights are not normally distributed, since they are proportional to a third power of the linear dimension.

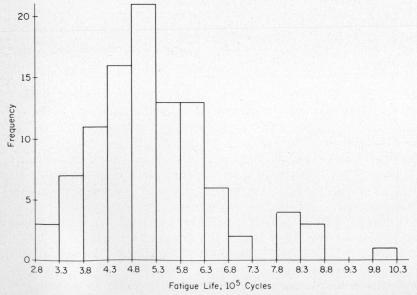

Figure 11.8   Histogram for the life of 100 metal members subjected to fatigue tests.

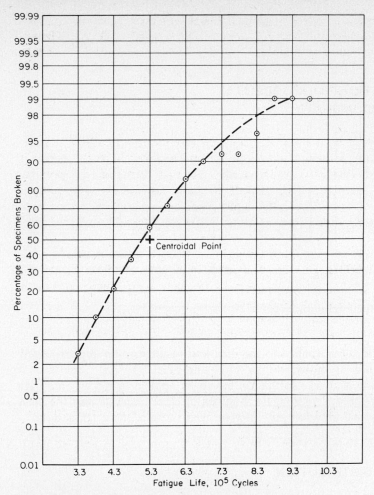

Figure 11.9 Cumulative frequency diagram for the data of Fig. 11.8 plotted on normal probability paper.

Therefore, changing the variable to the cube root of the weight will produce normal distribution. The same would apply in particle grading, where the size of particles is determined by a linear test but is measured by weight, for example, in the sieve analysis of aggregate.

   If we have no prior information as to which transformation should be used, we have to resort to trial and error. The transformation that yields the "best" straight line when the cumulative frequency of the transformed variable is plotted on normal probability paper is considered most suitable.

   As an illustration of rectification by transformation, Fig. 11.8 shows a histogram for fatigue tests on 100 metal members.[2] This is markedly skewed, and the skewness is confirmed by the cumulative frequency plot in Fig. 11.9.

---

[2] J. Pope and N. Bloomer, "Statistics as Applied to Fatigue Testing." *Metal Fatigue Symposium*, Nottingham University, England, 1955.

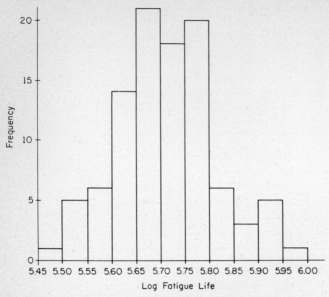

Figure 11.10 Histogram for logarithm of life for the data of Fig. 11.8.

Log transformation was applied to the data and resulted in an approximately normal distribution, as shown in Figs. 11.10 and 11.11.

We may note that transformation has to be applied to the original data before grouping; for this reason, the number of class intervals and the class frequency after transformation are different from those in the original data.

LOGNORMAL DISTRIBUTION

In general terms, a random variable X whose logarithms $Y(=\log_e X)$ are normally distributed is said to have a lognormal distribution. Its density function is given by

$$p(x) = \frac{1}{\zeta x \sqrt{2\pi}} e^{-(\log_e x - \lambda)^2/2\zeta^2} \qquad [5.26]$$

where $x > 0$ and $\zeta > 0$. The mean μ and variance σ^2 of the distribution can be shown to be, respectively,

$$\mu = e^{(\lambda + \zeta^2/2)} \quad \text{and} \quad \sigma^2 = (e^{\zeta^2} - 1)e^{(2\lambda + \zeta^2)},$$

and λ and ζ are the parameters of the distributions expressed as

$$\lambda = \mu_y = \log_e \mu - \frac{\zeta^2}{2} \quad \text{and} \quad \zeta^2 = \sigma_y^2 = \log_e \left(1 + \frac{\sigma^2}{\mu^2}\right).$$

If σ/μ is not large, say $\leqslant 0.30$, then $\zeta^2 \simeq \sigma^2/\mu^2$ and $\zeta \simeq \sigma/\mu$.

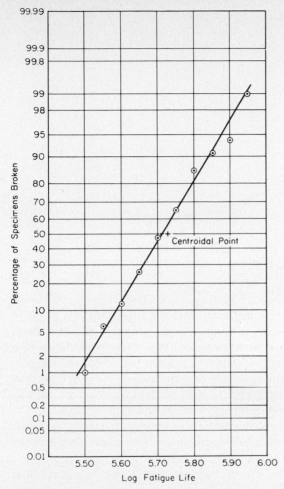

Figure 11.11 Cumulative frequency diagram for the data of Fig. 11.10, plotted on a normal probability paper.

The probability density of a lognormal distribution is shown in Fig. 11.12. As in any case of normal distribution, the range of Y is $-\infty$ to $+\infty$, but the range of X is 0 to $+\infty$. Since

$$Y = \log_e X$$

(although logarithms to any base can be used, the difference being only in a constant coefficient),

$$\text{when } X = 1, \quad Y = 0,$$
$$\text{when } X > 1, \quad Y > 0, \quad \text{and}$$
$$\text{when } 0 \leqslant X < 1, \quad -\infty \leqslant Y < 0.$$

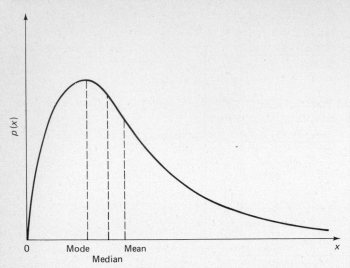

Figure 11.12   Lognormal distribution.

It is evident that X cannot be negative, since the logarithm of a negative number is not defined. This fact has contributed, albeit probably in a small measure, to the use of the lognormal distribution when a finite probability of a negative value is physically absurd. However, the main reason for the use of a lognormal distribution is that the behavior of some variates is well described by a lognormal distribution. This applies to some hydrological events, such as daily water flow, rainfall, or flood discharge, to the volume of air traffic, to the distribution of small particle sizes, to the strength of some materials, or to fatigue life. For dealing with such problems, lognormal probability paper, in which the abscissae are plotted to a logarithmic scale, is useful.

On the basis of Eq. (5.19), the probability that X will assume values between $X = X_1$ and $X = X_2$ is

$$P(X_1 < X < X_2) = \int_{X_1}^{X_2} \frac{1}{\zeta x \sqrt{2\pi}} e^{-(\log_e x - \lambda)^2/2\zeta^2} \, dx.$$

Let
$$z = \frac{\log_e x - \lambda}{\zeta}.$$

Then,
$$dz = \frac{dx}{\zeta x}.$$

Thus,
$$P(X_1 < X < X_2) = \frac{1}{\sqrt{2\pi}} \int_{(\log_e X_1 - \lambda)/\zeta}^{(\log_e X_2 - \lambda)/\zeta} e^{-z^2/2} \, dz$$

$$= F(z_2) - F(z_1)$$

where $z_1 = (\log_e X_1 - \lambda)/\zeta$, $z_2 = (\log X_2 - \lambda)/\zeta$, and $F(z_2)$ and $F(z_1)$ are found conveniently from Table A.6.

EXAMPLE

From past records, it is estimated that the total annual rainfall in a catch basin has a lognormal distribution with mean $\mu = 1800$ mm and standard deviation $\sigma = 360$ mm.

a. What is the probability that in future years the annual rainfall will be between 800 and 2000 mm?

b. What is the probability that the annual rainfall will be at least 1000 mm?

Solution

a. We have $\sigma/\mu = 360/1800 = 0.20 < 0.30$. Therefore,

$$\zeta \simeq \frac{\sigma}{\mu} = 0.20; \qquad \lambda = \log_e \mu - \zeta^2/2 = \log_e(1800) - 0.02,$$

that is,
$$\lambda = 7.48.$$

Using Table A.6,

$$P(800 < x < 2000) = F\left[\frac{\log_e(2000) - 7.48}{0.20}\right] + F\left[\frac{|\log_e(800) - 7.48|}{0.20}\right]$$

$$= F\left(\frac{0.12}{0.20}\right) + F\left(\frac{0.80}{0.20}\right)$$

$$= F(0.6) + F(4.0)$$

$$= 0.2257 + 0.5$$

$$= 0.7257.$$

b. $P(x \geqslant 1000) = 0.5 + F\left[\frac{|\log_e(1000) - 7.48|}{0.20}\right]$

$$= 0.5 + F(2.85)$$

$$= 0.5 + 0.4978$$

$$= 0.9978. \qquad \blacksquare\ \blacksquare$$

The use of lognormal distribution can be illustrated by its application in the field of soil testing. Let us assume that the "true" mean of the shear strength of a particular soil is τ_t. Using a small number of soil samples, n, we measure the shear strength τ. The mean value $\bar{\tau}[=(\sum \tau)/n]$ will deviate from the true value τ_t. The substructure is then designed on the basis of a reduced shear strength given by

$$\tau_d = \frac{\bar{\tau}}{L}$$

where L is a safety factor. Provided that a correct method of soil stability analysis is available, the probability of soil failure is expressed by

$$P\left[\left(\tau_t - \frac{\tau}{L}\right) < 0\right] = \alpha$$

where α is the level of significance (considered on page 209). Now, a normal distribution of the random variable τ is not likely, since τ cannot take negative values (implied by the normal range $-\infty$ to $+\infty$). Instead, a lognormal distribution is assumed with a range from zero to ∞. The probability of soil failure can, therefore, be expressed as

$$P\left[\left(\log \tau_t - \overline{\log \frac{\tau}{L}}\right) < 0\right] = \alpha$$

where $\overline{\log(\tau/L)} = [\sum \log(\tau/L)]/n$. Since L is a constant, we can write the above probability statement as

$$P[(\log \tau_t - \overline{\log \tau} + \log L) < 0] = \alpha,$$

Assuming that the standard deviation of the population, σ, is known from past records, we have the statistic

$$z = \frac{\overline{\log \tau} - \log \tau_t}{\sigma/\sqrt{n}}.$$

Substituting in the equation for probability, we obtain

$$P\left[\left(\log L - \frac{\sigma}{\sqrt{n}} z\right) < 0\right] = \alpha$$

or

$$P\left[\left(z > \frac{\sqrt{n}}{\sigma} \log L\right)\right] = \alpha.$$

In a given case, the values of n, σ, and L are known; hence, the probability of failure P can be found readily corresponding to the z values from Table A.6. Other combinations of the various factors are also possible.

As an example, let us consider the case when $n = 3$, $\sigma = 0.06$ kN/m^2, and $L = 1.2$; we want to find the probability α. We obtain

$$z = \frac{\sqrt{3}}{0.06} \log_{10} 1.2 = \left[\frac{1.732}{0.06}\right] \times 0.07918 = 2.285.$$

The corresponding probability α from Table A.6 (for the one-sided test) is

$$\alpha = 0.5 - F(z) = 0.5 - 0.4889 = 0.011.$$

If σ is not known and is estimated from the sample as s, then the t statistic, given by

$$t = \frac{\log \tau - \log \tau_t}{s/\sqrt{n}},$$

should be used. (The t distribution was introduced in Chapter 6 and will be considered further in Chapter 15.)

CONFIDENCE INTERVAL ESTIMATION

In Chapter 6, we introduced the basic ideas of sampling and sampling distributions; specifically, we showed that a sample mean is a reliable estimate of the mean of the sampled populations. This was followed by a general discussion of statistical inference in Chapter 7 where we introduced briefly the concepts of parameter estimation and hypothesis testing. We have already illustrated the procedure of hypothesis testing in Chapters 8 and 9 and we shall develop the subject further in Chapters 14, 15, and 16. Our purpose here is to expand on the notion of estimation and, in particular, of interval estimation.

Each of the possible samples drawn from the population yields a *point estimate* of the population parameter sought. Obviously, when we take only *one* sample we cannot ascertain by how much we have missed the parameter. In order to overcome this difficulty, we construct an *interval estimate* in such a way that we can state the *degree of confidence* that the interval includes, between its end points, the parameter being estimated. Because of the associated statement of confidence, we call such an interval a *confidence interval*. Let us demonstrate the procedure for a normally distributed population.

When observations are normally distributed, it follows that $[1 - 2F(z)]$ represents the probability of a value falling outside the range $\mu \pm z\sigma$. This probability is called the level of significance of a statistical test and is denoted by α (see Fig. 11.13; also refer to page 295 and Fig. 15.5). Thus, when $z = 1.96$, $[1 - 2F(z)] = 0.05$, and we say that the level of significance α is 5 percent. This means that if we obtain an observation that deviates from the mean by at least $\pm 1.96\sigma$, we can say that the observation is *significantly* different from the body of the data described by the given normal distribution, and the probability of our being in error is 5 percent. In other words, if we draw such a conclusion a large number of times, we shall be wrong in 5 percent of all the cases.

The term *significant* is used in the statistical sense of the word and means that the probability of the observed difference being due to chance alone is equal to the level of significance. A difference may be *statistically significant* but quite unimportant and not significant from the practical point of view.

From the fact that there is a 5 percent probability of an observation having a deviation from the mean greater than $|1.96\sigma|$, it follows that there is a 95 percent probability that an observation will fall within the range $\mu \pm 1.96\sigma$, and this degree of confidence is referred to as the 95 percent confidence level. Thus, the *confidence level* (or confidence coefficient) is described by $2F(z)$ expressed as a percentage (see Fig. 11.13). The limits $(\mu - z\sigma)$ and $(\mu + z\sigma)$ are called *confidence limits*, and they describe between them the confidence interval. Thus, we can say that if α measures our lack of confidence that a certain value x is not exceeded, then $(1 - \alpha)$ is the measure of our confidence or ability to prove that x is not exceeded. We can also think of the confidence

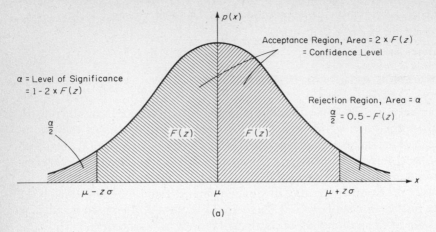

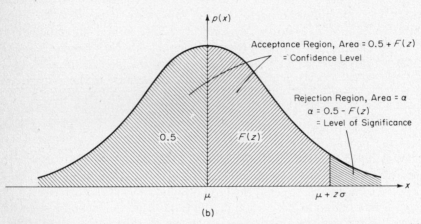

Figure 11.13 Level of significance in two-sided and one-sided tests: (a) two-sided test; (b) one-sided test.

level as the area of the acceptance region whereas the significance level would be the area of the rejection region.

More formally, we can express the probability that an observation x_0 falls between the limits $(\mu - z\sigma)$ and $(\mu + z\sigma)$ by

$$P(\mu - z\sigma \leqslant x_0 \leqslant \mu + z\sigma) = 1 - \alpha. \tag{11.3}$$

We can extend this treatment to the sample mean $\bar{x}$. Noting that $\sigma_{\bar{x}} = \sigma/\sqrt{n}$ [from Eq. (6.10)],[3] the probability that a sample mean $\bar{x}$ will fall between the limits of $\mu \pm z\sigma_{\bar{x}}$ is

$$P(\mu - z\sigma_{\bar{x}} \leqslant \bar{x} \leqslant \mu + z\sigma_{\bar{x}}) = 1 - \alpha. \tag{11.4}$$

[3] When sampling is without replacement or from a finite population, then we use

$$\sigma_{\bar{x}} = \sqrt{\frac{N-n}{N-1}} \frac{\sigma}{\sqrt{n}} \quad \text{instead of} \quad \sigma_{\bar{x}} = \frac{\sigma}{\sqrt{n}}.$$

TABLE 11.2   VALUES OF z FOR A SPECIFIED PERCENTAGE OF
RESULTS TO LIE WITHIN THE RANGE $\mu \pm z\sigma$

Level of significance (percentage of results outside the range), percent	z	Confidence level (percentage of results within the range), percent
10	1.645	90
5	1.960	95
2	2.326	98
1	2.576	99
0.1	3.291	99.9
0.01	3.891	99.99

The values of z corresponding to the more commonly used values of the level of significance are presented in Table 11.2.

The confidence interval, which can be calculated for any statistic, is of considerable importance as it expresses the reliability of our estimate of a parameter: the narrower the interval, the more precise the estimate.

If we know μ and σ, then we can say that, for example, the 99.74 percent confidence interval for the mean of a sample of size n is $\mu \pm (3\sigma/\sqrt{n})$. In the converse and more common case when μ is unknown, we can express the 99.74 percent confidence interval for μ as $\bar{x} \pm (3\sigma/\sqrt{n})$. This asserts that the true mean lies within the interval, with a 99.74 percent probability of our being right.

More generally, when the parameter μ is unknown, our objective is to find a confidence interval for μ, based on a known sample mean $\bar{x}$. We can in fact deduce an expression similar to that in Eq. (11.4) where μ replaces $\bar{x}$; we do this by multiplying Eq. (11.4) throughout by $\sigma_{\bar{x}}$, followed by subtracting $\bar{x}$ from each term, and finally multiplying throughout by (-1), and obtain

$$P(\bar{x} - z\sigma_{\bar{x}} \leqslant \mu \leqslant \bar{x} + z\sigma_{\bar{x}}) = 1 - \alpha. \qquad (11.5)$$

The confidence interval related to Eq. (11.5) is shown in Fig. 11.14.

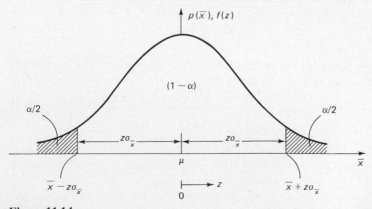

Figure 11.14

When σ is not known but only estimated, the confidence limits of the mean must perforce be wider. If, nevertheless, we want to find the confidence interval for μ from the sample information, first we must estimate σ by s; in this case, the sampling distribution is no longer normal but follows a t distribution. We can still use Eq. (11.5) after replacing z with t, where the t value, for a sample of size n, is found from Table A.7 corresponding to $(n - 1)$ degrees of freedom. This is discussed in Chapter 15; Chapter 16 deals with the confidence limits for variance. We can also obtain confidence intervals for $(\mu_1 - \mu_2)$ and (σ_1/σ_2) when two populations are being compared.

We should stress the fact that all our statements are in terms of probability and it is not possible to *prove* whether or not an observation belongs to a population.

EXAMPLE

The breaking strength of a certain type of cloth was measured on a random sample of four specimens with the following results (in kPa): 1250, 1190, 1220, 1200. From past records, the standard deviation is known to be 35 kPa. Assuming normal distribution, find the 99 percent confidence interval for the average breaking strength of the cloth population.

We first calculate the mean strength from the sample:

$$\bar{x} = \frac{\sum x}{n} = \frac{4860}{4} = 1215 \text{ kPa}.$$

We know that $\sigma = 35$ kPa. Hence,

$$\sigma_{\bar{x}} = \frac{\sigma}{\sqrt{n}} = \frac{35}{\sqrt{4}} = 17.5 \text{ kPa}.$$

Therefore, from Eq. (11.5),

$$P(\bar{x} - z\sigma_{\bar{x}} \leqslant \mu \leqslant \bar{x} + z\sigma_{\bar{x}}) = 1 - \alpha = 0.99.$$

From Table A.6, the z value corresponding to a probability of

$$\frac{1 - \alpha}{2} = 0.495$$

is $z = 2.575$. Thus the 99 percent confidence interval for the population average breaking strength is given by

$$\bar{x} \pm z\sigma_{\bar{x}} = 1215 \pm (2.575 \times 17.5) = [1170, 1260] \text{ kPa}. \qquad \blacksquare \blacksquare$$

EXAMPLE

Imagine that a coin was tossed 576 times and 256 heads were obtained. Are we justified in suspecting that the coin is biased or the experimenter dishonest? Use a level of significance of 1 percent.

We assume the null hypothesis $H_0 : p = \frac{1}{2}$ versus the alternative hypothesis $H_a : p \neq \frac{1}{2}$. Thus, since $p = q = \frac{1}{2}$ and n is large, we can use the

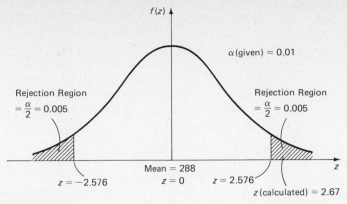

Figure 11.15

normal distribution as an approximation to binomial. We have,

$$n = 576$$
$$\mu = np = 288 \quad \text{(a value obviously expected)}$$
$$\sigma = \sqrt{npq} = 12.$$

The observed value is

$$x = 256.$$

Hence,
$$z = \frac{|x - \mu|}{\sigma} = 2.67.$$

From Table 11.2, we find that a deviation of 2.576σ is exceeded only in 1 percent of all cases and the observed deviation is larger than the tabulated value. Figure 11.15 shows that the calculated z falls in the rejection region. We conclude, therefore, at the 1 percent level of significance, that the observed value does not belong to the population (of all the possible sets of 576 throws of a coin); the probability of our making a wrong accusation of dishonesty is 1 percent. ■ ■

EXAMPLE
A manufacturer produces a special alloy steel with an average tensile strength of 180 MPa. A certain change in the composition of the alloy is said to increase the strength. The standard deviation of the tensile strength is known to be 2 MPa and the change in composition is not expected to change this value. An experiment was conducted on 16 tensile pieces made from the alloy of changed composition and the mean strength was 182 MPa. Assume normality.

    a. Is this a one-sided or two-sided test? Why?
    b. State the null hypothesis and the alternative hypothesis.

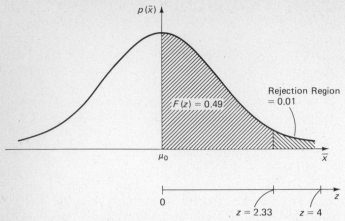

Figure 11.16

    c. Using a level of significance of 1 percent, can the manufacturer claim that the change in the composition increases the tensile strength?

    d. What is the probability of the manufacturer's reaching a wrong conclusion?

Solution

    a. This is a one-sided test because we are interested only in the increase in the tensile strength.

    b. Denote the mean of the population by μ_0 and that of the sampling distribution of the mean by μ. Then, the null hypothesis is $H_0 : \mu = \mu_0$ versus the alternative hypothesis $H_a : \mu > \mu_0$.

    c. Since the underlying distribution is assumed to be normal, with a known standard deviation, the fraction $(\bar{x} - \mu_0)/\sigma_{\bar{x}}$ is also normally distributed. Thus,

$$z = \frac{\bar{x} - \mu_0}{\sigma_{\bar{x}}} = \frac{\bar{x} - \mu_0}{\sigma/\sqrt{n}} = \frac{182 - 180}{2/\sqrt{16}} = 4.$$

The tabulated value of z from Table A.6, corresponding to $\alpha = 0.01$ (see Fig. 11.16) is $z = 2.33$. Since $z_{\text{calc}} > z_{\text{tab}}$, we reject the null hypothesis and accept the alternative hypothesis that the change in composition does increase the mean strength.

    d. This probability is in fact equal to the level of significance, $\alpha = 0.01$.   ■ ■

EXAMPLE

    The interval diameters of a random sample of 300 bushings were measured, and 10 of them were found to be outside the specification limits.

If the process is designed to produce no more than 2 percent defective bushings, can we conclude that the manufacturing process is out of control? Use $\alpha = 5$ percent.

We assume that the population proportion of defectives is $p_0 \leqslant 0.02$. Thus, the null hypothesis is $H_0:p \leqslant 0.02$ and the alternative hypothesis is $H_a:p > 0.02$. On the basis of $p = 0.02$, we have, from the binomial distribution, mean $= np = 300 \times 0.02 = 6$ bushings; and $\sigma = \sqrt{np(1-p)} = \sqrt{(300 \times 0.02 \times 0.98)} = 2.4$. Applying the normal approximation to the binomial distribution, we calculate the statistic z as

$$z = \frac{x - \mu}{\sigma} = \frac{9.5 - 6}{2.4} = 1.458.$$

[We must use 9.5 instead of 10 in order to include the entire probability rectangle associated with 10 (see continuity correction on page 281).] From Table A.6, for $\alpha = 0.05$ (one-sided test), $F(z) - 0.50 - 0.05 = 0.45$; hence, $z = 1.645$, which defines the critical region. Since $1.458 < 1.645$, we accept the null hypothesis that $p \leqslant 0.02$, and therefore conclude that the manufacturing process is in control. ■ ■

CONFIDENCE INTERVAL FOR A POPULATION PROPORTION

In Chapter 8, we found that the mean and standard deviation of the binomial distribution for the number of successes are, respectively,

$$\mu = np \qquad\qquad [8.6]$$

and $$\sigma = \sqrt{np(1-p)} \qquad\qquad [8.7]$$

where p is the proportion of successes in the population and n is the number of trials. We can readily convert a sampling distribution for the *number of successes* to the corresponding distribution of *proportion of successes*. If r is the number of successes in a sample of n observations, then the proportion of successes in the sample is $\hat{p} = r/n$. Thus, by dividing Eqs. (8.6) and (8.7) by n, we find the mean and standard deviation of the sample proportion to be, respectively,

$$\mu_p = p \qquad\qquad (11.6)$$

and $$\sigma_p = \sqrt{\frac{p(1-p)}{n}}. \qquad\qquad (11.7)$$

If p is not too close to 0 or 1 and n is large, then the distribution of the sample proportion, $\hat{p}$, is approximately normal with μ_p and σ_p given by Eqs. (11.6) and (11.7); this follows from the central limit theorem (see Chapter 6). Generally, we do not know the value of population proportion p and, therefore, we have to estimate it by the sample proportion $\hat{p}$; hence, we write Eq. (11.7) as

$$s_p = \sqrt{\frac{\hat{p}(1 - \hat{p})}{n}}. \tag{11.8}$$

The confidence limits for the population proportion p, corresponding to a probability of $(1 - \alpha)$, can now be written as

$$P\left[\hat{p} - z\sqrt{\frac{\hat{p}(1 - \hat{p})}{n}} \leqslant p \leqslant \hat{p} + z\sqrt{\frac{\hat{p}(1 - \hat{p})}{n}}\right] = 1 - \alpha. \tag{11.9}$$

EXAMPLE

Screws produced by an automatic machine are to be checked. Samples of 60 screws were checked by a go–no-go gauge, and it was found that in 30 successive samples the following number of defective screws was obtained:

> 5, 4, 3, 1, 2, 0, 0, 0, 1, 2, 0, 1, 2, 1, 0, 1, 1,
> 0, 1, 0, 0, 1, 2, 0, 1, 0, 1, 0, 0, 1.

Determine the 95 percent confidence interval for the population proportion of defectives. Assume normality.

We have the mean number of defectives per sample:

$$\bar{x} = \frac{\sum \text{number of defectives}}{30} = \frac{31}{30}.$$

Therefore, the mean proportion of defectives $= \hat{p} = \bar{x}/60 = 0.017$. Hence,

$$\sqrt{\frac{\hat{p}(1 - \hat{p})}{n}} = \sqrt{\frac{(0.017 \times 0.983)}{60}} = 0.0167.$$

Thus, from Eq. (11.9),

$$P\left(\hat{p} - z\sqrt{\frac{\hat{p}(1 - \hat{p})}{n}} \leqslant p \leqslant \hat{p} + z\sqrt{\frac{\hat{p}(1 - \hat{p})}{n}}\right) = 1 - \alpha = 0.95.$$

From Table A.6, the z value corresponding to a probability of

$$\frac{1 - \alpha}{2} = 0.475$$

is $z = 1.96$. Thus, the 95 percent confidence interval for the population proportion of defectives is

$$\hat{p} \pm z\sqrt{\frac{\hat{p}(1 - \hat{p})}{n}} = 0.017 \pm (1.96 \times 0.0167) = [-0.016, 0.050].$$

Since a proportion of defectives cannot be negative, we can put the lower limit as zero and write the confidence interval as $[0, 0.050]$.   ■ ■

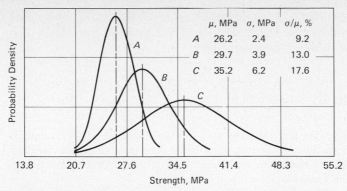

Figure 11.17 Normal distribution curves for concrete with a minimum strength (exceeded by 99 percent of results) of 20.7 MPa and different values of standard deviation. [From A. M. Neville, *Properties of Concrete*, 3rd ed. (London and Marshfield, Mass.; Pitman Books, 1981).]

SPECIFYING A MINIMUM VALUE

When a material such as concrete is used in construction, it is common to specify a certain minimum strength. Because of the statistical probability of encountering a test result falling below any specified minimum, the word is generally not taken to mean an absolute minimum. We require a specified confidence level, that is, we stipulate that not less than a prescribed percentage of test results falls above the "minimum." If this is, say, 99 percent, the area of *one* tail[4] is 1 percent, that is, $z = 2.326$ [see Fig. 11.13(b)].

If the material used, for example, is concrete, the mix is proportioned so as to give a certain *mean* strength. This mean has to be chosen so that with the variance that is characteristic of the process of manufacture, the "minimum" has a value exceeded by 99 percent of the test results.

We can state the problem as follows: let x_m be the "minimum" strength, μ the mean strength, and σ the standard deviation. Also, $z_m = (x_m - \mu)/\sigma$. Then,

$$F(z_m) + 0.5 \geqslant 0.99. \tag{11.10}$$

Since x_m is specified by the designer, the value of μ that satisfies Eq. (11.10) depends on σ. This is illustrated in Fig. 11.17 for $x_m = 20.7$ MPa and three different values of σ. In all cases, the area under the normal curve to the left of the abscissa $x_m = 20.7$ MPa is the same.

It is clear that the higher the value of σ the higher the necessary value of μ for the specified x_m, and if the cost of manufacture is related to μ, which is generally the case, then a higher value of σ requires the use of a more expensive

---

[4] Note that Table 11.2 has been prepared for results falling within a range, that is, with two tails taken into account.

material. On the other hand, a reduction in σ demands a closer control of manufacture and, therefore, a higher cost so that in practice the choice of σ (and therefore μ) is a result of a compromise.

SOLVED PROBLEMS

11-1. Foil strain gauges are produced with a mean resistance of 120.0 ohms. If the specification limits are 120 ± 0.5 ohms, what is the maximum allowable standard deviation that will permit no more than one gauge in 1000 to be defective? It is assumed that the resistance of the gauges is normally distributed.

Solution.   Given $\mu = 120.0$ ohm, $x - \mu = 0.5$ ohm. Refer to Fig. 11.18. The area under the normal curve inside the specification limits must be

$$1 - \frac{1}{1000} = 0.999.$$

Then,   half this area $= \dfrac{0.999}{2} = 0.4995.$

For this value of $F(z)$, Table A.6 gives $z = 3.27$. Hence,

$$\sigma = \frac{x - \mu}{z} = \frac{0.5}{3.27}$$

$$= 0.153 \text{ ohm.}$$

11-2. A certain process of manufacture produces records whose mass is normally distributed with a standard deviation of 5 g. What must be the mean mass if the probability of obtaining a mass exceeding 210 g is to be 0.01?

Solution.   Given $\sigma = 5$ g and $x = 210$ g. The area under the normal curve is

$$F(z) = 0.5000 - 0.01$$

$$= 0.4900.$$

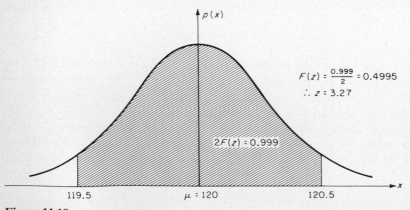

Figure 11.18

The corresponding z from Table A.6 is

$$z = 2.33.$$

But

$$z = \frac{x - \mu}{\sigma}.$$

Therefore, $210 - \mu = z\sigma = 2.33 \times 5 = 11.65.$

Hence, $\mu = 198.35 \text{ g} \simeq 198 \text{ g}.$

11-3. Results from a tensile test on 36 aluminum alloy specimens chosen at random from a certain mill were grouped as follows:

Tensile strength (MPa)	155–165	165–175	175–185	185–195	195–205	205–215	215–225
Frequency	1	4	7	11	9	3	1

a. Find the mean and standard deviation of the tensile strength of the specimens.
b. Plot on normal probability paper the tensile strength versus fractional cumulative frequency. Draw "by eye" a straight line through the points and obtain the mean and standard deviation from the graph; observe whether the results appear to follow the normal distribution.
c. Estimate the probability of obtaining a random measurement that has a deviation from the mean of between -10 and 20 MPa.
d. Calculate the range in which we would expect the mean of the population to fall with a probability of 95 percent.

Solution
a. Take origin at 160 MPa and a class width $w = 10$ MPa (see Table 11.3). We have

$$\text{mean} = \bar{x} = 160 + w \times \frac{\sum f_i X_i'}{\sum f_i} = 160 + 10 \times \frac{108}{36} = 190 \text{ MPa}$$

and standard deviation

$$s = w \sqrt{\frac{\sum f_i X_i'^2 - (\sum f_i X_i')^2/n}{n - 1}} = w \sqrt{\frac{386 - (108)^2/36}{35}}$$

$$= 1.33 \times w = 1.33 \times 10$$

$$= 13.3 \text{ MPa}.$$

b. The cumulative frequency is plotted on normal probability paper in Fig. 11.19 using the upper boundary of each class interval. We find that the mean is 189.7 MPa and the standard deviation 12.7 MPa. The graph indicates that the results follow a normal distribution very closely.

c. Given $\mu - x_1 = 10$ MPa, and $x_2 - \mu = 20$ MPa

$$\mu \text{ (estimated from the sample mean)} = 190 \text{ MPa}$$

$$s \text{ (estimated from the sample)} = 13.3 \text{ MPa}.$$

TABLE 11.3

Class interval, MPa	Class midpoint, x_i	Frequency, f_i	Cumulative frequency, F	Fractional cumulative frequency, F/n	Deviation from origin in terms of class width, X_i'	$f_i X_i'$	$f_i X_i'^2$
155–165	160	1	1	0.028	0	0	0
165–175	170	4	5	0.139	1	4	4
175–185	180	7	12	0.333	2	14	28
185–195	190	11	23	0.639	3	33	99
195–205	200	9	32	0.889	4	36	144
205–215	210	3	35	0.972	5	15	75
215–225	220	1	36	1.000	6	6	36
Totals		$\sum f_i = 36$				$\sum f_i X_i' = 108$	$\sum f_i X_i'^2 = 386$

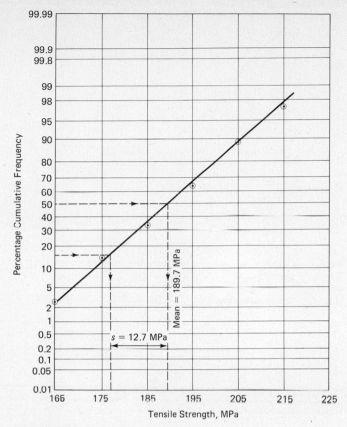

Figure 11.19

(Refer to Fig. 11.20.) Then,

$$z_1 = \frac{\mu - x_1}{s} = \frac{10}{13.3} = 0.752.$$

From Table A.6,

$$F(z_1) = 0.2740.$$

Also

$$z_2 = \frac{x_2 - \mu}{s} = \frac{20}{13.3} = 1.504.$$

Therefore,

$$F(z_2) = 0.4337.$$

The probability that a random measurement will fall within the limits $(190 - 10)$ MPa and $(190 + 20)$ MPa, that is, between 180 and 210 MPa, is

$$F(z_1) + F(z_2) = 0.2740 + 0.4337 = 0.7077$$
$$= 70.77 \text{ percent.}$$

d. Table A.6 gives the area under the normal curve on one side of the mean. Thus for a probability of 95 percent the area required $= 0.95/2 = 0.475$ (see Fig. 11.21). The

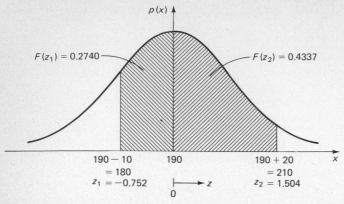

Figure 11.20

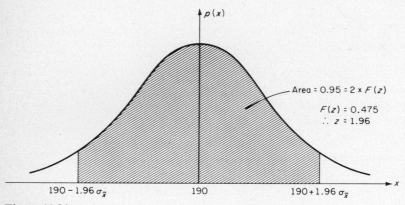

Figure 11.21

corresponding z from Table A.6 is $z = 1.96$. The range within which we would expect the population mean to fall is

$$190 \pm zs_{\bar{x}} = 190 \pm 1.96 \times \frac{13.3}{\sqrt{36}}$$

$$= 190 \pm 4.3 \text{ MPa}.$$

11-4. A steel company made numerous studies on the life span of their plate products immersed in water of a particular city. The results showed that the life span of such plate products was normally distributed, with a mean $\mu = 2160$ days and standard deviation $\sigma = 252$ days.

    a. What is the probability that the mean of a sample of 121 plates will not differ from μ by more than 60 days?

    b. Find the 95 percent confidence limits for the mean of a sample of 121 plates and for a single plate.

    c. What should be the size of a sample in future studies if it is required that the probability of the sample mean being in error by more than 90 days is 5 percent?

Solution

a. Given $\mu = 2160$ days and $\sigma = 252$ days, we find

$$\sigma_{\bar{x}} = \frac{\sigma}{\sqrt{n}} = \frac{252}{\sqrt{121}} = 22.9$$

and
$$z = \frac{\bar{x} - \mu}{\sigma_{\bar{x}}} = \frac{60}{22.9} = 2.62.$$

From Table A.6 for such a value of z, $F(z) = 0.4956$. This is the area to one side of the mean of the normal curve. For a deviation in either direction, the area is $2 \times 0.4956 = 0.9912$. Therefore, the probability that the mean life span of 121 plates will not differ from $\mu = 2160$ days by more than 60 days is 99.12 percent.

b. For 95 percent confidence limits the area under the normal curve is 0.95. Therefore, the area to either side of the mean is $0.95/2 = 0.475$, for which (from Table A.6) $z = 1.96$. Hence, the deviation of the mean life span of 121 plates is

$$z\sigma_{\bar{x}} = \frac{z\sigma}{\sqrt{n}} = \frac{1.96 \times 252}{\sqrt{121}} = 44.8 \text{ or } 45 \text{ days.}$$

Thus the 95 percent confidence limits for the mean life span of 121 plates are

$$\mu \pm z\sigma_{\bar{x}} = 2160 \pm 45 \text{ days.}$$

For a single plate, the deviation of its life span from μ is $z\sigma = 1.96 \times 252 = 494$ days. Thus the range in which a single observation will fall with a probability of error of 5 percent is 2160 ± 494 days.

c. Table A.6 uses the area to one side of the mean. Thus,

$$\text{required area} = \frac{1 - 0.05}{2} = 0.475$$

$$\text{corresponding } z = 1.96.$$

The given deviation is $\bar{x} - \mu = 90$ days. From

$$z = \frac{\bar{x} - \mu}{\sigma_{\bar{x}}} = \frac{\bar{x} - \mu}{\sigma/\sqrt{n}} = \frac{90}{252/\sqrt{n}} = 1.96$$

we find
$$\sqrt{n} = 5.49$$
or
$$n = 30.$$

Hence the sample size to be used is 30.

11-5. On a construction project the shear strength of 50 soil specimens was measured, and the following values (in kN/m^2) were observed:

2450	3300	3400	3650	3800
2650	3150	3100	3500	2850
3050	4300	3300	3300	3150
2100	3300	3650	3150	3550
2900	3250	3000	3400	3750
3900	3600	3150	3600	3000
4200	3700	3050	3300	2350
4150	2950	3200	3900	3200
3200	3450	2500	3050	2650
3050	2800	2700	3450	3400

a. Group these strengths into a frequency distribution with class width $w = 250$ kN/m^2, starting with 2000 kN/m^2.

b. Draw a histogram and a frequency polygon.

c. Calculate the mean, an estimate of the standard deviation, and the coefficient of variation from the grouped data; indicate the mean on the histogram.

d. What is the range of the given data? Find also the mode and the median of the grouped data.

e. By plotting the fractional cumulative frequency on normal probability paper, check whether the distribution of the data is approximately normal.

f. Assuming normal distribution, find the minimum shear strength that can be used for design, accepting a definite risk that 1 percent of test samples will have a strength less than this minimum. Indicate whether any of the 50 samples fall below this strength.

g. Calculate the standard error of the mean and explain its significance.

h. Obtain the equations to the normal probability curve and the normal frequency curve for the given data. Draw the normal probability curve.

i. Estimate the probability that a random test result will have a deviation from the mean lying between -200 and $+500$ kN/m^2.

j. Estimate the probability that a mean of a sample of 36 soil specimens from the same site will exceed 3500 kN/m^2.

k. Find the limits for the mean of a sample of 36 soil specimens at the 1 percent and 5 percent level of significance.

l. What should be the size of a sample in future tests in order that the probability of the sample mean being in error by more than 400 kN/m^2 be not more than 0.1?

Solution

a. The required grouping of the test results is shown in Table 11.4.

b. The histogram and the frequency polygon are shown in Fig. 11.22.

c. If the arbitrary origin is taken as 2125 kN/m^2, then the deviation of the class midpoint from this origin, X_i', is calculated as shown in Table 11.4, with a class width $w = 250$ kN/m^2. Thus from this table we get the mean:

$$\bar{x} = 2125 + \frac{w \sum f_i X_i'}{\sum f_i} = 2125 + \frac{250 \times 228}{50}$$

$$= 3265 \text{ kN/m}^2.$$

The estimate of the standard deviation is

$$s = w \sqrt{\frac{\sum f_i X_i'^2 - [(\sum f_i X_i')^2 / \sum f_i]}{n - 1}}$$

$$= 250 \sqrt{\frac{1210 - [(228)^2/50]}{49}}$$

$$= 466 \text{ kN/m}^2.$$

The coefficient of variation $V = s/\bar{x} \times 100 = 46{,}600/3265 = 14.27$ percent.

d. Range $= 4300 - 2100 = 2200$ kN/m^2 (from the raw data). For the grouped data, mode is the midpoint of the class interval with the highest frequency $= 3125$ kN/m^2. Median is the value that divides the histogram into two equal areas $= 3250$ kN/m^2 (by inspection).

TABLE 11.4

Class interval, kN/m²	Class midpoint, x_i	Frequency, f_i	Cumulative frequency, F	Fractional cumulative frequency, F/n	Deviation from origin in terms of class width, X_i'	$f_i X_i'$	$f_i X_i'^2$
2000–2250	2125	1	1	0.02	0	0	0
2250–2500	2375	2	3	0.06	1	2	2
2500–2750	2625	4	7	0.14	2	8	16
2750–3000	2875	4	11	0.22	3	12	36
3000–3250	3125	14	25	0.50	4	56	224
3250–3500	3375	11	36	0.72	5	55	275
3500–3750	3625	7	43	0.86	6	42	252
3750–4000	3875	4	47	0.94	7	28	196
4000–4250	4125	2	49	0.98	8	16	128
4250–4500	4375	1	50	1.00	9	9	81
Totals		$\sum f_i = 50$				$\sum f_i X_i' = 228$	$\sum f_i X_i'^2 = 1210$

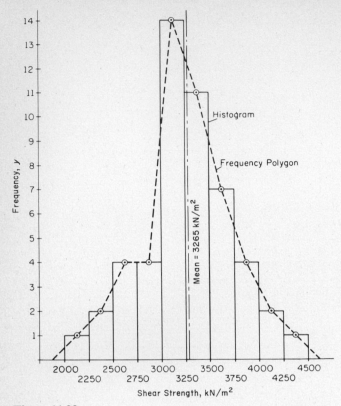

Figure 11.22

e. The fractional cumulative frequency (in percent) is plotted against the upper-class boundary on normal probability paper, Fig. 11.23. It can be seen that the plotted points closely follow a straight line drawn "by eye." From this graph, the mean is $3250 \ kN/m^2$ and the standard deviation $s = 475 \ kN/m^2$. Both these values are close to those calculated from the grouped data, and we conclude that the distribution of the given values is sensibly normal.

f. For a 1 percent risk the tail area of the normal probability curve (and we are interested in one tail only) is 0.01. Therefore, the area $F(z)$ is $0.50 - 0.01 = 0.49$. For this value of $F(z)$ Table A.6 gives $z = 2.33$. But

$$z = \frac{\text{deviation from the mean}}{s}.$$

Hence,   deviation from the mean $= zs = 2.33 \times 466$

$$= 1086 \ kN/m^2.$$

Therefore, the minimum shear strength used in design is

$$3265 - 1086 = 2179 \ kN/m^2.$$

Among the data in hand only 1 specimen has a strength that falls below this minimum.

g. The standard error of the mean is $s/\sqrt{n} = 466/\sqrt{50} = 66 \ kN/m^2$. Thus there is a 68.26 percent probability that the mean of the population (i.e. of all the soil repre-

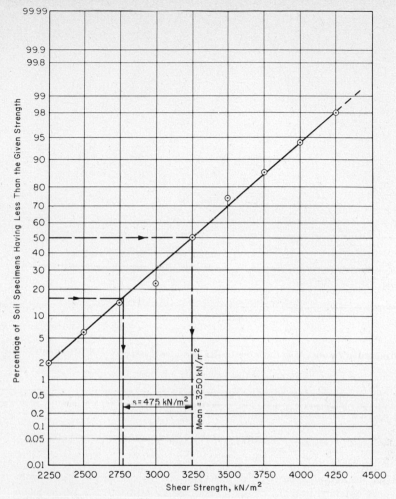

Figure 11.23

sented by the test specimens) lies within the range 3265 ± 66, i.e. between, say, 3200 and 3330 kN/m².

   h. Equation (10.18) gives the normal probability curve as

$$f(z) = \frac{1}{\sqrt{2\pi}} e^{-z^2/2}$$

$$= 0.3989 e^{-z^2/2}$$

where $z = X/s$ is the deviation from the mean of the grouped data in terms of standard deviation.

   From Eq. (10.14), the equation to the normal frequency curve is

$$y = \frac{N}{\sigma\sqrt{2\pi}} e^{-z^2/2}$$

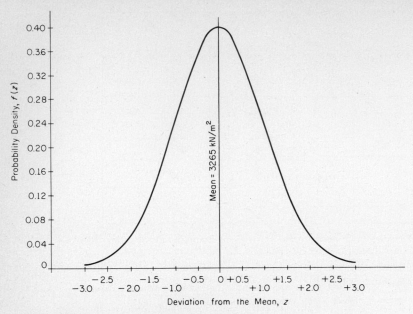

Figure 11.24

where σ is estimated by s and N is the area under the histogram.

$$N = w\sum f_i = 250 \times 50.$$

Hence,
$$y = \frac{250 \times 50}{466\sqrt{2\pi}} e^{-z^2/2}$$

$$= 10.7012e^{-z^2/2}$$

where z is as defined in (f).

To plot the normal *probability* curve, the values of the ordinate $f(z)$ (the probability density) are obtained from Table A.5 for selected deviations $\pm z$ from the mean 3265 kN/m^2. The normal probability curve is shown in Fig. 11.24.

i. To find the probability that a random measurement will have a deviation from the mean lying between -200 and $+500 \text{ kN/m}^2$, we calculate

$$z_1 = \frac{|\text{deviation}|}{s} = \frac{200}{466} = 0.43.$$

The corresponding area under the normal curve is given in Table A.6 as $A_1 = 0.1664$. (Refer to Fig. 11.25.)

Also,
$$z_2 = \frac{500}{466} = 1.073.$$

From Table A.6, $A_2 = 0.3583$;

$$\text{total area under normal probability curve} = A_1 + A_2$$
$$= 0.1664 + 0.3583$$
$$= 0.5247.$$

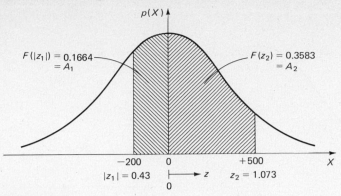

Figure 11.25

Thus there is a 52.47 percent probability that a single test has a deviation from the mean of 3265 kN/m², falling between -200 and $+500$ kN/m².

    j. From Eq. (6.8) after taking $s = \sigma$ (assuming that we have available σ from the finite population with size $N = 50$), we obtain

$$s_{\bar{x}} = s\sqrt{\frac{N-n}{n(N-1)}} = 466\sqrt{\frac{50-36}{36 \times 49}} = 41.5 \text{ kN/m}^2$$

$$\text{deviation } X = 3500 - 3265 = 235 \text{ kN/m}^2.$$

Therefore,
$$z = \frac{X}{s_{\bar{x}}} = \frac{235}{41.5} = 5.66.$$

From Table A.6, the area under the normal curve for such a value of z can be taken as 0.5. Therefore, the area under the curve for a value of $z > 5.66$ is considered to be zero. Thus the required probability is zero.

    k. For the 5 percent level of significance the total area under the normal curve outside the appropriate $\pm$ deviations from the mean is 0.05. Therefore,

$$\text{area inside the appropriate} \pm \text{deviations} = 1 - 0.05 = 0.95.$$

(See Fig. 11.26.) The area on either side of the mean is 0.95/2. Hence, from Table A.6, $z = 1.96$. Therefore,

$$\text{deviation } X = zs_{\bar{x}} = 1.96 \times 41.5 = 81 \text{ kN/m}^2.$$

Thus the limits of the mean at the 5 percent level of significance, or the 95 percent confidence limits, are 3265 ± 81 kN/m².

    Similarly, for the 1 percent level of significance $z = 2.575$,

$$\text{deviation } X = zs_{\bar{x}} = 2.575 \times 41.5 = 107 \text{ kN/m}^2.$$

Thus the limits at the 1 percent level of significance are 3265 ± 107 kN/m².

    l. The value of z for a 10 percent probability of the mean $\bar{x}$ being in error by more than 400 kN/m² is the value corresponding to the area under the normal curve of $(1.00 - 0.10)/2 = 0.45$; from Table A.6, $z = 1.645$. To find the size of the sample n, we use Eq. (6.11) where (again assuming $s = \sigma$)

$$s_{\bar{x}} = \frac{s}{\sqrt{n}}.$$

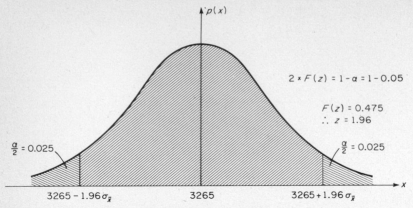

Figure 11.26 Limits for the mean at $\alpha = 5$ percent.

Now,
$$z = \frac{\text{deviation}}{s_{\bar{x}}} = \frac{400}{466/\sqrt{n}}$$

$$= 1.645.$$

Hence,
$$\sqrt{n} = 1.916$$

or
$$n = 3.67.$$

Therefore use a sample size of $n = 4$.

11-6. A patent tire was claimed to be 90 percent effective in minimizing skidding. In a sample of 100 tires tested for skid, 70 tires exhibited improvement against skidding. By using the normal approximation to the binomial distribution, determine whether the manufacturer's claim is justified. Use a 1 percent level of significance. State the null and alternative hypotheses.

Solution. We start by accepting the manufacturer's claim that his tires are 90 percent effective in minimizing skidding. Denote this by p. Thus, the null hypothesis is $H_0 : p = 0.9$, and the alternative hypothesis is $H_a : p < 0.9$. We are not interested in testing whether $p > 0.90$, since in this case we would be more than satisfied. The test is therefore a one-sided one.

From the binomial distribution (Chapter 8), for $p = 0.9$ and therefore $q = 0.1$, we have: mean, $\mu = np = 0.9 \times 100 = 90$ tires; and $\sigma = \sqrt{npq} = \sqrt{(100 \times 0.9 \times 0.1)} = 3$ tires. Using the normal distribution as an approximation, we calculate the z statistic as

$$z = \frac{x - \mu}{\sigma} = \frac{70 - 90}{3} = -6.67.$$

It should be noted that z is distributed normally with mean 0 and variance 1,[5] as shown in Fig. 11.27; the rejection area is measured by the given $\alpha = 0.01$. Therefore, $F(z) = 0.50 - 0.01 = 0.49$. Hence, from Table A.6, the corresponding $z = -2.325$ [z is negative since the area $F(z)$ is in the opposite direction of positive z]. Since $|z_{\text{calc}}| > |z_{\text{tab}}|$ (i.e., since $6.67 > 2.325$) the null hypothesis that $p = 0.9$ is rejected at the 1 percent level of significance, that is, the probability of our conclusion being wrong is $\alpha = 0.01$.

[5] See page 180.

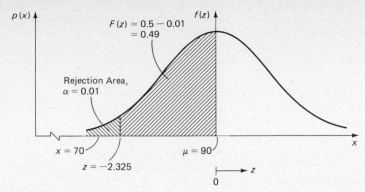

Figure 11.27

PROBLEMS

11-1. Tests on 16 tubes drawn at random from a normal population have yielded the mean value of resistance $\bar{y} = 20$ microohms and $\sum(y_i - \bar{y})^2 = 260$.
  a. Estimate the population mean and variance.
  b. Calculate the standard deviation of the sample mean.
  c. Find the 99 percent confidence interval for the mean.

11-2. Of 10,000 children entering grade 1 in a given year, 5170 are male. Using the approximation of normal distribution, establish whether the figures suggest that the numbers of males and females are not equally distributed. Use $\alpha = 1$ percent.

11-3. In a true-false examination, find the probability that a student can guess the answers to: **(a)** 14 or more out of 27, **(b)** 22 or more out of 40 questions.

11-4. From past experience, it has been found that a particular machine produces piston rings of which 10 percent are defective. Find the probability that in a random sample of 500 rings the following will be defective: **(a)** at most 50, **(b)** between 50 and 60, **(c)** 65 or more.

11-5. The mass in milligrams of a certain pharmaceutical product is distributed normally with a variance of 0.0025 (mg)². Find the size of the sample necessary to estimate, at the 0.5 percent level of significance, the mean mass within 0.025 mg.

11-6. The diameter of a certain shaft is normally distributed with a mean of 2.79 cm and a standard deviation of 0.01 cm. The specification limits are 2.77 ± 0.03.
  a. If 1000 shafts were produced, how many would be unacceptable? What are the limits for the 1 percent level of significance about the mean? Using these limits, how many of the 1000 shafts would one expect to be rejects?
  b. What is the probability that a diameter measurement would deviate from the true mean by ± 0.02 cm?
  c. Estimate the size of a sample in future measurements in order that the probability will not be greater than 0.05 of the sample mean being in error by more than ± 0.01 cm.

11-7. Fit a normal frequency curve to the data given in Problem 2-1. Draw both the histogram and the fitted curve on the same set of coordinate axes. Compare the two plots and comment. (NOTE: Group the precipitations into a frequency distribution with class width $w = 1$ cm, starting with 9.0 cm.)

11-8. Find the equations for the normal probability and frequency curves representing the data in Problem 2-3. From a plot on normal probability paper of the cumulative frequency distribution, estimate the mean and standard deviation of the population distribution. Compare these values with those obtained previously and comment.

11-9. From the 64 values of hardness given in the first table of Problem 4-5:
a. Estimate the 90 percent confidence limits for hardness (estimated by a mean of 10 readings).
b. Fit a normal frequency curve to the data. (NOTE: Group the hardness values into a frequency distribution with class width $w = 1$, starting with 49.)
c. Test for normality of the distribution of hardness number by means of a plot on normal probability paper. Comment on the result.

11-10. Fit a normal frequency curve to the data of Problem 4-6 and calculate what proportion of results will in the long-run fall below 17.2 MPa. Check this proportion from a plot of the cumulative frequency distribution on normal probability paper. (NOTE: Group the strength values into a frequency distribution with class width $w = 1.7$ MPa, starting with 15.15 MPa.)

11-11. The "minimum" strength of concrete on a certain job is specified to be 28.0 MPa, the minimum being defined as a value exceeded by $\frac{9}{10}$ of all tests. If the coefficient of variation is 11.8 percent, find the mean strength of the concrete. What would the mean strength have to be if the coefficient of variation increased to 19.5 percent?

11-12. A fixed flow is known to have a bedload of 10 kg/s. An electromagnetic flowmeter was used to take a large number of readings one-half of which fell between 9.5 and 10.5 kg/s; a plot of the results indicated that they follow a normal distribution.
a. Determine the precision index h for the flowmeter.
b. An alarm will ring if the flowmeter reads 9 kg/s or less; how many false alarms will ring in a 14-day period knowing that the flow is checked twice daily? If one wishes to reduce the number of false alarms by a factor of 3 what should be the value of the flowmeter precision index h?

11-13. The sample average range of a random sample of 100 advanced rifles was found to be 501 m. From past records, the standard deviation is known to be 10 m. Find the 99 percent confidence interval for the true average range. Assume normality. If the standard deviation of 10 m were based on the sample, indicate how much your answer would change.

11-14. The average shear resistance of a spot weld is 2.80 MPa with a standard deviation of 0.14 MPa. A modification to welding is being considered which is supposed to increase the average shear resistance. An experiment is to be conducted to ascertain the properties of the new weld. If the average shear resistance is increased by as much as 0.21 MPa, such a change should be detected with a probability of 0.99. If there is no change, this should be determined with a probability of 0.95. Assume normality.
a. How many measurements are required?
b. If the sample mean is 3.10 MPa, should we conclude that the average shear resistance has been increased?

Chapter 12

Rejection of Outliers

This is a short chapter but the subject matter considered is of great importance, and yet rarely discussed. Probably every engineer or scientist has encountered observations which, he is convinced, are incorrect. Specifically, in a group of readings or in a supposedly homogeneous sample, one of the observations may be very different from all the others. In statistical terminology, such an observation is called an *outlier;* less formally, it can be called wild, unrepresentative, rogue or spurious, or termed a maverick. The question arises: Is the experimenter justified in discarding the outlier and in treating the data as if the "faulty" observation did not exist?

Popular attitudes range from "never dare to tamper with the data!" to "if in doubt, throw it out!" It is our purpose in this chapter to discuss the statistical approach to the problem.

REASONS FOR OUTLIERS

There are two broad possible causes of an outlier being included in a sample. The first is that a mistake has occurred, for instance in reading or recording a measurement. This could be as extreme as an impossible value, when there is no difficulty in reaching a decision, or simply a value remote from other values in the sample, as shown in Fig. 12.1. A second possibility is that an additional variable has entered the picture; for example, an overload of the grid may have appreciably reduced the voltage which had previously been reasonably constant, or a changed wind direction may have caused an excessive amount of solid matter in the air. We thus have an observation from a different population. Such a population may have a different mean or the same mean but a larger variance.

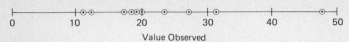

Value Observed

Figure 12.1 A distribution of values which may give rise to the investigation of an outlier.

In the former case, we are dealing with a location error, in the latter with a scalar error.

Under such circumstances we may encounter an observation that will not fall within the expected range, that is one whose deviation from the mean will be greater than expected. However, what is it that we expect or are justified in expecting? Table 11.2 showed that, when the variate is normally distributed, 95 percent of all observations are expected to fall within 1.96σ of the mean, that is, the chance of an observation falling outside the range $(\mu - 1.96\sigma, \mu + 1.96\sigma)$ is 1 in 20. For a deviation of $\pm 2.58\sigma$ the chance is 1 in 100, for $\pm 3.29\sigma$ it is 1 in 1000, and for $\pm 4.89\sigma$, one in a million.[1]

It is thus reasonable under normal circumstances to reject an observation from a population assumed to be normally distributed which differs from the mean by more than a specified deviation, $z\sigma$; the value of z depends on the size of the sample. Such a rejection is justified either because we were probably wrong to assume that the sample containing the extreme observation came from the specific population that we are testing (as the occurrence of such a large deviation is unlikely in a sample from the population in question), or because we are interested in testing representative samples, and a sample containing such a large deviation is not representative. It is important to appreciate this reasoning and not simply to reject indiscriminately observations that appear to be more widely scattered than we would like. In particular, if large deviations occur in a number of samples, we should suspect the presence of additional factors, probably of intermittent character; the experiment must then be carefully examined.

Under industrial conditions, it is important to distinguish between the two cases mentioned in the last paragraph, namely, whether the outlier is caused by a real factor or is just an improbable result. If the outlier is caused by a real factor, we may want to identify it. The factor causing the different product may then be eliminated or, in some cases, deliberately used to obtain a better or a new product.

Furthermore, it is important not to overlook the possibility that an apparent outlier is merely a manifestation of the fact that our assumed mathematical model for the distribution of the data is incorrect. It is only when we are confident that this is not the case that we can think in terms of an outlier that may be rejected. For instance, we know that the tail of a lognormal distribution is longer than that of a normal distribution so that a value that can be judged to be an outlier to a normal distribution may not be an outlier to a lognormal distribution. In the latter case, the "suspect" value would be consistent with the remainder of the data in the sample. Thus, it is the propriety of the normal

---

[1] These are values for both tails and should be distinguished from the case where we are interested only in a value smaller *or* greater than the mean by a certain number of standard deviations.

distribution model that has to be considered before proceeding to testing for the rejection of an outlier.

In the first place, what to pick for scrutiny as a suspect outlier is a subjective judgment, but the criteria for rejection should be statistically sound. In the present chapter, we shall discuss only three of them relating to normally distributed populations. We should add that, since the test criteria involve extreme sample values (usually the largest or the least), they are very sensitive to departure from normality. This is not a desirable feature of the procedures but it is unavoidable.

REJECTION ON BASIS OF ESTIMATED VARIANCE

In *Nair's method*, the maximum deviation from the sample mean $\bar{x}$ that can be expected for *single* values in samples of size n is related to the estimated variance of the population; the estimate variance must be based on a larger sample than the one containing the outlier.

Let x_m be the greatest or smallest value of x that can be expected in a sample of size n at a given significance (probability) level; the levels considered are 10 percent, 5 percent, 1 percent, and 0.1 percent, but data for other levels are also available. Let s_e be the estimated standard deviation, the estimate being based on data with v degrees of freedom. Table A.8 gives the values of $|x_m - \bar{x}|/s_e$ that are not normally expected to be exceeded in samples of size n between 3 and 9. If a deviate larger than the tabulated value is observed, then the observation may be rejected as being significantly different from the remainder of the sample. The level of significance at which the rejection is decided upon represents the risk of error; for example, a 5 percent level of significance means that there is a 5 percent probability that we reject a value which does correctly belong to the sample in question.

EXAMPLE

Twenty-five observations on the masses of material from a packing machine have given an estimate of standard deviation as 0.40 kg. Assume that masses, in kilograms, taken by a customer on 5 packages from his consignments are 100.4, 100.2, 100.5, 100.2, and 99.2. The question is whether the value of $x_m = 99.2$ can be discarded. Use a 5 percent level of significance.

Since $\bar{x} = 100.1$ and $s_e = 0.40$,

$$\frac{|x_m - \bar{x}|}{s_e} = \frac{0.9}{0.40} = 2.25.$$

We now enter Table A.8 with the value of 2.25 for $n = 5$ and the number of degrees of freedom[2] $v = 25 - 1 = 24$. The extreme deviates in Table A.8 are 2.23 at the 5 percent level of significance, and 2.85 at the

---

[2] See Chapter 4.

1 percent level. Thus, the value $x_m = 99.2$ can be rejected with a 5 percent risk of error of wrong rejection.

Once the extreme deviate has been rejected, the sample mean becomes 100.32 kg and the standard deviation estimated from the sample is $s = \sqrt{0.0225}$; this is based on the number of degrees of freedom $v = 4 - 1 = 3$. It may be of interest to compare the standard deviation from this sample with the value of 0.40 estimated for 24 degrees of freedom. This is done by means of the F test (considered in Chapter 16). We calculate the F statistic as

$$F = \frac{(0.4)^2}{0.0225} = 7.11.$$

From Table A.14, for $v_1 = 24$ and $v_2 = 3$, at the 5 percent level of significance F_{tab} is 8.64. Since F_{calc} is less than 8.64, we conclude that the variation in the estimates of variance given by the two samples is due to chance alone.   ■ ■

CHAUVENET'S CRITERION

Another criterion of rejection of outliers is due to Chauvenet, an American astronomer, who suggested the following simple test. An observation in a sample of size n is rejected if it has a deviation from the mean greater than that corresponding to a $(1/2n)$ probability. The probability is calculated on the assumption of a normal distribution, using an estimate of variance on the basis of the sample considered. For example, if $n = 10$, then $(1/2n) = 0.05$, which is the probability of a deviate of at least 1.96σ. Thus an outlier which deviates from the mean by at least $1.96s$ would be rejected.[3] The mean and standard deviation of the remaining 9 observations are then calculated and used in further work.

To simplify calculations, Table A.9 gives the maximum values of $|x_m - \bar{x}|/s$ for different values of n; an outlier exceeding the tabulated value can be rejected.

For example, for the 5 masses given in the preceding example, $s = 0.52$, and

$$\frac{|x_m - \bar{x}|}{s} = \frac{0.9}{0.52} = 1.73.$$

For $n = 5$, Table A.9 gives the maximum value of $|x_m - \bar{x}|/s$ as 1.64. We are justified, therefore, in rejecting the outlier, and both Chauvenet's and Nair's methods lead to the same conclusion, but this need not always be the case.

We should also note that the rejection of an outlier decreases s. When Chauvenet's criterion is used, this could easily lead to successive rejection of extreme observations—a procedure that must never be used. We should also add

---

[3] Since σ is unknown, we estimate it from the sample by s.

that, in a large sample, Chauvenet's criterion leads to an excessively high probability of rejection of an outlier so that this method cannot be recommended.

DIXON-TYPE TESTS

Intuitively, we can look for a single, say upper, possible outlier in a set of independent observations, ordered in ascending order as $x_1, x_2, \ldots, x_n$, by examining the statistics of the type

$$T = \frac{x_n - x_{n-1}}{D} \qquad (12.1)$$

or

$$T = \frac{x_n - \bar{x}'}{D} \qquad (12.2)$$

where $\bar{x}'$ is the sample mean excluding the suspect outlier x_n, and D is some measure of the dispersion of the sample, also excluding x_n.

In order to determine the quantitative aspects of the test, we should look at the problem of rejection of outliers in terms of a null hypothesis. The null hypothesis expresses some basic probability model for the data with no contemplation of outliers; the alternative hypothesis represents a model which can incorporate or explain the outlier or outliers. Such an alternative hypothesis could be a deterministic one in which all but one of the observations are assumed to belong to the given population while one specific observation is quite different. Another alternative hypothesis would be a different distribution from that assumed by the null hypothesis (e.g., lognormal rather than normal).

The measure D, particularly appropriate in the case of a normal distribution, is the standard deviation of the distribution (known independently of the sample in hand) or its estimate from the sample, excluding the suspected outlier. What is important is that D must be in the same units as the numerator of Eq. (12.1) or (12.2) so that the test statistics given by those equations are independent of the units of measurement.

When the standard deviation of the distribution is not known we can use a test of the type

$$T = \frac{x_n - x_{n-1}}{x_n - x_1} \qquad (12.3)$$

when we are examining an upper outlier, or

$$T = \frac{x_2 - x_1}{x_n - x_1} \qquad (12.4)$$

when we are concerned with a lower outlier.

This is a two-sided test for which the critical values at the 5 percent and 1 percent levels are given in Table A.10 for sample size n between 3 and 30.

A disadvantage of the tests given by Eqs. (12.3) and (12.4) is that they are vulnerable to the *masking* effect of x_{n-1} or x_1. In general, by masking we mean the tendency of a specific value of an observation other than the outlier considered to influence the outcome of the test on the suspected outlier. For instance, if the next-in-rank observation is also an outlier, the first outlier may fail to be detected; in consequence, the second outlier would not even be examined. To remedy this, there exist other Dixon-type tests. Thus, to avoid the masking of a single upper outlier x_n by x_{n-1}, we can use the statistic

$$T = \frac{x_n - x_{n-2}}{x_n - x_1}. \tag{12.5}$$

The critical values for this test are given in Table A.10.

Another method of avoiding masking when two adjacent outliers are suspected is to test them as a pair. For instance, in the sample 9, 10, 10, 11, 13, 13, 15, 16, 20, 21, 22, 957, 958, if we consider 958 alone as a possible outlier, the denominator of the statistic of Eq. (12.1) will be large because it involves 957, so that 958 might not be found to be an outlier. In consequence, 957 would *not* be examined. On the other hand, testing 958 and 957 together would identify both as outliers.

There is, however, a danger of *swamping* in considering the two observations n and $n-1$ together. For instance, in a sample 9, 10, 10, 11, 13, 13, 15, 16, 20, 21, 22, 28, 958, the two values 958 and 28 considered together might be found to be outliers. Common sense should prevent us from falling into this trap.

EXAMPLE

Density measurements of concrete cylinders (in kg/m^3) from the same mix were as follows:

$$2301, \quad 2330, \quad 2332, \quad 2332, \quad 2340, \quad 2340,$$
$$2341, \quad 2343, \quad 2343, \quad 2345, \quad 2346, \quad 2349.$$

Should the value 2301 be considered to be an outlier? Assume that no prior information on the standard deviation is available.

Solution. Using Eq. (12.4), we find

$$T = \frac{2330 - 2301}{2349 - 2301} = 0.604.$$

Table A.10 gives for $n = 12$ and $\alpha = 0.05$, $T = 0.376$. Since the calculated value is greater than the observed value, we conclude that the value 2301 can be considered to be an outlier. It is clear that no remaining value is suspect.   ■ ■

Outliers can also be tested for distributions other than normal.[4]

---

[4] See V. Barnett and T. Lewis, *Outliers in Statistical Data* (New York: John Wiley & Sons, 1978).

Two final comments should be made. First, if an outlier is rejected, it is good practice always to report it. This guards against total and repeated failure to spot some disturbance or occurrence in the data, and in the longer run can lead to establishing or discovering a latent factor.

Our second remark concerns action following the performance of a statistical test on an outlier. The decision to reject an observation should be based on experience and must not be made lightly. It is important to realize that in rejecting an observation we *may* be, in our ignorance, throwing away vital information which *could* lead to the discovery of a hitherto unrecognized factor. It is possible that the data including the suspect value can suggest a new hypothesis. In such a case, fresh data should be obtained to test the new hypothesis.

PROBLEMS

12-1. Ten measurements of the diameter of a shaft were as follows: 6.06, 5.92, 6.01, 6.01, 5.99, 5.99, 6.02, 6.03, 6.02, and 5.97 (cm). Using Chauvenet's criterion, determine whether any one of the observations can be considered as an outlier.

12-2. Twenty observations of deflection of similar beams have given an estimate of the standard deviation as 0.5 cm. If the deflections of 6 beams are 3.4, 3.2, 3.5, 3.2, 4.6, and 3.4 cm, determine whether the deflection of any beam can be considered abnormal, using the following methods: **(a)** Nair's method; **(b)** Chauvenet's criterion. After discarding the appropriate measurement, recalculate the mean and compare it with the original mean deflection.

12-3. A student using a cathetometer was measuring the height of a mercury column in a manometer. The results in centimeters were as follows: 8.92, 8.98, 9.01, 8.99, 9.02, 8.97, 9.02, 9.03, 9.00, 9.06.

  a. Determine whether any measurement should be discarded as an outlier using Chauvenet's criterion.
  b. After rejecting the outlier, recompute the mean and compare it with the original mean.

12-4. Measurements of the spring constant (in MN/m) of identical glue-laminated beams were as follows: 672, 675, 676, 678, 666, 672, 680, 681, 676, 665, 670, 671, 664, 620. Assuming no prior information on the variance is known, use the Dixon test to check whether the value 620 is an outlier. Use $\alpha = 0.05$.

12-5. Apply Chauvenet's criterion to determine whether the value 620 in Problem 12-4 is an outlier. Would Nair's method be applicable here? Why?

Chapter 13

Distributions of Extremes

One of the important engineering problems that must be solved by a statistical approach is the estimation of the life of a structure or of manufactured components. The variable may be age, time of usage, or the number of occasions on which a load or a stress level is applied, and so on. The success (or failure) of a system, for example, a structure, is often measured by its ability to perform under the maximum demand, such as certain loads to which it is subjected. Of concern here, then, is the estimation of the largest design parameters, such as floods, winds, bridge loads, that may occur or be encountered during the lifetime of the structure. Likewise, the capacity of a system may depend on extreme values of its components, for example, the strength of the weakest link in a chain, or the tensile strength of brittle material when the weakest one of its many microscopic elements fails.

FAILURE FUNCTIONS

Let us look at the case of age, that is, the length of use prior to failure; the problem is then to determine the life distribution, which can also be called the distribution of failure times. Such a distribution, being continuous, can be described by a probability density function (see page 84) $p(t)$, where t is time. The cumulative distribution function [see Eq. (5.20) and page 196]

$$P(t) = \int_0^t p(t)\,dt \qquad (13.1)$$

can then be used to describe the probability of failure at any time between zero and t.

The probability that an item will function up to a time t, that is, will fail only after time t is

$$R(t) = 1 - P(t) \qquad (13.2)$$

and this is called the *reliability function*.

In practice, we are often interested not merely in the total survival or failure numbers but in the failure rate at or near a given instant t; this is defined as the ratio of probability of failure in the interval $(t, t + \Delta t)$ divided by Δt, to the probability of survival up to time t, that is, the failure rate is

$$G(t, \Delta t) = \frac{(1/\Delta t) \int_t^{t+\Delta t} p(t)\, dt}{R(t)}. \qquad (13.3)$$

The limit of this function, when $\Delta t \to 0$, represents the *instantaneous failure rate or hazard rate*, viz.

$$Z(t) = \frac{p(t)}{R(t)}. \qquad (13.4)$$

This function gives the probability that an item which has survived until time t will fail immediately thereafter; therefore, it is known also as the *conditional failure rate function*. The function is of interest in actuarial work, where the question is of the type: if a man has survived up to the age of 89, what is the probability of his surviving up to 90? A similar problem arises when we want to decide the probability of subsequent survival of mechanical components after they have been in service for a given time.

The conditional failure rate function, therefore, is of considerable value, but its correct interpretation is important. We must realize that since $R(t) < 1$,

$$Z(t) > p(t).$$

The relation between $Z(t)$ and $R(t)$ can be established directly. From Eqs. (13.1) and (13.2),

$$p(t) = -\frac{dR(t)}{dt}.$$

Substituting in Eq. (13.4), we find that

$$Z(t) = -\frac{dR(t)}{R(t)}\frac{1}{dt}$$

or

$$Z(t) = -\frac{d \log_e R(t)}{dt}. \qquad (13.5)$$

Hence,

$$R(t) = \exp\left[-\int_0^t Z(t)\, dt \right] \qquad (13\text{-}6)$$

The pattern of the failure function can be illustrated simply by the "bathtub curve" shown in Fig. 13.1. This figure shows that the highest failure rate occurs during the very early life of a being or a manufactured component or natural product. Then follows a long, nearly level period and finally the product

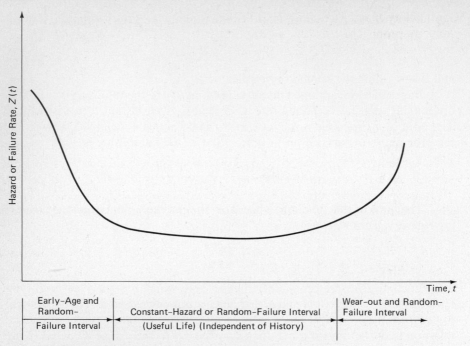

Hazard or Failure Rate, $Z(t)$

Time, t

| Early–Age and Random–Failure Interval | Constant-Hazard or Random-Failure Interval (Useful Life) (Independent of History) | Wear-out and Random-Failure Interval |

Figure 13.1   The "bathtub" curve for a typical hazard function.

enters a wear-out phase, where a drastic increase in failure rate occurs because of age factors.

In summary, therefore, we can define *reliability* as the probability that a system, or one of its components, will function acceptably for a specified time. A study of this subject, known as reliability theory, may help us to improve the reliability of a system. This can be achieved, for example, (i) by using more reliable components, (ii) by using the system at a lower stress, or (iii) by adding components in parallel or making redundant arrangements (discussed on page 247). Of course, the latter will tend to increase the cost, weight, or size, so that their use may be constrained. We use, therefore, the reliability theory to maximize the reliability of the system subject to the constraints present.

Reliability theory developed largely in the electronic industry, where electronic components tend to fail suddenly with very little loss of efficiency prior to failure. As will be shown in the next section, the appropriate hazard rate, $Z(t)$, in such cases, is constant, that is, if a component is functioning at time t, it is "as good as new." In other cases, the hazard rate can be proportional to time (t), that is,

$$Z(t) = \frac{1}{\lambda} + \frac{t}{\lambda_0},$$

where λ = mean time to failure and λ_0 = a positive constant greater than zero and based on previous experience. This is so with random vibrations, since the probability that a vibrating system peaks in the next instant is assumed to be directly proportional to the time since the system was last at equilibrium. In other cases, a decreasing hazard function, such as

$$Z(t) = \frac{1}{\lambda} - \frac{t}{\lambda_0},$$

is more appropriate, for example, strength of concrete improves with age, and the life expectancy of an airplane engine increases shortly after it has survived initial testing.

Generally, thus, once an appropriate model for time to failure has been formulated and its parameters estimated, the model may be used to predict life, to develop optimum initial burn-in or run-in procedures, to establish part-replacement schedules and inventory schemes, or to plan future reliability test programs.

EXPONENTIAL DISTRIBUTION

The simplest distribution describing failure times is the exponential distribution, which, it will be shown, has a constant instantaneous failure rate; that is, the probability of failure at all ages is constant.

The exponential probability density function can be written as

$$p(t) = \frac{1}{\lambda} e^{-t/\lambda}$$

for $t \geqslant 0$ and $\lambda \geqslant 0$, where λ is the mean time to failure.

The cumulative probability of failure [Eq. (13.1)] is then

$$P(t) = \int_0^t \frac{1}{\lambda} e^{-t/\lambda} \, dt$$

or
$$P(t) = 1 - e^{-t/\lambda}. \tag{13.7}$$

It can readily be observed that the probability density function is always nonnegative; its total area from $t = 0$ to $t = \infty$ is equal to 1, as can be deduced from Eq. (13.7) by putting $t = \infty$.

From Eq. (13.2)

$$R(t) = e^{-t/\lambda}. \tag{13.7a}$$

The failure rate is given by Eq. (13.3) as

$$G(t, \Delta t) = \frac{1}{\Delta t R(t)} \int_t^{t + \Delta t} \frac{1}{\lambda} e^{-t/\lambda} \, dt$$

that is,
$$G(t, \Delta t) = \frac{1}{\Delta t} (1 - e^{-\Delta t/\lambda}). \tag{13.8}$$

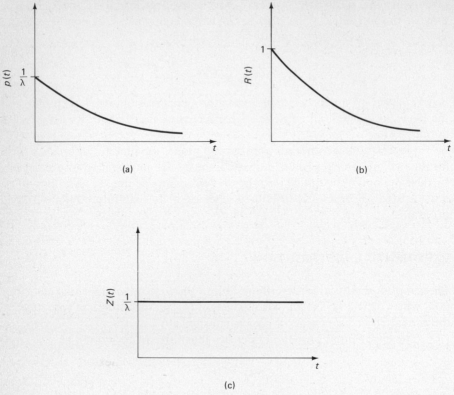

Figure 13.2 Exponential distribution: (a) probability density function (PDF); (b) reliability function; (c) hazard of instantaneous failure rate.

Equation (13.4) gives the instantaneous failure rate

$$Z(t) = \frac{1}{\lambda} \tag{13.9}$$

from which it can be seen that the instantaneous failure rate is constant and is equal to the reciprocal of the mean time to failure, λ.

The exponential distribution, its reliability function, and the instantaneous failure rate are plotted in Fig. 13.2.

It should be noted that most complex system modeling assumes that only random component failures need be considered, and hence the exponential distribution is used. This assumption is reasonable since all early-age failures would have been removed by burn-in, and the time to occurrence of wear-out failures (e.g., with electronic components) is usually very long.

EXAMPLE
    The lifetime of a particular electronic component is known to be exponentially distributed with a mean life of 1000 h. What proportion of such components will fail before 800 h?

The mean life $\lambda = 1000$ hours. Thus, from Eq. (13.7),

$$P(t) = 1 - e^{-t/1000}$$

that is, for $t = 800$ h

$$P(800) = 1 - e^{-800/1000}$$

or, $$P(800) = 0.551.$$

Therefore, we can say that approximately 55 percent of components will fail before 800 h.   ■ ■

The exponential distribution can be derived from the Poisson distribution (considered in Chapter 9) by dealing with the average time between incidents (failures, accidents, or arrivals) instead of the average number of incidents per unit time. From Eq. (9.1), the probability of no incident occurring in an interval of time of length t, that is, for $r = 0$, is

$$P_0 = e^{-t/\lambda} \tag{13.10}$$

where t/λ is the mean frequency of incidents; that is, $1/\lambda$ is the average number of incidents per unit time. We may note that t can be any interval of time and does not have to begin at time 0.

Let us consider the time that elapses after t until the next incident occurs, and denote this time as a random variable t_1. Then, the probability that $t_1 > t$ is equal to the probability that no incidents occur in the time interval of length t. The former probability is given by the reliability function [see Eq. (13.2)] as $1 - P(t)$. Using Eq. (13.10), we can write the equality of the two probabilities as

$$1 - P(t) = e^{-t/\lambda}$$

whence $$P(t) = 1 - e^{-t/\lambda}$$

which is Eq. (13.7).

Thus, we can observe that times between incidents (failures, accidents, or other events) follow an exponential distribution. It should be mentioned that the exponential distribution, as well as the Poisson distribution, has a memoryless property, since future behavior is independent of present or past behavior.

We shall now apply the exponential distribution to predict the probability of time between arrivals of vehicles at a particular point on a highway. The determination of the length of the time interval between vehicle arrivals is important to the traffic engineer: if this length is too short, a vehicle attempting to merge or cross the traffic stream will be forced either to remain stationary or to interrupt the traffic stream. Wishing to predict the probability of a certain time between successive cars, a traffic engineer collected data of the gaps in traffic at a certain point on a freeway. From these data, he found that the mean gap length or time between successive cars is 8.33 s. What is the probability of a gap length of 9 to 11 s?

We have the mean time between arrivals

$$\lambda = 8.33 \text{ s}.$$

Using Eq. (13.7), we obtain

$$P(11) - P(9) = 1 - e^{-11/8.33} - (1 - e^{-9/8.33})$$
$$= e^{-1.08} - e^{-1.32}$$
$$= 0.072$$

which is the probability of a gap length of 9 to 11 s

MEAN TIMES TO AND BETWEEN FAILURES

The mean time to the first failure, MTTF, can be shown to be

$$\text{MTTF} = \bar{T} = \int_0^\infty R(t)\, dt. \tag{13.11}$$

For the case when the useful life of the component has a constant failure rate, that is, exponential distribution, we found that $R(t) = e^{-t/\lambda}$ [Eq. (13.7a)]. Hence, we can show that

$$\text{MTTF} = \bar{T} = \lambda. \tag{13.12}$$

Now, the mean time between two successive component failures, MTBF, is given by

$$\frac{1}{\text{MTBF}} = \sum_{j=1}^{m} \frac{1}{\bar{T}_j} \tag{13.13}$$

where m is the number of components in the system, and $\bar{T}_j$ is the MFFT of the jth component. During the useful life of a component, MTBF and MTTF are equal (see Fig. 13.1).

EXAMPLE

An aircraft has an electronic system composed of a computer, radar, and an auxiliary unit with MTBFs of 160, 90, and 400 h, respectively. Determine the MTBF of the system and the reliability of the system for a 10-h operating time. Assume that $p(t) = (1/\lambda)e^{-t/\lambda}$.

TABLE 13.1

Component	MTBF	Equivalent failure rate, failures per 1000 h
Computer	160	6.25
Radar	90	11.11
Auxiliary Unit	400	2.50
	Total =	19.86

The MTBF for a system composed of a number of components in series during useful life is determined by first converting the individual MTBFs into failure rates, adding these to obtain the system failure rate and then converting this to the MTBF of the system, as shown in Table 13.1.

Therefore, System MTBF $= 1000/19.86 = 50.35$ h $= \lambda$. From Eq. (13.7a), for 10-h operating time,

$$R_{\text{system}} = e^{-t/\lambda}$$
$$= e^{-10/50.35} \simeq 0.82.$$

■ ■

RELIABILITY OF A SYSTEM WITH SERIES OR PARALLEL COMBINATIONS

Let us consider a system constructed of n components in series, as shown in Fig. 13.3(a), with reliabilities $R_1, R_2, \ldots, R_n$. If we assume that the components are independent, as is usually the case, then by the multiplication rule of probability given in Chapter 5, the reliability of the system is

$$R_{\text{series sys.}} = (R_1)(R_2) \ldots (R_i) \ldots (R_n). \tag{13.14}$$

It is seen from Eq. (13.14) that the reliability of a series system is never greater than that of its least reliable component. On the other hand, the reliability of a system consisting of a parallel combination of n components, as shown in Fig. 13.3(b), is given by

$$R_{\text{parallel sys.}} = (1 - R_1)(1 - R_2) \ldots (1 - R_i) \ldots (1 - R_n). \tag{13.15}$$

Thus, a parallel combination is at least as reliable as its most reliable component. It follows that a low reliability of a system can be improved by using parallel redundancy. The reliability of a mixed combination, such as that in Fig. 13.3(c), is obtained by writing the appropriate relation between the events of interest, determining the probabilities of these events, and hence the system's reliability.

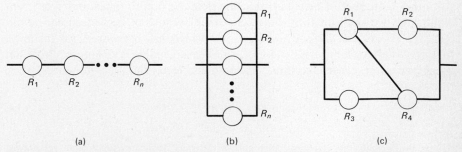

Figure 13.3 Combinations of components: (a) series combination; (b) parallel combination; (c) mixed system.

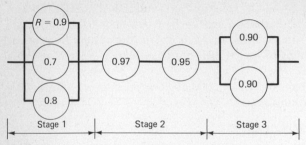

Figure 13.4   System of four electronic devices.

EXAMPLE

Consider the system, shown in Fig. 13.4, in which four different electronic devices must work in series to produce a given response. The reliabilities, R, of the various components are shown on the figure. Find the reliability of the system.

Let R_1, R_2, and R_3 be the reliabilities of stages, 1, 2, and 3, respectively. Then, $R_{\text{system}} = (R_1)(R_2)(R_3)$.

For stage 1: $R_1 = 1 - (1 - 0.9) \times (1 - 0.7) \times (1 - 0.8) = 0.994$.

For stage 2: $R_2 = (0.97 \times 0.95) = 0.9215$.

For stage 3: $R_3 = 1 - (1 - 0.90) \times (1 - 0.90) = 0.99$.

Thus, $R_{\text{system}} = (0.994 \times 0.9215 \times 0.99) = 0.91$.   ■ ■

We can note that where the reliability of a system must be very high, as, for instance, in nuclear power plants or spacecraft, and such systems depend on the functioning of many components, numerous component redundancies are introduced in their design.

WEIBULL DISTRIBUTION

Although a number of distributions may describe failure times under different conditions, we shall mention only one other because of its widespread applicability. This is the Weibull distribution,[1] which has been used, for instance, to describe fatigue failure in structures, ball-bearing failure, and failure of vacuum tubes and some other electronic components. Here, the instantaneous failure rate is given by

$$Z(t) = m\gamma t^{m-1} \tag{13.16}$$

[1] W. Weibull, "A Statistical Distribution of Wide Applicability," *Journal of Applied Mechanics*, vol. 18, Sept. 1951, pp. 293–297.

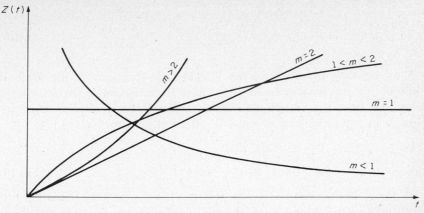

Figure 13.5 Failure rate for Weibull distribution for different values of the shape parameter m.

where m is the shape parameter and γ the scale parameter. Different values of γ stretch or compress the distribution graph in the t-direction.

    For different values of m, different shapes of the instantaneous rate function are obtained (Fig. 13.5): for $m < 1$, the rate decreases with time; for $m = 2$, it increases linearly; for $1 < m < 2$, the rate increases at a decreasing gradient; for $m > 2$, it increases at an increasing gradient; and finally, for $m = 1$, the instantaneous rate function is constant. We note that in the case of $m = 1$, Eq. (13.16) reduces to Eq. (13.9) with $\lambda = 1/\gamma$ so that the exponential distribution can be considered to be a special case of the Weibull distribution, but there the connection between the two distributions ends. We conclude, therefore, that by a proper choice of its shape parameter, m, the Weibull distribution can be used for all the three phases of the mortality "bathtub" curve of Fig. 13.1. This is in contrast to the normal distribution which is generally used to model wear-out failures or stress failures (when the random variable is the stress level rather than time).

    Substituting in Eq. (13.6), the reliability function of the Weibull distribution can be written as

$$R(t) = e^{-\gamma t^m}. \tag{13.17}$$

    If we substitute in Eq. (13.2) for $R(t)$ from Eq. (13.6) we can write $P(t)$ for the Weibull distribution as

$$P(t) = 1 - e^{-\gamma t^m}. \tag{13.18}$$

    From Eq. (13.1), the probability density function can be expressed in terms of the cumulative distribution as

$$p(t) = \frac{dP(t)}{dt}$$

so that, for the Weibull distribution,

$$p(t) = m\gamma t^{m-1} e^{-\gamma t^m} \tag{13.19}$$

with $t \geqslant 0$, $\gamma > 0$, and $m > 1$.

Thus, we have obtained all the fundamental functions of the Weibull distribution, but the parameters m and γ have to be estimated from the data or, preferably, from the underlying theory of the physical behavior involved. One simple way of estimating m and γ is graphically. From Eq. (13.17),

$$\log_e R(t) = -\gamma t^m$$

so that $\qquad\qquad \log_e[-\log_e R(t)] = m \log_e t + \log_e \gamma. \tag{13.20}$

In an actual experiment we test N items; those that have failed are not replaced. If the ith failure occurs at time t_i, then it can be shown that an unbiased estimate of the cumulative distribution function (CDF) for $t = t_i$ is

$$P(t_i) = \frac{i}{N+1}. \tag{13.21}$$

Thus, from Eq. (13.2),

$$R(t_i) = \frac{N+1-i}{N+1}$$

whence $\qquad\qquad -\log_e R(t_i) = \log_e\left(\frac{N+1}{N+1-i}\right).$

Substituting in Eq. (13.20), we obtain

$$\log_e\left[\log_e\left(\frac{N+1}{N+1-i}\right)\right] = m \log_e t_i + \log_e \gamma. \tag{13.22}$$

Thus, if we plot $\log_e[(N+1)/(N+1-i)]$ against t_i on log-log paper (i.e. we plot $\log_e[-\log_e R(t)]$), it follows from Eq. (13.20) that, for a one-parameter distribution, the experimental points will scatter about a straight line if the distribution is of the Weibull type. The slope of the line gives m, and γ can then be found from $\log_e \gamma$ at a value of t_i corresponding to $\log_e[(N+1)/(N+1-i)] = 1$.

EXAMPLE

In a large production run of electronic communications equipment, a certain relay was being used for a critical application. It was decided to obtain the Weibull model for the number of actuations before failure of this relay. Twenty relays were subjected to a life test and the numbers of actuations to failure obtained are given in Table 13.2.

Solution. The data are first ranked starting with the lowest number of actuations: The number of relays tested is $N = 20$. The values of $\log_e[(N+1)/(N+1-i)]$ are obtained, where i is the rank of a particular relay failing, the least event having the rank $i = 1$. The resulting values are given in Table 13.3.

TABLE 13.2

Relay number	Number of actuations to failure (10^5)
1	3.65
2	8.40
3	9.00
4	5.89
5	9.60
6	6.10
7	11.95
8	4.72
9	12.40
10	3.34
11	18.07
12	8.50
13	13.03
14	11.02
15	6.62
16	1.90
17	7.92
18	20.63
19	4.20
20	13.42

TABLE 13.3

Rank i	Actuations to failure, $t_i(10^5)$	$\dfrac{21}{21-i}$	$\log_e\left(\dfrac{21}{21-i}\right)$
1	1.90	1.05	0.049
2	3.34	1.11	0.104
3	3.65	1.17	0.157
4	4.20	1.24	0.215
5	4.72	1.31	0.270
6	5.89	1.40	0.336
7	6.10	1.50	0.405
8	6.62	1.62	0.482
9	7.92	1.75	0.560
10	8.40	1.91	0.647
11	8.50	2.10	0.742
12	9.00	2.33	0.846
13	9.60	2.63	0.967
14	11.02	3.00	1.099
15	11.95	3.50	1.253
16	12.40	4.20	1.435
17	13.03	5.25	1.658
18	13.42	7.00	1.946
19	18.07	10.50	2.351
20	20.63	21.00	3.045

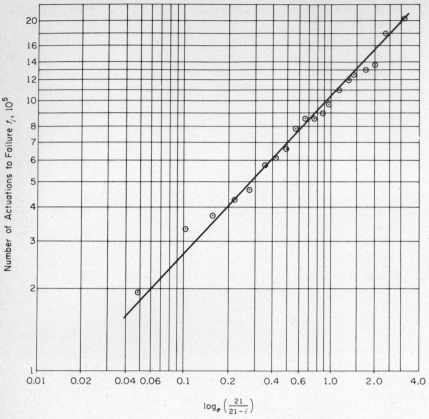

Figure 13.6   Plot of t_i versus $\log_e[21/(21 - i)]$ on log–log scale.

The values of t_i and $\log_e[21/(21 - i)]$ are plotted on log-log paper as shown in Fig. 13.6. Since the plotted points lie approximately on a straight line (fitted by eye), there is a good indication that the data follow a Weibull distribution. The slope of the line yields $m = 1.7$. To find γ, we require t_i corresponding to $\log_e[21/(21 - i)] = 1$. From Fig. 13.6, we observe that for $\log_e[21/(21 - i)] = 1$, $t = 10.2 \times 10^5$. Therefore, from Eq. (13.22),

$$m \log_e(10.2 \times 10^5) = -\log_e \gamma$$

whence
$$\gamma = (10.2 \times 10^5)^{-1.7}$$
$$= 0.61 \times 10^{-10}.$$

With the values of the parameters m and γ determined, the probability density function $p(t)$ and the associated cumulative distribution $P(t)$ are explicitly defined. We can then estimate, for example, the overall proportion of relays that would survive a certain number of actuations before failure.

Where the observed lifetimes fall into a fairly narrow range, it is often necessary to include a third parameter in the Weibull distribution, the minimum lifetime, in order that a sufficiently sensitive measure of the parameter m may be made. If we denote this *location parameter* by L, the expression for the reliability function of the Weibull distribution [Eq. (13.17)] then becomes

$$R(t) = e^{-\gamma(t-L)^m} \tag{13.23}$$

■ ■

Recently, it was shown[2] that the *median* cumulative distribution function (CDF) associated with a ranked failure is independent of any distribution. This is a useful fact because, for small samples, the use of the mean CDF [Eq. (13.21)] gives rise to some bias since the true CDF of the parent population is not equally likely to lie above or below the experimental distribution. This bias may be removed by assigning the median value of the CDF at the ith failure. While tables of median ranks are required for this purpose, an excellent approximation for the median CDF can be shown to be

$$P(t_i) = \frac{i - 0.3}{N + 0.4} \tag{13.24}$$

and hence the corresponding reliability is given by

$$R(t_i) = 1 - P(t_i) = \frac{N - i + 0.7}{N + 0.4}. \tag{13.25}$$

The CDF given by Eq. (13.24) has an equal chance of being too high or too low, a condition which is required for proper line-fitting by the method of least squares (Chapter 17). The reader may like to solve the previous example on page 250 by using Eq. (13.24) and generating data for the ratio $20.4/(20.7 - i)$ and $\log_e[20.4/(20.7 - i)]$, plotting the results and comparing the two straight lines.

DISTRIBUTION OF EXTREME VALUES

The Weibull distribution was developed in a study of strength of materials, where the problem is that of finding the weakest element. This is a particular case of determining extreme values—a field of special interest in the study of floods and in hydrology in general.

---

[2] Private communication from Professor C. Mischke, Iowa State University, Ames, Iowa, U.S.A.

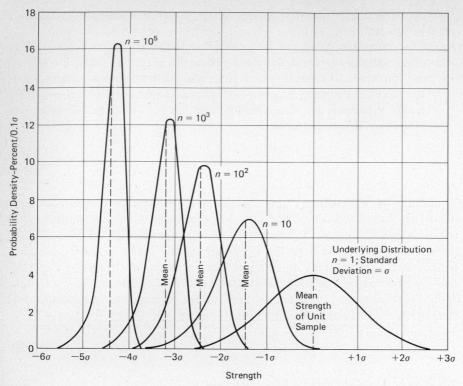

Figure 13.7 Strength distribution in samples of size n for an underlying normal distribution. (From J. Tucker, "Statistical Theory of the Effect of Dimensions and of Method of Loading upon the Modulus of Rupture of Beams," *ASTM Proceedings*, vol. 41, 1941, pp. 1072–1088.

The essential problem is that of determining the distribution of smallest or largest values in samples of size n drawn at random from a certain given underlying distribution $p(x)$. The important point is that the extremes are not fixed but are new statistical variates depending on the underlying distribution and on the sample size.

In many practical engineering problems, the exact form of the distribution is not known and assumptions regarding its form have to be made. In the particular case when the underlying distribution is normal,[3] the variation in the mean and standard deviation of samples of sample size n in terms of the mean and standard deviation of sample of unit sample size is as shown in Fig. 13.7. This figure shows that the larger the specimen of a given material the lower the strength. We can also see that the distribution of strength of specimens of a given physical size becomes progressively more skewed (to the left) with an increase in the sample size. Since the influence of physical size on strength de-

---

[3] L. C. H. Tippett, "On the Extreme Individuals and the Range of Samples Taken from a Normal Population," *Biometrika*, vol. 17, 1925, pp. 364–387.

pends on the standard deviation of strength (for a given mean strength of the specimens of unit size), it follows that the physical size effect is smaller the greater the homogeneity of the material. Figure 13.7 can also explain why the physical size effect virtually disappears beyond a certain physical size of the specimen. For instance, for each successive tenfold increase in physical size of the specimen it loses progressively a smaller amount of strength.[4]

In a more general case when the underlying probability density function is $p(x)$ and the cumulative distribution function is

$$P(x) = \int_{-\infty}^{x} p(x)\,dx \qquad (13.26)$$

then the distribution of the smallest value in samples of size n is given by the probability density function

$$g_n(x) = np(x)[1 - P(x)]^{n-1} \qquad (13.27)$$

and the corresponding cumulative distribution function is

$$G_n(x) = \int_{-\infty}^{x} g_n(x)\,dx \qquad (13.28)$$

or $$G_n(x) = 1 - [1 - P(x)]^n. \qquad (13.28a)$$

The mode of $g_n(x)$ is the solution of the equation

$$\frac{d}{dx} g_n(x) = 0 \qquad (13.29)$$

but the solution does not exist in all cases. If the underlying distribution is limited, the distribution of the smallest value decreases monotonically.

From Eq. (13.27), the solution of Eq. (13.29) can be written as

$$(n - 1)[p(\hat{x})]^2 = p'(\hat{x})[1 - P(\hat{x})] \qquad (13.30)$$

where $\hat{x}$ is the mode of the smallest value and $p'(\hat{x})$ is the value of the derivative $dp(x)/dx$ at $x = \hat{x}$.

Equation (13.30) is used in the majority of "weakest link" problems of various sorts. (The adage that a chain is no stronger than its weakest link is a classical example of the importance of the extreme value in a distribution.) Values of $\hat{x}$ for two probability density functions $p(x)$ are given in Table 13.4.

In Table 13.4, ξ is distributed with a probability density function $h(\xi) = e^{-\xi}$ for $\xi \geqslant 0$. This is a simple function so that the distribution of the smallest value of x can readily be sketched or plotted.

Table 13.4 shows that the mode of the smallest value $\hat{x}$ for a sample of given size depends on the underlying distribution $p(x)$ from which the samples are drawn. The last column shows how the mode, mean, and variance of the smallest value in a sample of size n (e.g., minimum strength) vary for two common distributions: normal and Weibull.

[4] A. M. Neville, *Properties of Concrete*, 3rd ed. (London and Marshfield, Mass.: Pitman Books, 1981).

TABLE 13.4 PROPERTIES OF THE NORMAL AND WEIBULL DISTRIBUTIONS

$p(x)$	Mode of smallest value $\hat{x}$ for samples of size n	Distribution of smallest values in samples of size n (n is large)	Characteristics of the distribution of the smallest value in samples of size n
Normal [Eq. (10.16)] $$p(x) = \frac{1}{\sigma\sqrt{2\pi}}\exp\left[-\frac{(x-\mu)^2}{2\sigma^2}\right]$$	$$\hat{x} = \mu - \sigma\sqrt{2\log_e n}$$ $$+ \sigma\frac{\log_e(\log_e n) + \log 4\pi}{2\sqrt{2\log_e n}}$$	$$x_n = \mu - \sigma\sqrt{2\log_e n}$$ $$+ \sigma\frac{\log_e(\log_e n) + \log 4\pi}{2\sqrt{2\log_e n}}$$ $$+ \frac{\sigma}{\sqrt{2\log_e n}}\log_e \xi$$	Most probable value decreases as a multiple of $\sqrt{\log_e n}$. Variance decreases as n increases and is equal to $$\frac{\pi^2\sigma^2}{12\log_e n}$$
Weibull [Eq. (13.19)] $$p(x) = m\gamma x^{m-1}\exp[-\gamma x^m]$$	$$\hat{x} = \frac{1}{(\gamma n)^{1/m}}\left[1 - \frac{1}{m}\right]^{1/m}$$	$$x_n = \left[\frac{\xi}{n\gamma}\right]^{1/m}$$	Most probable value decreases as $n^{-1/m}$. Mean value decreases as $n^{-1/m}$. Variance decreases as $n^{-2/m}$.

Source: B. Epstein, "Statistical Aspects of Fracture Problems," *Journal of Applied Physics*, vol. 19, Feb. 1948, pp. 140–147.

FLOOD FREQUENCY ANALYSIS

Experience has shown that the logarithms of a series of annual flood peaks, Q, are approximately normally distributed. (The transformation of a variate to its logarithmic value was discussed on page 202.) Thus, if we take as the random variable $Y = \log Q$, with $\mu =$ mean of Y, and $\sigma =$ standard deviation of Y, then we can write the probability density function (PDF) of Q (since we are interested in the flood peaks and *not* in their logarithmic values) as

$$p(Q) = \frac{1}{\sqrt{2\pi}\,\sigma y}\, e^{-(y-\mu)^2/2\sigma^2} \tag{13.31}$$

for $Q \geqslant 0$. Otherwise,

$$p(Q) = 0.$$

Now, the probability of not exceeding a certain flow Q_0 is

$$P(Q \leqslant Q_0) = \frac{1}{\sqrt{2\pi}\,\sigma} \int_{-\infty}^{y_0} \frac{e^{-(y-\mu)^2/2\sigma^2}}{y}\, dy. \tag{13.32}$$

Hence, the probability of exceeding a flow Q_0—an event known as *exceedance*—is

$$P(Q > Q_0) = \bar{P}(Q_0) = \frac{1}{T_r} = 1 - \frac{1}{\sqrt{2\pi}\,\sigma} \int_{-\infty}^{y_0} \frac{e^{-(y-\mu)^2/2\sigma^2}}{y}\, dy \tag{13.33}$$

where T_r is called the return period in years and is defined as the average number of years before a certain value, that is, a peak flow, either recurs or is again exceeded.

In practice, Eq. (13.33) is usually treated graphically by plotting the observed annual flood peaks, Q_i, versus their estimated probability of exceedance, $\bar{P}(Q_i)$, on logarithmic probability paper [or $\log Q_i$ versus $\bar{P}(Q_i)$ on arithmetic probability paper].

Several expressions have been suggested for estimating the probability of exceedance for an event in an annual flood series; the most common one of these is

$$\bar{P}(Q_m) = \frac{1}{T_{r_m}} = \frac{m}{N+1} \tag{13.34}$$

where m is the rank of the event, Q_m, with $m = 1$ for maximum and $m = N$ for minimum event; N the length of the record in years; and $\bar{P}(Q_m)$ the estimated probability of any Q being equal or greater than Q_m. Equation (13.34) should be compared with Eq. (13.21).

EXAMPLE

Flow records are available for a particular river near a proposed dam site for the period 1949–1950 to 1964–1965 (the year beginning on October 1 in each case). The data are given in Table 13.5.

TABLE 13.5

Year	Peak flow, $Q \, (m^3/s)$
1949–1950	4800
1950–1951	3000
1951–1952	1410
1952–1953	1960
1953–1954	2900
1954–1955	5100
1955–1956	5700
1956–1957	1260
1957–1958	660
1958–1959	1270
1959–1960	2400
1960–1961	1270
1961–1962	1510
1962–1963	2150
1963–1964	680
1964–1965	2550

TABLE 13.6

Rank, m	Peak flow, $Q(m^3/s)$	$T_r = \dfrac{N+1}{m}$	$\log_{10} Q$
1	5700	17.000	3.756
2	5100	8.500	3.708
3	4800	5.666	3.681
4	3000	4.250	3.477
5	2900	3.400	3.463
6	2550	2.833	3.406
7	2400	2.428	3.381
8	2150	2.125	3.332
9	1960	1.888	3.292
10	1510	1.700	3.179
11	1410	1.545	3.149
12	1270	1.417	3.104
13	1270	1.307	3.104
14	1260	1.214	3.101
15	680	1.133	2.832
16	660	1.063	2.819

a. Plot the annual flood frequency curve for the dam site on
  i. arithmetic probability paper.
  ii. logarithmic probability paper.
b. Estimate the flood peaks for 1 year in 2 years, 1 in 10, 1 in 20, 1 in 100, and 1 year in 1000 years, that is, for return periods of 2, 10, 20, 100, and 1000 years.

Solution
  a. The data are first ranked, beginning with rank $m = 1$ for the maximum peak flow Q. Values of $T_r = m/(N + 1)$ and $\log_{10} Q$ are found (see Table 13.6).

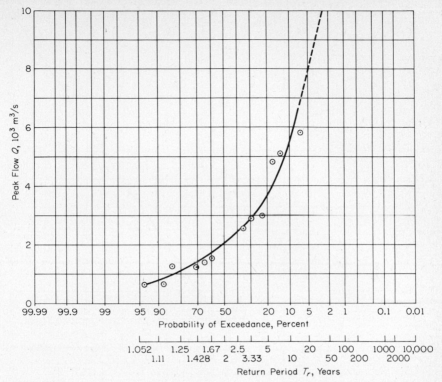

Figure 13.8

It should be observed that plotting either $\log_{10} Q$ or $\log_e Q$ is equally correct, since the two are related by a constant, namely, $\log_e Q = 2.3026$ $\log_{10} Q$.

   i. The relation between the peak flow Q and the return period T_r, plotted on probability paper, is shown in Fig. 13.8. It should be noted that the return period T_r is the inverse of the probability of exceedance [Eq. (13.34)]. The curve was fitted by eye, but the nonlinear character of the relationship is readily seen.

   ii. This nonlinear relationship can be rectified into a linear one if the return period T_r is plotted against $\log_{10} Q$ as shown in Fig. 13.9.

   b. To estimate the peak flows for the required return periods, we use the straight-line relationship in Fig. 13.9 (fitted by eye). Thus, for

$$2 \text{ years: } \log_{10} Q = 3.243, \text{ or } Q = 1750 \text{ m}^3/\text{s}$$
$$10 \text{ years: } \log_{10} Q = 3.692, \text{ or } Q = 4924 \text{ m}^3/\text{s}$$
$$20 \text{ years: } \log_{10} Q = 3.800, \text{ or } Q = 6309 \text{ m}^3/\text{s}$$
$$100 \text{ years: } \log_{10} Q = 4.000, \text{ or } Q = 10{,}000 \text{ m}^3/\text{s}$$
$$1000 \text{ years: } \log_{10} Q = 4.220, \text{ or } Q = 16{,}595 \text{ m}^3/\text{s}.$$

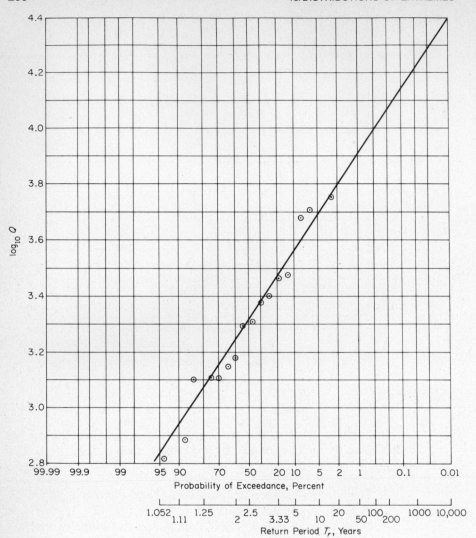

Figure 13.9   Plot of $\log_{10} Q$ versus T_r for the data of Fig. 13.8.

In order to increase the reliability of the estimated frequency values, Gumbel made use of the distribution of extreme values.[5] In this approach, we consider the extreme values $X_1, X_2, \ldots, X_N$ observed, respectively, in N samples of equal size n. Now, if X is an exponentially distributed and unlimited variable, then the cumulative probability P that any of the N extremes will be less than X, as N and n approach infinity, is

$$P = e^{-e^{-y}} \tag{13.35}$$

[5] E. J. Gumbel, "Statistical Theory of Extreme Values and Some Practical Applications," National Bureau of Standards, *Applied Mathematics*, Ser. 33, Feb. 1954.

TABLE 13.7 EXPECTED MEAN μ_N AND EX-
PECTED STANDARD DEVIATION
σ_N FOR DIFFERENT SIZES OF
SAMPLE OF LARGEST VALUES

N	μ_N	σ_N
15	0.51	1.02
20	0.52	1.06
30	0.54	1.11
40	0.54	1.14
50	0.55	1.16
60	0.55	1.17
70	0.55	1.19
80	0.56	1.19
90	0.56	1.20
100	0.56	1.21
150	0.56	1.23
200	0.57	1.24
500	0.57	1.26
∞	0.57	1.28

Source: E. J. Gumbel, "Statistical Theory of Extreme
Values and Some Practical Applications," National
Bureau of Standards, *Applied Mathematics*, Ser. 33, Feb.
1954.

where y is the reduced variate given by

$$y = a(X - \hat{X}).\tag{13.36}$$

Here, $\hat{X}$ is the mode of the distribution, and a the dispersion parameter. Although it is possible to determine explicit expressions for $\hat{X}$ and a, these cannot be strictly used to estimate return periods from *limited samples*, and Gumbel used an approach based on the method of least squares[6] to determine these values from the annual series. By minimizing the squares of the deviations measured in a direction perpendicular to the derived straight line X versus y (on Cartesian coordinates), the following equations are found:

$$\hat{X} = \bar{X} - \sigma_x \frac{\mu_N}{\sigma_N}\tag{13.37}$$

and

$$a = \frac{\sigma_N}{\sigma_X}.\tag{13.38}$$

The quantities μ_N and σ_N, obtained theoretically, are functions of the sample size only, the sample consisting of N largest values from the original N samples; they are given in Table 13.7.

Equation (13.36) indicates that a plot of X versus the reduced variate y is linear on a Cartesian coordinate system; this observation led Powell[7] to

---

[6] This method is discussed on page 369.

[7] R. W. Powell, "A Simple Method of Estimating Flood Frequency," *Civil Engineering*, vol. 13, 1943, pp. 105–107.

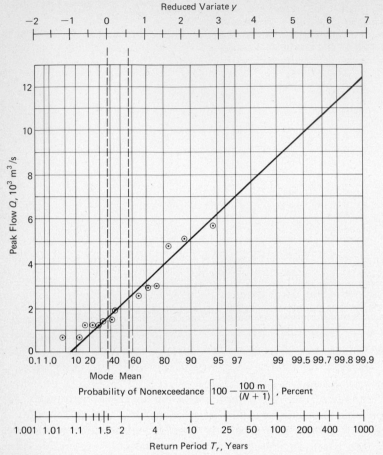

Figure 13.10   Gumbel plot of flood frequency curve for the example on page 257.

introduce the so-called *Gumbel* or *extremal probability paper.* Gumbel's distribution is such that the arithmetic average of the annual series will have a return period of 2.33 years when N is large (see Fig. 13.10). A typical Gumbel probability paper is shown in Fig. 13.10 where the data (Q versus T_r) of the example on page 257 are plotted. (The straight line is drawn by eye.) Note the location of the mode $\hat{X}$ and the arithmetic mean of the peak flow Q.

As a further development it has been shown that more accurate results can be predicted from a *Gumbel logarithmic plot,* that is, by plotting $\log_{10} Q$ (instead of Q) versus the return period T_r on Gumbel probability paper. This is illustrated in the following example.

EXAMPLE

Discharge data at a gauging station on a river were collected for the 40-year period from 1921 to 1960; the flow record is shown in Table 13.8.

TABLE 13.8

Year	Peak discharge, Q 10^3 (m³/s)	Year	Peak discharge, Q 10^3(m³/s)
1921	46	1941	72
1922	35	1942	45
1923	47	1943	78
1924	37	1944	58
1925	22	1945	90
1926	151	1946	24
1927	21	1947	25
1928	54	1948	256
1929	34	1949	110
1930	55	1950	95
1931	56	1951	35
1932	62	1952	39
1933	109	1953	31
1934	30	1954	94
1935	56	1955	33
1936	199	1956	132
1937	66	1957	76
1938	52	1958	32
1939	148	1959	71
1940	34	1960	14

Construct a Gumbel log plot and derive the linear equation relating the reduced variate y and $X(= \log_{10} Q)$.

Solution. First, the data are ranked. The values of the return period T_r (with $N = 40$) and of $\log_{10} Q$ are then found. The results are tabulated in Table 13.9.

Now, from Eq. (13.36), the reduced variate y is given by $y = a(X - \hat{X})$. From Table 13.7 for $N = 40$, $\mu_N = 0.54$ and $\sigma_N = 1.14$. Using the latter value, Eq. (13.38) gives

$$a = \frac{\sigma_N}{\sigma_X} = \frac{1.14}{0.28} = 4.07.$$

Using Eq. (13.37), we obtain

$$\hat{X} = \bar{X} - \frac{\sigma_X \mu_N}{\sigma_N} = 1.739 - 0.28 \times \frac{0.54}{1.14}$$

or
$$\hat{X} = 1.606.$$

Hence, the linear relationship is given by

$$y = 4.07(X - 1.606).$$

This line, as well as the observed values, is shown plotted in Fig. 13.11. We can readily observe the good fit afforded by this approach. ■ ■

TABLE 13.9

Rank, m	$Q\ 10^3\ (m^3/s)$	$T_r = \dfrac{(N+1)}{m}$	$X = \log_{10} Q$	$X - \bar{X}$	$(X - \bar{X})^2$
1		41.0	2.408	0.669	0.4476
2		20.5	2.299	0.560	0.3136
3		13.7	2.179	0.440	0.1936
4		10.3	2.170	0.431	0.1858
5		8.2	2.121	0.382	0.1459
6		6.8	2.041	0.302	0.0912
7		5.9	2.037	0.298	0.0888
8		5.1	1.978	0.239	0.0571
9		4.6	1.973	0.234	0.0548
10		4.1	1.954	0.215	0.0462
11		3.7	1.892	0.153	0.0234
12		3.4	1.881	0.142	0.0202
13		3.2	1.857	0.118	0.0139
14		2.9	1.851	0.112	0.0125
15		2.7	1.820	0.081	0.0066
16		2.6	1.792	0.053	0.0028
17		2.4	1.763	0.024	0.0006
18		2.3	1.748	0.009	0.0001
19		2.2	1.748	0.009	0.0001
20		2.1	1.740	0.001	0.0000
21		2.0	1.732	−0.007	0.0000
22		1.9	1.716	−0.023	0.0005
23		1.8	1.672	−0.067	0.0045
24		1.7	1.663	−0.076	0.0058
25		1.6	1.653	−0.086	0.0074
26		1.58	1.591	−0.148	0.0219
27		1.52	1.568	−0.171	0.0292
28		1.47	1.544	−0.195	0.0380
29		1.41	1.544	−0.195	0.0380
30		1.37	1.532	−0.207	0.0428
31		1.33	1.532	−0.207	0.0428
32		1.28	1.519	−0.220	0.0484
33		1.24	1.505	−0.234	0.0548
34		1.21	1.491	−0.248	0.0615
35		1.17	1.477	−0.262	0.0686
36		1.14	1.398	−0.341	0.1163
37		1.11	1.380	−0.359	0.1289
38		1.08	1.342	−0.397	0.1576
39		1.05	1.322	−0.417	0.1739
40		1.03	1.146	−0.593	0.3516
			$\sum = 69.579$		3.0973

$$\bar{X} = \frac{\sum X}{N} = \frac{69.579}{40} = 1.739$$

$$\sigma_x = \sqrt{\frac{\sum (X - \bar{X})^2}{N}} = \sqrt{\frac{3.0973}{40}} = 0.28$$

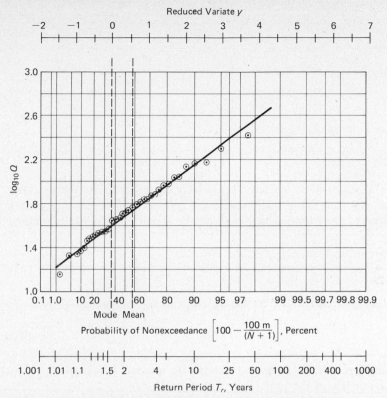

Figure 13.11 Gumbel log plot for the data of Fig. 13.10.

WIND FREQUENCY ANALYSIS

It has been found that Eq. (13.35) can satisfactorily represent the statistical distribution of many climatological extremes, for example, the distribution of maximum wind velocity, V. We can thus write the probability $P(V)$ that the maximum wind velocity in any one year is less than V.

$$P(V) = e^{-e^{-y}} \tag{13.39}$$

where $y = a(V - \hat{V})$, a = scale factor for the data (measuring its dispersion), and $\hat{V}$ = the mode of the data. The values of the parameters a and $\hat{V}$ are obtained from anemometer records at selected stations in any one locality. Following our definition for the return period T_r,[8] the probability that a certain velocity is *not* exceeded in any one year is $[1 - (1/T_r)]$. Thus, by taking logarithms of both sides of Eq. (13.39) and putting $P(V) = 1 - (1/T_r)$, we obtain

$$V = \hat{V} - \frac{1}{a} \log_e \left[-\log_e \left(1 - \frac{1}{T_r} \right) \right]. \tag{13.40}$$

[8] For example, if we wish to design a structure to resist the once-in-50-years wind, the return period is $T_r = 50$.

TABLE 13.10

Class	1	2	3	4	5	6	7	8	9	10
Yield strength (kg/mm^2: 1.275)^b	32^a	33	34	35	36	37	38	39	40	42
Cumulative frequency	10	33	81	161	224	289	336	369	383	389

^{a} Minimum strength = 30.25 (kg/mm^2: 1.275).
^{b} 1 kg/mm^2 = 9.81 N/mm^2.
Source: W. Weibull, "A Statistical Distribution Function of Wide Applicability," *Journal of Applied Mechanics,* vol. 18, Sept. 1951, pp. 293–297.

For the gradient-wind velocity $\bar{V}_G$ (which corresponds to the gradient wind, i.e., one that is moving freely under the influence of pressure gradients and is unaffected by the frictional stresses near the ground surface) with a return period T_r,

$$\bar{V}_G = \hat{V} - \frac{1}{a} \log_e \left[-\log_e \left(1 - \frac{1}{T_r} \right) \right]. \tag{13.41}$$

For large values of T_r, say $T_r > 10$, Eq. (13.41) can be approximated by

$$\bar{V}_G = \hat{V} + \frac{1}{a} \log_e T_r. \tag{13.42}$$

The mean wind velocity $\bar{V}_z$ at height z above the ground is related to $\bar{V}_G$ by means of a power law of the type

$$\bar{V}_z = \bar{V}_G \left(\frac{z}{z_G} \right)^\alpha \tag{13.43}$$

where z_G and α are functions of the ground roughness.[9] From these values of mean wind velocities, the mean wind pressures are found, and it is to resist these that the structure is designed.

The extreme value distribution has been used extensively also in interpreting fatigue tests and forecasting fatigue life of various materials.[10]

SOLVED PROBLEM

13-1. The yield values for a certain grade of steel were found to be as listed in Table 13.10. Assuming that the Weibull distribution is applicable, calculate the appropriate parameters, and compare the expected and observed values by the χ^2 test.

Assume also that the normal distribution is applicable, and find the corresponding value of χ^2.

Solution. The minimum yield strength is 30.25 (kg/mm^2: 1.275) and this is used as an estimate of L, $\hat{L}$. This is subtracted from all the other observed yield values. The

[9] A. Davenport, "The Application of Statistical Concepts to the Wind Loading of Structures," *Proceedings Institution of Civil Engineers,* vol. 19. Aug. 1961, pp. 449–471.

[10] A. M. Freudenthal and E. J. Gumbel, "On the Statistical Interpretation of Fatigue Tests," *Proceedings Royal Society of London,* vol. 215–216, 1952–1953, p. 309.

TABLE 13.11

Class	Yield strength, t_i (kg/mm²: 1.275)	$t_i - \hat{L}$ (kg/mm²: 1.275)	Cumulative frequency, i	$\dfrac{390}{390-i}$	$\log_e\left(\dfrac{390}{390-i}\right)$
1	32	1.75	10	1.026	0.026
2	33	2.75	33	1.092	0.088
3	34	3.75	81	1.262	0.232
4	35	4.75	161	1.703	0.532
5	36	5.75	224	2.350	0.854
6	37	6.75	289	3.861	1.351
7	38	7.75	336	7.222	1.977
8	39	8.75	369	18.571	2.922
9	40	9.75	383	55.714	4.020
10	42	11.75	389	390.000	5.966

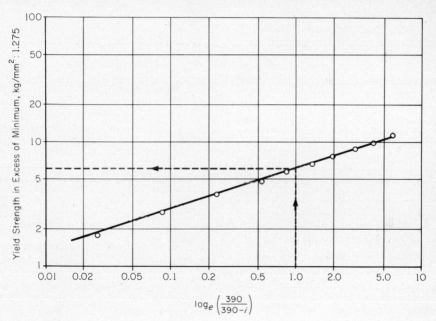

Figure 13.12

expression for $R(t_i)$ is then

$$R(t_i) = \frac{N+1-i}{N+1} = \frac{390-i}{390}.$$

We can tabulate the values as in Table 13.11.

The values of $(t_i - \hat{L})$ and $\log_e[390/(390 - i)]$ are plotted on log-log graph paper as shown in Fig. 13.12. The slope of the straight line (fitted by eye) gives a value of 2.93 for the Weibull parameter m; the value of $(t_i - \hat{L})$ corresponding to $\log_e[390/(390 - i)] = 1$ is $6.07 \times 1.275 = 7.74$ kg/mm². Therefore, from Eq. (13.22),

$$m \log_e(7.74) = -\log_e \gamma$$

whence

$$\gamma = 7.74^{-2.93} = 0.0025.$$

TABLE 13.12

Class	$(t_i - \hat{L})^{2.93} = T$	$0.0025 \times T$	$e^{-0.0025T}$	Estimated e
1	10.484	0.026	0.974	10
2	39.440	0.099	0.906	37
3	97.887	0.245	0.783	85
4	195.702	0.489	0.613	151
5	342.574	0.856	0.425	224
6	548.050	1.370	0.254	291
7	821.557	2.054	0.128	340
8	1172.430	2.931	0.053	369
9	1609.910	4.025	0.018	383
10	2781.311	6.953	0.001	390

TABLE 13.13

Class	E	O	$|O - E|$	$(O - E)^2/E$
1	10	10	0	0.000
2	27	23	4	0.593
3	48	48	0	0.000
4	66	80	14	2.970
5	73	63	10	1.370
6	67	65	2	0.060
7	49	47	2	0.082
8	29	33	4	0.552
9	14	14	0	0.000
10	7	6	1	0.143
				$\chi^2 = 5.770$

In order to estimate the frequencies of yield as predicted by the Weibull distribution, we equate the two expressions for the reliability function $R(t)$:

$$e^{-\gamma(t_i - \hat{L})^m} = \frac{N + 1 - i}{N + 1}.$$

Therefore,

$$e^{-0.0025(t_i - 38.57)^{2.93}} = \frac{390 - i}{390}$$

so that

$$i = 390 - 390e^{-0.0025(t_i - 38.57)^{2.93}}$$

where t_i is in kg/mm^2.

The estimated frequencies are calculated as in Table 13.12.

To test the hypothesis that the observed yield strengths fit a Weibull distribution, we calculate χ^2 (see Table 13.13).

Since we have 9 independent classes and we must estimate three parameters from the observed data, the number of degrees of freedom is $9 - 3 = 6$. From Table A.11, a χ^2 value of 5.770 for 6 degrees of freedom is significant at the 50 percent level so that we have no evidence to reject the hypothesis that the Weibull distribution fits the observed data.

To fit a normal distribution to the data, we first estimate the mean and standard deviation as shown in Table 13.14.

TABLE 13.14

Class midpoint, x_i	$X_i = x_0 - x_i$	X_i^2	f_i	$f_i X_i$	$f_i X_i^2$
$32 = x_0$	0	0	10	0	0
33	1	1	23	23	23
34	2	4	48	96	192
35	3	9	80	240	720
36	4	16	63	252	1008
37	5	25	65	325	1625
38	6	36	47	282	1692
39	7	49	33	231	1617
40	8	64	14	112	896
42	10	100	6	60	600
			$\sum = 389$	$\sum = 1621$	$\sum = 8373$

TABLE 13.15

$z = X/s$	0	± 0.5	± 1.0	± 1.5	± 2.0	± 2.5	± 3.0	± 3.5	± 4.0
$f(z)$	0.3989	0.3521	0.2420	0.1295	0.0540	0.0175	0.0044	0.0009	0
$f(z) \times n/s$	75.98	67.07	46.10	24.67	10.29	3.33	0.84	0.17	0
$X = zs$	0	1.02	2.04	3.06	4.08	5.10	6.12	7.14	8.16
$x = \bar{x} + X$	36.17	37.19	38.21	39.23	40.25	41.27	42.29	43.31	44.33
$x = \bar{x} - X$	36.17	35.15	34.13	33.11	32.09	31.07	30.05	29.03	28.01

The mean is

$$\bar{X} = x_0 + \frac{1621}{389} = 32 + 4.167 = 36.167$$

and the standard deviation

$$S = \sqrt{\frac{\sum f_i X_i^2 - [(\sum f_i X_i)^2/n]}{n-1}}$$

$$= \sqrt{\frac{8373 - 6754.86}{388}}$$

$$= \sqrt{4.170} = 2.042.$$

Ordinates of the fitted normal curve, for $n/s = 190.48$, are obtained using Table A.5 (see Table 13.15).

The normal curve is shown in Fig. 13.13 and the values obtained from it are then used to obtain χ^2 (see Table 13.16).

Since the estimated frequency of the last class is rather small, we pool the last two classes; the number of degrees of freedom is then $8 - 2 = 6$, because we estimated two parameters from the observed data. Table A.11 gives the value of 17.527 as significant at the 1 percent level so that we conclude that the normal distribution does not satisfactorily fit the observed data.

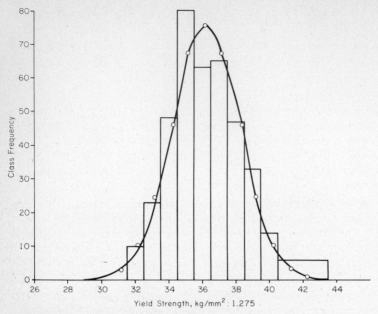

Figure 13.13

TABLE 13.16

Upper-class boundary	E	O	|O − E|	$\dfrac{(O − E)^2}{E}$
32	8	10	2	0.500
33	19	23	4	0.842
34	41	48	7	1.195
35	66	80	14	2.970
36	76	63	13	2.224
37	69	65	4	0.232
38	53	47	6	0.679
39	29	33	4	0.552
40	12	14	2	0.333
42	2	6	4	8.000
				$\chi^2 = 17.527$

As an exercise, solve again this problem by taking the reliability in the form of Eq. (13.20), that is,

$$R(t_i) = \frac{N - i + 0.7}{N + 0.4}$$

and compare the results of the two methods.

PROBLEMS

13-1. The backup electrical power of a nuclear power plant is supplied by five identical engines; the emergency power can be provided by at least two engines starting automatically. The operational life t of each engine has an exponential distribution with a mean = 10 years. Determine the reliability of the emergency backup system for a period of 3 years.

13-2. Find the reliability of the system composed of stages 1 and 2 only in Fig. 13.4.

13-3. A planning study on the design of a bridge recommended a probability of 25 percent that the bridge will be flooded over in the next 30 years. Calculate the return period of this design flood.

13-4. One-hundred-year records of earthquakes in a region show that there were 12 earthquakes of intensity 6 or more. It is known that the occurrence of such high-intensity earthquakes in this region follows a Poisson process. Calculate:

    a. the probability that such earthquakes will occur in the next 3 years;
    b. the probability that no such earthquake will occur in the next 10 years;
    c. the return period of an intensity-6 earthquake.

13-5. Twenty electric motors were run to destruction and the times to failure (in hours) were as follows: 106.2, 159.6, 194.3, 215.9, 227.6, 271.6, 274.3, 297.7, 299.0, 345.5, 357.6, 373.4, 398.0, 430.5, 447.9, 485.3, 512.4, 548.9, 564.5, 608.9. Estimate the parameters for a Weibull model to fit the observed failure times using the simplified model without the location parameter [Eq. (13.17)]. What proportion of the motors will last more than two weeks (336 hours)?

13-6. Measurement of the size of fly ash revealed the distribution shown in Table 13.17. Fit a Weibull model to the observed values and compare the goodness of fit using χ^2. Also, fit a normal distribution to the data and calculate χ^2. Solve also this problem by using Eq. (13.25). Use $\alpha = 0.10$.

13-7. The values of annual maximum instantaneous flows of a river for the years 1942 through 1965 are listed in Table 13.18.

TABLE 13.17

Particle diameter in 20 μm, t_i	Cumulative frequency, i
2^a	3
3	14
4	34
5	56
6	85
7	126
8	150
9	175
10	188
11	197
12	202
13	208
14	211

[a] Minimum diameter = 1.5 (μm:20).

Source: W. Weibull, "A Statistical Distribution Function of Wide Applicability," *Journal of Applied Mechanics*, vol. 18, Sept. 1951, pp. 293–297; after J. M. Dalla Valle, *Micromeritics*, (New York: Pitman Publishing Corporation, 1948), p. 57, Fig. 2.

TABLE 13.18

Year	Flow Q, m^3/s	Year	Flow Q, m^3/s
1942	2750	1954	1150
1943	7200	1955	7150
1944	1750	1956	2000
1945	8600	1957	2600
1946	2800	1958	4670
1947	1890	1959	2350
1948	4780	1960	4300
1949	7270	1961	5900
1950	4370	1962	5300
1951	1580	1963	4300
1952	5200	1964	2800
1953	5420	1965	1800

TABLE 13.19

Capacitor rank, m	Breakdown voltage, V
1	900
2	870
3	845
4	840
5	830
6	830
7	800
8	800
9	780
10	760
11	750
12	710
13	700
14	700
15	670
16	620
17	600
18	520

a. Plot the data on a graph of discharge versus return period.

b. Compute the mean and standard deviation of the extreme value distribution.

c. Estimate the return periods of a flow of 5500 m^3/s and of the average flood.

d. Estimate the magnitude of flows with return periods of 10, 15, and 25 years.

13-8. The breakdown voltage of a capacitor is affected by the largest size of the conductivity particle present; for practical purposes it is the smallest breakdown voltage that is of interest.

The breakdown voltages listed in Table 13.19 (in rank order) have been measured on 18 capacitors. Using probability paper, obtain an expression for the proportion of capacitors having a specified breakdown voltage. (Note that because the smallest value is critical, ranking is in a decreasing order of magnitude.)

Chapter 14

Chi-Squared Distribution and Tests for Goodness of Fit

In this chapter, we shall consider the ways of checking whether the data which we have obtained do, in fact, agree with the underlying theoretical chance distribution which we assumed for these data. One of the ways of performing this task is by the goodness of fit testing. Two tests will be considered, namely: the χ^2 test,[1] suitable for discrete distributions, and the Kolmogorov–Smirnov (K–S) test for continuous distributions. Before considering the χ^2 test, we shall briefly discuss the χ^2 distribution.

χ^2 DISTRIBUTION

This is another continuous chance distribution, defined as the sum of the squares of v independent standardized normal variates. If x_i is a normal variate with mean μ_i and standard deviation σ_i, then

$$z_i = \frac{x_i - \mu_i}{\sigma_i} \tag{14.1}$$

(i.e., z_i is a standardized normal variate with mean $= 0$ and variance $= 1$) and, by definition,

$$\chi_v^2 = \sum_{i=1}^{i=v} z_i^2 = \sum_{i=1}^{i=v} \left(\frac{x_i - \mu_i}{\sigma_i} \right)^2.$$

---

[1] Sometimes written chi, pronounced *ki* as in kite.

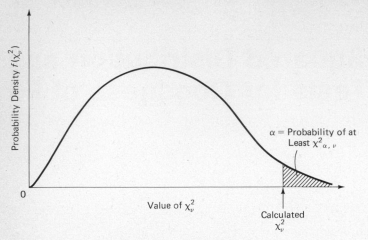

Figure 14.1   Probability density function of χ^2.

The probability density function of the χ^2 distribution is given by

$$f(\chi_v^2) = \frac{(\chi_v^2)^{[v/2-1]}e^{-\chi_v^2/2}}{2^{(v/2)}\Gamma(v/2)} \tag{14.2}$$

where

$$\Gamma\left(\frac{v}{2}\right) = \int_0^\infty x^{[(v/2)-1]}e^{-x}\,dx$$

is the so-called gamma function, and v = degrees of freedom. A graph of the probability density function is shown in Fig. 14.1.

The χ^2 probability distributions are unimodal and skewed to the right. As can be seen from Eq. (14.2), the χ^2 distribution is defined by only *one parameter*, namely v, the number of degrees of freedom. As v increases, skewness becomes less marked, as shown in Fig. 14.2. In fact, it can be shown that, as $v \to \infty$, the limit of the χ^2 distribution is the normal distribution. Of course, the area under the χ^2 probability density function represents probability so that the total area under the curve equals unity. Table A.11 in the Appendix contains values of $\chi_{v,\alpha}^2$ for various values of v and of level of significance α. A value $\chi_{v,\alpha}^2$ denotes the point on the horizontal axis (Fig. 14.1) such that a proportion α of the area under the χ^2 curve with v degrees of freedom lies to the right of $\chi_{v,\alpha}^2$; the value α represents the probability of encountering χ_v^2 greater than $\chi_{v,\alpha}^2$. Because the χ^2 distribution is nonsymmetrical, extreme values of χ^2 have to be tabulated for both tails. The mean of the χ_v^2 distribution is $E(\chi_v^2) = v$, and its variance is Var $(\chi_v^2) = 2v$.

The sum of two independent χ^2 distributions is also a χ^2 distribution with a number of degrees of freedom which is the sum of the degrees of freedom of the constituent distributions. This is of interest in pooling variances.

The χ^2 distribution can be used to investigate the sampling distribution of s^2, the estimate of the variance of the population [see Eq. (4.7)]. Let us consider the distribution of s^2 in repeated sampling from a specified normal

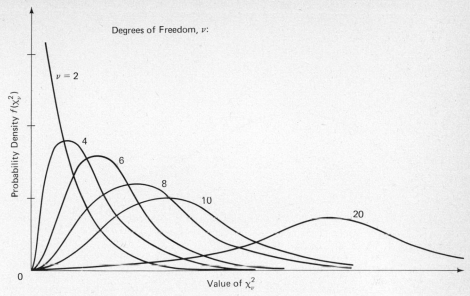

Figure 14.2 Plots of the χ^2 probability density function for various degrees of freedom, v.

distribution having a mean μ and variance σ^2. It can be shown that the distribution of s^2 is independent of μ, but is related to each sample size, n, and to each value of σ^2 by the following relation

$$s^2 = \frac{\chi^2 \sigma^2}{(n-1)}.$$ (14.3)

In standardized form, Eq. (14.3) is written as

$$\chi^2 = \frac{(n-1)s^2}{\sigma^2}.$$ (14.4)

This equation can be readily used for testing of a hypothesis.

EXAMPLE

A ready-mix concrete company claims that the variance of the compressive strength of a particular mix is 5 MPa. Tests on a sample of size $n = 10$ cylinders produced a mean compressive strength $\bar{x} = 30$ MPa and an estimate of variance $s^2 = 9.8$ MPa. Do the results from the sample justify the company's claim? Use $\alpha = 0.05$.

The null hypothesis is $H_0: \sigma^2 = 5$ MPa with the alternative hypothesis $H_a: \sigma^2 > 5$ MPa. This is a one-sided test with the entire rejection area located in the right-hand tail of the χ^2 distribution, Fig. 14.3. From Eq. (14.4),

$$\chi_v^2 = \frac{(n-1)s^2}{\sigma^2} = \frac{9 \times 9.8}{5} = 17.64.$$

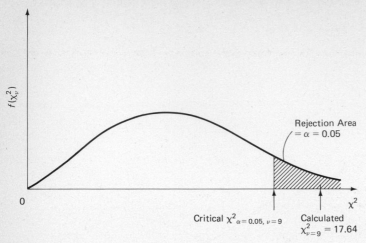

Figure 14.3

Since this value of χ^2 falls in the rejection region, we conclude that the null hypothesis is false and that the company's claim cannot be justified. ■ ■

Let us now consider a two-tailed test.

EXAMPLE

A researcher has found over a long period of time that his pressure gauge has a standard deviation of $\sigma_0 = 1$ Pa. In a recent experiment, he recorded the following measurements: $x_1 = 38.5$ Pa, $x_2 = 41.5$ Pa, $x_3 = 40.0$ Pa, $x_4 = 42.2$ Pa, and $x_5 = 37.8$ Pa. Has the precision of the gauge altered? Use $\alpha = 0.10$.

By inspection, $\bar{x} = 40.0$ Pa. From Eq. (4.7), we find s^2, which is an unbiased estimator of σ^2:

$$s^2 = \frac{\sum\limits_{i=1}^{5} (x_i - \bar{x})^2}{n - 1}$$

$$= \frac{(-2.2)^2 + (1.5)^2 + (0)^2 + (1.5)^2 + (2.2)^2}{4}$$

$$= 3.54.$$

Now, we are interested in detecting $\sigma_0^2 > 1$ *and* $\sigma_0^2 < 1$, and we should, therefore, employ a two-tailed test. Thus, using $\alpha = 0.10$, we place 0.05 in each tail, as shown in Fig. 14.4. The null hypothesis is $H_0: \sigma^2 = \sigma_0^2$ with the alternative hypothesis $H_a: \sigma^2 \neq \sigma_0^2$. We shall reject the null hypothesis when calculated $\chi^2 > 9.488$ or $\chi^2 < 0.711$. Using Eq. (14.4), the calculated value of the test statistic is

$$\chi^2 = \frac{(n-1)s^2}{\sigma_0^2} = \frac{4 \times 3.54}{1^2} = 14.18.$$

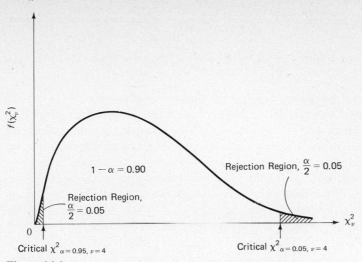

Figure 14.4

Since the test statistic falls in one of the rejection regions, the data justify rejecting the null hypothesis that $\sigma^2 = \sigma_0^2 = 1$ Pa^2. We can therefore conclude that the precision of the pressure gauge has altered, and the probability of this decision being wrong is α, the level of significance. ■ ■

THE χ^2 TEST

This test enables us to find whether observed frequencies differ *significantly* from frequencies expected from an assumed model. The test requires, in general, the use of frequencies and not percentages. In the χ^2 test, as in all tests of significance, we postulate a null hypothesis that there is no significant difference between the distributions being compared, that is, we assume that they are drawn from the same population. We measure the probability of the actual difference occurring due to chance alone, and if this probability is very small, we reject the null hypothesis and infer that a real difference exists. We should note, as discussed in Chapter 7, that we can never formally prove the null hypothesis to be correct.

To perform the χ^2 test, we compare each expected class frequency E with the observed frequency O, and compute for each class the term

$$\frac{(O - E)^2}{E}.$$

The statistic χ^2 is then defined as

$$\chi^2 = \sum \frac{(O - E)^2}{E} \tag{14.5}$$

the summation extending over all classes and with the constraint condition that

$$\sum_{i=1}^{k} O_i = \sum_{i=1}^{k} E_i = N \qquad (14.6)$$

where N is the total frequency and k is the number of classes.

The calculated value is then compared with tabulated values of χ^2 (see Table A.11); the latter are values that cannot be exceeded by the calculated value when there is *no real difference* at a specified level of significance, that is, with a given probability.

To find the requisite probability, we locate on the table the appropriate number of degrees of freedom (see the following section) and find the highest tabulated value that is exceeded by the calculated value. At the head of the column containing this tabulated value we read off the probability of the null hypothesis not being true. It is usual to reject the null hypothesis at the 5 percent or the 1 percent level of significance (i.e., a probability of 0.05 and 0.01, respectively).

If the level of significance is higher, we generally do not reject the null hypothesis, but this does not necessarily mean that the observed distribution is the same as the hypothetical one. It is possible that we simply do not have adequate data in hand, and further tests should be made before a reliable conclusion can be drawn.

We should note that the χ^2 test determines the probability of obtaining the values of $|O - E|$ of *at least* the magnitude observed and not of exactly that magnitude.

Equation (14.5) defines χ^2 as a criterion to measure the discrepancies between the observed and the expected values. We shall gain a better understanding of the χ^2 test if we examine how reasonable it is as a criterion. Consider any class: the discrepancy between the observed and expected values is $(O - E)$. The degree of this discrepancy can be better judged if it is relative; hence, we divide the term $(O - E)$ by E (since E is a better basis for comparison than O) to yield the quotient $(O - E)/E$. Such quotients will be either positive or negative and their sum might be close to zero, thus impairing its efficiency. It is better, therefore, to square the quotients and then sum them up. However, in situations involving relative values it is judicious to consider the sum of weighted square quotients. For example, in the case when the values are $O = 11$ and $E = 10$, the discrepancy quotient is 10 percent and this is far less significance (since it can happen by chance) than the 10 percent discrepancy quotient in a case when $O = 330$ and $E = 300$. For this reason, we multiply each squared quotient by its expected value, E, and then sum up all the classes, yielding

$$\sum_{\text{all classes}} E\left(\frac{O - E}{E}\right)^2$$

which we call χ^2. Thus,

$$\chi^2 = \sum_{\text{all classes}} \frac{(O - E)^2}{E}. \qquad [14.5]$$

DEGREES OF FREEDOM IN THE χ^2 TEST

The concept of degrees of freedom, denoted by v, was introduced and defined in Chapter 4. Applying the definition to problems involving the use of the χ^2 test, we find that:

   a. The number of degrees of freedom is $v = k - 1$ if the expected frequencies can be calculated without having to estimate any population parameters from the sample. We subtract one from k, the number of classes, because of the constraint of Eq. (14.6). In other words, since the total is fixed, we can arbitrarily assign expected frequencies to only $(k - 1)$ classes.

   b. The number of degrees of freedom is $v = k - 1 - m$ if the expected frequencies can be calculated only after estimating m number of population parameters from the sample (e.g., the mean μ, standard deviation σ). For instance, if we are determining the goodness of fit of observed data having six classes to a theoretical binomial distribution, we need to calculate the parameter p from the observed sample. This would then yield the expected frequencies. Thus, in this case, $v = k - 1 - m$, with $k = 6, m = 1$, that is, $v = 4$. If we were comparing the same observed data to a normal distribution, we would have to estimate the parameters μ and σ ($m = 2$) from the sample before being able to calculate the expected frequencies. Hence, the number of degrees of freedom in this case is $v = 6 - 1 - 2 = 3$.

EXAMPLE

   Three shifts, A, B, and C are in competition to produce similar units that must pass a standard test before being declared acceptable. In the first week, they produced 2, 9, and 10 faulty units, respectively. It is assumed that the total number of units produced by each of the three shifts is identical and very large. Can we conclude that there is no difference in the quality of workmanship between the three shifts? Use a level of significance of 5 percent.

   We adopt the null hypothesis that there is no significant difference between shifts so that the expected number of faulty units per shift is $(2 + 9 + 10)/3 = 7$. More formally, we can state the null hypothesis as $H_0: p_1 = p_2 = p_3 = \frac{1}{3}$ (i.e., a uniform distribution), against the alternative hypothesis H_a: at least one p is different from $\frac{1}{3}$. The total number of faulty units is $N = 2 + 9 + 10 = 21$. Hence, expected frequency, for each of the three shifts, will be equal to $N \times p = 21 \times \frac{1}{3} = 7$, as before. We can set out the data as in Table 14.1. Hence,

$$\chi^2 = \frac{5^2}{7} + \frac{2^2}{7} + \frac{3^2}{7} = 5.428.$$

   The number of degrees of freedom is 2 since, given the total number of rejected units, we can assign arbitrarily only two classes. Table A.11 gives $\chi^2 = 5.991$ at the 5 percent level of significance, and we cannot conclude, therefore, that there is a difference in workmanship between the three shifts. In other words, we do not have enough evidence to reject the null hypothesis.

TABLE 14.1

Shift	O	E	$|O - E|$
A	2	7	5
B	9	7	2
C	10	7	3

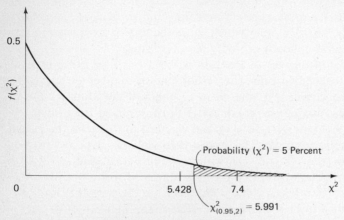

Figure 14.5   Probability density function of the χ^2 variable ($v = 2$) for the example on page 279.

If the foreman of shift A is not satisfied with this conclusion, we answer that we do not deny that a difference *may* exist, but the evidence available is inadequate to regard the difference as established.

The same foreman, still unconvinced, may collect further evidence. Let us assume that at the end of the second week, all conditions having remained unaltered, the numbers of rejected units have increased to 3, 13, and 14. Now the expected number of unacceptable units per shift is $(3 + 13 + 14)/3 = 10$. Hence,

$$\chi^2 = \frac{7^2}{10} + \frac{3^2}{10} + \frac{4^2}{10} = 7.4.$$

With 2 degrees of freedom ($v = k - 1 = 3 - 1$), this value is significant at the 5 percent level, and we consider our suspicions confirmed: the workmanship in the three shifts is not of uniform quality; that is, at least one p is different from $\frac{1}{3}$ (see Fig. 14.5).   ■ ■

MINIMUM CLASS FREQUENCY

The preceding example illustrates the point that the χ^2 test is sensitive to the size of the sample used. In general, the test should not be used when an *expected* class frequency is less than 5, as the relative frequency for such a class is very

TABLE 14.2

Pressure (Pa)	2.0	2.2	2.4	2.6	2.8
Class	A	B	C	D	E
Observed number of rejects, O	2	3	6	6	3
Expected number of rejects, E	$1\frac{1}{2}$	$5\frac{1}{2}$	6	$5\frac{1}{2}$	$1\frac{1}{2}$

small. However, it is usually possible to combine adjacent classes with a frequency below 5 in order to reach or exceed this value.

EXAMPLE

Five pressures are used in extruding a difficult shape, and the numbers of rejects are given in Table 14.2. From numerous past records the expected numbers of rejects are also listed. Using $\alpha = 5$ percent, check whether there is a significant difference between the observed and expected numbers of rejects produced by the five pressures.

To satisfy the requirement of an expected class frequency of not less than 5, we combine A and B, and D and E:

Class	A and B	C	D and E
O	5	6	9
E	7	6	7

Hence,
$$\chi^2 = \frac{2^2}{7} + 0 + \frac{2^2}{7}.$$

That is $\chi^2 = 1.143$ with 2 degrees of freedom ($v = k - 1 = 3 - 1$). A value of 1.386 can be obtained with a probability of 50 percent; therefore, we conclude that there is no significant difference between the observed and expected numbers of rejects for the pressures: (A and B), C, and (D and E).

A close examination of Table A.11 reveals that if the calculated value of χ^2 is smaller than the number of degrees of freedom v, we can conclude that χ^2 is not significant. ■ ■

CONTINUITY CORRECTION

We should note that χ^2 is a continuous variable and, if the actual distribution is discontinuous, we have to apply a *continuity correction*. This can be done only when the number of degrees of freedom is 1. The correction consists of reducing by 0.5 the values of observed frequency that are greater than the expected frequency, and increasing those that are smaller. Failure to apply the correction leads to too high a value of calculated χ^2. Thus, without the correction, we may wrongly reject the null hypothesis at a specified level of significance.

TABLE 14.3

	Heads	Tails
Observed	17	33
Expected E	25	25
Observed, corrected O	17.5	32.5
$\lvert O - E \rvert$	7.5	7.5

If, however, the null hypothesis is not rejected without the correction being applied, the correction would not affect our conclusion (see also page 200).

EXAMPLE

We toss a coin 50 times and obtain 17 heads. Are we justified in suspecting that the coin is biased? Use $\alpha = 1$ percent.

The number of degrees of freedom is 1. The null hypothesis is $H_0 : p = \frac{1}{2}$ versus $H_a : p \neq \frac{1}{2}$. Therefore, the expected number of heads $= N \times p = 50 \times \frac{1}{2} = 25$.

We tabulate the data as shown in Table 14.3.

Hence,
$$\chi^2 = \frac{7.5^2}{25} + \frac{7.5^2}{25} = 4.5.$$

From Table A.11, $\chi^2_{v=1, \alpha=0.05} = 3.841$, and $\chi^2_{v=1, \alpha=0.01} = 6.635$. The calculated χ^2 is therefore significant at the 5 percent level but not at the 1 percent level; we have thus a good, but not an overwhelming, reason to suspect the coin. However, we cannot reject the null hypothesis at the level of significance $\alpha = 1$ percent specified *a priori*. ■ ■

TOO GOOD A FIT

Table A.11 gives the values of χ^2 for probabilities of 0.001 to 0.10, that is, for levels of significance of 0.1 to 10 percent which are the usual levels at which the rejection of the null hypothesis is considered. The table also contains, however, values for probabilities of 0.50 to 0.99. The occurrence of χ^2 corresponding to a probability higher than about 0.99 makes us suspect that the data have been "rigged." This has been shown to have been the case, for instance, with some of the test results reported by Mendel's disciples. Too high a value of χ^2 may also occur when, for example, spurious pulses of uniform frequency are mixed with pulses being observed, or, in general, when there is a lack of randomness.

EXAMPLE

In the statistics laboratory we ask students to draw samples of 4 from a bowl containing red and black balls in equal proportions, the drawn balls being returned into the bowl after each test; 160 samples are drawn and the students report their results, given in Table 14.4. We compare the observed distribution with that expected, that is, with the binomial distribution. Are the results suspicious? Use a 5 percent level of significance.

TABLE 14.4

Number of red balls in sample, r	0	1	2	3	4
Number of samples with r red balls observed, O	9	40	59	41	11
Number of samples with r red balls expected, E	10	40	60	40	10
$|O - E|$	1	0	1	1	1

Hence,
$$\chi^2 = \frac{1}{10} + \frac{1}{60} + \frac{1}{40} + \frac{1}{10} = 0.24.$$

The number of degrees of freedom is $v = k - 1 = 5 - 1 = 4$.

Table A.11 gives $\chi^2 = 0.297$ at the 99 percent level of significance. Therefore, the probability of obtaining χ^2 *as small* as calculated is less than 1 percent, and we are justified, therefore, in suspecting that the experiment was not performed but that the "results" were arbitrarily written down so as to appear plausible in the students' eyes. ■ ■

χ^2 AS A MEASURE OF GOODNESS OF FIT

As mentioned earlier, the χ^2 test is used to test the goodness of fit; in this case the null hypothesis states that there is no significant difference between the observed distribution and a postulated standard distribution. The preceding example involved the binomial distribution, but perhaps a better illustration is offered by the data in Chapter 9 on the number of deaths caused by a horse kick. On the assumption of Poisson distribution, we calculated there the expected number of deaths per army corps per annum, and we can now apply the χ^2 test to find how well the observed data fit the assumed distribution. The data for the example are repeated in Table 14.5.

Hence,
$$\chi^2 = \frac{1^2}{66} + \frac{2^2}{20} + \frac{1^2}{5} = 0.415.$$

Since we deduced the expected frequencies by first estimating np, the mean number of deaths/corps/annum, from the observed sample (see page 165), the number m is 1. Here we are imposing a restriction by assuming that the mean of the population (expected frequencies) is equal to the mean of the sample

TABLE 14.5

Number of deaths per corps per annum, r	0	1	2	3	4
Observed number of corps with r deaths, O	109	65	22	3	1
Expected number of corps with r deaths, E	109	66	20	4	0.6 ≃ 1
$|O - E|$		0	1	2	1

(observed frequencies). Thus the number of degrees of freedom in this case is $v = k - 1 - m = 4 - 1 - 1 = 2$. With $v = 2$, Table A.11 gives $\chi^2 = 0.446$ at the 80 percent level of significance. Thus the goodness of fit is good and we are satisfied that the observed distribution is a Poisson distribution.

CONTINGENCY TABLES

Up to now, we have dealt with one-way classification tables where observed frequencies occupy a single row (or a single column). However, the χ^2 tests can also be written down in a somewhat different form. For example, if we compare two methods of treatment in order to establish whether or not there is a significant difference between them, we can set out the results in the form of a contingency table (Table 14.6).

Instead of the χ^2 calculations given in Eq. (14.5), we can use a formula:

$$\chi^2 = \frac{(B_1 A_2 - A_1 B_2)^2 \times T_t}{A_t B_t T_1 T_2} \tag{14.7}$$

where the terms are as defined in Table 14.6.

To prove this formula we have first to generate the expected table. If the rows and columns in Table 14.6 are independent of each other (this being the null hypothesis), then the probability that a random element will belong to cell $(1, 1)$ is

$$p_{11} = p_{r1} p_{c1}$$

where
$$p_{r1} = \frac{A_t}{T_t} \quad \text{and} \quad p_{c1} = \frac{T_1}{T_t}.$$

Therefore,
$$p_{11} = \frac{A_t T_1}{T_t^2}.$$

Hence, the expected value is

$$E_{11} = p_{11} \times T_t = \frac{A_t T_1}{T_t}.$$

Similarly,
$$E_{12} = p_{12} \times T_t = \frac{A_t T_2}{T_t},$$

$$E_{21} = p_{21} \times T_t = \frac{B_t T_1}{T_t},$$

TABLE 14.6

Item	Number of successes	Number of failures	Totals
Method A	A_1	A_2	A_t
Method B	B_1	B_2	B_t
Totals	T_1	T_2	T_t

and
$$E_{22} = p_{22} \times T_t = \frac{B_t T_2}{T_t}.$$

Applying Eq. (14.5), we find

$$\chi^2 = \frac{\left[A_1 - \left(\dfrac{A_t T_2}{T_t}\right)\right]^2}{\dfrac{A_t T_1}{T_t}} + \frac{\left[A_2 - \left(\dfrac{A_t T_2}{T_t}\right)\right]^2}{\dfrac{A_t T_2}{T_t}}$$

$$+ \frac{\left[B_1 - \left(\dfrac{B_t T_1}{T_t}\right)\right]^2}{\dfrac{B_t T_1}{T_t}} + \frac{\left[B_2 - \left(\dfrac{B_t T_2}{T_t}\right)\right]^2}{\dfrac{B_t T_2}{T_t}}$$

which, after some algebraic operations, will reduce to the form given by Eq. (14.7).

The number of degrees of freedom is 1, as only one of the values of A_1, A_2, B_1, B_2 can be assigned arbitrarily, all the others being governed by the totals T_1, T_2, A_t, and B_t.

It can easily be shown that Eq. (14.7) gives the same result as the calculation of χ^2 by Eq. (14.5). It should be noted that the tabulated values must be adjusted by the continuity correction (page 281) *before* applying Eq. (14.7).

We should realize that for problems of this type there is generally no theoretical basis available to determine the expected frequency for each category or cell. What we have to do then is to use the observed frequencies in order to calculate the expected frequencies on the assumption that the null hypothesis of independence is true.

Let us consider a more general case: to test the hypothesis that rows and columns in Table 14.7 represent an independent classification. We do this by computing an expected number E_{ij} for each cell and using the χ^2 test.

By independence we mean that the proportion of each row total to that belonging in, say, the jth column, is the same for all rows. The same meaning of independence applies when the words columns and rows are interchanged in the preceding statement. This requirement can be expressed mathematically by saying that the probability of any random element belonging in the (i, j)th cell is equal to the product of the probability of its belonging to the ith row

TABLE 14.7 OBSERVED DATA

	1	2	3	$\cdots$	c	Row totals
1	O_{11}	O_{12}	O_{13}		O_{1c}	R_1
2	O_{21}	O_{22}	O_{23}		O_{2c}	R_2
$\vdots$	$\vdots$	$\vdots$	$\vdots$	$\vdots$	$\vdots$	$\vdots$
r	O_{r1}	O_{r2}	O_{r3}		O_{rc}	R_r
Column totals	C_1	C_2	C_3	$\cdots$	C_c	N

(R_i/N) multiplied by the probability of its belonging to the jth column (C_j/N), that is, R_iC_j/N^2. Hence, the expected number is the sample size N multiplied by the estimated probability, that is,

$$E_{ij} = \frac{R_iC_j}{N^2} \times N = \frac{R_iC_j}{N}.$$

On this basis, we construct the expected table and proceed to compute the χ^2:
In such cases the number of degrees of freedom, v, is given as follows.

a. The number of degrees of freedom is $v = (r-1)(c-1)$ if the expected frequencies can be computed without estimating population parameters from the observed sample (i.e., when the population parameters required in calculating the expected frequencies are *known*). This value can be readily deduced in the following way. If in the expected table we leave out a single number in each row and column, such numbers can then be determined from the known fixed totals of each row and column. Thus, we have freedom in assigning numbers to only $(r-1)(c-1)$ classes in the table, the others being uniquely determined. Another way of deducing the expression for v is as follows. We have a total of rc cells with the total N fixed, and hence there is one constraint. Also, $(r-1) + (c-1) = (r+c-2)$ independent parameters have been estimated from the sample. Thus, $v = rc - 1 - (r+c-2) = rc - r - c + 1 = (r-1)(c-1)$.

b. The number of degrees of freedom is $v = (r-1)(c-1) - m$ when the population parameters are *not known* but are estimated from the observed sample to compute the expected frequencies. Here, we are imposing m additional constraints by assuming that m population parameters are equal to the corresponding sample statistics.

If the calculated χ^2 exceeds the tabulated value for a probability α, we reject the hypothesis and conclude that rows and columns do not represent an independent classification. If this conclusion is indeed wrong, then we are committing a Type I error (see Chapter 7) and the measure of the risk involved is the probability α, the level of significance.

THE KOLMOGOROV–SMIRNOV (K–S) TEST

It is possible to adapt the χ^2 test for the purpose of determining the goodness of fit of continuous distributions. However, the procedure becomes subjective because the continuous random variable does not provide natural cells or categories into which we can group our data. A more appropriate test is the Kolmogorov–Smirnov (K–S) test which is easier to perform and which does not require a minimum expected frequency in each cell. Unlike the χ^2 test, which compares data in grouped cells, the K–S test compares the original data with the characteristics of a theoretical model hypothesized independently of the observed data. The test depends on the absolute deviation, D, between the hypothetical (theoretical) and observed cumulative relative frequencies. Thus, the

TABLE 14.8

Interval	Observed frequency	Observed relative frequency	Observed cumulative frequency, S_i	Fractional cumulative frequency of distribution (from Table 11.3), F_i	$\|F_i - S_i\|$
$-\infty$ to 165	1	0.028	0.028	0.028	0.000
165–175	4	0.112	0.140	0.139	0.001
175–185	7	0.195	0.335	0.333	0.002
185–195	11	0.304	0.639	0.639	0.000
195–205	9	0.249	0.888	0.889	0.001
205–215	3	0.084	0.972	0.972	0.000
215 to ∞	1	0.028	1.000	1.000	0.000
	Total $= \overline{36}$				

statistic D for the K–S test can be expressed as

$$D = \underset{i=1}{\overset{n}{\text{Max}}} |F_i - S_i| \qquad (14.8)$$

where F_i is the theoretical cumulative distribution function and S_i is observed cumulative frequency.

  The distribution of this random sample statistic is independent of the hypothetical distribution of the variate; the sample size n is its only parameter. The null hypothesis is stated as $H_0 : x$ has the assumed distribution, versus the alternative hypothesis, H_a : the distribution of x is other than the assumed one. If the value of D in Eq. (14.8) exceeds the tabulated values of D_{crit} (based on chance) in Table A.12, then the assumed theoretical distribution is rejected at the specified level of significance, α.

  Let us apply this test to Solved Problem 11-3, using $\alpha = 0.01$. From the last column of Table 14.8, we find that the maximum value of $|F_i - S_i|$ is $D = 0.002$. Since the sample size is $n = 36$, we estimate D_{crit} from Table A.12 to be 0.27 for $\alpha = 0.01$. D being smaller than D_{crit} means that we cannot reject the null hypothesis, that is, the agreement between the observed and theoretical values is close and we conclude that the tensile strength of that particular aluminum alloy follows a normal distribution.

SOLVED PROBLEMS

  14-1. An experiment was conducted to test the effect of the rate of loading on the type of failure in steel rods. Twenty-four specimens were tested to failure, 12 at a fast-loading rate and the other 12 at a slow rate. It was found that 11 of the slow specimens showed a complete cone failure, whereas only 5 of the fast specimens showed this type of failure. Establish whether the rate of loading influences the shape of the failure zone for the given steel. Use $\alpha = 5$ percent.

TABLE 14.9

	Failure A	Failure B	Total
Slow method	11	1	12
Fast method	5	7	12
Total	16	8	24

TABLE 14.10

	Failure A	Failure B	Total
Slow method	8	4	12
Fast method	8	4	12
Total	16	8	24

Solution. The null hypothesis is H_0:shape of failure zone is independent of the rate of loading. There are two criteria here and hence a two-way classification. Let a complete cone failure be denoted as A failure and all other types of failure as B. Then the *observed* 2×2 contingency table is as shown in Table 14.9.

Based on the hypothesis of independence, the expected values are calculated to be as in Table 14.10.

The number of degrees of freedom is $v = (r - 1)(c - 1) = (2 - 1)(2 - 1) = 1$. The value of χ^2 *without the continuity correction* is

$$\chi^2 = \frac{(3)^2}{8} + \frac{(3)^2}{8} + \frac{(3)^2}{4} + \frac{(3)^2}{4} = 6.75.$$

The value of χ^2 *with the continuity correction* is

$$\chi^2 = \frac{(2.5)^2}{8} + \frac{(2.5)^2}{8} + \frac{(2.5)^2}{4} + \frac{(2.5)^2}{4} = 4.69.$$

From Table A.11, $\chi^2_{v=1,\alpha=0.05} = 3.841$. Therefore, this result is significant at the 5 percent level, and hence the rate of loading does influence the shape of the failure zone at the above level of significance.

14-2. Five machines, A, B, C, D, and E are experimentally used to make precision tools. The following are the numbers of tools made by the five machines and the numbers rejected:

Machine	A	B	C	D	E	Total
Number made	20	18	16	24	22	100
Number rejected	12	16	10	14	18	70

Test the hypothesis that there is no difference in the performance of the machines. Use a level of significance of $\alpha = 5$ percent.

Solution. The observed number of tools in each category is listed in Table 14.11.

$$\frac{\text{Expected number of}}{\text{rejects from any machine}} = \frac{\text{total number of rejects}}{\text{total number of tools made}} \times \frac{\text{number of tools made by}}{\text{that particular machine.}}$$

TABLE 14.11

Machine	A	B	C	D	E	Total
Rejected	12	16	10	14	18	70
Accepted	8	2	6	10	4	30
Total	20	18	16	24	22	100

TABLE 14.12

Machine	A	B	C	D	E	Total
Rejected	14.0	12.6	11.2	16.8	15.4	70
Accepted	6.0	5.4	4.8	7.2	6.6	30
Total	20	18	16	24	22	100

TABLE 14.13

Machine	A	B	C	D	E	Total
Observed rejected	4	16	18	14	18	70
Observed accepted	8	2	6	10	4	30
Expected rejected	8.4	12.6	16.8	16.8	15.4	70
Expected accepted	3.6	5.4	7.2	7.2	6.6	30

The expected numbers are shown in Table 14.12.

$$\chi^2 - \sum \frac{(O-E)^2}{E} = \frac{(12-14)^2}{14} + \frac{(16-12.6)^2}{12.6} + \frac{(10-11.2)^2}{11.2}$$

$$+ \frac{(14-16.8)^2}{16.8} + \frac{(18-15.4)^2}{15.4} + \frac{(8-6)^2}{6} + \frac{(2-5.4)^2}{5.4}$$

$$+ \frac{(6-4.8)^2}{4.8} + \frac{(10-7.2)^2}{7.2} + \frac{(4-6.6)^2}{6.6} = 7.458.$$

For $v = (r-1)(c-1) = (2-1) \times (5-1) = 1 \times 4 = 4$ degrees of freedom, Table A.11 gives a value of $\chi^2 = 9.488$ for $\alpha = 0.05$ and $v = 4$. Since $\chi^2_{calc.} < \chi^2_{tab.}$, we have no reason to reject the null hypothesis, and we conclude that there is no difference in the performance of the five machines.

14-3. Test the null hypothesis in Solved Problem 14-2 using the following data:

Machine	A	B	C	D	E	Total
Number made	12	18	24	24	22	100
Number rejected	4	16	18	14	18	70

Use $\alpha = 10$ percent.

Solution. We calculate the observed and expected numbers as before (Table 14.13).

Since the expected number in A is smaller than 5, we pool the expected numbers of A and B and at the same time, pool the observed rejects of A and B. Thus,

$$\chi^2 = \frac{(20-21)^2}{21} + \frac{(18-16.8)^2}{16.8} + \frac{(14-16.8)^2}{16.8} + \frac{(18-15.4)^2}{15.4}$$

$$+ \frac{(10-9)^2}{9} + \frac{(6-7.2)^2}{7.2} + \frac{(10-7.2)^2}{7.2} + \frac{(4-6.6)^2}{6.6} = 3.463.$$

The number of degrees of freedom is $v = (r-1)(c-1) = (2-1)(4-1) = 3$, since we pooled the expected numbers in A and B. From Table A.11, for $v = 3$, the probability is approximately 50 percent. Therefore, there are no grounds for rejection of the null hypothesis. However, nothing can be said about the difference between the machines A and B until further tests have been made.

14-4. The manufacturer of a particular casting kept the following record of the number of defective units produced in 50 shifts:

Number of defectives per shift, r	0	1	2	3	4	5	6	7	8
Shifts with r defectives, O	2	6	10	10	7	6	4	3	2

Determine whether the data support the hypothesis that the number of defective castings is completely random, that is, we are not justified in suspecting that different shifts produce significantly different numbers of defective castings. Use $\alpha = 10$ percent.

Solution. If the distribution is random, it will not differ significantly from a Poisson distribution. Therefore, we start by fitting a Poisson distribution to the observed data (Table 14.14).

$$\text{Mean number of defectives per shift} = np = \frac{175}{50} = 3.5.$$

Using the cumulative Poisson probability graph of Fig. 9.2, we obtain the data given in Table 14.15, where $E = 50 \times P_r = $ expected number of shifts with r defective castings.

TABLE 14.14

Number of defectives per shift, r	Shifts with r defectives, O	$r \times O$
0	2	0
1	6	6
2	10	20
3	10	30
4	7	28
5	6	30
6	4	24
7	3	21
8	2	16
Totals	$\sum O = 50$	$\sum (r \times O) = 175$

TABLE 14.15

r	0	1	2	3	4	5	6	7	8
P cumulative	0.03	0.13	0.32	0.535	0.725	0.86	0.93	0.97	0.99
P_r	0.03	0.10	0.19	0.215	0.19	0.135	0.07	0.04	0.02
E	1.5	5.0	9.5	11.0	9.5	7.0	3.5	2.0	1.0

TABLE 14.16

Number of defectives	0 and 1	2	3	4	5	6, 7, and 8	$\sum$
Observed numbers of shifts, O	8	10	10	7	6	9	50
Expected number of shifts, E	6.5	9.5	11	9.5	7.0	6.5	50

Since the expected number of shifts producing 0 defectives and those producing 6, 7, and 8 defectives are smaller than 5, we pool the expected numbers of shifts of 0 and 1 defectives, and 6, 7, and 8 defectives, respectively; at the same time the corresponding numbers of observed shifts O are pooled, as shown in Table 14.16.

$$\chi^2 = \sum \frac{(O-E)^2}{E} = \frac{(8-6.5)^2}{6.5} + \frac{(10-9.5)^2}{9.5} + \frac{(10-11)^2}{11}$$

$$+ \frac{(7-9.5)^2}{9.5} + \frac{(6-7)^2}{7} + \frac{(9-6.5)^2}{6.5}$$

$$= 0.346 + 0.026 + 0.091 + 0.658 + 0.143 + 0.961$$

$$= 2.225.$$

The number of degrees of freedom is $v = k - 1 - m = 6 - 1 - 1 = 4$. The value of k is 6 after pooling the classes, and $m = 1$, since we have one added constraint in assuming that the means (np) of the observed and expected distributions are the same. Thus, from Table A.11, for $v = 4$ and $\alpha = 0.10$, the value of χ^2 is 7.779, which is greater than the calculated χ^2. Hence, there is no justification in claiming that the identity of the shift affects the number of defective castings produced.

PROBLEMS

NOTE: State the null hypothesis and the alternative hypothesis for all problems.

14-1. A product is supposed to contain 5 percent of defective items. We take a sample of 100 items and find it to contain 12 defectives. Are we justified in suspecting that the consignment is not up to specification? Use $\alpha = 1$ percent.

14-2. For the data given in Problem 9-1, use the χ^2 to determine whether the distribution differs significantly from a Poisson distribution. Use $\alpha = 10$ percent.

14-3. For the data given in Problem 9-3, use the χ^2 test to check on the goodness of fit of the assumed Poisson distribution. Use $\alpha = 5$ percent.

14-4. A course is taught in two classes. In class A there are 27 failures out of 202 students taking the course. In class B there are 9 failures out of 199 students. Can we conclude that class B receives better instruction? Use $\alpha = 1$ percent.

TABLE 14.17

	Improvement	No improvement
New nozzle	30	20
Regular nozzle	19	31

14-5. A number of machines of two types were used over a period of time; the records of their serviceability are as follows:

Type	Broken down	Temporarily out of order	Always serviceable
A	11	132	212
B	58	29	13

Can we conclude that type A is superior insofar as it leads to "less trouble"? Use $\alpha = 5$ percent.

14-6. Of 10,000 children entering grade 1 in a given year, 5170 are male. Use the χ^2 test to determine whether the figures suggest that the numbers of males and females differ significantly. Use $\alpha = 1$ percent.

14-7. Samples of 100 items each were taken from two machines producing the same product. Among those from machine A there were 17 defectives, but there were only 3 defectives among those from machine B. Should we conclude that there is a significant difference between the two machines? Use $\alpha = 5$ percent.

14-8. At the end of the first semester the number of failures in three sections of a class, the sections being chosen at random and each with 30 students, was 2, 9, 10, respectively. Can we conclude that the three instructors differ in their marking? Use **(a)** 5 percent level of significance; **(b)** 1 percent level of significance.

14-9. In order to improve the performance of a certain engine a new carburetor nozzle was designed. A lot of 100 identical engines was divided randomly into two sublots of fifty engines. One sublot was fitted with the new nozzle and the other with the regular nozzle. The engine test results are shown in Table 14.17. Test the hypothesis that the new nozzle has no effect in improving engine performance. Use a 5 percent level of significance.

14-10. Four parallel electrical circuit tripping devices are simultaneously subjected to a current surge and the number of those which have broken the circuit is noted in each of 80 tests. The intention of the device is to have a 50 percent probability of tripping under the given current. The frequency of each number of circuit breaks is as follows.

No. of breaks	0	1	2	3	4
Frequency	5	15	30	25	5

Using the K–S test, determine whether the actual distribution conforms to the theoretical binomial distribution ($n = 4$, $p = 0.5$). Use $\alpha = 0.05$.

Chapter 15

Comparison of Means

In Chapter 7 we presented some of the basic principles of statistical inference and in subsequent chapters we applied these principles to various problems including estimation and hypothesis testing. In the present chapter we are concerned with comparing means of samples for the purpose of determining whether the observed difference is due to chance only, or whether we should suspect some real cause to be responsible and hence consider the difference to be statistically significant. This comparison of means is carried out by hypothesis testing. It is instructive, therefore, to expand on this approach.

HYPOTHESIS FORMULATION

A hypothesis is an assertion subject to verification or proof. We have seen that, for our purposes, there are two types of hypotheses: the null hypothesis, H_0, and the alternative hypothesis, H_a. The principle of null hypothesis testing is to examine the postulate that any observed difference between two population parameters, or between the true value of some parameter and a hypothesized value, is attributed only to random sampling errors. The object of the test is to establish whether the differences observed in our experimental results arise from the application of different treatments or processes or whether they merely arise due to chance. If, for example, we observe a difference that could occur by chance less than once in a thousand times, then we are quite justified in treating the difference as statistically significant, thus contradicting the null hypothesis, and concluding that there is a real difference. As we have emphasized before, there is no statistical test capable of providing a complete certainty in our decision, and judgment should always be exercised in interpreting the results: while a result may be statistically significant, there may be practical or economic reasons why decisions cannot be taken as indicated by the statistical test of hypothesis.

In stating hypotheses, it is usual to make the null (H_0) and alternative (H_a) hypotheses complementary. For example, suppose we are studying the yield stress of a steel alloy, with its mean value denoted as μ. If we write H_0: $\mu = 350$ MPa, then $H_a: \mu \neq 350$ MPa; or, if $H_0: \mu \leqslant 350$ MPa, then $H_a: \mu > 350$ MPa. Thus, we observe that if the values specified by H_a lie on both sides of H_0, the test is called a two-sided test, as in the first case, whereas the test with $H_0: \mu \leqslant 350$ MPa versus $H_a: \mu > 350$ MPa is a one-sided test since all the values specified by H_a are to one side of H_0. We shall elaborate this point later on in the chapter. At this stage, we should point out that, when the alternative hypothesis H_a specifies a deviation from equality in one direction, deviations from equality in the opposite direction are of no interest. For example, in quality control and acceptance of merchandise, we are interested only in detecting a proportion of defectives in the product *greater than* the maximum acceptable level, in which case the product can be rejected. If the proportion of defectives is *less than* the acceptable level, so much the better.

Since the decisions we make in hypothesis testing are based on sample information and not on certainty, there is a chance of errors in these decisions. As we have seen in Chapter 7, there are two possible kinds of errors:

a. If we accept H_0 when H_a is true, this is a Type I error.
b. If we accept H_a when H_0 is true, this is a Type II error.

The probabilities of Type I and II errors are denoted by α and β, respectively. These errors, sometimes referred to as inference errors, and their probabilities are discussed in the next section.

INFERENCE ERRORS AND
THEIR PROBABILITIES

Suppose that we have determined the compressive strength of concrete supplied by two ready-mix concrete manufacturers and found that the mean strength of the concrete from supplier A was 48.3 MPa and the standard deviation was 2.8 MPa, the corresponding values for the concrete from supplier B being 63.5 and 2.8 MPa, respectively. In each case the result was obtained from a sample of 10 specimens. We have no doubt that the latter concrete has a higher strength because the difference between the means (15.2 MPa) is more than five times the value of the standard deviation of the values in either sample. It is, therefore, highly improbable that the two samples have been drawn from the same population and that their difference is due to chance. This conclusion is intuitively obvious and statistical proof is not necessary.

When, however, the difference is smaller—for example, if concrete B has a mean strength of 50.4 MPa with the standard deviation remaining at

2.8 MPa—it is far from obvious that this concrete is *really* superior to concrete *A*. We can use statistical methods in an attempt to infer whether or not there is a real difference between the strengths of the two concretes; however, our answer cannot be *guaranteed* to be correct, but it has only a specified probability of being correct. It is important at this stage to know the type of inference error that we may commit.

A Type I error is said to have been made if we infer that there is a real difference between the two samples, while in fact the observed difference is due to chance only. To reduce the risk of a Type I error, we may insist on a higher level of significance of the difference being studied before we accept the difference as real; for example, we may require a 1 percent level of significance, rather than 5 percent, that is, a probability of only 1 percent that such a difference may occur by chance and not be due to real causes. (The choice in a practical case depends on judgment and experience.)

However, a decrease in the risk of a Type I error increases the chances of committing a Type II error. This type of error is said to occur if we conclude that there is no real difference between two samples, while the difference does in fact exist. A Type II error may be due to the inaccuracy of our estimate or to the inadequacy of our data for a satisfactory test of the hypothesis. The errors of inference were summarized on page 131.

The situation is illustrated in Fig. 15.1. Sample (1) may belong to the same population as sample (2). Conversely, it is possible that the two samples belong to two distinct populations which overlap at their tails, so that there is always a small chance that a sample (1) belonging to population *B* is so near the mean of population *A* that sample (1) can be erroneously believed to belong to *A*.

Let us consider the distribution curves of Fig. 15.2 and assume that we want the probability of Type I error, α, to be 1 percent. This means that the criterion for the rejection of the null hypothesis is a value of the abscissa at least equal to the value indicated by *X* such that the area under curve *A* to

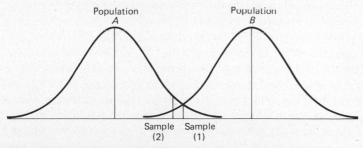

Figure 15.1 Normal distribution curves for two populations. To which population does sample (1) belong? If we infer that it does not belong to *A* while, in fact, it does, we have committed a Type I error. If we infer that (1) does belong to *A* while, in fact, it does not, we have committed a Type II error. [In the diagram, the area under the normal distribution curve for population *A* to the right of sample (1) represents 2.5 percent of the total area under the curve.]

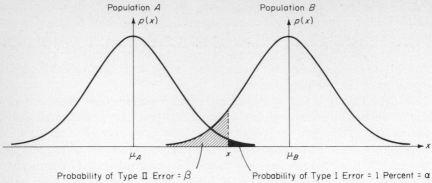

Figure 15.2   Graphical representation of the probability of obtaining a Type II error, assuming that a Type I error of 1 percent is acceptable.

the right of X is 1 percent of the total area under the curve. The probability of Type II error, β, is then equal to the shaded area under curve B. This probability can be calculated from the knowledge of the mean of the population B, μ_B, the standard deviation of the means of the sample drawn from this population, $s_B/\sqrt{n}$, and from the value of X. This probability is

$$P(\bar{x} < X) = P\left(\frac{\bar{x} - \mu_B}{s_B/\sqrt{n}} < \frac{X - \mu_B}{s_B/\sqrt{n}}\right) = \beta$$

where $\bar{x}$ is the observed sample mean. The value of the probability β can be found with the aid of Table A.6.

In Fig. 15.2, we have illustrated the relation between α, β, and the critical value X for a one-sided test. We shall now present such a relation for a two-sided test of significance. Consider the sampling distribution of a sample mean $\bar{x}$ from a normally distributed population with mean μ and variance σ^2. Let us adopt a null hypothesis $H_0 : \mu = \mu_A$ versus $H_a : \mu \neq \mu_A$. For a given α and H_0, we can construct the acceptance and rejection regions as shown in Fig. 15.3(a). Now, if H_0 is false, the true sampling distribution of $\bar{x}$ will not be centered over μ_A [Fig. 15.3(a)] but will be centered over the true population mean, say μ_B [Fig. 15.3(b)]. Thus if $\bar{x}$, computed from the sample drawn from the population, falls in the acceptance region when μ really equals μ_B, H_0 will be *erroneously* accepted and a Type II error committed. The probability of this happening is equal to the portion of the area under the curve of $\bar{x}$, centered over μ_B, that overlaps the area under the curve of $\bar{x}$, centered over μ_A, lying between the critical values of $\bar{x}$, as shown in Fig. 15.3(b).

It is not possible to reduce both Type I and II errors in a given test without changing the sample size. For a given sample size, the smaller the Type I error the larger the Type II error (see Solved Problem 15-2). Usually, the tests of significance are arranged so that there is a specified risk of committing a Type I error (this risk is expressed as the level of significance of the test) without a provision for controlling the risk of a Type II error, which depends on the true unknown value of the parameter in question. However, if the resulting Type II

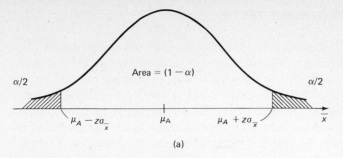

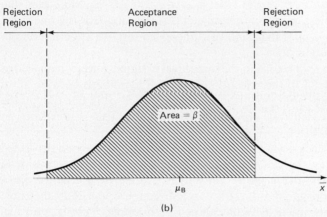

(b)

Figure 15.3 Relation between α and β in a two-sided test.

TABLE 15.1 EXAMPLES OF TYPE I AND TYPE II ERRORS

Engineering problem	Type I error	Type II error
	Selection of a more expensive device that *seems* to behave more dependably than others but does not really do so	Failure to select the truly best device
Parachute opening device	Not serious	Extremely serious (safety)
Electric relay in a cheap toy	Serious (economics)	Not very serious

error is unacceptably high, the probability of committing it can be decreased by increasing the sample size, but this, of course, means a higher cost. The choice of sample size for specified risks of committing errors of both types is discussed fully in Chapter 22 and the relation between α, β, and sample size n is considered on page 300. Here, it suffices to say that the level of acceptability of the error of either type depends on the consequences of its occurrence: we must err on the safe side; this, indeed, is common engineering sense (see Table 15.1).

ONE-SIDED AND TWO-SIDED TESTS

There are two general questions that we may seek to answer by means of a statistical test of significance. The first one: is μ significantly different from μ_0? Here, we are not interested in whether $\mu > \mu_0$ or $\mu < \mu_0$; the null hypothesis can be wrongly rejected in favor of either of these possibilities, and the test is therefore two sided. The null hypothesis is rejected if the proportional area under *two* tails is smaller than that corresponding to the specified level of significance, that is, when the absolute value of the calculated statistic is greater than the tabulated statistic.

The second question is of the type: is $\mu > \mu_0$? If $\mu \not> \mu_0$, we accept the null hypothesis regardless of how much smaller μ is than μ_0. This is a one-sided test, and the sign of $\mu - \mu_0$ is material. In a one-sided test, we are interested in one tail of the distribution only.

It is important to realize that, at the same level of significance, α, a one-sided test is more likely to lead to the rejection of the null hypothesis because all of the α area under the probability distribution curve is located in one tail; on the other hand, in a two-sided test, only $\alpha/2$ is in each tail. This is illustrated in Fig. 15.4.

It is advisable to decide whether we should apply a one-sided or a two-sided test before commencing the calculations so as to avoid the tendency to lean toward the test that will give a more "convenient" result. As a general rule, a one-sided test is appropriate if a deviation in a direction opposite to that postulated would have no practical significance. For example, if we require fuel

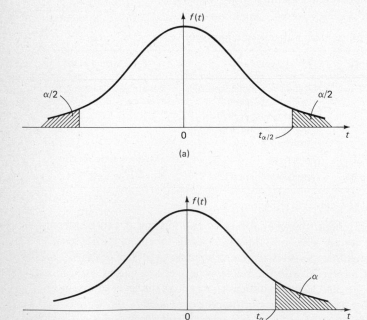

Figure 15.4 Tail areas for a given α in (a) two-sided, and (b) one-sided tests.

with a certain minimum octane rating level, we would test whether the actual rating is significantly lower than that specified, but we would not be concerned if it were higher. Another example of a one-sided test is afforded by the traffic speed problem, considered on page 309, since the question asked concerns an increase in speed.

The concepts of one-sided and two-sided normal distribution tests are illustrated in Fig. 15.5, and these are similar to the t tests. See also Solved Problems 15-1 and 15-2.

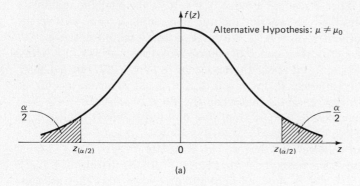

(a)

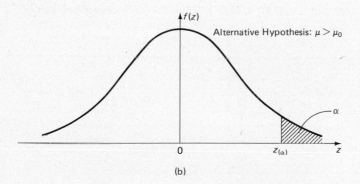

(b)

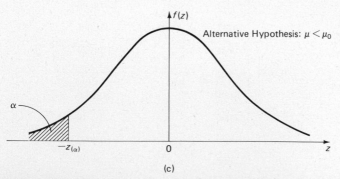

(c)

Figure 15.5   Two-sided and one-sided normal tests with null hypothesis $\mu = \mu_0$: (a) two-sided test; (b) one-sided test with positive z; and (c) one-sided test with negative z.

RELATION BETWEEN α, β, AND
SAMPLE SIZE n

We have mentioned earlier that the probabilities of Type I and II errors and the sample size n are interrelated. This can be best illustrated by means of an example. Let us consider a machine that produces a certain type of bolt. From past records, it is known that when the proportion of defective bolts p is no more than $p = 0.10$, the machine requires only minor repairs and this can be tolerated; however, when p reaches a value of $p = 0.30$, the machine requires a major overhaul. Hence, we can assume the null hypothesis $H_0 : p = 0.10$ versus the alternative hypothesis $H_a : p = 0.30$. We agree to take a sample of size $n = 10$ bolts and decide on a critical value for the number of defectives as $r < 2$. Thus, we shall accept H_0 if $r < 2$ and reject H_0 (or accept H_a) if $r \geqslant 2$. Using Eq. (8.1), we can calculate the values of P_r for $p = 0.10$ and $p = 0.30$, given $n = 10$, as shown in Table 15.2. Hence, we see that when $H_0 : p = 0.10$ is true, $\alpha = P(r \geqslant 2)$ $= 0.2639$; and, when $H_a : p = 0.30$ is true, $\beta = P(r < 2) = 0.1493$. The results are shown graphically in Fig. 15.6.

       It is important to point out that we can calculate β only after a specific value for an alternative has been given, that is, $p = 0.30$. Furthermore, α and β are not complementary, that is, they need not add up to one, since they are conditional probabilities based on different conditions. Specifically, we can lower both α and β by increasing the sample size n. Suppose we increase the sample

TABLE 15.2

Number of defectives, r	Probabilities	
	When $p = 0.10$ $P_r = {}_{10}C_r(0.10)^r(0.90)^{10-r}$	When $p = 0.30$ $P_r = {}_{10}C_r(0.30)^r(0.70)^{10-r}$
0	0.3487	$\beta = 0.1493 \begin{cases} 0.0282 \\ 0.1211 \end{cases}$
1	0.3874	
2	0.1937	0.2335
3	0.0574	0.2668
4	0.0112	0.2001
5	0.0015	0.1029
6	$\alpha = 0.2639$ 0.0001	0.0368
7	0.0000	0.0090
8	0.0000	0.0014
9	0.0000	0.0002
10	0.0000	0.0000
	$\sum = 1.0000$	$\sum = 1.0000$

-- - - Critical value of r (between rows 1 and 2)

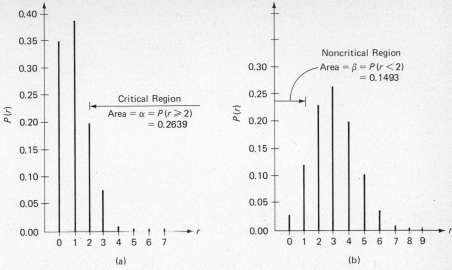

Figure 15.6 Binomial distribution plots: (a) H_0 is true ($p = 0.10$); (b) H_a is true ($p = 0.30$).

size from $n = 10$ to $n = 20$, with an arbitrarily chosen critical region defined by $r \geqslant 4$. Using Eq. (8.1), with $p = 0.10$ and $p = 0.30$, for $n = 20$, we calculate $\alpha = 0.1329$ and $\beta = 0.1070$. Thus, with $p = 0.10$, $\alpha = P(r \geqslant 4) = 0.1329$; and, with $p = 0.30$, $\beta = P(r < 4) = 0.1070$. We can see then that we have decreased both α and β by doubling the sample size. Of course, larger sample sizes involve increased costs so that a sound sampling plan would balance the risks of making an incorrect decision and the cost involved. Such sampling plans are discussed in Chapter 22.

    The *power* of a significance test is defined as the probability of rejecting a false null hypothesis and is equal to $(1 - \beta)$. Thus, for a given α, we say that one test is more powerful than another if $(1 - \beta)$ for the former is greater than for the latter for all values of the parameter in question. Typical power curves are shown in Fig. 15.7 for a two-sided and a one-sided test. The complement of the *power curve* is the *operating characteristic* curve (OC curve) which is widely used in industrial quality control. This subject is further discussed in Chapter 22.

    When we apply the statistical decision theory to practical problems of studying a population parameter, we may encounter the following alternatives, given a null hypothesis H_0 versus a simple alternative hypothesis H_a:

    i. Given a decision rule, compute the probabilities α and β.
    ii. Given α (e.g., 0.05 or 0.01) arrive at a decision rule and compute β.
    iii. Decide on α and β and arrive at a decision rule on the parameter being studied.

Alternative (i) is illustrated in the Solved Example on page 300, and alternatives (ii) and (iii) are illustrated in Solved Problem 15-2.

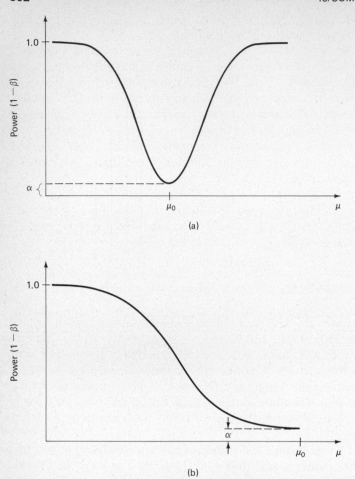

Figure 15.7 Power of test $(1 - \beta)$: (a) two-sided test; (b) one-sided test (rejection area in the lower tail of the sampling distribution).

PROCEDURE FOR HYPOTHESIS TESTING

As we mentioned earlier, in order to test a null hypothesis, we examine sample data from the relevant population so as to decide whether or not they are compatible with the null hypothesis. The data refer to a specific population parameter, for example, the population mean, which is the subject matter of this chapter.[1]

In general, the procedure for hypothesis testing includes the following steps.

1. State the null and alternative hypotheses, H_0 and H_a.

2. Select the significance level, α, and the size of sample, n, to be tested.

---

[1] The hypothesis tests for the binomial and Poisson parameters are considered in Chapters 8 and 9, respectively, and for the population variance in Chapter 16.

3. Describe the population of interest, for example, size of the population sampled, or whether normally distributed.
4. Select the relevant statistic; for example, if we are testing a hypothesis about the population mean, then the sample mean $\bar{x}$ (from that population) is the relevant statistic. We shall also require information about the form and parameters of the sampling distribution of the statistic (Chapter 6) in order to model the problem at hand. For instance, if sampling is from a normally distributed population with mean μ and variance σ^2, then the sampling distribution of the sample mean $\bar{x}$ (sample size $= n$) is also normally distributed with mean μ and variance σ^2/n as parameters.
5. Specify the test statistic and its distribution, such as z, t, χ^2, or F; this statistic is computed from the sample data. For instance, when sampling is from a normally distributed population with a known variance, the test statistic is z given by

$$z = \frac{\bar{x} - \mu_0}{\sigma_{(\bar{x} - \mu_0)}} = \frac{\bar{x} - \mu_0}{\sigma_{\bar{x}}} = \frac{\bar{x} - \mu_0}{\sigma/\sqrt{n}}$$

where μ_0 is a known parameter.[2] The test statistic z is normally distributed with mean $= 0$ and variance $= 1$, as shown in Chapter 5. When sampling is from a normally distributed population with unknown variance, estimated from the sample as s^2, then the test statistic becomes

$$t = \frac{\bar{x} - \mu_0}{s/\sqrt{n}}$$

which follows a t distribution with the number of degrees of freedom $v = n - 1$.
6. Determine the rejection and acceptance regions as set by the level of significance α.
7. Compute the value of the test statistic for the data collected.
8. Make statistical decisions and draw conclusions.

As we have mentioned before, if the calculated statistic falls in the rejection region, we reject H_0. On the other hand, if we accept H_0, then the calculation of β (which depends on the true unknown value of the parameter in question) is sometimes necessary because, if β is small, we could accept H_0, realizing the risk of an erroneous decision.

---

[2] $\mathrm{Var}(\bar{x} - \mu_0) = \mathrm{Var}\, \bar{x} + \mathrm{Var}\, \mu_0$ (by rule 7, Chapter 5)

$\qquad\qquad\qquad = \mathrm{Var}\, \bar{x} + 0$ (by rule 2, Chapter 5)

$\qquad\qquad\qquad = \sigma_{\bar{x}}^2 = \dfrac{\sigma^2}{n}$ [by Eq. (6.10)].

Hence,

$$\sigma_{(\bar{x} - \mu_0)} = \frac{\sigma}{\sqrt{n}}.$$

We should note that in the illustrative examples and solved problems in this chapter (and elsewhere in the book) the procedural steps in hypothesis testing will not be specifically identified.

NORMAL DISTRIBUTION TEST

One-Sample Test

We frequently want to determine whether a set of observations (i.e., a sample) accords with the hypothesis that the population mean has a specific value. The standard deviation of the population may be known (as in quality control work when a large amount of previous data is available) or may have to be estimated from the standard deviation of the actual observations (as is usually the case in experimental work). In the latter case, the sample must be sufficiently large (say, $n \geqslant 30$) for a close estimate of the population standard deviation σ to be possible.

To answer our question, we apply the normal distribution test, provided, of course, that the underlying distribution is normal. The test consists of calculating the z statistic given by

$$z = \frac{|\mu - \bar{x}|}{\sigma/\sqrt{n}} \tag{15.1}$$

where μ = the population mean,
$\bar{x}$ = the sample mean,
n = the sample size, and
$\sigma/\sqrt{n}$ = the standard deviation of the mean [from Eq. (6.10)].

As mentioned earlier, if σ of the population is not known, but is estimated from the sample by s, Eq. (15.1) still applies *provided* that the sample size $n \geqslant 30$. In such cases, we use $\sigma_{\bar{x}} = \sigma/\sqrt{n} \simeq s_{\bar{x}} = s/\sqrt{n}$, based on Eq. (6.11), and the statistic z is then given by

$$z = \frac{|\mu - \bar{x}|}{s/\sqrt{n}}. \tag{15.2}$$

We can now find from Table A.6 the probability of obtaining a value of z at least this large. This probability is represented by $1 - 2 \times F(z)$. The factor 2 is appropriate here, since we are generally interested in testing the significance of the difference $|\mu - \bar{x}|$, and are not concerned with whether $\mu > \bar{x}$ or $\mu < \bar{x}$. When the probability given by Table A.6 is small (below a specified minimum), we reject the hypothesis.

If the underlying population is not infinite but consists of N items, then z is modified to

$$z = \frac{|\mu - \bar{x}|}{(\sigma/\sqrt{n})\sqrt{(N-n)/(N-1)}}. \tag{15.3}$$

EXAMPLE

The mean ultimate strength of a certain aluminum alloy wire is stated by the manufacturer to be 250 MPa. A contractor buys a consignment of wire and tests specimens from 35 coils. The mean value from these tests is 247.4 MPa with a standard deviation of 11.2 MPa. Is the contractor justified in concluding that the consignment does not accord with the manufacturer's statement? Use $\alpha = 5$ percent.

The null hypothesis is $H_0: \mu = 250$ versus $H_a: \mu < 250$, that is, this is a one-sided test. We have $\bar{x} = 247.4$, and $s = 11.2$. Because the sample size is large ($n = 35$), we can use the normal distribution test and take the standard deviation of the mean as

$$\frac{11.2}{\sqrt{35}} = 1.89.$$

From Eq. (15.1),

$$z = \frac{250 - 247.4}{1.89} = 1.37.$$

Since this is a one-sided test, Fig. 15.5(c) is appropriate; the critical value of z, given by $\alpha = 0.05$, is obtained from Table A.6 as follows: $0.5 - F(z) = \alpha = 0.05$; therefore $F(z) = 0.45$, or $z_{\text{critical}} = 1.645$. Since $z_{\text{calc}} < z_{\text{crit}}$, that is, z_{calc} falls in the acceptance region, we conclude that the consignment belongs to the manufacturer's stated population and advise the contractor to accept the wire.　■ ■

EXAMPLE

The sampling distribution of the mean tensile strength of a certain plastic is normally distributed with mean $\mu = 100$ kPa and variance $\sigma^2 = 25$ kPa. Based on a sample size of $n = 9$ measurements, calculate the probability β of accepting the null hypothesis when μ is actually equal to $\mu_1 = 105$ kPa, given $\alpha = 0.05$.

The null hypothesis is $H_0: \mu = 100$ versus $H_a: \mu = 105$. This is a one-sided test and, therefore, we can use Fig. 15.2. Similarly to the previous example, we find $0.5 - F(z) = \alpha = 0.05$, or $F(z) = 0.45$, and, hence, from Table A.6, $z = 1.645$. Also $\sigma_{\bar{x}} = \sigma/\sqrt{n} = \sqrt{25}/\sqrt{9} = 5/3$. Therefore, the boundary of the acceptance region is $X = 100 + z\sigma_{\bar{x}} = 100 + 1.645 \times (5/3) = 102.7$ kPa. Now, β is equal to the area under the normal distribution curve located to the left of 102.7 kPa. Thus, the corresponding z value is

$$z = \frac{\mu_1 - X}{\sigma_{\bar{x}}} = \frac{105 - 102.7}{5/3} = 1.38.$$

From Table A.6, $F(z) = 0.4162$. Therefore, $\beta = P(\text{accept } H_0 \text{ when } \mu = 105) = P(z > 1.38) = 0.5 - 0.4162 = 0.0838$, or about 8 chances in 100.　■ ■

EXAMPLE

A machine was considered to be in good working order when it produced steel rods having a mean length of 25.00 cm. The standard deviation of the rod length had always been about 1 cm. A sample of 36 rods is taken and the average length of these rods is found to be 25.30 cm.

    a. State the null and alternative hypotheses.

    b. For the given sample results, check whether the machine is working properly. Assume $\alpha = 0.05$.

    c. If the alternative hypothesis is that mean length $\mu_a = 25.50$ cm, and the critical region in part (b) is used, what is the probability (β) of a Type II error?

Solution.

    a. The null hypothesis is $H_0: \mu = 25.00$ cm, and $H_a: \mu \neq 25.00$ cm.

    b. Since the sample size $n = 36$ is greater than 30, we can assume, using the central limit theorem, that the sampling distribution of the sample mean $\bar{x}$ follows a normal distribution, with mean μ and variance $\sigma_{\bar{x}}^2 = \sigma^2/n = 1^2/36$.

Thus, the appropriate test statistic is z given by

$$z = \frac{\bar{x} - \mu}{\sigma_{\bar{x}}} = \frac{25.30 - 25.00}{1/6} = 1.8.$$

Since this is a two-sided test [see Fig. 15.5(a)], for $\alpha = 0.05$, we have $0.5 - F(z) = \alpha/2 = 0.025$. Hence, $F(z) = 0.475$, and $z_{\text{crit}} = 1.96$. Since $z_{\text{calc}} < z_{\text{crit}}$, we cannot reject the null hypothesis. The acceptance region is bounded by $(25.00 \pm z_{\text{crit}}\sigma_{\bar{x}})$ or $(25.00 \pm 1.96 \times 1/6)$, that is, 25.33 and 24.67 cm, as shown in Fig. 15.8.

    c. The probability β of accepting H_0, given $\mu = 25.50$ cm, is the area shown in Fig. 15.8. Calculating the z value corresponding to the limit 24.67 cm, with $\mu_a = 25.50$, we have

$$z = \frac{|24.67 - 25.50|}{\sigma_{\bar{x}}} = 4.98.$$

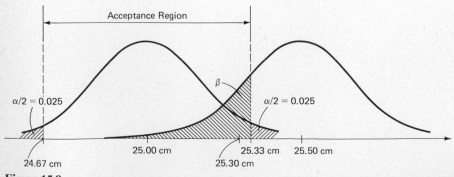

Figure 15.8

From Table A.6, $F(z) \simeq 0.5$. The z value corresponding to the limit 25.33 cm is

$$z = \frac{|25.33 - 25.50|}{\sigma_{\bar{x}}} = 1.02.$$

From Table A.6, $F(z) = 0.3461$. Therefore, $\beta = 0.5 - 0.3461 = 0.1539$. Thus, the probability of accepting H_0 given that $\mu = 25.50$ cm is approximately 15 percent. ■ ■

Two-Sample Test

The normal distribution can also be used to compare the means of two random samples. For example, given two different sample means, $\bar{x}_1$ and $\bar{x}_2$, with $d = |x_1 - x_2|$ and sample sizes n_1 and n_2, the question is whether we are willing to attribute the difference d to chance errors of sampling or whether we should conclude that the populations from which the samples are drawn have unequal means μ_1 and μ_2 (see Fig. 15.9). In this case, the null hypothesis is $H_0 : \mu_1 - \mu_2 = 0$ (or $\mu_1 = \mu_2$) versus $H_a : \mu_1 - \mu_2 \neq 0$ (or $\mu_1 \neq \mu_2$). If the two samples are independent (i.e., the probabilities of selecting the elements in one sample are not affected by the selection in the other sample), then their mean $\bar{x}_1$ and $\bar{x}_2$ are independent random variables and, hence, d is also a random variable. It was shown in Chapter 5 that the mean and variance of the sampling distribution of d are

$$\mu_{(\bar{x}_1 - \bar{x}_2)} = \mu_d = 0 \tag{15.4}$$

and

$$\sigma^2_{(x_1 - \bar{x}_2)} = \sigma_d^2 = \sigma_{\bar{x}_1}^2 + \sigma_{\bar{x}_2}^2 = \frac{\sigma_1^2}{n_1} + \frac{\sigma_2^2}{n_2}. \tag{15.5}$$

This is not surprising as the variability of the difference between two independent random variables must be greater than the variability of either of the two variables, as one of them may happen to be very large just when the other one is particularly small. In other words, each variable contributes some of its variability to the variability of the differences.

If we assume that the variances of the two underlying populations are equal, that is, $\sigma_1^2 = \sigma_2^2 = \sigma^2$, Eq. (15.5) becomes

$$\sigma_d^2 = \sigma^2 \left(\frac{1}{n_1} + \frac{1}{n_2} \right). \tag{15.6}$$

Now, if both the underlying populations are normally distributed, then the test statistic

$$z = \frac{|\bar{x}_1 - \bar{x}_2| - |\mu_1 - \mu_2|}{\sigma_{(\bar{x}_1 - \bar{x}_2)}} \tag{15.7}$$

is normally distributed with mean $= 0$ and variance $= 1$. By invoking the null hypothesis, we can write the statistic z as

$$z = \frac{|\bar{x}_1 - \bar{x}_2|}{\sigma_d} = \frac{|d|}{\sigma_d}. \tag{15.8}$$

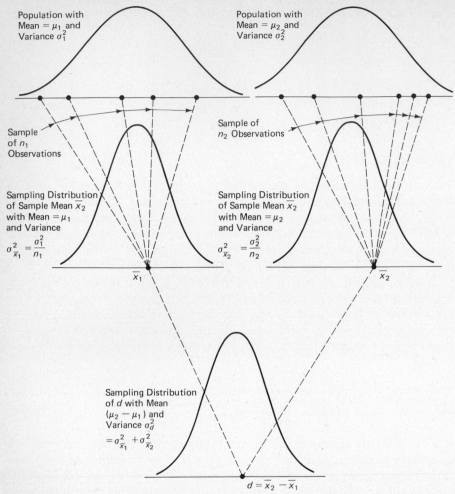

Figure 15.9 Sampling distribution of d ($=\bar{x}_2 - \bar{x}_1$) resulting from two parent populations sampled.

We note that, as in Eq. (15.1), the significance of the difference of means is measured by the ratio of the difference to its standard deviation. We can now use Table A.6 in the usual manner to decide whether this calculated z value falls in the critical region as defined by a given level of significance α. If so, we reject the null hypothesis and conclude that the population parameters μ_1 and μ_2 are indeed different.

If the variance σ^2 of the two underlying populations is not known, then Eq. (15.8) no longer applies. However, when the sizes of the two samples, n_1 and n_2, are large (say, $n \geqslant 30$), then σ_d in Eq. (15.8) is estimated quite precisely from the variance estimates, s_1^2 and s_2^2, from the two samples. We note that since the two samples are large, the variances of the two sample means will be approximately normally distributed (see the central limit theorem, page 117).

Thus, we can write

$$\sigma_d^2 \simeq s_d^2 = s_{\bar{x}_1}^2 + s_{\bar{x}_2}^2 = \frac{s_1^2}{n_1} + \frac{s_2^2}{n_2}. \qquad (15.9)$$

Hence, we can write Eq. (15.8) as

$$z = \frac{|\bar{x}_1 - \bar{x}_2|}{\sqrt{\dfrac{\sum(x_1 - \bar{x}_1)^2}{n_1(n_1 - 1)} + \dfrac{\sum(x_2 - \bar{x}_2)^2}{n_2(n_2 - 1)}}} \qquad (15.10)$$

where x_1 and x_2 are the individual measurements in samples 1 and 2, respectively. For convenience, the more common values of the areas between $(d - z\sigma_d)$ and $(d + z\sigma_d)$ are given in Table 15.3.

EXAMPLE

Traffic studies before and after traffic control improvements were made at a certain intersection in a city. The condensed data are given in Table 15.4. Does the difference between the two mean speeds represent a significant increase? Use $\alpha = 1$ percent and assume that the "before" and "after" means are independent.

TABLE 15.3 PROBABILITY FOR NORMAL DISTRIBUTION

z	Probability of $|\bar{x}_1 - \bar{x}_2|$ being smaller than $z\sigma_d$, percent
0.524	40
0.674	50
1.036	70
1.282	80
1.645	90
1.960	95
2.326	98
2.576	99
3.291	99.9

TABLE 15.4

Time	Mean speed $\bar{x}$, km/h	Number of speed observations, n	Standard deviation, s, km/h
Before	29.3	140	5.65
After	30.9	160	5.07

The estimates of the standard deviations of the two population means are

$$\frac{s_1}{\sqrt{n_1}} = \frac{5.65}{\sqrt{140}} = 0.478$$

and

$$\frac{s_2}{\sqrt{n_2}} = \frac{5.07}{\sqrt{160}} = 0.401.$$

From Eq. (15.9), the standard deviation of the difference of means is

$$\sigma_d \simeq s_d = \sqrt{0.478^2 + 0.401^2} = 0.624.$$

We now calculate z [given by Eq. (15.8)]:

$$z = \frac{|\bar{x}_1 - \bar{x}_2|}{s_d} = \frac{30.9 - 29.3}{0.624} = 2.56.$$

This is a one-sided test, since we are checking the null hypothesis $\mu_1 = \mu_2$ against the alternative hypothesis $\mu_1 > \mu_2$. From Table A.6, we find the probability of obtaining by chance a value of z of at least this magnitude as $(0.5000 - 0.4948) = 0.0052 = 0.52$ percent. We conclude, therefore, that the observed increase in the mean speed is significant and not due to chance error. ■ ■

THE t TEST

The hypothesis testing methods discussed in the preceding sections were appropriate for:

   i. sample(s) of any size drawn from normally distributed population(s) whose variance σ^2 is known; and
   ii. sample(s) of large size ($n \geqslant 30$) drawn from underlying population(s) whose variance σ^2 is unknown but is estimated from the sample(s) because the statistic $(\bar{x} - \mu)/s_{\bar{x}}$ is approximately normally distributed.

It should be noted that in case (ii) the underlying population(s) need not be normally distributed. However, for a small sample from a normally distributed population whose variance σ^2 is unknown, the ratio $(\bar{x} - \mu)/s_{\bar{x}}$ is described by Student's t statistic.[3] For the t test to be applicable, it is essential that $\bar{x}$ and s_x are independent of one another; this is, of course, the case with random samples drawn from a normal distribution.

One-Sample Test

In Chapter 6 we defined the random variable t as

$$t = \frac{z}{\sqrt{\chi^2/\nu}} \tag{15.11}$$

---

[3] Student was the pseudonym of W. S. Gosset, a chemist at the Guinness brewery in Dublin.

where z is defined by Eq. (15.1),

$$\chi^2 = \frac{vs^2}{\sigma^2},$$

and v = the number of degrees of freedom = $n - 1$, with reference to χ^2.

The density function of t can be shown to be

$$f(t) = \frac{1}{\sqrt{\pi v}} \times \frac{\Gamma\left(\dfrac{v+1}{2}\right)}{\Gamma\left(\dfrac{v}{2}\right)} \left(1 + \frac{t^2}{v}\right)^{-(v+1)/2}$$

for $-\infty < t < +\infty$. (The Γ function is defined on page 274.) Thus, we can write Eq. (15.11) as

$$t = \frac{(\bar{x} - \mu)\dfrac{\sqrt{n}}{\sigma}}{\sqrt{n-1} \times \dfrac{s}{\sigma(\sqrt{n-1})}} = \frac{(\bar{x} - \mu)}{s/\sqrt{n}}$$

or

$$t = \frac{\bar{x} - \mu}{s/\sqrt{n}} = \frac{\bar{x} - \mu}{s_{\bar{x}}}. \tag{15.12}$$

Values of the statistic t are given in Table A.7 in terms of the number of degrees of freedom v. This number is the same as that for the estimate s. As we have seen in Chapter 4, for a sample of size n, v for s is $(n-1)$. For a large sample size ($n \geqslant 30$) the t distribution closely approximates the normal distribution.

The one-sided and two-sided t tests are similar to those for the normal distribution tests (see Fig. 15.5) except that t and $f(t)$ replace z and $f(z)$, respectively.

Although, as mentioned earlier, the t test is applicable to samples drawn from normally distributed populations, a fairly large departure from normality (provided the distribution is symmetrical and modal) does not seriously affect the outcome of a two-sided t test even if the samples are as small as 10 or even 5. However, a one-sided t test is more seriously affected because of the skewness of the sampling distribution. When the departure from normality is very large, the use of nonparametric test methods is preferable (see page 320).

Two-Sample Test

We have seen earlier that we can compare the means of two random small-sized samples by computing the statistic z from Eq. (15.8), based on the null hypothesis $H_0: \mu_1 - \mu_2 = 0$. If σ in Eq. (15.6) is known, then the problem is solved using the normal distribution test. If, as is often the case, σ is unknown, then we must use the following procedure. It can be shown that the statistic χ^2 has the additive property, that is, the sum

$$\chi_1^2 + \chi_2^2 = \frac{(n_1 - 1)s_1^2}{\sigma^2} + \frac{(n_2 - 1)s_2^2}{\sigma^2}$$

has a χ^2 distribution with $(n_1 + n_2 - 2)$ degrees of freedom and is independent of the random variable $(\bar{x}_1 - \bar{x}_2)$. Hence, substituting Eqs. (15.8) and (15.9) and $\chi^2 = \chi_1^2 + \chi_2^2$ into Eq. (15.11), we find

$$t = \frac{|\bar{x}_1 - \bar{x}_2|}{s_c \sqrt{\dfrac{1}{n_1} + \dfrac{1}{n_2}}}. \tag{15.13}$$

This statistic has a t distribution with $(n_1 + n_2 - 2)$ degrees of freedom, where s_c^2 is the combined population variance estimated from the two samples and given by

$$s_c^2 = \frac{(n_1 - 1)s_1^2 + (n_2 - 1)s_2^2}{n_1 + n_2 - 2}. \tag{15.14}$$

Thus, each estimated variance is weighted by the number of degrees of freedom available for its calculation. This is the *only* method of obtaining a combined variance. Averaging of variances without considering the numbers of degrees of freedom involved is incorrect. Averaging of standard deviations is also incorrect.

The combined or pooled variance can also be computed from

$$s_c^2 = \frac{\sum(x_1 - \bar{x}_1)^2 + \sum(x_2 - \bar{x}_2)^2}{n_1 + n_2 - 2}. \tag{15.15}$$

Equation (15.13) can also be expressed as

$$t = \frac{|\bar{x}_1 - \bar{x}_2|}{s_d} = \frac{|d|}{s_d} \tag{15.16}$$

where

$$s_d = s_c \sqrt{\frac{n_1 + n_2}{n_1 n_2}}. \tag{15.17}$$

We should note that the process of pooling leads to the most advantageous use of all the information provided by the sample data. However, since the null hypothesis being examined by the t test assumes that the two samples belong to the same population, the two variance estimates must be consistent with this hypothesis, that is, the two variances must not be significantly different.

The probability of $\bar{x}_1 - \bar{x}_2$ exceeding ts_d, if drawn by chance from the same population, represents the odds *against* the null hypothesis and, similarly to the case in Chapter 11, is known as the level of significance. Values of t for various levels of significance and degrees of freedom are given in Table A.7.

We usually specify the level of significance at which we are prepared to reject the null hypothesis as 5 percent or 1 percent. If the calculated t is greater than the tabulated value at the specified level of significance, we reject the null hypothesis and conclude that the difference is significant. If the calculated t is not greater than the tabulated t at, say, the 5 percent level of significance, the null hypothesis is accepted, but we cannot tell whether there is no difference between the means being compared or whether the data are inadequate to establish whether or not there is a difference. As previously stated, there is no question of ever proving the null hypothesis. We must remember also that statistical considerations are not the sole basis for drawing inferences; a physical appreciation of the problem, judgment, and experience should also be brought into the picture.

We can now answer the question posed on page 294. The difference between the mean strengths of the two concretes is $50.4 - 48.3 = 2.1$ MPa; and

$$s_d = 2.8 \sqrt{\frac{20}{100}} = 1.25 \text{ MPa.}$$

Hence,
$$t = \frac{2.1}{1.25} = 1.68.$$

For $20 - 2 = 18$ degrees of freedom, Table A.7 gives $t = 1,734$ at the 10 percent level of significance, and we conclude, therefore, that there is no significant difference between the strengths of the two concretes.

We should note that for a given probability (i.e., a specified level of significance) the size of the sample required to make a decision possible increases as the difference between the means decreases.

EXAMPLE

The slopes of two types of valley walls were measured. Sample *A* comprised slopes at whose base talus and slope wash have accumulated, indicating that considerable time has elapsed since stream erosion was active against the slope base. Sample *B* comprised slopes at whose base stream erosion has recently been active. We wish to determine whether the slopes of sample *A* differ significantly from those of *B*. In other words, do the data indicate that a slope, if left to weather and waste without basal cutting, tends to decline in angle rather than retreat in parallel planes?[4] Use $\alpha = 1$ percent.

Sample	Mean slope, $\bar{x}$	Standard deviation, s	Sample size, n
A	38.23°	2.70°	34
B	44.82°	3.27°	172

We assume *a priori* that the two population variances are equal and, of course, the two samples are independent of one another.

From Eq. (15.14) the pooled estimate of variance is

$$s_c^2 = \frac{33 \times 2.7^2 + 171 \times 3.27^2}{33 + 171} = 10.142$$

and
$$s_c = 3.2°.$$

[4] A. N. Strahler, "Statistical Analysis in Geomorphic Research," *Journal of Geology*, Jan. 1954, p. 12.

Using Eq. (15.17), we obtain

$$s_d = 3.2 \sqrt{\frac{1}{34} + \frac{1}{172}} = 0.60$$

and from Eq. (15.16),

$$t = \frac{44.82 - 38.23}{0.60} = 10.98.$$

The number of degrees of freedom is $172 + 34 - 2 = 204$, and Table A.7 gives the probability of less than 0.1 percent of obtaining a value of t equal to or greater than 10.98. Therefore, the null hypothesis can be rejected, and we conclude that the absence of erosion at the base of a slope leads to a decline in the angle of the slope, but when erosion takes place, the slope retreats parallel to itself.   ■ ■

The distribution of t is unimodal and symmetrical about the value $t = 0$. The variability of t is greater than that of z because t is affected by the variations both in $\bar{x}$ and in s, while the variability of z depends on the variability of $\bar{x}$ alone. The variability of t decreases with an increase in the sample size n because s is then established on better information. In the limit, when n is infinitely large, s becomes σ and the t and z distributions are identical.

For the above reason, when we require a specific value of α, the critical value of t is greater than that of z. The value of t, at a given value of α, decreases with an increase in the sample size n, and, as expected, when n is infinitely large, the values of t and z are identical.

In practical terms, we consider a sample size $n \geqslant 30$ as large, and use the t test only for smaller samples. We do so because, at this sample size, the difference between the t and z values is small (see Tables A.7 and A.6).

We may note that t itself is not normally distributed but becomes so when the number of degrees of freedom v approaches infinity. This can be seen from a comparison of the values of t for $v = \infty$ (Table A.7) and the values of z for the corresponding $2F(z)$ (Table A.6), for example, at the 10 percent level of significance $t = 1.645$. Now for $z = 1.645$, $2F(z) = 0.90$, which corresponds to the 10 percent level of significance.

THE t TEST FOR PAIRED DATA

The comparison of means discussed in the preceding pages is applicable when the two samples have been drawn independently of one another; for example, they may represent products of two factories, and we may want to compare these products in order to determine whether there is a significant difference between them. If, however, the samples are drawn from one source and then subjected to two different treatments whose effects are being studied, we can use a somewhat different technique, although the t test on the difference of means is still permissible.

In the case of paired variables, we consider the mean difference between two samples as the variate and compare it with *its* standard deviation, that is, we apply the *t* test to the paired data. In this manner, the effect of the test-to-test variation is eliminated, but this advantage is offset by a loss in precision due to the standard deviation being based on fewer degrees of freedom (the number of *pairs* less one, instead of the total number of observations less two).

It should be stressed that this technique can be used only when the pairs of samples are truly correlated; pairing by random choice or by arrangement of samples in each group by rank is not permitted. Because of the somewhat confusing terminology, it is important to distinguish between a test for the difference between means and a test for the mean difference between pairs of observations.

INTERPRETATION OF RESULTS

When the data are truly paired, we can apply either form of the *t* test. Which one is more convenient to use will depend on whether the variation between tests, which may be made under different conditions, obscures the difference between two members of a pair forming one test. This is illustrated by the next example.

Having a choice of tests of significance, the reader may wonder what to do when one test indicates a significant difference between two sets of values while the other does not. We should remember that failure to detect a significant difference does not mean that there is none, but only that we cannot say with a sufficiently high probability of being right that a difference is present. Thus if *any* method of test shows a definitely significant difference, its testimony is vital, even though another method fails to show a similar result.

EXAMPLE

The influence of the size of the test specimen on the tensile strength of briquettes was tested as shown in Table 15.5. Seven mixes were made and, from each, one large and one small concrete specimen were prepared and tested.

TABLE 15.5

Strength of specimen, kN/m^2		
Small, x_2	Large, x_1	Difference, kN/m^2 $x_2 - x_1$
4404	4140	264
4326	3984	342
3788	3842	-54
3475	3053	422
3418	3145	273
2262	1813	449
7415	6867	548
$\sum x_2 = 29{,}088$	$\sum x_1 = 26{,}844$	$\sum(x_2 - x_1) = 2244$

Test whether there is a significant difference between the strengths of the two types of specimens. Use $\alpha = 5$ percent. Hence,

$$\bar{x}_2 = \frac{\sum x_2}{n_2} = \frac{29{,}088}{7} = 4155.43 \text{ kN/m}^2$$

and
$$\bar{x}_1 = \frac{26{,}844}{7} = 3834.86 \text{ kN/m}^2.$$

Since the data are paired, we consider $x_2 - x_1$ as the variable. Let $y = x_2 - x_1$. Then,

$$\bar{y} = \frac{\sum y}{n} = \frac{2244}{7} = 320.57 \text{ kN/m}^2.$$

Now, the standard deviation of y is

$$s = \sqrt{\frac{\sum (y - \bar{y})^2}{n - 1}}$$

$$= \sqrt{\frac{224{,}731.71}{6}} = 193.53 \text{ kN/m}^2.$$

The standard deviation of $\bar{y}$ is

$$s_{\bar{y}} = \frac{s}{\sqrt{n}}$$

$$= \frac{193.53}{\sqrt{7}} = 73.15 \text{ kN/m}^2.$$

With a null hypothesis $\mu_{\bar{y}} = 0$, we now apply the t test to $\bar{y}$ by comparing it to a zero mean difference:

$$t = \frac{|\bar{y} - 0|}{s_{\bar{y}}} = 4.38.$$

The number of degrees of freedom is 6 ($v = n - 1 = 7 - 1$), and Table A.7 gives $t = 3.707$ at the 1 percent level of significance. The difference in strength is thus significant and the null hypothesis is rejected.

Let us now ignore the pairing and apply the t test to the mean difference of strengths.

Using Eq. (15.15), we compute the combined population variance s_c^2:

$$s_c^2 = \frac{\sum (x_1 - \bar{x}_1)^2 + \sum (x_2 - \bar{x}_2)^2}{2n - 2}$$

$$= \frac{14{,}484{,}406.90 + 15{,}442{,}547.80}{12}$$

$$= 2{,}493{,}912.89.$$

The standard deviation of the difference of means is given by Eq. (15.17):

$$s_d = s_c \sqrt{\frac{2}{n}}$$

$$= 1579.21 \sqrt{\frac{2}{7}} = 844.12 \text{ kN/m}^2.$$

The mean difference of strengths is

$$\bar{x}_2 - \bar{x}_1 = 4155.43 - 3834.86 = 320.57 \text{ kN/m}^2.$$

With the null hypothesis $H_0 : \mu_2 - \mu_1 = d = 0$, we now apply the t test:

$$t = \frac{|\bar{x}_2 - \bar{x}_1|}{s_d}$$

$$= \frac{320.57}{844.12} = 0.380.$$

The number of degrees of freedom is $(2n - 2) = 12$. Table A.7 gives $t = 2.179$ at the 5 percent level. The difference thus appears to be not significant.

It is clear that the conclusion from the last test is due to the considerable difference in the level of strength of the different mixes. The paired test is more discriminating, and we conclude that there is a significant difference between the tensile strengths of the specimens of the two sizes.

■ ■

In a more general way, it is instructive to list some of the advantages and disadvantages of paired comparisons. The advantages are:

i. The test does not require the assumption of equal variance for the two populations being compared.
ii. The two random samples need not be independent.
iii. Pairing reduces the variance resulting from any extraneous factors and thus increases the power of the test.

The disadvantages are:

i. Sample sizes must be equal.
ii. A paired test has $(n - 1)$ degrees of freedom while an unpaired test has $2(n - 1)$ degrees of freedom; this leads to loss of information so that the accuracy of conclusions can become unreliable if pairing is not necessary.
iii. The test assumes that the variance $\sigma_d (\simeq s_d)$ does not depend on the level of the measured variable.

CASE OF NONHOMOGENEOUS VARIANCES

Equation (15.13) was obtained on the assumption that the variances of the two sampled populations being compared are not significantly different (i.e., are homogeneous), this being implicit in the hypothesis that the two samples belong to the same population. The homogeneity of variances is examined by the F test (see Chapter 16).

However, in some cases, the condition of homogeneity of variances may not be satisfied, but we may still want to test the significance of the difference of two means. This is the case, for example, when errors of measurement in the two samples are due to different causes so that the estimates of variance cannot correctly be pooled. The t test cannot, therefore, be applied, and we use a test in which the ratio of the standard deviations of the two sample means, $s_{\bar{x}_1}/s_{\bar{x}_2} = \tan \theta$, is considered in determining the significance of the difference of the means. The difference $\bar{x}_1 - \bar{x}_2$ is considered significant if

$$\frac{|\bar{x}_1 - \bar{x}_2|}{\sqrt{s_{\bar{x}_1}^2 + s_{\bar{x}_2}^2}} > d \tag{15.18}$$

where d is given in Table A.13 for two levels of significance and for different values of θ, v_1, and v_2. The numbers of degrees of freedom in the two samples, v_1 and v_2, are equal to $n_1 - 1$ and $n_2 - 1$, respectively (n_1 and n_2 are the sample sizes).

EXAMPLE

Imagine that we have used two different methods to determine a physical constant. Each method yields a mean value, and we want to determine at $\alpha = 1$ percent whether or not there is a real discrepancy between the two results. Because different methods have been used, the variances may differ and cannot be pooled. Let the results be

$$\bar{x}_1 = 5.289 \qquad \bar{x}_2 = 5.261$$
$$s_{\bar{x}_1}^2 = 0.00008 \qquad s_{\bar{x}_2}^2 = 0.00001$$

for $n_1 = 13$ and $n_2 = 60$.

We may check that the F test yields

$$F = \frac{s_{\bar{x}_1}^2}{s_{\bar{x}_2}^2} = 8$$

which, for the degrees of freedom $v_1 = 12$ and $v_2 = 59$, shows a significant difference at the 1 percent level (F from Table A.14 is 2.50). We calculate

$$\tan \theta = \sqrt{\frac{0.00008}{0.00001}} = 2.828$$

whence $\theta = 70.5°$. Now,

$$\sqrt{s_{x_1}^2 + s_{x_2}^2} = 0.0095.$$

Therefore, $$d = \frac{|\bar{x}_1 - \bar{x}_2|}{\sqrt{s_{\bar{x}_1}^2 + s_{\bar{x}_2}^2}} = \frac{0.028}{0.0095} = 2.95.$$

Table A.13 gives the values of θ of $60°$ and $75°$; therefore, we have to interpolate. For the 5 percent level of significance the values of d are for $v_1 = 12$:

$$v_2 = 24 \quad \begin{cases} \theta = 60° & d = 2.142 \\ \theta = 75° & d = 2.168 \end{cases}$$

$$v_2 = \infty \quad \begin{cases} \theta = 60° & d = 2.120 \\ \theta = 75° & d = 2.163. \end{cases}$$

As all these values are close to one another, we shall take simply the arithmetic mean of the four values of d; this is $d = 2.15$.

For the 1 percent level of significance, the four values of d at the same points are: 2.938, 3.020, 2.909, and 3.014. Hence, the arithmetic mean is 2.97.

We can, therefore, conclude that the difference between the means $\bar{x}_1$ and $\bar{x}_2$ is significant at the 5 percent level but not quite at the 1 percent level. ■ ■

A special case arises when the standard deviation is not constant for either group but varies with the level of x, the variation being the same in both groups. For example, in testing the strength of concrete it has been found that the standard deviation is proportional to strength.[5] In such a case, logarithmic transformation has to be applied to the variate. The variance of the natural logarithm of the original variate is approximately equal to the square of the coefficient of variation V^2. We can, therefore, use Eq. (15.16), substituting $\log_e x$ for x, and V^2 for s_c^2. Then

$$t = \frac{|\log_e \bar{x}_1 - \log_e \bar{x}_2|}{\sqrt{\dfrac{V_1^2(n_1 - 1) + V_2^2(n_2 - 1)}{n_1 + n_2 - 2} \times \dfrac{n_1 + n_2}{n_1 n_2}}} \tag{15.19}$$

where $\bar{x}_1$ and $\bar{x}_2$ are the sample means, n_1 and n_2 the sample sizes, and V_1 and V_2 the coefficients of variation. Note that t has $(n_1 + n_2 - 2)$ degrees of freedom.

If n is large, we can consider V^2 to be the variance of $\log_e \bar{x}$ and not an estimate, and Eq. (15.19) reduces to

$$t = \frac{|\log_e \bar{x}_1 - \log_e \bar{x}_2|}{\sqrt{\left(\dfrac{V_1^2}{n_2} + \dfrac{V_2^2}{n_1}\right) \times \dfrac{n_1 + n_2}{n_1 + n_2 - 2}}}. \tag{15.20}$$

---

[5] A. M. Neville, "The Relation Between Standard Deviation and Mean Strength of Concrete Test Cubes," *Magazine of Concrete Research*, vol. 10, no. 31, July 1959.

TABLE 15.6 SUMMARY OF TEST METHODS FOR COMPARISON OF MEANS[a]

Null hypothesis[b]	Conditions of applicability	Equation to be used
$\mu = \mu_0$	μ and σ are known, and the population is normally distributed and is $\begin{cases} \text{infinite} \\ \text{finite} \end{cases}$	Eq. (15.1) (normal distribution test) Eq. (15.3) (normal distribution test)
$\mu = \mu_0$	μ is known but σ is unknown; s, estimated from a small sample, is used.	Eq. (15.12) (t test)
$\mu_1 = \mu_2$	$\bar{x}_1$ and $\bar{x}_2$, estimators of μ_1 and μ_2, are means of large samples (independent of one another). The means can be considered as normally distributed.	Eqs. (15.8) and (15.10) (normal distribution test)
$\mu_1 = \mu_2$	$\bar{x}_1$ and $\bar{x}_2$, estimators of μ_1 and μ_2, are means of small samples whose variances are homogeneous.	Eq. (15.13) (t test)
$\mu_1 = \mu_2$	$\bar{x}_1$ and $\bar{x}_2$, estimators of μ_1 and μ_2, are means of samples whose variances are not homogeneous.	Eq. (15.18)

[a] μ = population mean, $\bar{x}$ = sample mean, σ = standard deviation of population, and s = estimate of standard deviation from the sample used.
[b] See Fig. 15.5 for the alternative hypothesis.

CHOICE OF APPROACH

The various tests of the null hypothesis of no difference between two means have been described in the preceding pages, and it may be convenient to have them summarized in one table. This is done in Table 15.6.

DISTRIBUTION-FREE OR NONPARAMETRIC TESTS

In certain applications, we may be confronted with sampling distributions arising from populations with unknown parameters. In such cases, we should not make assumptions about such parameters other than those of random sampling and continuity of the distribution. Tests that deal with such distributions are, therefore, called distribution-free tests; since they do not involve the use of parameters, they are also known as nonparametric tests.

SIGN TEST

This is the simplest of all nonparametric tests. Let us consider an example (see Table 15.7). The degree of corrosion of a pipe made of a new alloy is to be investigated. Pipe pieces made from the new alloy and from the standard

TABLE 15.7 DEPTH OF MAXIMUM PITS
(in 10^{-2} mm)

Pair	Standard pipe, A	New alloy pipe, B	Sign of difference $(A - B)$
1	20	25	−
2	26	29	−
3	31	28	+
4	42	37	+
5	35	40	−
6	19	29	−
7	33	41	−
8	38	43	−
9	29	21	+
10	27	35	−
11	40	47	−
12	37	41	−

alloy are paired. The pairs are placed at the same depth of the same soil, positioned in the same manner, and for the same length of time. The corrosion of the pipes in each pair is then compared and the pipe that is more corroded is given a plus rating, the other pipe a minus rating.

Is there a significant difference in the degree of corrosion in the pipe due to a change in the alloy? Use $\alpha = 5$ percent.

If we apply the null hypothesis that the two alloys are affected by corrosion to the same degree, the number of plus signs should be approximately equal to the number of minus signs. Such a number in a sample of size n is a random variable with a binomial distribution, with $n = 12$, $p = q = \frac{1}{2}$. The expected number of minus signs is the mean $np = (12)(\frac{1}{2}) = 6$. However, the observed number of minus signs is 9. The probability that 9 or more minus signs are observed is:

$$\sum_{r=9}^{r=12} P_r = P_9 + P_{10} + P_{11} + P_{12}.$$

We find from Table A.2 that, for $p = 0.5$, $q = 0.5$, $n = 12$, $r = 9$, and $r' = 4$, the corresponding value from the table is 0.9270. Therefore, the required probability is $1 - 0.9270 = 0.0730$. Bearing in mind that this is a two-sided test, the probability of 0.0730 is compared to 0.5α, that is, 0.025. Since $0.0730 > 0.025$, there is no strong evidence that there is a difference in the degree of corrosion in the pipes made from the two alloys.

Applying the normal test as an approximation to the binomial distribution, we find[6]

$$\text{mean} = np = 6, \qquad \sigma = \sqrt{npq} = \sqrt{(12)(\tfrac{1}{2})(\tfrac{1}{2})} = 1.732$$

$$z = \frac{8.5 - 6}{1.732} = \frac{2.5}{1.732} = 1.442$$

---

[6] Since we need to approximate the area of the histogram to the right of $x = 9$, we decrease 9 by $\frac{1}{2}$ in order better to fit a continuous normal distribution to a discrete binomial distribution.

and from Table A.6,
$$F(z) = 0.4254.$$

The required probability $= 0.5 - 0.4254 = 0.0746$, which is greater than $\frac{1}{2}\alpha$, that is, 0.025; therefore, we arrive at the same conclusion.

It is evident from this example that the sign test does not take account of the magnitude of the observed differences and is, therefore, not very sensitive. This deficiency is rectified by the Wilcoxon signed rank test.

The usefulness of the sign test should not be underestimated. Because of its simplicity, the sign test can be sometimes used instead of a standard parametric test even when quantitative data are available: in applying the sign test, samples do not even have to be independent, nor are assumptions made concerning the distribution of the underlying populations.

WILCOXON SIGNED RANK TEST

In this test, the absolute values of the differences are first ranked and then these ranks are affixed with the associated sign of the difference. For no significant difference between the means of the two samples, the total of the ranks associated with positive differences and that associated with negative differences should be about the same. Otherwise, there may be a significant difference between the means of the two samples. This is so if the probability of obtaining by chance alone a signed rank total less than or equal to the smaller of the signed rank totals is less than a critical value at the appropriate significance level. Let us apply this test to the previous example (see Table 15.8).

We notice that some of the observed differences are tied for rank. In such cases, Wilcoxon suggested that the tied values be assigned the mean of the respective ranks. For example, pairs 2 and 3 have the same differences, corresponding to ranks 1 and 2. The mean rank of $(1 + 2)/2 = 1.5$ is assigned to each of the two differences.

TABLE 15.8   DEPTH OF MAXIMUM PITS (in 10^{-2} mm)

Pair	Pipe A	Pipe B	Difference	Rank	Signed rank
1	20	25	-5	$5\frac{1}{2}$	$-5\frac{1}{2}$
2	26	29	-3	$1\frac{1}{2}$	$-1\frac{1}{2}$
3	31	28	3	$1\frac{1}{2}$	$1\frac{1}{2}$
4	42	37	5	$5\frac{1}{2}$	$5\frac{1}{2}$
5	35	40	-5	$5\frac{1}{2}$	$-5\frac{1}{2}$
6	19	29	-10	12	-12
7	33	41	-8	10	-10
8	38	43	-5	$5\frac{1}{2}$	$-5\frac{1}{2}$
9	29	21	8	10	10
10	27	35	-8	10	-10
11	40	47	-7	8	-8
12	37	41	-4	3	-3

If there is no difference in the degree of corrosion in the pipes made from the two alloys, we would expect the sum of the positive ranks to be nearly equal numerically to the sum of the negative ranks.

$$\text{Sum of all ranks} = 1 + 2 + \cdots + n$$

$$= \frac{n(n + 1)}{2} = \frac{(12)(13)}{2} = 78$$

and, hence, the expected sum of either positive or negative signed ranks is

$$\frac{78}{2} = 39.$$

Now, the observed sum of negative ranks is

$$5.5 + 1.5 + 5.5 + 12 + 10 + 5.5 + 10 + 8 + 3 = 61$$

and the observed sum of positive ranks is

$$1.5 + 5.5 + 10 = 17.$$

To check for a significant difference, we compare the absolute value of the smaller sum of ranks, that is, 17 to the critical value of R given in Table A.15; this is $R = 14$ for $n = 12$, at the 5 percent level of significance. Since $17 > 14$, the null hypothesis cannot be rejected and we can conclude that there is no difference in the degree of corrosion in the pipes made from the two different alloys.

Note that the values given in Table A.15 are for a two-sided test. If a one-sided test is performed, the levels of significance given at the top of the table must be halved.

RANK TEST FOR TWO INDEPENDENT SAMPLES

When the samples are not paired and their probability distributions are assumed to differ only in their means, we can use a modified rank test to check for significant difference. We shall illustrate the test by considering the previous data on pipe corrosion but assuming that the data are not paired (see Table 15.9).

We arrange all observations in order of magnitude and rank them. If no significant difference exists, we would expect the sum of ranks for both samples to be nearly the same. For the above data, the sum of ranks in sample A is $1 + 2 + 5.5 + \cdots + 22 = 132.5$; the sum of ranks in sample B is $3 + 4 + 7 + \cdots + 24 = 167.5$. Let $T_1 =$ the sum of ranks of the smaller sample (in this case $T_1 = 132.5$), and $T_2 = n_1(n_1 + n_2 + 1) - T_1$ (in this case $T_2 = 167.5$). Then let T be the smaller sum of ranks T_1 or T_2.

Entering Table A.16, with n_1 (size of sample A) $= 12$ and n_2 (size of sample B) $= 12$, we find the critical value T as 115. For a two-sided test, since $T_2 > T$,

TABLE 15.9

Sample	Depth of maximum pits (in 10^{-2} mm)	Rank
A	19	1
A	20	2
B	21	3
B	25	4
A	26	$5\frac{1}{2}$
A	26	$5\frac{1}{2}$
B	28	7
A	29	9
B	29	9
B	29	9
A	31	11
A	33	12
A	35	$13\frac{1}{2}$
B	35	$13\frac{1}{2}$
A	37	$15\frac{1}{2}$
B	37	$15\frac{1}{2}$
A	38	17
A	40	$18\frac{1}{2}$
B	40	$18\frac{1}{2}$
B	41	$20\frac{1}{2}$
B	41	$20\frac{1}{2}$
A	42	22
B	43	23
B	47	24

the difference in corrosion is not significant and the null hypothesis is accepted at the 5 percent level. If T_2 had been below the critical value T, we would have had to reject the null hypothesis at the 5 percent level. It should be noted that, for unequal sample sizes, n_1 applies to smaller samples. Again, for a one-sided test, the level of significance equals 0.5α, that is, $2\frac{1}{2}$ percent in this case.

It can be shown[7] that, when the sample size n is large ($n > 25$), the Wilcoxon's T statistic becomes approximately normally distributed with mean and standard deviation given, respectively, by

$$\mu_T = \frac{n(n+1)}{4} \tag{15.21}$$

and

$$\sigma_T = \sqrt{\frac{n(n+1)(2n+1)}{24}}. \tag{15.22}$$

In such a case, we can calculate the usual z statistic as

$$z = \frac{T - \mu_T}{\sigma_T} \tag{15.23}$$

[7] W. H. Kruskal and W. A. Wallis, "Use of Ranks in One-Criterion Variance Analysis," *J. Am. Statist. Assoc.* Vol. 47, 1952, pp. 583–621.

and the hypothesis test is continued in the usual way, using Table A.6. It should be mentioned that the Wilcoxon test offers a very efficient alternative to the t test for paired data when doubts exist about the applicability of the latter test.

From the foregoing, it can be seen that nonparametric tests are easily applied. Because of this and other advantages mentioned earlier, their use has increased considerably. However, when justifiable assumptions about the form and/or parameters of the population sampled can be made, nonparametric tests become less efficient than tests utilizing correct assumptions.

SOLVED PROBLEMS

15-1. It is suspected that the state of stress in a steel wire affects the percentage loss in the ultimate tensile strength in the wire when such a wire has been immersed in a calcium chloride solution. Twelve lengths of wire were obtained, and each one was cut into four specimens. Two of these were stressed, one in solution, one in air; the other two were unstressed, likewise one in solution, one in air.

Table 15.10 gives the percentage loss in the ultimate tensile strength for the appropriate pairs. Establish whether stressing affects the percentage loss in strength caused by immersion in the solution. Use $\alpha = 1$ percent.

Solution. Since the samples are paired, we shall apply the t test to find the significance of the mean difference between the unstressed and stressed specimens (see Table 15.11).

$$\text{Mean difference } \bar{d} = \frac{14.6}{12} = 1.217$$

and

$$\text{estimated standard deviation } s = \sqrt{\frac{\sum d^2 - [(\sum d)^2/n]}{n-1}}$$

$$= \sqrt{\frac{31.88 - [(14.6)^2 \, 12]}{11}}$$

$$= \sqrt{1.283} = 1.13.$$

TABLE 15.10

Test number	Stressed	Unstressed
1	10.4	7.1
2	8.1	8.4
3	8.5	7.2
4	9.7	8.3
5	8.2	6.8
6	10.1	8.5
7	7.9	7.9
8	9.8	8.2
9	8.4	8.4
10	8.7	6.5
11	9.3	7.0
12	8.6	8.8

TABLE 15.11

Test number	Stressed	Unstressed	Difference, d	d^2
1	10.4	7.1	3.3	10.89
2	8.1	8.4	−0.3	0.09
3	8.5	7.2	1.3	1.69
4	9.7	8.3	1.4	1.96
5	8.2	6.8	1.4	1.96
6	10.1	8.5	1.6	2.56
7	7.9	7.9	0	0
8	9.8	8.2	1.6	2.56
9	8.4	8.4	0	0
10	8.7	6.5	2.2	4.84
11	9.3	7.0	2.3	5.29
12	8.6	8.8	−0.2	0.04
Totals			$\sum d = 15.1 - 0.5 = 14.6$	$\sum d^2 = 31.88$

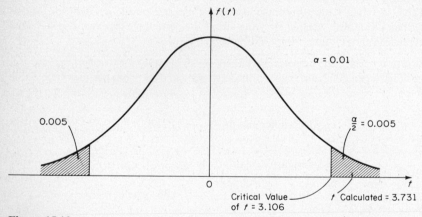

Figure 15.10

Therefore,

$$s_{\bar{d}} = \frac{s}{\sqrt{n}} = \frac{1.13}{\sqrt{12}}.$$

Hence,

$$t = \frac{|\bar{d} - 0|}{s_{\bar{d}}} = \frac{1.217}{1.13} \times \sqrt{12} = 3.731.$$

This is a two-sided test, since we are checking the null hypothesis that $\bar{d} = 0$ against the alternative hypothesis $\bar{d} \neq 0$. For $v = n - 1 = 12 - 1 = 11$, Table A.7 gives, for the 1 percent level of significance, $t = 3.106$. Since the calculated $t > 3.106$, the difference is significant at the 1 percent level (see Fig. 15.10). In other words, there is strong evidence to support the contention that the state of stress affects the percentage loss in ultimate strength after immersion in a calcium chloride solution.

The χ^2 test can be used to give a quick, albeit rough, check on the significance of the difference. We calculate the expected numbers of positive and negative signs of the difference on the basis of the null hypothesis and compare these with the observed

TABLE 15.12

Strength loss, x_1	Deviation, $(x_1 - \bar{x}_1)$	$(x_1 - \bar{x}_1)^2$
10.4	1.425	2.031
8.1	−0.875	0.766
8.5	−0.475	0.226
9.7	0.725	0.526
8.2	−0.775	0.601
10.1	1.125	1.266
7.9	−1.075	1.156
9.8	0.825	0.681
8.4	−0.575	0.331
8.7	−0.275	0.076
9.3	0.325	0.106
8.6	−0.375	0.141
$\sum x_1 = 107.7$	$\sum(x_1 - \bar{x}_1) = +4.425$ −4.425 = 0	$\sum(x_1 - \bar{x}_1)^2 = 7.907$

numbers of positive and negative signs. In tabular form:

	$+ve$ sign	$-ve$ sign
observed number of signs O	8	2
expected number of signs E	5	5

$$\chi^2 = \sum \frac{(O - E)^2}{E} = \frac{(8 - 5)^2}{5} + \frac{(2 - 5)^2}{5} = \frac{9}{5} + \frac{9}{5} = 3.6.$$

For $v = 1$, from Table A.11, the probability of obtaining such a value of χ^2 by chance is between 0.10 and 0.05. Therefore, we suspect the null hypothesis and should test the significance by the t test (as already done)

As a somewhat more accurate alternative, the binomial distribution can be used to calculate the possibility of obtaining the distribution of positive and negative signs actually observed.

If the specimens had not been paired, that is, if we had measured the loss in strength on immersion in the solution for 12 consignments of wire using stressed specimens and for another 12 consignments using unstressed specimens, pairing would have not been possible. In such a case, the t test must be applied to the difference of means, but the procedure is permissible even when the data are paired. Thus, we have

a. for stressed specimens (Table 15.12):

$$\bar{x}_1 = \frac{107.7}{12} = 8.975.$$

b. for unstressed specimens (Table 15.13):

$$\bar{x}_2 = \frac{\sum x_2}{n} = \frac{93.1}{12} = 7.758.$$

The pooled estimate of variance is

$$s_c^2 = \frac{\sum(x_1 - \bar{x}_1)^2 + \sum(x_2 - \bar{x}_2)^2}{(n_1 - 1) + (n_2 - 1)}$$

$$= \frac{7.907 + 6.788}{11 + 11} = \frac{14.695}{22} = 0.668.$$

TABLE 15.13

Strength loss, x_2	Deviation, $(x_2 - \bar{x}_2)$		$(x_2 - \bar{x}_2)^2$
7.1		−0.6583	0.433
8.4	0.6417		0.412
7.2		−0.5583	0.312
8.3	0.5417		0.293
6.8		−0.9583	0.918
8.5	0.7417		0.550
7.9	0.1417		0.020
8.2	0.4417		0.195
8.4	0.6417		0.412
6.5		−1.2583	1.583
7.0		−0.7583	0.575
8.8	1.0417		1.085
$\sum x_2 = 93.1$	$\sum(x_2 - \bar{x}_2) = +4.1919$	$-4.1915 \simeq 0$	$\sum(x_2 - \bar{x}_2)^2 = 6.788$

The standard deviation of the difference of means is

$$s_d = s_c \sqrt{\frac{n_1 + n_2}{n_1 n_2}}$$

$$= \sqrt{\frac{0.668}{6}} = 0.3337.$$

The difference of means $= \bar{x}_1 - \bar{x}_2 = 8.975 - 7.758 = 1.217$. Hence,

$$t = \frac{1.217}{0.3337} = 3.647.$$

The number of degrees of freedom $= 24 - 2 = 22$.

From Table A.7, $t = 2.819$ at the 1 percent level of significance and 3.792 at the 0.1 percent level for a two-sided test. The difference is, therefore, highly significant.

15-2. The ultimate strengths of prestressing wires manufactured by a steel company have a mean of 2000 N and a standard deviation of 100 N. By employing a new manufacturing technique, the company is claiming that the ultimate strength is now increased. To verify this claim, a contractor tests a sample of 50 wires produced by the new process and finds that the mean ultimate strength is 2050 N.

    a. Do the data support the manufacturer's claim at the 1 percent level of significance?

    b. What is the probability β of accepting the old process when, in fact, the new process has increased the mean ultimate strength to 2050 N, assuming still $\sigma = 100$ N?

Solution

    a. We have to decide between two hypotheses: either $\mu = 2000$ N, and there is really no change in ultimate strength; or $\mu > 2000$ N, and there is a change in ultimate strength.

    Since we are testing whether the new process is better than the old one (and not better *or* worse), a one-sided test is appropriate. Thus, for a one-sided test at $\alpha = 0.01$, assuming a normal distribution, $F(z) = 0.5 - 0.01 = 0.49$. The corresponding critical value of z from Table A.6 is $z = 2.33$. The decision is: if the calculated $z > 2.33$, reject

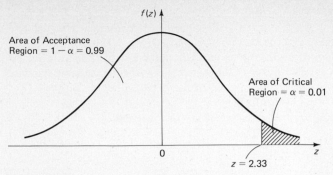

Figure 15.11

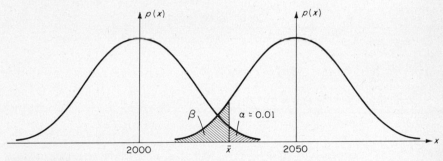

Figure 15.12

the hypothesis $\mu = 2000$ N, otherwise accept the hypothesis $\mu = 2000$ N (see Fig. 15.11). From Eq. (15.1),

$$\text{the actual } z = \frac{\bar{x} - \mu}{\sigma/\sqrt{n}} = \frac{2050 - 2000}{100/\sqrt{50}} = \frac{50}{100/\sqrt{50}} = 3.54.$$

Since $3.54 > 2.33$, the results are highly significant and we conclude that the hypothesis $\mu = 2000$ N should be rejected and the manufacturer's claim should be accepted.

To calculate the critical mean strength for rejecting the old process at $\alpha = 0.01$ with $n = 50$, we have the critical value $z = 2.33$, $\sigma = 100$ N, $\mu = 2000$ N; thus, from Eq. (15.1),

$$z = \frac{\bar{X} - \mu}{\sigma/\sqrt{n}} = \frac{\bar{X} - 2000}{100/\sqrt{50}} = 2.33.$$

Therefore, $\bar{X} = 2033$ N.

We can rephrase the above conclusion by saying that we reject the hypothesis $\mu = 2000$ N, since $2050 > 2033$.

b. The two hypotheses are now: $\mu = 2000$ N against the alternative of $\mu = 2050$ N. The distributions of the mean ultimate strengths corresponding to the above hypotheses are shown in Fig. 15.12. The probability of committing a Type II error is β, which is the area under the right-hand normal curve corresponding to

$$z = \frac{2033 - 2050}{100/\sqrt{50}} = \frac{-17}{(100/7.08)} = -1.21.$$

Therefore, $\beta = 0.5 - F(1.21) = 0.5 - 0.3869 = 0.1131 \simeq 0.11.$

The decision in this case becomes: Reject the hypothesis $\mu = 2000$ N if $\bar{X} \geqslant 2033$ N (the probability of Type I error, α, is 0.01). Accept the hypothesis that $\mu = 2000$ N if $\bar{X} < 2033$ N (the probability of Type II error, β, is 0.11).

If the probability for Type II error is too high and we wish to limit it, for example, to $\beta = 0.05$, what should the size of the sample n be? Assume the same standard deviation.

$$\text{Critical } z = \frac{\bar{X} - 2000}{100/\sqrt{n}} = 2.33 \qquad \text{for} \quad \alpha = 0.01.$$

Hence, $\bar{X} = 2000 + 233/\sqrt{n}$.

$$\beta = 0.05 = 0.5 - F\left(\frac{2050 - \bar{X}}{100/\sqrt{n}}\right).$$

Thus,

$$0.45 = F\left(\frac{2050 - 2000 - 233/\sqrt{n}}{100/\sqrt{n}}\right)$$

$$= F\left(\frac{\sqrt{n}}{2} - 2.33\right).$$

From Table A.6, for $F(z) = 0.45$ the corresponding z is 1.645. Therefore,

$$1.645 = \sqrt{n}/2 - 2.33, \qquad \sqrt{n} = 7.95, \qquad \text{or} \quad n = 62.$$

Then,

$$\text{critical } \bar{X} = 2000 + \frac{233}{\sqrt{n}} = 2000 + \frac{233}{\sqrt{62}} = 2029 \text{ N}.$$

The decision changes in this case to:
1. reject the hypothesis that $\mu = 2000$ N if $\bar{X} \geqslant 2029$ N ($\alpha = 0.01$),
2. accept the hypothesis that $\mu = 2000$ N if $\bar{X} < 2029$ N (now $\beta = 0.05$) and it is agreed to test 62 wires.

In this problem, we were given α and n and computed β in the first part, while in the second part we were required to compute n for specified values of α and β. In a similar manner, we can calculate α, given n and β.

Although in the present case we have applied the normal distribution, the procedure would be the same when we use other distributions, for example, the t distribution, as applicable.

These computations can be much simplified by the use of operating characteristic curves, which are discussed in Chapter 22.

PROBLEMS

NOTE: State the null hypothesis and the alternative hypothesis for all problems.

15-1. A brand of cement is sold in bags containing 50 kg. We choose 11 bags at random and find their masses in kilograms: 49.2, 50.1, 49.8, 49.7, 50.1, 50.5, 49.6, 49.9, 50.4, 50.2, and 49.7. Are these results consistent with the assumption that the bags belong to a population with a mean of 50 kg? Use $\alpha = 10$ percent.

15-2. To check two weighing machines, 8 samples were weighed on each machine. Do the results suggest that there is a significant difference between the two machines? Use the paired t test, with $\alpha = 5$ percent.

| Machine A | 10.063 | 8.051 | 9.036 | 9.067 | 3.056 | 5.076 | 5.074 | 2.006 |
| Machine B | 10.063 | 8.050 | 9.033 | 9.062 | 3.060 | 5.070 | 5.070 | 2.000 |

15-3. In order to test his laboratory, a manufacturer took 13 samples of his product, halved each of them, and had one-half tested in his laboratory (A) and the other in an independent laboratory (B). Is there a significant difference between the test results of the two laboratories? Use $\alpha = 5$ percent.

Sample no.	1	2	3	4	5	6	7	8	9	10	11	12	13
Laboratory A	17.2	17.0	17.4	18.0	18.3	15.2	13.2	18.7	16.7	19.4	14.7	17.7	16.9
Laboratory B	19.1	19.8	17.9	18.0	18.3	15.0	14.3	18.2	17.7	19.3	16.7	16.8	16.7

15-4. The mean resistance of a box has been established by the manufacturer to be 250 ohms. A purchaser tests 10 boxes and finds the following values: 246, 261, 249, 254, 235, 242, 235, 231, 266, and 239. Does the consignment meet the specification if values within the 10 percent level of significance are tolerated?

15-5. In a laboratory, it was suspected that the measurements of viscosity obtained in the morning were lower than in the afternoon. Ten samples were, therefore, split in half, one-half of each being tested in the morning, the other in the afternoon. Do the data suggest that the "afternoon viscosity" is higher? Apply the paired t test, using $\alpha = 5$ percent (see Table 15.14).

15-6. Results of chemical analyses for the content of A in materials from two sources are as follows:

	Content of A, percent					
Source 1	93.12	93.57	92.81	94.32	93.77	93.52
Source 2	92.54	92.38	93.21	92.06	92.55	

TABLE 15.14

	Viscosity (coded)	
Sample no.	Morning	Afternoon
1	43	45
2	48	48
3	48	50
4	50	53
5	55	54
6	50	52
7	72	73
8	75	75
9	73	72
10	54	56

Test the hypothesis that there is no difference in the content of A between the two sources. Use $\alpha = 1$ percent.

15-7. The strength of two alloys was compared, 10 samples of each being tested. Alloy A had a mean strength of $31,400 \text{ kN/m}^2$ with a coefficient of variation of 19 percent; the corresponding values for alloy B were $27,100 \text{ kN/m}^2$ and 15 percent. Can we conclude that the strengths of the two alloys do not differ at the 1 percent level of significance?

15-8. Measurements of a certain angle in castings over two periods yielded the following data:

$$n_1 = 154 \qquad n_2 = 149$$
$$\theta_1 = 90.0° \qquad \theta_2 = 89.7°$$
$$s_1 = 3.6° \qquad s_2 = 3.5°.$$

Does this mean that the angle is becoming smaller? (If the angle were increasing, we would not worry.) Use $\alpha = 5$ percent.

15-9. In order to determine whether the use of rubber packing between the concrete specimen and the platen of the testing machine affects the observed strength, two specimens were made from each of six batches of concrete (see Table 15.15). Of each pair of specimens, one was tested with the packing, the other without. Is there a significant difference between the strengths obtained by the two test methods? Use $\alpha = 1$ percent.

15-10. To compare the tensile strength of two cements, six mortar briquettes were made with each cement, and the following strengths (kN/m^2) were recorded:

Cement A: 4600, 4710, 4820, 4670, 4760, 4480

Cement B: 4400, 4450, 4700, 4400, 4170, 4100.

Is there a significant difference between the tensile strengths of the two cements? Use $\alpha = 5$ percent.

15-11. The resistance (in ohms) of 40 boxes supplied from each of three manufacturers was found to be as listed in Table 15.16. Test whether there is a significant difference between the mean values of Groups A and B, and Groups B and C. Use $\alpha = 10$ percent.

TABLE 15.15

	Tensile strength, MPa	
Batch no.	With packing	Without packing
1	2.76	2.48
2	2.72	2.00
3	2.65	2.28
4	2.62	2.10
5	2.96	2.38
6	2.48	2.14

Source: P. J. F. Wright, "Statistical Methods in Concrete Research," *Magazine of Concrete Research,* vol. 5, no. 15, March 1954, p. 143. The original data were in psi units.

TABLE 15.16

			Group A				
6040	7240	6160	7000	7160	8000	7360	6800
6040	5680	6320	6120	8240	8040	7760	7040
6720	6920	7600	6600	6920	7280	6400	6200
8120	8120	8000	7800	7320	7560	7200	7280
7560	7520	7520	6840	6640	7160	7280	6680

			Group B				
7040	7640	6480	6000	6640	6880	6200	6480
6160	6480	7320	6680	6440	6600	6280	7480
7320	6320	7880	7520	8760	8280	7880	7040
6720	6600	8080	7120	6600	7960	6440	5960
6680	6600	6600	6040	6080	6720	6640	6600

			Group C				
7240	7240	6840	7240	7320	7080	7320	7720
7280	7360	7320	7440	7240	7240	8400	8440
7800	7720	7640	7640	7520	7720	7640	7600
8600	8520	8880	8800	8440	8400	7320	8800
7520	7520	6320	5680	7440	7640	6960	8920

15-12. For the data in Problem 8-8, calculate the average mean strength of the 10-cm as well as the 20-cm specimens for the 7 mixes. Apply the t test to the difference in the two averages, and, hence, establish whether there is a real difference between the strengths of the 10- and 20-cm cubes. Use $\alpha = 10$ percent.

15-13. Concrete is formed by pressurized compaction with a view to increasing its compressive strength. To test whether this is true, six sample cylinders are made by this new method and another six cylinders are made by the standard method. The results in MPa are as follows:

New method	33.1	31.0	34.5	33.8	35.9	29.0
Standard method	27.6	29.0	26.2	30.3	31.7	29.6

Check, at the 5 percent level, whether the new method has increased the compressive strength of concrete using:
   a. the sign test, assuming the samples are paired;
   b. the Wilcoxon signed rank test, assuming paired samples;
   c. the test for two independent samples, assuming no pairing.

Chapter 16

Comparison of Variances and Their Properties

In the tests on the significance of means, we either assumed that the two samples whose means were being compared had the same standard deviation (or, strictly speaking, standard deviations belonging to the same population of standard deviations) or we allowed for the inequality of the standard deviations (as on page 318). However, it is often important to know with some degree of certainty whether the standard deviations of two samples are the same, that is, they do not differ significantly; such standard deviations are said to be *homogeneous*. For example, if we want to establish that two samples belong to the same population, we should test their means and determine that they do not differ significantly, and also test their standard deviations and determine that they do not differ significantly. If is, of course, possible for one of these conditions to be satisfied but not the other. Although we refer to standard deviations, it is really variances that are the statistic being studied.

To illustrate the type of problem, let us imagine that we wish to compare the precision of one instrument with that of another, or the variability in the grading by one professor with that by another, or the stability of one manufacturing process with that of another. To achieve the above we might compare two population variances σ_1^2 and σ_2^2, using the ratio of the sample variances s_1^2 and s_2^2. If s_1^2/s_2^2 is nearly equal to one, we would find little evidence to show that σ_1^2 and σ_2^2 are unequal whereas a very large or very small value of s_1^2/s_2^2 would provide evidence of a difference in the population variances.

THE F TEST

From the previous discussion, there arises the question: how large or how small must s_1^2/s_2^2 be in order that sufficient evidence exists to reject the null hypothesis

$H_0 : \sigma_1^2 = \sigma_2^2$? The answer to this question is found by studying the distribution of

$$\frac{s_1^2/\sigma_1^2}{s_2^2/\sigma_2^2}$$

in repeated sampling. If s_1^2 and s_2^2 are variances computed from independent random samples of size n_1 and n_2 drawn from normally distributed populations with variances σ_1^2 and σ_2^2, respectively, then the random variable

$$F = \frac{s_1^2/\sigma_1^2}{s_2^2/\sigma_2^2} \tag{16.1}$$

follows a distribution called the *F* distribution, with $v_1 = (n_1 - 1)$ and $v_2 = (n_2 - 1)$ degrees of freedom associated with the numerator and denominator, respectively. The importance of the need for the samples to be independent and drawn from normally distributed populations should be stressed.

Adopting the null hypothesis $H_0 : \sigma_1^2 = \sigma_2^2$, reduces Eq. (16.1) to

$$F = \frac{s_1^2}{s_2^2}. \tag{16.2}$$

The random variable *F* given by Eq. (16.1) is also defined as the ratio of two χ^2 variables, each divided by its number of degrees of freedom:

$$F = \frac{\chi_1^2/v_1}{\chi_2^2/v_2} = \frac{v_1 s_1^2/\sigma_1^2 v_1}{v_2 s_2^2/\sigma_2^2 v_2} = \frac{s_1^2/\sigma_1^2}{s_2^2/\sigma_2^2} \tag{16.3}$$

since

$$\chi^2 = \frac{v s^2}{\sigma^2}. \tag{6.14}$$

The sampling *F* distribution was introduced in Chapter 6. The *F* distribution has a probability density function given by

$$f(F) = \frac{\left(\dfrac{v_1}{v_2}\right)^{v_1/2} F^{[(v_1/2)-1]} \Gamma\left[\dfrac{v_1 + v_2}{2}\right]}{\left[\left(\dfrac{v_1}{v_2}\right)F + 1\right]^{(v_1+v_2)/2} \Gamma\left(\dfrac{v_1}{2}\right)\Gamma\left(\dfrac{v_2}{2}\right)} \tag{16.4}$$

when $0 < F < \infty$, and $f(F) = 0$, otherwise, (The Γ function is defined on page 274.)

A typical probability density function is shown in Fig. 16.1. As always, the total area under the curve of an *F* distribution is equal to unity and, like the χ^2 distribution (Chapter 14), *F* assumes only nonnegative values. There exists a family of *F* curves, each determined by two parameters: the degrees of freedom associated with the numerator (v_1) and the degrees of freedom associated with the denominator (v_2). All the curves are continuous, unimodal, and skewed to the right; however, those with large numbers of degrees of freedom tend toward symmetry. The shape of the *F* distribution curve is similar to that of the χ^2 distribution which it approaches as v_2 becomes larger. The upper percentage points

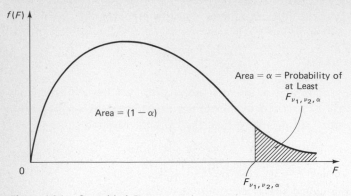

Figure 16.1   One-sided F test.

of the F distribution are given in Table A.14 for levels of significance $\alpha = 0.05$ and 0.01.

The associated degrees of freedom v_1 and v_2 are, in fact, those for the variances s_1^2 and s_2^2, respectively. If the two samples are of size n_1 and n_2, the corresponding numbers of degrees of freedom are $v_1 = n_1 - 1$ and $v_2 = n_2 - 1$, since, as explained in Chapter 3, by calculating the deviations $(x_i - \bar{x})$ from the sample mean $\bar{x}$, we lose 1 degree of freedom because of the constraint equation, namely,

$$\sum_{i=1}^{n_1} (x_i - \bar{x}_1) = 0 \qquad \text{for sample 1}$$

and

$$\sum_{i=1}^{n_2} (x_i - \bar{x}_2) = 0 \qquad \text{for sample 2.}$$

In an F test, we are interested in testing the hypothesis that s_1^2 and s_2^2 are both estimates of the same variance σ^2; that is, we test the null hypothesis $H_0: \sigma_1^2 = \sigma_2^2 = \sigma^2$. For an alternative hypothesis of the form $H_a: \sigma_1^2 > \sigma_2^2$, a one-sided test would be appropriate. The ratio s_1^2/s_2^2, given by Eq. (16.2), is compared with the upper percentage points of the F distribution, given in Table A.14. The value of $F_{v_1, v_2, \alpha}$ is a point on the F distribution with v_1 and v_2 degrees of freedom such that a proportion α of the distribution lies above it, as shown in Fig. 16.1. If, for example, we find $s_1^2/s_2^2 > F_{v_1, v_2, 0.05}$, where s_1^2 and s_2^2 are based on v_1 and v_2 degrees of freedom, respectively, then the result is significant at the 5 percent level of significance; in other words, we have reasonable evidence that the null hypothesis H_0 is untrue.

If there is no prior reason to expect one variance to be larger than the other, so that the alternative hypothesis is of the form $H_a: \sigma_1^2 \neq \sigma_2^2$, then a two-sided test is appropriate. Here, we put the larger of the two-sample variances (be it s_1^2 or s_2^2) in the numerator in order to compare the resulting ratio with the upper percentage points of the F distribution given by $F_{v_1, v_2, \alpha/2}$. We are using $\alpha/2$ because, in this case, the rejection region will be divided between the lower and upper tails, as shown in Fig. 16.2. It can be shown that

$$F_{v_2, v_1, [1 - (\alpha/2)]} = \frac{1}{F_{v_1, v_2, \alpha/2}}. \qquad (16.5)$$

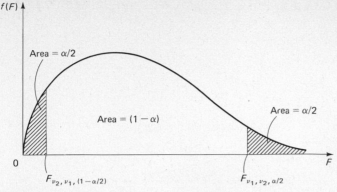

Figure 16.2 Two-sided F test.

If the calculated F exceeds the tabulated value, the probability that the difference between the two variances is caused by chance alone is smaller than the specified probability (0.05, 0.01 or 0.001), and we are justified in rejecting the null hypothesis (with the given probability of committing a Type I error).

It has been shown that the larger the sample the more accurately the variance is determined. For this reason, the larger the samples being compared, the lower the value of F at which the null hypothesis is rejected with a given probability of a correct decision. This is evident in Table A.14.

EXAMPLE

In tests on a plastic, the following data were obtained for two samples from two sources.

Source	Sample size, n	Estimate of standard deviation, s
A	11	300
B	21	200

Can we say that the standard deviation of plastic from source A is greater than from source B at the 5 percent level of significance? We have:

$$s_1 = 300 \qquad v_1 = 11 - 1 = 10$$
$$s_2 = 200 \qquad v_2 = 21 - 1 = 20.$$

Here, the null hypothesis is $H_0: \sigma_1^2 = \sigma_2^2$ versus the alternative hypothesis $H_a: \sigma_1^2 > \sigma_2^2$. Thus, this is a one-sided test. From Eq. (16.2),

$$F = \left(\frac{300}{200}\right)^2 = 2.25.$$

From Table A.14, $F = 2.35$ at the 5 percent level of significance. Therefore, the difference between the variances is not significant, as shown

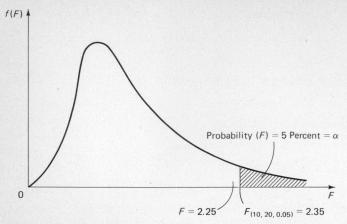

Figure 16.3   Probability density function of the F variable for $v_1 = 10$ and $v_2 = 20$ for the example on page 337.

in Fig. 16.3. However, since $F_{\text{calculated}}$ is quite close to $F_{\text{tabulated}}$, we would be wise to take further specimens and repeat the F test for the enlarged samples; this procedure will reduce the Type I error.   ■ ■

It may be of interest to mention that the value of F for $v_1 = 1$ and v_2 degrees of freedom is equal to the value of t^2 with v_2 degrees of freedom. For example, for a level of significance $\alpha = 0.05$, $v_1 = 1$ and $v_2 = 2$, $F = 18.51$ from Table A.14. Now, the corresponding value of t from Table A.7 with $v = v_2 = 2$ is 4.303. Thus, $F = t^2$ (see page 123).

If variance is a function of the level of the mean, and the populations whose variability is being compared have different means, the F test cannot be applied directly to the variances. For example, if the standard deviation is directly proportional to the mean strength of the population,[1] then it is the squares of the coefficients of variations that have to be tested for homogeneity. The square of the coefficient of variation is approximately equal to the variance of the natural logarithm of the original variate; we can imagine thus that we are dealing with the variance of a log-transformed variable.

STANDARD DEVIATIONS OF VARIOUS STATISTICS

It may be appropriate here to list the standard deviations of various statistics for a sample of size n and an estimate of variance s^2. Equation (6.10) showed that

$$\text{standard deviation}^2 \text{ of the mean} = \frac{s}{\sqrt{n}}. \qquad (16.6)$$

[1] See Chapter 15.

[2] This standard deviation and those that follow are known as standard errors (see Chapter 11).

We can now list the following without proof:

$$\text{standard deviation of variance} = s^2 \sqrt{\frac{2}{(n-1)}} \qquad (16.7)$$

$$\text{standard deviation of standard deviation} = \frac{s}{\sqrt{2(n-1)}} \qquad (16.8)$$

$$\text{standard deviation of the coefficient of variation} = \frac{V}{\sqrt{2(n-1)}}. \qquad (16.9)$$

When the sample size n is large (say, $n \geqslant 30$) we can substitute n for the term $(n-1)$ in Eqs. (16.7) to (16.9).

Equations (16.6) to (16.9) are valid only when the underlying distribution is normal, but even then the standard deviations of variance, of standard deviation, or of the coefficient of variation are not normally distributed.[3] These standard deviations are useful as only an approximate guide to the precision of the estimate of the appropriate statistic and are not greatly used.

COMPARISON OF STANDARD DEVIATIONS
OF LARGE SAMPLES

In the case of very large samples (say, $n > 120$), the central limit theorem (Chapter 6) makes it possible to test the significance of a difference between two *standard deviations* by the normal distribution test of Chapter 15 instead of the F test. This will not seem strange if we are quite clear about the fact that we treat the standard deviation as the variate.

The procedure is as follows. We compute a pooled estimate of the assumed common variance, s_c^2, as given by Eq. (15.14),

$$s_c^2 = \frac{(n_1 - 1)s_1^2 + (n_2 - 1)s_2^2}{(n_1 - 1) + (n_2 - 1)} \qquad [15.14]$$

where s_1^2 and s_2^2 are variances of the two samples, and n_1 and n_2 are the respective sample sizes. Since the sample sizes are large we can write n for $(n-1)$ and write Eq. (15.14) as

$$s_c^2 = \frac{n_1 s_1^2 + n_2 s_2^2}{n_1 + n_2}. \qquad (16.10)$$

We now use the modified form of Eq. (16.8) to write the variance of the distribution of sample standard deviations s_c as

$$\frac{s_c^2}{2n_1} \quad \text{and} \quad \frac{s_c^2}{2n_2}$$

for the two distributions, respectively.

---

[3] Variance has a distribution close to χ^2 but as n increases, the distribution tends to normal.

Since the variance of a difference is equal to the sum of variances (see Rule 7, page 91), the standard deviation of the difference s_d is given by

$$S_{(s_1 - s_2)} = s_d = s_c \sqrt{\frac{1}{2n_1} + \frac{1}{2n_2}}. \tag{16.11}$$

Assuming that the null hypothesis $H_0 : \sigma_1^2 = \sigma_2^2$ is true, we can apply the normal distribution test of Eq. (15.8), that is, compare the difference of the observed standard deviations s_1 and s_2 with s_d:

$$z = \frac{|s_1 - s_2|}{s_d}$$

in which z is a random variable which approximately follows the standard normal distribution. The probability of encountering z at least this large is given in Table A.6.

EXAMPLE

Shear test specimens of soil were obtained on two sites, as follows:

Site	Number of specimens	Standard deviation, kN/m^2
1	120	300
2	150	150

Is there a significant difference between the variabilities on the two sites, i.e., are the two standard deviations significantly different? Use $\alpha = 1$ percent.

We have to apply a two-sided test, since we are checking the null hypothesis $H_0 : \sigma_1^2 = \sigma_2^2$ against the alternative hypothesis $H_a : \sigma_1^2 \neq \sigma_2^2$. Thus,

$$s_c^2 = \frac{120 \times 300^2 + 150 \times 150^2}{120 + 150}$$

$$= 52{,}500.$$

Now, $\quad s_d = \sqrt{52{,}500 \left(\frac{1}{2 \times 120} + \frac{1}{2 \times 150} \right)} = 19.8 \text{ kN/m}^2.$

Hence, $\quad z = \frac{300 - 150}{19.8} = 7.58.$

The probability of obtaining such a value of z by chance is extremely low, and we conclude that the difference between the standard deviations is highly significant. ■■

CONFIDENCE LIMITS FOR VARIANCE

By analogy to the confidence limits of the mean, the confidence limits of variance give the limits within which the true population variance lies with a specified probability.

If s^2 is the variance calculated from a sample with v degrees of freedom, then the limits are given by

$$\frac{v}{\chi^2_{(v,\alpha)}} s^2 \quad \text{and} \quad \frac{v}{\chi^2_{v,(1-\alpha)}} s^2 \tag{16.12}$$

where χ^2 has a value corresponding to v degrees of freedom and to the 5 percent level of significance for the lower limit, and to the 95 percent level of significance for the upper limit.

Thus, we have a 5 percent probability of σ^2 falling below the lower limit and a 5 percent probability of σ^2 falling above the upper limit. The confidence limits, therefore, contain the true value of σ^2 with a 90 percent probability. Similarly, if we take χ^2 at the 1 percent level of significance, the confidence limits contain the true value of σ^2 with a 98 percent probability.

EXAMPLE

Tests on 10 concrete tension specimens yielded an estimate of the population variance of 40,000 (standard deviation of 200 kN/m^2). Find the 90 percent confidence limits for the population variance.

For $v = 9$, we find from Table A.11 that $\chi^2 = 16.919$ at the 5 percent level of significance and $\chi^2 = 3.325$ at the 95 percent level of significance. Thus, the lower limit of σ^2 is

$$\frac{9}{16.919} \times 40,000 = 21,300$$

and the upper limit is

$$\frac{9}{3.325} \times 40,000 = 108,500.$$

Hence, we conclude, with a 90 percent probability of being correct, that

$$21,300 \leqslant \sigma^2 \leqslant 108,500$$

or
$$146 \leqslant \sigma \leqslant 329. \qquad \blacksquare\ \blacksquare$$

In the case of large samples, say $n > 30$, we can take advantage of Eq. (16.8) for the standard deviation of the standard deviation; this is equal to $s/\sqrt{2n}$ [using n for $(n-1)$].

For instance, if in the previous example we tested 50 specimens, the standard deviation remaining at 200 kN/m^2, we would find the standard deviation of the standard deviation to be

$$\frac{200}{\sqrt{2 \times 50}} = 20 \text{ kN/m}^2.$$

Since the standard deviation is not normally distributed, we have to use the t distribution. At the 5 percent level of significance and $v = 49$, $t \simeq 2.010$ (from Table A.7). Thus the confidence limits are

$$200 \pm 2.010 \times 20$$

that is, $$160 \leqslant \sigma \leqslant 240.$$

It is apparent how an increase in sample size decreases the width of the confidence interval at a given level of significance.

BARTLETT'S TEST

The F test can be used to compare two variances only. If more than two variances are involved, then a test of homogeneity of variances, known as Bartlett's test, may be applied. This is a special application of the χ^2 test, in which we compare the difference between the total number of degrees of freedom times the natural logarithm of the pooled estimate of variance and the sum, extended over all samples, of the product of the degrees of freedom and the natural logarithm of the estimate of variance. Thus, if n_i is the sample size, s_i^2 is the estimate of variance from sample i, and $\bar{s}^2$ is the pooled estimate of variance, then Bartlett's test requires the calculation of

$$\chi^2 = 2.3026\{\log \bar{s}^2 \times \sum(n_i - 1) - \sum[(n_i - 1) \log s_i^2]\}. \tag{16.13}$$

The coefficient 2.3026 is introduced by conversion of natural logarithms to those to base 10, since

$$\log_e a = 2.3026 \log_{10} a.$$

When all samples are of the same size n, Eq. (16.13) reduces to

$$\chi^2 = 2.3026(n - 1)(k \log \bar{s}^2 - \sum \log s_i^2) \tag{16.14}$$

where k is the number of samples whose variances are being compared.

The computations are conveniently set out in Table 16.1.

Now, $$\bar{s}^2 = \frac{\sum\sum(x - \bar{x}_i)^2}{\sum(n_i - 1)}$$

and, substituting the other summations in Eq. (16.13), χ^2 can be calculated. This enables us to test the hypothesis that all the variances are homogeneous, using Table A.11 with $(k - 1)$ degrees of freedom. If the calculated value of χ^2 is greater than the tabulated value at a specified level of significance, we conclude that the variances are not homogeneous. The level of significance represents, as always, the probability of our having reached the wrong conclusion.

The value of χ^2 as calculated from Eq. (16.13) is biased toward the high side so that we may wrongly reject the null hypothesis. If χ^2 indicates acceptance, then, after correction for bias, the hypothesis would be even more likely to be correct so that we need not worry about the bias. However, rejection at

TABLE 16.1

Sample number	Sample size	Sum of squares of deviations	Degrees of freedom, ν	Estimated variance, s_i^2	Logarithm of variance	Product	Reciprocal of ν
1	...	...	...	...	...	...	...
...							
i	n_i	$\displaystyle\sum_i^{n_i}(x-\bar{x}_i)^2$	n_i-1	$\dfrac{\sum(x-\bar{x}_i)^2}{n_i-1}$	$\log s_i^2$	$(n_i-1)\log s_i^2$	$\dfrac{1}{n_i-1}$
...	...	...	...	...	...	...	...
k							
	$\displaystyle\sum_1^k\sum_1^{n_i}(x-\bar{x}_i)^2$		$\displaystyle\sum(n_i-1)$		$\displaystyle\sum\log s_i^2$	$\displaystyle\sum[(n_i-1)\log s_i^2]$	$\displaystyle\sum\dfrac{1}{n_i-1}$

TABLE 16.2

Machine	Coded results, x_i	$\bar{x}_i$	$\sum(x_i - \bar{x})^2$	s_i^2	log s_i^2
1	2, 3, 5, 2	3.0	6.00	2.00	0.30103
2	3, 4, 4, 1	3.0	6.00	2.00	0.30103
3	3, 3, 3, 4	3.25	0.75	0.25	−0.60206
4	2, 1, 3, 4	2.5	5.00	1.67	0.22272
5	5, 2, 2, 5	3.5	9.00	3.00	0.47712
Totals				$\sum s_i^2 = 8.92$	$\sum \log s_i^2 = 0.69984$

the 5 percent level has to be checked by calculating a corrected value of χ^2, say χ_c^2. This is given by

$$\chi_c^2 = \frac{\chi^2}{C} \tag{16.15}$$

where

$$C = 1 + \frac{1}{3(k-1)} \left[\sum \left(\frac{1}{n_i - 1} \right) - \frac{1}{\sum(n_i - 1)} \right]. \tag{16.16}$$

Often, a considerable computational effort can be saved by applying an F test to the largest and smallest variances before Bartlett's test. If the F test indicates that the largest variance is not significantly different from the smallest one, then we can reasonably assume that the variances lying in between do not differ significantly, and all the variances can be regarded as homogeneous.

EXAMPLE

The performance of five testing machines was compared by testing four specimens, all from the same source, in each machine (see Table 16.2). Does the variability of the different machines differ significantly? Use $\alpha = 10$ percent.

The null hypothesis is $H_0: \sigma_1^2 = \sigma_2^2 = \sigma_3^2 = \sigma_4^2 = \sigma_5^2$ versus the alternative hypothesis H_a: any two (or more) variances are different. From Table 16.2,

$$\bar{s}^2 = \frac{3 \times 8.92}{5 \times 3} = 1.784$$

and hence,

$$\log \bar{s}^2 = 0.25139.$$

From Eq. (16.14),

$$\chi^2 = 2.3026 \times 3(5 \times 0.25139 - 0.69984)$$
$$= 3.85.$$

The number of degrees of freedom is 4, and Table A.11 gives $\chi^2 = 7.779$ at the 10 percent level of significance. Since the test indicates an acceptance of the null hypothesis, there is no need to apply the correction of Eq. (16.16), and we conclude that there is no significant difference between the variances of the test results of the five machines. ■ ■

PROPAGATION OF ERRORS

If a quantity Q is a function of two or more measured quantities, it is clear that the errors in these measured values will affect the value of Q.

Suppose that we want to determine a quantity Q which is obtained from two measured quantities x_1 and x_2; for example, let

$$Q = ax_1 \pm bx_2. \tag{16.17}$$

Assume that we have a large number of observations of x_1 and x_2, and hence of Q. We can compute the standard deviations of x_1 and x_2, and we want to determine the standard deviation of Q.

Let μ_Q, μ_1, and μ_2 be the true mean values of the three quantities. Then

$$\mu_Q = a\mu_1 \pm b\mu_2. \tag{16.18}$$

If ΔQ, Δx_1, and Δx_2 denote the deviations of observations from the appropriate means, then

$$\Delta Q = a\,\Delta x_1 \pm b\,\Delta x_2$$

and $\qquad (\Delta Q)^2 = a^2(\Delta x_1)^2 + b^2(\Delta x_2)^2 \pm 2ab\,\Delta x_1\,\Delta x_2. \tag{16.19}$

We can write Eq. (16.19) for each set of observations. The mean value of $(\Delta Q)^2$ then represents the variance of Q, σ_Q^2. Similarly, the mean value of $(\Delta x_1)^2$ is the variance of x_1, $\sigma_{x_1}^2$, and the mean value of $(\Delta x_2)^2$ is the variance of x_2, $\sigma_{x_2}^2$.

The mean value of $\Delta x_1\,\Delta x_2$ is the *covariance* of x_1 and x_2, and is a measure of correlation between x_1 and x_2 (see page 92).

If the variables x_1 and x_2 are independent, that is, not correlated, the covariance is zero. Under such circumstances, the mean values of the various terms of Eq. (16.19) yield the relation

$$\sigma_Q^2 = a^2\sigma_{x_1}^2 + b^2\sigma_{x_2}^2. \tag{16.20}$$

When $a = b = 1$, that is, for $Q = x_1 \pm x_2$, we have

$$\sigma_Q^2 = \sigma_{x_1}^2 + \sigma_{x_2}^2. \tag{16.21}$$

Thus, the variance of a sum or of a difference of two *independent* variables is equal to the sum of the variances of the variables. The argument can be extended to any number of variables.

Equation (16.21) is of great importance in apportioning errors to various causes and forms the basis of the analysis of variance, which is the subject of Chapter 20.

In a more general way, Eq. (16.20) depicts the propagation of errors. For example, if Q is the perimeter of an isosceles triangle, x_1 the length of the base, and x_2 the length of the side, then

$$Q = x_1 + 2x_2.$$

From Eq. (16.20), the variance of the perimeter is

$$\sigma_Q^2 = \sigma_{x_1}^2 + 4\sigma_{x_2}^2$$

and the standard deviation of the perimeter is

$$\sigma_Q = \sqrt{\sigma_{x_1}^2 + 4\sigma_{x_2}^2}.$$

Let us now consider a more general case where the dependent variable Q is given by

$$Q = \sum_{i=1}^{n} a_i X_i.$$

All the terms a_i are constants and the values X_i are random variables. We can use the concepts of expectation discussed in Chapter 5. Thus, it can be shown that

$$E(Q) = \mu_Q = \sum_{i=1}^{n} a_i E(X_i) \tag{16.22}$$

and

$$\text{Var}(Q) = \sigma_Q^2 = \sum_{i=1}^{n} [a_i^2 \, \text{Var}(X_i)] + 2 \sum_{i=1}^{n-1} \sum_{j=i+1}^{n} a_i a_j \, \text{Cov}(X_i, X_j) \tag{16.23}$$

where the covariance is

$$\text{Cov}(X_i, X_j) = r_{ij} \sigma_{X_i} \sigma_{X_j}, \tag{16.24}$$

r_{ij} being the correlation coefficient between X_i and X_j (see Chapter 18). If X_i and X_j are uncorrelated, then $r_{ij} = 0$ and Eq. (16.23) reduces to

$$\text{Var}(Q) = \sigma_Q^2 = \sum_{i=1}^{n} a_i^2 \, \text{Var}(X_i) = \sum_{i=1}^{n} a_i^2 \sigma_{X_i}^2. \tag{16.25}$$

For example, if $Q = X_1 \pm X_2$, that is, $a_1 = a_2 = 1$, then, by Eq. (16.22),

$$E(Q) = \mu_Q = E(X_1) + E(X_2) = \mu_{X_1} + \mu_{X_2}$$

and, from Eq. (16.23),

$$\text{Var}(Q) = \sigma_Q^2 = \text{Var}(X_1) + \text{Var}(X_2) + 2 \, \text{Cov}(X_1, X_2)$$
$$= \sigma_{X_1}^2 + \sigma_{X_2}^2 \pm 2 r_{12} \sigma_{X_1}^2 \sigma_{X_2}^2.$$

If the variables X_1 and X_2 are uncorrelated, then

$$\sigma_Q^2 = \sigma_{X_1}^2 + \sigma_{X_2}^2, \text{ as shown by Eq. (16.21).}$$

Equation (16.20) was derived for the case when Q is a sum or a difference of two quantities. Let us now consider the case when Q is a product of two quantities, for example,

$$Q = a x_1 x_2 \tag{16.26}$$

where a is a constant assumed free from error.

Using the same notation as before, a typical measurement of Q inclusive of error ΔQ is

$$Q + \Delta Q = a(x_1 + \Delta x_1)(x_2 + \Delta x_2). \tag{16.27}$$

Expanding Eq. (16.27) and subtracting from it Eq. (16.26), we obtain for one set of observations the value of error

$$\Delta Q = a(x_1 \Delta x_2 + x_2 \Delta x_1 + \Delta x_1 \Delta x_2).$$

The error product term is a second-order quantity and can, therefore, be ignored, so that

$$\Delta Q = a(x_1 \Delta x_2 + x_2 \Delta x_1). \tag{16.28}$$

This expression can be written for any set of measurements. For n measurements we can write the variance σ_Q^2 as

$$\sigma_Q^2 = \frac{\sum (\Delta Q)^2}{n}$$

that is,

$$\sigma_Q^2 = \frac{a^2}{n} \left[x_1^2 \sum (\Delta x_2)^2 + x_2^2 \sum (\Delta x_1)^2 + 2x_1 x_2 \sum (\Delta x_1 \Delta x_2) \right]$$

which reduces to

$$\sigma_Q^2 = a^2 (x_1^2 \sigma_{x_2}^2 + x_2^2 \sigma_{x_1}^2) + 2x_1 x_2 \, \mathrm{Cov}(x_1, x_2). \tag{16.29}$$

If x_1 and x_2 are independent quantities, then $\mathrm{Cov}(x_1, x_2) = 0$ and Eq. (16.29) becomes

$$\sigma_Q^2 = a^2 (x_1^2 \sigma_{x_2}^2 + x_2^2 \sigma_{x_1}^2). \tag{16.30}$$

Let us now turn to the more general case of Q which is any function of two variables x_1 and x_2

$$Q = f(x_1, x_2). \tag{16.31}$$

Then, a typical measurement is

$$Q + \Delta Q = f(x_1 + \Delta x_1, x_2 + \Delta x_2).$$

If this function is continuous, so that it has derivatives (and the majority of functions determined experimentally satisfy this requirement), we can expand it in a Taylor series. Using the first two terms only, we find that

$$Q + \Delta Q = f(x_1, x_2) + \left[\left(\frac{\partial Q}{\partial x_1} \right) \frac{x_1 + \Delta x_1 - x_1}{1!} + \left(\frac{\partial Q}{\partial x_2} \right) \frac{x_2 + \Delta x_2 - x_2}{1!} + \cdots \right]. \tag{16.32}$$

Subtracting Eq. (16.31) from Eq. (16.32), we obtain as a first-order approximation

$$\Delta Q = \frac{\partial Q}{\partial x_1} \Delta x_1 + \frac{\partial Q}{\partial x_2} \Delta x_2.$$

Hence,

$$\sum (\Delta Q)^2 = \left(\frac{\partial Q}{\partial x_1} \right)^2 \sum (\Delta x_1)^2 + \left(\frac{\partial Q}{\partial x_2} \right)^2 \sum (\Delta x_2)^2 + 2 \frac{\partial Q}{\partial x_1} \frac{\partial Q}{\partial x_2} \sum (\Delta x_1 \Delta x_2).$$

If x_1 and x_2 are independent, $\mathrm{Cov}(x_1, x_2) = 0$ so that the third term on the right-hand side of the equation is equal to zero. Dividing by the number of observations n, we find

$$\sigma_Q^2 = \left(\frac{\partial Q}{\partial x_1} \right)^2 \sigma_{x_1}^2 + \left(\frac{\partial Q}{\partial x_2} \right)^2 \sigma_{x_2}^2. \tag{16.33}$$

Equation (16.33) was derived for Q, which is a function of two variables only. For a general case, when

$$Q = g(X_1, X_2, \ldots, X_n)$$

the mean and variance of Q may be obtained using the definition of expectation (Chapter 5), as

$$E(Q) = \mu_Q = \int_{-\infty}^{+\infty} g(x_1, x_2, \ldots) p(x_1, x_2, \ldots) \, dx_1 \, dx_2 \, dx_3 \ldots dx_n$$

and

$$\mathrm{Var}(Q) = \sigma_Q^2 = \int_{-\infty}^{+\infty} [g(x_1, x_2, \ldots) - \mu_Q]^2 p(x_1, x_2, \ldots) \, dx_1 \, dx_2 \, dx_3 \ldots dx_n.$$

In many applications, the probability density function $p(x_1, x_2, \ldots)$ is not known, and information is limited to the means and variances of the random variables $X_1, X_2, \ldots, X_n$. To circumvent this problem, once again we expand $g(X_1, X_2, \ldots)$ in a Taylor series about the mean values, $\mu_{X_1}, \mu_{X_2}, \ldots$. Thus,

$$Q = g(\mu_{X_1}, \mu_{X_2}, \ldots, \mu_{X_n}) + \sum_{i=1}^{n} (X_i - \mu_{X_i}) \frac{\partial Q}{\partial X_i}$$

$$+ \frac{1}{2} \left\{ \sum_{i=1}^{n} (X_i - \mu_{X_i})^2 \frac{\partial^2 Q}{\partial X_i^2} + 2 \sum_{i=1}^{n-1} \sum_{j=i+1}^{n} (X_i - \mu_{X_i})(X_j - \mu_{X_j}) \frac{\partial^2 Q}{\partial X_i \partial X_j} \right\}$$

$$+ \cdots \tag{16.34}$$

where all the derivatives are evaluated at their expected values, that is, at $X_i = \mu_{X_i}, X_j = \mu_{X_j}, \ldots, X_n = \mu_{X_n}$; in general, this is not possible, but evaluation at the observed values is usually good enough. By equating the expectations of both sides of Eq. (16.34) and applying the expectation rules in Chapter 5, we deduce the second-order approximate mean of Q as

$$E(Q) = \mu_Q \approx g(\mu_{X_1}, \mu_{X_2}, \ldots, \mu_{X_n}) + \frac{1}{2} \sum_{i=1}^{n} \sigma_{X_i}^2 \frac{\partial^2 Q}{\partial X_i^2}$$

$$+ \sum_{i=1}^{n-1} \sum_{j=i+1}^{n} \mathrm{Cov}(X_i, X_j) \frac{\partial^2 Q}{\partial X_i \partial X_j}. \tag{16.35}$$

Furthermore, for simplicity, we consider only the first-order approximation $\mathrm{Var}(Q)$, which can be shown to be a function of only the means and variances of the variables $X_1, X_2, \ldots, X_n$. Thus,

$$\mathrm{Var}(Q) = \sigma_Q^2 \approx \sum_{i=1}^{n} \left(\frac{\partial Q}{\partial X_i}\right)^2 \sigma_{X_i}^2 + 2 \sum_{i=1}^{n-1} \sum_{j=i+1}^{n} \mathrm{Cov}(X_i, X_j) \left(\frac{\partial Q}{\partial X_i}\right) \left(\frac{\partial Q}{\partial X_j}\right). \tag{16.36}$$

If X_i and X_j are uncorrelated, that is, $\mathrm{Cov}(X_i, X_j) = 0$, then Eq. (16.35) reduces to

$$E(Q) = \mu_Q \approx g(\mu_{X_1}, \mu_{X_2}, \ldots, \mu_{X_n}) + \frac{1}{2} \sum_{i=1}^{n} \sigma_{X_i}^2 \frac{\partial^2 Q}{\partial X_i^2} \tag{16.37}$$

and Eq. (16.36) reduces to

$$\text{Var}(Q) = \sigma_Q^2 \approx \sum_{i=1}^{n} \left(\frac{\partial Q}{\partial X_i} \right)^2 \sigma_{X_i}^2. \tag{16.38}$$

It should be noted that, for many practical applications, the first-order approximation for the mean μ_Q, given by

$$E(Q) = \mu_Q \cong g(\mu_{X_1}, \mu_{X_2}, \ldots, \mu_{X_n}) \tag{16.39}$$

is adequate. For greater accuracy in estimating the mean and variance of Q, reference can be made to the work of Tukey.[4]

Equation (16.33) is especially useful because it can be employed to deduce several relationships, for example, Eq. (15.9). Let us denote by d the difference between two means $\bar{x}_1$ and $\bar{x}_2$, of sample size n_1 and n_2, respectively,

$$d = \bar{x}_1 - \bar{x}_2.$$

Applying Eq. (16.33), we find the variance of the difference to be

$$\sigma_d^2 = \left(\frac{\partial d}{\partial \bar{x}_1} \right)^2 \sigma_{\bar{x}_1}^2 + \left(\frac{\partial d}{\partial \bar{x}_2} \right)^2 \sigma_{\bar{x}_2}^2$$

whence $\qquad \sigma_d^2 = (1)^2 \sigma_{\bar{x}_1}^2 + (-1)^2 \sigma_{\bar{x}_2}^2 = \sigma_{\bar{x}_1}^2 + \sigma_{\bar{x}_2}^2.$

Using Eq. (6.11), we have $\sigma_{\bar{x}_1}^2 \cong s_{\bar{x}_1}^2 = s_1^2/n_1$ and

$$\sigma_{\bar{x}_2}^2 \cong s_{\bar{x}_2}^2 = \frac{s_2^2}{n_2}.$$

Thus, putting s_d^2 as an estimate of σ_d^2, we have

$$s_d^2 = \frac{s_1^2}{n_1} + \frac{s_2^2}{n_2}. \tag{15.9}$$

EXAMPLE

A company assembles a particular machine which requires the union of male and female parts made by different manufacturers, A and B. Samples of parts were taken and their means $\bar{x}$ and standard deviations s were calculated; the results are shown in Table 16.3. Determine the 95 percent confidence limits on the tolerance of fit.

We shall assume that the data are normally distributed. From Table A.6, $z = 1.96$. Now,

$$d = 1.270 - 1.230 = 0.040 \text{ cm.}$$

From Eq. (15.9),

$$s_d = \left[\frac{(0.040)^2}{50} + \frac{(0.045)^2}{36} \right]^{1/2} = 0.0094 \text{ cm.}$$

---

[4] J. W. Tukey, *Technical Reports 10, 11 and 12*, Statistical Techniques Research Group (Princeton, N.J.: Princeton University, 1952).

TABLE 16.3

	Female (A)	Male (B)
$\bar{x}$, cm	1.270	1.230
s, cm	0.040	0.045
n	50	36

Thus, the tolerance is $0.040 \pm (z)(s_d) = 0.040 \pm (1.96)(0.0094) = 0.040 \pm 0.018$ cm. Hence, at the 95 percent confidence level, the maximum tolerance is 0.058 cm and the minimum tolerance is 0.022 cm. If these limits fall outside the specification limits, the company may reject the parts.

■ ■

EXAMPLE

The refractive index N of the glass of a prism is to be determined on the basis of several measurements of the angle of the prism, A, and the angle of minimum deviation, D. The mean values and standard deviations of the angles are A: 56°; 1° and D: 41°; 0.5°.

If the refractive index of the prism is given by

$$N = \frac{\sin \frac{1}{2}(A + D)}{\sin \frac{1}{2}A}$$

determine which angle contributes more to the error in N.

From Eq. (16.33), we can write

$$\sigma_N^2 = \left(\frac{\partial N}{\partial A}\right)^2 \sigma_A^2 + \left(\frac{\partial N}{\partial D}\right)^2 \sigma_D^2.$$

Now,
$$\frac{\partial N}{\partial A} = \frac{\left[\frac{1}{2} \cos \frac{1}{2}(A + D) \sin \frac{1}{2}A - \frac{1}{2} \sin \frac{1}{2}(A + D) \cos \frac{1}{2}A\right]}{\sin^2 \frac{1}{2}A}$$

$$= -\frac{\sin \frac{1}{2}D}{2 \sin^2 \frac{1}{2}A} = -\frac{(\sin 20.5°)}{2 \sin^2 28°}$$

$$= -0.794468$$

and
$$\frac{\partial N}{\partial D} = \frac{\frac{1}{2} \cos \frac{1}{2}(A + D)}{\sin \frac{1}{2}A} = \frac{\frac{1}{2}(\cos 48.5°)}{\sin 28°}$$

$$= 0.705708.$$

The standard deviations are $\sigma_A = 1° = 0.017453$ radians and $\sigma_D = 0.5° = 0.008726$ radians.

Substituting in the expression for σ_N^2, we obtain

$$\sigma_N^2 = (0.794468)^2(0.017453)^2 + (0.705708)^2(0.008726)^2$$

$$= 192.26 \times 10^{-6} + 37.92 \times 10^{-6}.$$

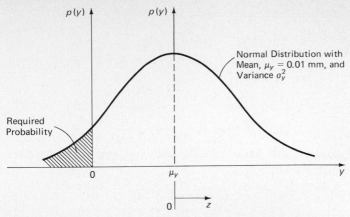

Figure 16.4

Thus the angle of the prism contributes more to the error in the refractive index than the angle of minimum deviation. ■ ■

EXAMPLE

Two mating parts, shaft A and bearing B, are approximately normally distributed and statistically independent with $\mu_A = 75.00$ mm, $\mu_B = 75.01$ mm, $\sigma_A = 0.005$ mm, and $\sigma_B = 0.0075$ mm. Calculate the probability of interference.

Let the expected difference between μ_A and μ_B be $E(y)$, that is, $E(y) - \mu_B - \mu_A$. Thus, $E(y) - \mu_y = 0.01$ mm. From Eq. (16.33) and since $y = B - A$, $\text{Var}(y) = \sigma_y^2 = (1)^2 \sigma_B^2 + (-1)^2 \sigma_A^2 = 0.00008125$. Since A and B are normally distributed, their difference y will also be normally distributed, as shown in Fig. 16.4; the nondimensional statistic $z = (y - \mu_y)/\sigma_y$ is also normally distributed with mean zero and variance 1. Interference will occur when diameter A exceeds that of B; thus, the required probability of interference is given by

$$P(y < 0) = P\left(z < \frac{0 - 0.01}{\sigma_y} = \frac{-0.01}{0.00901} = -1.109 \right).$$

From Table A.6, $F(z) = 0.3830$. Therefore, $P(y < 0) = 0.5 - 0.3830 = 0.1170$. Obviously, this is a relatively large probability and should be reduced by demanding better precision in the manufacture of the two mating parts. ■ ■

EXAMPLE

Given $Z = XY$, determine $E(Z)$ assuming: (a) X and Y are correlated, and (b) X and Y are uncorrelated. Based on assumption (b), evaluate $\text{Var}(Z)$.

    a. Expanding Z in Taylor's series and calculating the derivatives at $X = \mu_X$ and $Y = \mu_Y$, we have from Eq. (16.34),

$$Z = \mu_X \mu_Y + [(X - \mu_X)\mu_Y + (Y - \mu_Y)\mu_X] + (X - \mu_X)(Y - \mu_Y).$$

Taking expectations of both sides yields

$$E(Z) = E(XY) = E(\mu_X\mu_Y) + \mu_Y E(X - \mu_X)$$
$$+ \mu_X E(Y - \mu_Y) + E[(X - \mu_X)(Y - \mu_Y)].$$

Since $E(X - \mu_X) = E(Y - \mu_Y) = 0$,

$$E(Z) = \mu_X\mu_Y + E[(X - \mu_X)(Y - \mu_Y)] = \mu_X\mu_Y + \text{Cov}(X, Y)$$

or $$E(Z) = \mu_X\mu_Y + r_{XY}\sigma_X\sigma_Y.$$

b. If X and Y are uncorrelated, then $r_{XY} = 0$ and therefore $E(Z) = \mu_X\mu_Y$. By definition,

$$\text{Var}(Z) = \text{Var}(XY) = E[XY - E(XY)]^2$$
$$= E(X^2Y^2) - 2E(XY)E(XY) + [E(XY)]^2$$
$$= E(X^2Y^2) - [E(XY)]^2$$

or $$\text{Var}(XY) = E(X^2Y^2) - \mu_X^2\mu_Y^2.$$

Now, from Eq. (5.33),

$$E(X^2Y^2) = E[(X^2 - \mu_X^2)(Y^2 - \mu_Y^2)]$$
$$= E(X^2)E(Y^2).$$

From Eq. (5.35),

$$E(X^2Y^2) = (\sigma_X^2 + \mu_X^2)(\sigma_Y^2 + \mu_Y^2)$$
$$= \sigma_X^2\sigma_Y^2 + \mu_X^2\sigma_Y^2 + \mu_Y^2\sigma_X^2 + \mu_X^2\mu_Y^2.$$

Therefore, $$\text{Var}(XY) = \sigma_X^2\sigma_Y^2 + \mu_X^2\sigma_Y^2 + \mu_Y^2\sigma_X^2.$$

If we divide both sides by $\mu_X^2\mu_Y^2$, we derive the relationship between the coefficients of variations:

$$V_Z^2 = V_X^2 V_Y^2 + V_X^2 + V_Y^2.$$

In many practical problems, we find the product $V_X^2 V_Y^2$ is relatively small and, therefore, we can use

$$V_Z^2 \simeq V_X^2 + V_Y^2. \qquad\qquad ■ ■$$

EXAMPLE

The ultimate moment capacity M_u of a rectangular under-reinforced concrete beam is given by

$$M_u = A_s f_y \left(d - \frac{kA_s f_y}{f'_c b} \right)$$

where A_s = area of tension steel reinforcement;
 f_y = yield stress of steel reinforcement;
 d = depth to the center of area of reinforcement;
 b = width of beam;

f'_c = ultimate compressive strength of the concrete; and

k = factor dependent upon the shape of the compressive stress block in the concrete.

All variables are assumed to be random, independent, and normally distributed. We are given: $\bar{A}_s = 50$ mm^2, $\sigma_A = 3$ mm^2; $\bar{f}_y = 300$ MPa, $\sigma_{f_y} = 20$ MPa; $\bar{d} = 450$ mm; $\sigma_d = 10$ mm; $\bar{b} = 250$ mm; $\sigma_b = 6$ mm; $\bar{f'_c} = 30$ MPa; $\sigma_{f'_c} = 5$ MPa; $\bar{k} = 0.6$; $\sigma_k = 0.06$. Determine the expected value of M_u and its variance $\sigma^2_{M_u}$. Indicate which variables have the most significant influence on the error in M_u, that is, on σ_{M_u}.

Using Eq. (16.39), the mean $\bar{M}_u$ is

$$\bar{M}_u = \bar{A}_s \bar{f}_y \left(\bar{d} - \frac{\bar{k}\bar{A}_s\bar{f}_y}{\bar{f'_c}\bar{b}} \right) = 6732 \text{ N·m}.$$

To evaluate σ_{M_u} by Eq. (16.38), we require the following partial derivatives, all evaluated at the corresponding mean values of the variables:

$$\frac{\partial M_u}{\partial A_s} = f_y d - \frac{2kf_y^2 A_s}{f'_c b} = 134,280$$

$$\frac{\partial M_u}{\partial f_y} = A_s d - \frac{2kA_s^2 f_y}{f'_c b} = 22,380$$

$$\frac{\partial M_u}{\partial d} = A_s f_y = 15,000$$

$$\frac{\partial M_u}{\partial k} = -\frac{(A_s f_y)^2}{f'_c b} = -30,000$$

$$\frac{\partial M_u}{\partial f'_c} = \frac{kA_s^2 f_y^2}{f'^2_c b} = 600$$

and

$$\frac{\partial M_u}{\partial b} = \frac{kA_s^2 f_y^2}{f'_c b^2} = 72.$$

Thus,

$$\sigma^2_{M_u} = \left(\frac{\partial M_u}{\partial A_s}\right)^2 \sigma^2_{A_s} + \left(\frac{\partial M_u}{\partial f_y}\right)^2 \sigma^2_{f_y} + \left(\frac{\partial M}{\partial d}\right)^2 \sigma^2_d + \left(\frac{\partial M}{\partial k}\right)^2 \sigma^2_k$$
$$+ \left(\frac{\partial M}{\partial f'_c}\right)^2 \sigma^2_{f'_c} + \left(\frac{\partial M_u}{\partial b}\right)^2 \sigma^2_b$$

$$= 134,280^2 \times 3^2 + 22,380^2 \times 20^2 + 15,000^2 \times 10^2$$
$$+ (-30,000)^2 \times 0.06^2 + 600^2 \times 5^2 + 72^2 \times 6^2$$

whence $\sigma_{M_u} = 620$ N·m. It is observed from the above that the yield stress f_y, followed by A_s and d, in that order, are the variables that contribute most significantly to the error in calculating M_u, whereas the width of the beam, b, does not contribute to the variation in M_u and therefore it is reasonable to treat it as deterministic. ■ ■

EXAMPLE

Assume that the mean and variance of the vertical load on columns in a multistorey building are constant for all floors; determine the reduction factor C which specifies the load contribution from each floor, assuming: (a) loads on any two floors are statistically independent, and (b) loads on any two floors are correlated with the same positive correlation coefficient $r_{ij} = r$ for any two floors i and j.

We are given: $\beta =$ number of standard deviations from the mean $= 2$; $n =$ number of storeys $= 36$; coefficient of variation of load $V_X = 0.20$; and $r = 0.5$.

If X_i is the load on a column from the ith floor, then the total vertical load on the ground-floor columns will be $Q = \sum_{i=1}^{n} X_i$. Therefore, the mean $\mu_Q = n\mu_X$, and the variance, given by Eq. (16.23), is

$$\text{Var}(Q) = \sigma_Q^2 = n \, \text{Var}(X) + \text{Var } X \sum_{i=1}^{n-1} \sum_{j=i+1}^{n} r_{ij}.$$

a. When $r_{ij} = 0$, $\text{Var}(Q) = \sigma_Q^2 = n \, \text{Var}(X)$. Hence, $\sigma_Q = \sqrt{n}\sigma_X$. Thus, the coefficient of variation is $V_Q = \sigma_Q/\mu_Q = V_X/\sqrt{n}$. The design load is usually specified at β standard deviations from the mean. Therefore, for one floor, the specified design load, X_D, is $X_D = \mu_X + \beta\sigma_X = \mu_X(1 + \beta V_X)$; and for Q_D,

$$Q_D = \mu_Q + \beta\sigma_Q = n\mu_X\left(1 + \frac{\beta V_X}{\sqrt{n}}\right).$$

Therefore, the average load from each floor is

$$\frac{Q_D}{n} = \mu_X\left(1 + \frac{\beta V_X}{\sqrt{n}}\right)$$

which decreases with an increase in the number of floors, n. By definition, the reduction factor C is

$$C = \frac{Q_D}{nX_d} = \frac{1 + \beta V_X/\sqrt{n}}{1 + \beta V_X} = \frac{1 + (2 \times 0.20)/6}{1 + 2 \times 0.20} = 0.76.$$

b. If correlation between loads on any two floors is present and constant, then

$$\text{Var}(Q) = \sigma_Q^2 = n \, \text{Var}(X) + \text{Var}(X)[n(n - 1)r]; \quad \text{or}$$

$$\sigma_Q = \sigma_X\sqrt{[n + n(n - 1)r]}; \quad V_Q = \frac{\sigma_Q}{\mu_Q} = \sqrt{\frac{1 + (n - 1)r}{n}} \, V_X;$$

$$Q_D = \mu_Q + \beta\sigma_Q = n\mu_X\left[1 + \beta\sqrt{\frac{1 + (n - 1)r}{n}} \, V_X\right].$$

Therefore, $C = \dfrac{Q_D}{nX_D} = 0.92.$

It is observed that this reduction factor is larger than the one in (a); therefore, wrongly assuming no correlation between floor loads can lead to unsafe design. ■ ■

EXAMPLE

The cost P in dollars of a wastewater treatment plant is estimated as

$$P = 1000[(0.55 + 0.185Q)C_0 + (0.385 + 0.115Q)(C_s - 200) + 583Q^{0.84}]$$

in which Q = flow rate in million gal/day;
C_0 = concentration, in mg/liter, of influent BOD
(biological oxygen demand);
C_s = concentration of suspended solids in mg/liter.

We are given: $\bar{Q} = 10$ million gal/day; $\bar{C}_0 = 500$ mg/liter; $\bar{C}_s = 300$ mg/liter; and the following coefficients of variation: $V_Q = 0.30$, $V_{C_0} = 0.20$, $V_{C_s} = 0.15$. Assuming that Q, C_0, and C_s are random, normally distributed, and independent variables, determine the average capital cost of the plant, its standard deviation, and coefficient of variation.

From Eq. (16.39),

$$\bar{P} \simeq 1000[\{0.55 + 0.185(10)\}(500) + \{0.385 + 0.115 \times 10\}(300 - 200)$$
$$+ 583 \times 10^{0.84}] = \$5,386,700.$$

From Eq. (16.38),

$$\sigma_P^2 \simeq (1000)^2 \left[\left(\frac{\partial P}{\partial Q} \right)^2 \sigma_Q^2 + \left(\frac{\partial P}{\partial C_0} \right)^2 \sigma_{C_0}^2 + \left(\frac{\partial P}{\partial C_s} \right)^2 \sigma_{C_s}^2 \right]$$

$$\simeq (1000)^2 [\{0.185\bar{C}_0 + (0.115)(\bar{C}_s - 200) + 583 \times 0.84\bar{Q}^{(-0.16)}\}^2 \sigma_Q^2$$
$$+ (0.185\bar{Q})^2 \sigma_{C_0}^2 + (0.385 + 0.115\bar{Q})^2 \sigma_{C_s}^2]$$
$$= (1000)^2 (5,967,247).$$

Thus, $\sigma_P = \$2,442,795$, and the coefficient of variation in the cost is $V_P = \sigma_P/\bar{P} = 0.45$. ■ ■

EXAMPLE

The output voltage V_0 (see Fig. 16.5) is a function of the product of input voltage, V_1, transformer N, and amplifier K, that is,

$$V_0 = V_1 N K.$$

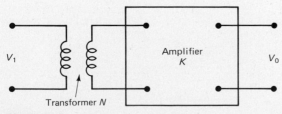

Figure 16.5

We are given: $\bar{V}_1 = 50$ V, $\sigma_{V_1} = 0.4$ V; $\bar{N} = 2$ to 1, $\sigma_N = 0.003$; $\bar{K} = 4$, $\sigma_K = 0.04$. If the design requirement for the voltage V_0 is 100 ± 3 percent, will the components (V, N, K) meet this requirement? Consider $\pm 3\sigma_{V_0}$ to be the maximum tolerance limits.

Assuming that V_1, N, and K are normally distributed random variables and are statistically independent, we have, using Eq. (16.39),

$$E(V_0) = \bar{V}_1 \bar{N} \bar{K} = 50 \times \frac{1}{2} \times 4 = 100 \text{ V}.$$

By Eq. (16.38),

$$\text{Var}(V_0) = \sigma_{V_0}^2 = \left(\frac{\partial V_0}{\partial V_1}\right)^2 \sigma_{V_1}^2 + \left(\frac{\partial V_0}{\partial N}\right)^2 \sigma_N^2 + \left(\frac{\partial V_0}{\partial K}\right)^2 \sigma_K^2.$$

The partial derivatives are evaluated at $V_1 = \bar{V}_1$, $N = \bar{N}$, and $K = \bar{K}$. Thus,

$$\frac{\partial V_0}{\partial V_1} = \bar{N}\bar{K}, \qquad \frac{\partial V_0}{\partial N} = \bar{V}_1\bar{K}, \qquad \frac{\partial V_0}{\partial K} = \bar{V}_1\bar{N}.$$

Hence, $\qquad\qquad\qquad \sigma_{V_0}^2 = 2.00 \quad \text{or} \quad \sigma_{V_0} = 1.414 \text{ V}.$

Therefore, the maximum tolerance limits for V_0 are $100 \pm 3\sigma_{V_0} = 100 \pm 4.242$ V, which is outside the design specification of 100 ± 3 percent. Therefore, the precisions of the independent variables V_1, N, and K require improvement in order to meet the given design specifications. ■ ■

SOLVED PROBLEMS

16-1. The water hardness of two samples taken from separate outlets in a power plant was checked. The coded results (parts per million) are shown in Table 16.4. Determine whether the variance of water hardness from location 1 is greater than from location 2. Use $\alpha = 5$ percent.

Solution. The null hypothesis is $H_0: \sigma_1^2 = \sigma_2^2$ versus $H_a: \sigma_1^2 > \sigma_2^2$. Estimate of variance:

$$s_1^2 = \frac{\sum x_1^2 - [(\sum x_1)^2/n_1]}{n_1 - 1} = \frac{29{,}101 - [(504)^2/9]}{8} = 109.6.$$

TABLE 16.4

Location 1	Location 2
$\sum x_1 = 504$	$\sum x_2 = 868$
$\sum x_1^2 = 29{,}101$	$\sum x_2^2 = 54{,}201$
$n_1 = 9$	$n_2 = 14$

Estimate of variance:

$$s_2^2 = \frac{\sum x_2^2 - [(\sum x_2)^2/n_2]}{n_2 - 1} = \frac{54,201 - [(868)^2/14]}{13} = 29.6$$

$$F = \frac{109.6}{29.6} = 3.71.$$

Using Table A.14 for $v_1 = n_1 - 1 = 9 - 1 = 8$, and $v_2 = n_2 - 1 = 14 - 1 = 13$, $F = 2.77$ at the 5 percent level of significance. Since the calculated $F > 2.77$, the difference in the water hardness of the two samples is significant at the 5 percent level, that is, we reject the null hypothesis and accept the alternative hypothesis with a probability of a wrong decision equal to 0.05.

16-2. A car manufacturing company carried out a series of tests on the rate of crack growth in tires under four different conditions. The summary of the results is shown in Table 16.5.

We want to determine whether the variability of the measurements under the four conditions is the same, i.e., whether the variances are homogeneous. Use $\alpha = 10$ percent (see Table 16.6).

Solution. The null hypothesis is $H_0 : \sigma_1^2 = \sigma_2^2 = \sigma_3^2 = \sigma_4^2$ versus H_a: one or more pairs of population variances differ.

We find

$$\bar{s}^2 = \frac{\sum v_i s_i^2}{\sum v_i} = \frac{4.625}{76} = 0.060855$$

whence 　　　　　　$\log \bar{s}^2 = 0.784296 - 2 = -1.215704.$

TABLE 16.5

Condition, k	Sample size, n	Variance of the rate of crack growth, σ_i^2
1	20	0.0349
2	25	0.0875
3	20	0.0652
4	15	0.0445

TABLE 16.6

k	$v_i = n_i - 1$	s_i^2	Sum of squares, $v_i s_i^2$	$\log s_i^2$	$v_i \log s_i^2$	$\dfrac{1}{v_i}$
1	19	0.0349	0.663	0.542825 − 2	10.313675 − 38	0.05263
2	24	0.0875	2.100	0.942008 − 2	22.608192 − 48	0.04167
3	19	0.0652	1.239	0.814248 − 2	15.470712 − 38	0.05263
4	14	0.0445	0.623	0.648360 − 2	9.077040 − 28	0.07143
$\sum$	76		4.625	2.947441 − 8	57.469619 − 152	0.21836
					= −94.530381	

From Eq. (16.13),

$$\chi^2 = 2.3026[76 \times (-1.215704) - (-94.530381)]$$
$$= 2.3026 \times 2.136877$$
$$= 4.920.$$

From Eq. (16.16), the correction factor is

$$C = 1 + \frac{1}{3(k-1)}\left[\sum\left(\frac{1}{v_i}\right) - \frac{1}{\sum v_i}\right]$$

$$= 1 + \frac{1}{3(4-1)}(0.21836 - 0.01316)$$

$$= 1.0228.$$

Thus,
$$\chi_c^2 = \frac{\chi^2}{C} = \frac{4.920}{1.0228} = 4.810$$

with $(k-1) = 4 - 1 = 3$ degrees of freedom.

Table A.11 gives $\chi^2 = 4.642$ at the 20 percent level of significance, and $\chi^2 = 6.251$ at the 10 percent level. We conclude, therefore, that there is no significant difference in the variances of the different tests and the null hypothesis cannot be rejected. We would, however, be wise to apply Bartlett's test again when more test results are available.

(NOTE: The correction C is not necessary, since the uncorrected χ^2 indicates that the difference is not significant; the computation of χ_c^2 is given solely as an illustration of the method of applying the correction.)

16-3. The following data were calculated from tensile tests on two samples of glass fibers; we can assume that the observations within each sample are normally distributed:

sample size $n_1 = 11$:

$$\sum_1^{11} x_1 = 33,000 \text{ kN/m}^2 \qquad \sum_1^{11} x_1^2 = 100.6 \times 10^6$$

sample size $n_2 = 6$:

$$\sum_1^6 x_2 = 16,800 \text{ kN/m}^2 \qquad \sum_1^6 x_2^2 = 48.84 \times 10^6.$$

a. Test the hypothesis that $s_1 = s_2$ against the alternative $s_1 \neq s_2$ at the 10 percent level of significance.

b. Assuming that the sample sizes are $n_1 = n_2 = 144$ and that the standard deviations of the two samples are $s_1 = 300 \text{ kN/m}^2$ and $s_2 = 320 \text{ kN/m}^2$, apply an appropriate test to the null hypothesis that $s_1 = s_2$.

Solution

a. $s_1 = \sqrt{\dfrac{\sum x_1^2 - [(\sum x_1)^2/n_1]}{n_1 - 1}} = 10^3 \times \sqrt{\dfrac{100.6 - [(33)^2/11]}{10}} = 400 \text{ kN/m}^2$

$s_2 = 10^3 \times \sqrt{\dfrac{48.84 - [(16.8)^2/6]}{5}} = 600 \text{ kN/m}^2.$

Hence, $$F = \frac{s_2^2}{s_1^2} = \left[\frac{600}{400}\right]^2 = 2.25.$$

Since this is a two-sided test, in order to use Table A.14, we must halve the level of significance, $\alpha = 10$ percent, that is, we use Table A.14 at the 5 percent level of significance. Furthermore, since $s_2 > s_1$ the number of degrees of freedom v_1 in Table A.14 must now refer to those for s_2, and v_2 for s_1. Thus, from Table A.14, for $\alpha = 5$ percent, $v_1 = n_2 - 1 = 5$ and $v_2 = n_1 - 1 = 10$, we find $F = 3.33$. Hence, since the calculated $F < 3.33$, the difference in the sample variances is not significant at the 10 percent level.

b. The samples can be considered large ($n \geqslant 30$); therefore, we can use the normal distribution test. The pooled estimate of the variance is

$$s_c^2 = \frac{300^2 + 320^2}{2} = 9.62 \times 10^4.$$

The standard deviation of the difference is

$$s_d = s_c \sqrt{\frac{1}{n}} = 100 \times \sqrt{\frac{9.62}{144}} = 25.85 \text{ kN/m}^2.$$

Hence, $$z = \frac{|s_1 - s_2|}{s_d} = \frac{|300 - 320|}{25.85} = 0.774.$$

Table A.6 gives the probability of obtaining at least this value of z by chance as about $0.5 - 0.28 = 0.22$. The difference cannot, therefore, be deemed significant.

16-4. A simply supported girder is loaded by a uniformly distributed load w per unit length. The center deflection Δ is given by

$$\Delta = \frac{5}{384} \frac{wl^4}{EI}$$

where the length l is measured as 40 ± 0.4 m, w as 2 ± 0.02 kN/m, and the flexural rigidity of the girder, EI, is known precisely. Calculate the resulting fractional standard deviation (or relative error) in Δ; that is, determine the quantity (σ_Δ/Δ).

Solution. From Eq. (16.33), we have

$$\sigma_\Delta^2 = \left(\frac{\partial \Delta}{\partial w}\right)^2 \sigma_w^2 + \left(\frac{\partial \Delta}{\partial l}\right)^2 \sigma_l^2.$$

No other terms are required, since the quantity EI does not vary. To simplify the computation, let us write

$$\Delta = \frac{5}{384} \frac{wl^4}{EI} = Cwl^4.$$

Therefore, $$\sigma_\Delta^2 = (Cl^4)^2(0.02)^2 + (4Cwl^3)^2(0.4)^2.$$

Dividing by Δ^2 yields

$$\left(\frac{\sigma_\Delta}{\Delta}\right)^2 = \left(\frac{0.02}{w}\right)^2 + 16\left(\frac{0.4}{l}\right)^2$$

$$= \left(\frac{0.02}{2}\right)^2 + 16\left(\frac{0.4}{40}\right)^2 = 0.0017.$$

Therefore, the fractional standard deviation in the center deflection $\sigma_\Delta / \Delta = 0.041$ or 4.1 percent, which is considerably larger than the error in either l or w. It can be observed that the error in the length l has a greater influence on the precision of the deflection than the load intensity w.

16-5. The heat transfer coefficient U for a system of two fluids separated by a partition of negligible thermal resistance is

$$U = \frac{h_1 h_2}{h_1 + h_2}$$

where h_1 and h_2 are the individual coefficients of the two fluids. The mean value of h_1 is 20 W/(m²·°C) with a percent standard deviation (σ_{h_1}/h_1) of 5 percent; the mean value of h_2 is 30 W/(m²·°C) with (σ_{h_2}/h_2) of 2 percent. Calculate the percentage standard error in U.

Solution. From Eq. (16.33), we find

$$\sigma_U^2 = \left(\frac{\partial U}{\partial h_1}\right)^2 \sigma_{h_1}^2 + \left(\frac{\partial U}{\partial h_2}\right)^2 \sigma_{h_2}^2$$

whence

$$\sigma_U^2 = \left[\frac{h_2(h_1 + h_2) - h_1 h_2}{(h_1 + h_2)^2}\right]^2 \sigma_{h_1}^2 + \left[\frac{h_1(h_1 + h_2) - h_1 h_2}{(h_1 + h_2)^2}\right]^2 \sigma_{h_2}^2$$

$$= \left[\frac{h_2^2}{(h_1 + h_2)^2}\right]^2 \sigma_{h_1}^2 + \left[\frac{h_1^2}{(h_1 + h_2)^2}\right]^2 \sigma_{h_2}^2.$$

Dividing by U^2 yields

$$\left(\frac{\sigma_U}{U}\right)^2 = \left[\frac{h_2}{(h_1 + h_2)}\right]^2 \left(\frac{\sigma_{h_1}}{h_1}\right)^2 + \left[\frac{h_1}{(h_1 + h_2)}\right]^2 \left(\frac{\sigma_{h_2}}{h_2}\right)^2.$$

Therefore,

$$\left(\frac{\sigma_U}{U}\right)^2 = \left[\frac{30}{(20 + 30)}\right]^2 (0.05)^2 + \left[\frac{20}{(20 + 30)}\right]^2 (0.02)^2$$

$$= \frac{9}{25}\left(\frac{25}{10^4}\right) + \frac{4}{25}\left(\frac{4}{10^4}\right)$$

whence,

$$\left(\frac{\sigma_U}{U}\right)^2 = \frac{241}{(25)(10^4)}.$$

Hence, the percentage standard error in the overall heat transfer coefficient is

$$\frac{\sigma_U}{U} = \frac{15.3}{(5)(10^2)} = 0.0306, \text{ or } 3.1 \text{ percent.}$$

PROBLEMS

16-1. Two different precision instruments were compared, 20 measurements being taken with instrument A and 30 with instrument B. The errors of instrument A had a variance of 15; those of B had a variance of 10. Assuming that the population of errors is normally distributed, test the hypothesis that:

a. $\sigma_A^2 = \sigma_B^2$.

TABLE 16.7

Laboratory	Sample size	Estimate of variance
A	91	267
B	92	388
C	89	552
D	90	860
E	90	480

b. $\sigma_A^2 = 1.75\sigma_B^2$.

c. $\sigma_A^2 \not> \sigma_B^2$.

Use $\alpha = 10$ percent for (a) and (b), and $\alpha = 5$ percent for (c).

16-2. In Problem 15-2, verify the assumption of equal variances of the two machines, A and B, versus the assumption that one variance is greater than the other. Use a 1 percent level of significance.

16-3. From numerous tests (which can be considered infinite) on a certain type of light bulb, it was found that the variance in burning time was 9000 h. A sample of 25 new-type light bulbs is found to have a variance of 13,000. Determine, at the 2 percent level of significance, whether or not the two variances are different.

16-4. The variability of six planimeters is to be tested. Six observations are taken on each planimeter, and the sample variances are computed. The coded results are as follows: 6.5, 9.4, 8.7, 12.4, 10.5, and 7.7. Determine, at the 1 percent level of significance, whether all the planimeters have the same variance.

16-5. Verify the assumption of equal variances in content A from the two sources 1 and 2 in Problem 15-6 versus the assumption that one variance is greater than the other. Use a 5 percent level of significance.

16-6. The variance of error of tests in five laboratories is given in Table 16.7. Establish whether there are any significant differences among them. Use $\alpha = 1$ percent.

16-7. Twenty-six shipments of cement were obtained from each of five plants. From each shipment, 15 test specimens were made, their average strengths being given in Table 16.8. A control supply of cement was also obtained, and on every occasion when tests were made on the shipped-in cement, similar tests were made on the control cement (which, of course, did not vary).

Comment on the suggestion that the shipment-to-shipment variability is no greater than the variability within the control cement. (HINT: The standard deviation of control represents the testing error. Is the standard deviation for shipments from a given plant significantly greater?) Use $\alpha = 1$ percent.

16-8. For the data of Problem 15-11 test the homogeneity of standard deviations. Use $\alpha = 5$ percent.

16-9. The standard deviation of the strength of beams of four different sizes was obtained using three series of tests, each test consisting of two specimens (see Table 16.9). Are the standard deviations homogeneous? Use $\alpha = 1$ percent.

16-10. The radius r of a cylinder is given as 6.1 ± 0.1 cm and the length l as 15.6 ± 0.2 cm. Find the volume of the cylinder and the associated standard error.

TABLE 16.8

Sample number	Compressive strength, MPa, for cement source number					
	Control	1	2	3	4	5
1	18.28	20.40	13.55	13.09	18.68	11.02
2	17.80	19.66	14.87	13.04	20.72	14.78
3	16.44	19.00	—	14.00	17.84	11.93
4	17.75	15.82	—	16.69	18.48	14.21
5	16.51	15.14	14.89	13.15	19.02	11.71
6	16.77	16.92	14.12	14.47	18.43	14.35
7	16.42	17.33	15.54	12.11	19.92	13.27
8	16.33	18.73	14.78	15.27	17.50	11.51
9	16.01	16.31	13.76	16.02	19.19	10.97
10	16.82	19.15	15.90	14.62	20.04	13.56
11	17.09	18.18	16.44	13.27	18.59	14.93
12	17.36	17.31	16.07	14.17	18.80	14.29
13	17.48	20.93	14.21	15.95	17.76	15.27
14	16.90	23.19	13.65	12.69	17.24	10.82
15	17.43	23.02	12.88	17.41	18.38	13.78
16	17.11	19.43	13.52	12.02	18.22	13.95
17	17.08	22.05	13.53	14.35	17.52	12.00
18	16.84	19.92	12.78	13.81	16.95	13.51
19	17.13	19.99	14.64	13.17	14.69	13.57
20	17.00	—	—	13.97	16.15	14.03
21	16.86	—	12.77	14.42	18.03	13.67
22	17.82	20.98	11.96	14.13	19.40	14.20
23	16.33	18.76	13.63	14.25	19.82	14.30
24	17.06	21.41	12.55	15.65	17.60	14.04
25	16.27	16.89	11.58	14.54	12.42	13.92
26	15.72	19.91	10.73	12.92	11.00	—

Source: S. Walker and D. L. Bloem, *Tests of Uniformity of Mortar Strengths of Cement Samples from Same Source* (Washington D.C.: National Ready Mixed Concrete Assn., Jan. 1957). The original data were in psi units.

TABLE 16.9

Beam size (in 2.54 cm)	Number of tests			Standard deviation, kN/m^2		
	Series A	Series B	Series C	Series A	Series B	Series C
6	17	10	6	503	248	131
9	24	8	2	490	138	76
12	16	10	4	538	324	83
18	8	3	2	386	228	221

Source: A. M. Neville, "Some Aspects of the Strength of Concrete," Part I, *Civil Engineering* (London), vol. 54, Oct. 1959, p. 1156. The original data were in psi units.

16-11. The value of the gravitation constant g is to be determined from $g = 2s/t^2$ by observing a body fall, where s is the distance traveled in time t. The experimenter has a choice of setting s at 1.22 m with t about $\frac{1}{2}$ s or of setting s at 4.88 m with t about 1 s. Assume that the standard deviation of s is 0.0006 m and that the standard deviation of recording time is 0.05 s. Calculate the variance of g for the two choices of s and t.

Which value of s is better in the sense of giving a smaller variance of the estimated value of g? Given

$$\frac{\partial g}{\partial s} = \frac{2}{t^2}, \qquad \frac{\partial g}{\partial t} = -\frac{4s}{t^3}.$$

16-12. The volume of a sphere is $V = \pi D^3/6$, where D is the diameter. What is the standard error in the volume, σv if D is measured and found to be 10.00 ± 0.16 cm? (NOTE: The standard error in D, σ_D, is 0.16 cm, as shown.)

16-13. The deflection δ of an eccentrically loaded hinged-end column is given as

$$\delta = e\left\{ \sec\left[\left(\frac{P}{EI}\right)^{1/2} \frac{l}{2} \right] - 1 \right\}.$$

If for a model column the load P is 10 ± 0.5 kN, the eccentricity e of 0.5 ± 0.05 mm, the moment of inertia $I = 400{,}000$ mm^4, the modulus of elasticity $E = 100 \pm 4$ kN/mm^2, and the length $l = 250$ mm, calculate the standard error in the deflection δ.

16-14. The energies of the various quantum states of a hydrogen atom are given by

$$E_n = -\frac{1}{2}\frac{me^4}{n^2\kappa^2} \qquad \text{with } n = 1, 2, 3, \ldots$$

If the mass of the electron m is known with a fractional standard deviation $\sigma_m/m = 0.1$ percent, the electron charge e with $\sigma_e/e = 0.2$ percent, and the constant κ with $\sigma_\kappa/\kappa = 0.1$ percent, what is the percent standard error in E_n, σ_{E_n}/E_n, for the state $n = 1$ and for the state $n = 2$?

Determine which of the measurements (m, e, or κ) should be increased in accuracy for best improvement in the precision of E_n.

16-15. The rate of crack growth, per load cycle, in metals, can be estimated from

$$\frac{dC}{dn} = a[(\Delta S)\sqrt{\pi C}]^b$$

in which $C =$ the crack length;
                 $n =$ number of cycles;
              $\Delta S =$ applied stress increment; and
       a and $b =$ constants.

We are given: $a = 10^{-7}$, $b = 2$, $\bar{C} = 3$ mm, $\sigma_C - 0.6$ mm, $\overline{\Delta S} = 350$ kPa, and $\sigma_{\Delta S} - 100$ kPa. Assume that C and ΔS are normally distributed and independent variables.

a. Determine the first-order mean and standard deviation of the crack growth rate per load cycle.

b. Evaluate the second-order mean crack growth rate per load cycle.

16-16. The noise intensity, in decibels, at a station C, transmitted from two noise sources A and B, located at fixed distances from C, is approximated by

$$D_C = 40 \log_e\left[2\frac{I_A}{(10)^2} + \frac{I_B}{(20)^2} \right]$$

where I_A and I_B are the noise intensities originating from A and B. We are given: $\bar{I}_A = 1500$ units, $\sigma_A = 150$ units, $\bar{I}_B = 2500$ units, and $\sigma_B = 250$ units. Assuming that I_A and I_B are statistically independent and normally distributed, determine the first-order mean and variance of D_C, that is, the number of decibels at C.

16-17. The Manning equation for the velocity of uniform flow V in m/sec in an open channel is

$$V = \frac{R^{2/3}S^{1/2}}{n}$$

where S = slope of the energy line,
           R = hydraulic radius in meters, and
           n = roughness coefficient of the channel.

We are given: $\bar{R} = 1$ m, $\sigma_R = 0.005$ m, $\bar{S} = 0.01$, $\sigma_S = 0.001$, $\bar{n} = 0.015$, and $\sigma_n = 0.005$. Assuming statistical independence between the normally distributed variables R, S, and n, calculate the first-order mean value and variance of the flow velocity V. Also, determine the second-order approximation for the mean flow velocity.

Chapter 17

Regression and Method of Least Squares

Relations between variables are often of interest: we may want to establish an association between the variables measured or, alternatively, we may look for a basis of prediction. Prediction (or forecast) is of course important in planning and decision making. One type of analysis primarily concerned with the association between variables is the regression analysis. This provides the basis on which estimates can be made of the values of a (dependent) variable from a knowledge of the values of one or more other (independent) variables. The decision on a proper selection of independent variables would normally be made by an engineer or scientist and based on his experience and prior knowledge as to which independent variables are likely to influence the values of the dependent variable.

The functional form of the relationship between the dependent variable and the independent variable(s) is deduced from either:

1. analytical or theoretical considerations; or
2. an inspection of the scatter diagram (described in the next section) of the data for a sample taken from some population.

The main objectives of regression analysis are:

1. to provide estimates of values of the dependent variable from values of the independent variable(s); and
2. to obtain measures of the error involved in using the regression line as a basis of estimation.

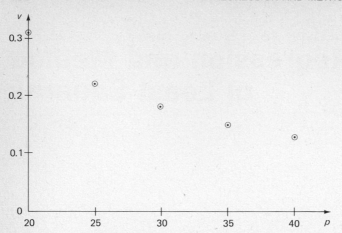

Figure 17.1   Scatter diagram for data in Solved Problem 17-1.

In this chapter, we shall deal with two-variable regression; multiple linear regression, involving two or more independent variables to estimate a dependent variable, is discussed in Chapter 19.

SCATTER DIAGRAM

A useful tool in examining the relationship between two variables is to plot the sample data on a graph; by examining such a plot we can (i) observe whether the variables are indeed related or not; and (ii) choose an appropriate model for estimation. Figure 17.1 shows a scatter diagram of the data given in Solved Problem 17-1; it is clear from the plot that the volume v (dependent variable) is not linearly related to the pressure p (independent variable).

TWO-VARIABLE LINEAR REGRESSION

In elementary work, we often establish numerical relations by determining the values of the variables at a number of points equal to the total number of variables. For example, if a linear relation $y = a + bx$ is postulated, two pairs of values (x_1, y_1) and (x_2, y_2) determine the constants in the equation. This is satisfactory, provided that the observed quantities are free from error.

In practice, error enters all our observations, and if we take further observations, say (x_3, y_3), we may obtain a point that does not fit exactly on the straight line through the original two points. This also applies, of course, to curves involving powers of x and y. Statistical methods help us to fit the "best" line to a given set of data, instead of simply drawing a line "by eye."

In seeking a "best" line, our main interest is in studying the association between the two variables, rather than estimating one variable from the other.

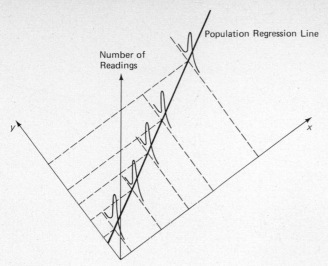

Figure 17.2 Linear regression line for a population.

Let us assume that we have a population consisting of all relevant pairs of observations, (y, x), of the dependent and independent variables. Let us denote the population regression line as

$$E(y|x) = \mu_{y|x} = a + bx \tag{17.1}$$

where $\mu_{y|x}$ is the mean of the dependent variable y, given a fixed value of x, that is, it is the mean of the conditional probability distribution.[1] Figure 17.2 shows the population regression line, with the variable y having a constant precision error independent of the level of the variable x. The same property is exhibited in Fig. 17.3, which also shows the intercept a and the slope b. Equation (17.1) joins the means of the distribution corresponding to all possible values of x. Any randomly selected y is represented by

$$y_p = a + bx_p + e_p \tag{17.2}$$

where e_p is the random deviation (error) of the observation y_p from the mean $\mu_{y|x_p}(= a + bx_p)$. The error e_p is shown in Fig. 17.3.

The following assumptions are involved in using the linear regression model given by Eq. (17.2):

    1. The values of y are random and independent of each other, so that, for instance, a low observed value of y does not necessarily imply that the following y value will also be low.

---

[1] Conditional probability distribution describes the probability of obtaining a particular experimental outcome, say y, for a given particular value of another variable, say x.

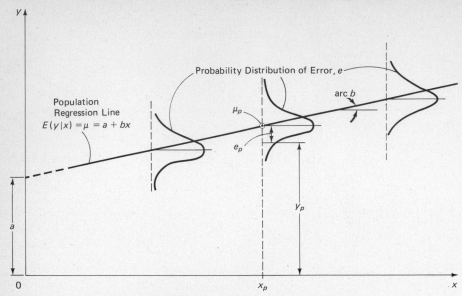

Figure 17.3   Linear regression line and error probability distribution for a population.

2. The values of x are fixed and without error and are therefore considered nonrandom.

3. The error e associated with y is normally distributed with a mean equal to zero and constant variance $\sigma_{y|x}^2$, that is, for each value of x, the probability distribution of y is normal about the mean, $\mu_{y|x}$ (see Fig. 17.3). If $\sigma_{y|x}^2 \neq$ constant, then the regression analysis must be modified by allowing more weight to those observations which have a smaller variance. (For further information see footnote.[2])

Generally, we deal with only a sample drawn from the population so that we cannot attain Eq. (17.1). However, this population regression line equation can be estimated from the sample by the equation,

$$\hat{y} = \hat{a} + \hat{b}x \tag{17.3}$$

in which $\hat{y}$ denotes the estimated mean of the conditional probability distribution of y corresponding to a given x; in other words, $\hat{y}$ is a point estimator (see Chapter 7) of $\mu_{y|x}$; $\hat{a}$ and $\hat{b}$ are estimates of the population parameters a and b, respectively. Equation (17.3) is deduced by the method of least squares, discussed in the next section. Figure 17.4 shows the population regression line and the sample regression line.

We cannot stress too strongly that extrapolation of the regression line outside the range of variables used in its derivation is not permitted without a valid reason.

---

[2] A Hald, *Statistical Theory with Engineering Applications* (New York: John Wiley & Sons, 1952).

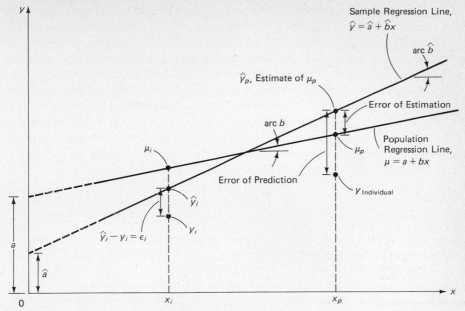

Figure 17.4 Population regression line and sample regression line.

In order to simplify the notation in this chapter we shall use the following symbols:

Definition	Symbol
Variance of a population y at $x = x_i$	σ_y^2
Estimate, from the sample, of σ_y^2	s_y^2
Mean of a population y at $x = x_i$	μ_i
Estimate, from the sample, of μ_i	$\hat{y}_i$
Variance of $\hat{y}_i$	$\sigma_{\hat{y}_i}^2$
Estimate, from the sample, of $\sigma_{\hat{y}_i}^2$	$s_{\hat{y}_i}^2$

METHOD OF LEAST SQUARES

There are two disadvantages in drawing the regression line using the "by eye" technique mentioned earlier. First, it is quite likely that different investigators will not draw identical regression lines for the same data. Furthermore, it will not be possible to evaluate from the sample data the precision of any prediction based on such a regression line, that is, we shall not be able to establish confidence limits on such predictions. These disadvantages can be avoided by using statistical methods for fitting the best line; the most common of these involves the application of the principle of least squares. This principle states that if y is a linear function of an independent variable x, the most probable position of a line $\hat{y} = \hat{a} + \hat{b}x$ is such that the sum of squares of deviations of all points (x_i, y_i) from the line is a minimum; the deviations are measured *in the direction of the y axis*. It should be stressed that the underlying assumption is that x is either free from error (being assigned) or subject to negligible error only, while y is the observed or measured quantity, subject to errors that have to be "reduced" by the method of least squares. The observed y is thus a random value from the population of values of y corresponding to a given x. Such a situation exists in controlled experiments, where we are interested in estimating a mean value of y, that is, μ_i, for each given value of x_i.

Suppose that our observations consist of n pairs of values:

$$\begin{cases} x_1, x_2, \ldots, x_n \\ y_1, y_2, \ldots, y_n \end{cases}$$

and imagine that the various pairs plot as points shown in Fig. 17.5. Assume further that from the physical nature of the relation between y and x we know that the relation is linear, or alternatively expect or suspect it to be linear. Therefore, we postulate the relation for the population mean of y as

$$E(y) = \mu = a + bx. \qquad [17.1]$$

As mentioned earlier, such an equation for the population regression line can be estimated by the sample regression equation:

$$\hat{y} = \hat{a} + \hat{b}x. \qquad [17.3]$$

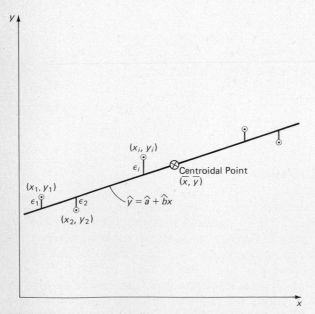

Figure 17.5 Regression line.

Our problem then is to find the values of $\hat{a}$ and $\hat{b}$ for the line of "best fit." For a point i on this line:

$$y_i - (\hat{a} + \hat{b}x_i) = 0 \tag{17.4}$$

but, if there is error in the measurement, there will be a residual ϵ_i (see Figs. 17.4 and 17.5) such that

$$y_i - (\hat{a} + \hat{b}x_i) = \epsilon_i. \tag{17.5}$$

With n observations we have n equations:

$$y_1 - (\hat{a} + \hat{b}x_1) = \epsilon_1$$
$$y_2 - (\hat{a} + \hat{b}x_2) = \epsilon_2$$
$$\vdots \qquad \vdots \qquad \vdots$$
$$y_n - (\hat{a} + \hat{b}x_n) = \epsilon_n.$$

Using the summation notation, we can write the sum of squares of residuals as

$$P = \sum \epsilon_i^2 \tag{17.6}$$

or

$$P = \sum [y_i - (\hat{a} + \hat{b}x_i)]^2 \tag{17.7}$$

the summation extending from $i = 1$ to $i = n$.

As stated before, we have to satisfy the condition that the sum of squares of residuals is a minimum, that is, P is a minimum. This occurs when

$$\left. \begin{array}{c} \dfrac{\partial P}{\partial \hat{a}} = 0 \\[2ex] \dfrac{\partial P}{\partial \hat{b}} = 0 \end{array} \right\} \tag{17.8}$$

or

$$\sum [y_i - (\hat{a} + \hat{b}x_i)] = 0 \tag{17.9}$$

and

$$\sum x_i [y_i - (\hat{a} + \hat{b}x_i)] = 0. \tag{17.10}$$

Omitting the subscripts, we can write Eq. (17.9) as

$$\sum y - \sum \hat{a} - \hat{b} \sum x = 0.$$

Since $\hat{a}$ is a constant, we have

$$\sum y = n\hat{a} + \hat{b} \sum x \tag{17.11}$$

or

$$\frac{\sum y}{n} = \hat{a} + \hat{b} \frac{\sum x}{n}.$$

Thus,

$$\bar{y} = \hat{a} + \hat{b}\bar{x}. \tag{17.12}$$

Equation (17.12) states that the line passes through the point $(\bar{x}, \bar{y})$, that is, through the point whose coordinates are the appropriate means of all observations; we can call this point the centroidal point of all observations. From the fact that the point $(\bar{x}, \bar{y})$ lies on the line, it follows that Eq. (17.3) can be written also as

$$\hat{y} - \bar{y} = \hat{b}(x - \bar{x}). \qquad [17.3a]$$

Returning now to Eq. (17.10), we have

$$\sum xy = \hat{a}\sum x + \hat{b}\sum x^2. \qquad (17.13)$$

Equations (17.11) and (17.13) are called the *normal equations*.

REGRESSION LINE

Solving the normal equations (17.11) and (17.13), we obtain

$$\hat{a} = \frac{\sum x^2 \sum y - \sum x \sum xy}{n\sum x^2 - (\sum x)^2} \qquad (17.14)$$

and[3]

$$\hat{b} = \frac{n\sum xy - \sum x \sum y}{n\sum x^2 - (\sum x)^2}. \qquad (17.15)$$

Hence, the equation to the line of "best fit" (i.e., the sample regression line) can be written as

$$\hat{y} = \frac{\sum x^2 \sum y - \sum x \sum xy}{n\sum x^2 - (\sum x)^2} + \frac{n\sum xy - \sum x \sum y}{n\sum x^2 - (\sum x)^2}x. \qquad (17.16)$$

In practice, it is more convenient to compute $\hat{a}$ and $\hat{b}$ separately [using Eqs. (17.14) and (17.15)], and to use the numerical values of $\hat{a}$ and $\hat{b}$ directly in writing $\hat{y} = \hat{a} + \hat{b}x$.

The line given by Eq. (17.16) is called the line of *regression of y on x*. In deriving the line, we assumed that x is the assigned variable (i.e., sensibly free from error) and that y is the observed quantity.

If, however, the properties of the variables are reversed, that is, if y is the assigned variable and x is the observed quantity, we find the constants in the equation to the sample regression line

$$\hat{x} = \hat{a}' + \hat{b}'y \qquad (17.17)$$

by minimizing the sum of squares of the x *residuals*. The equation to the line, known as the line of *regression of x on y*, is

$$\hat{x} = \frac{\sum y^2 \sum x - \sum y \sum xy}{n\sum y^2 - (\sum y)^2} + \frac{n\sum xy - \sum x \sum y}{n\sum y^2 - (\sum y)^2}y. \qquad (17.18)$$

$$\hat{x} = c + dy$$

---

[3] Note that

$$n\sum xy - \sum x \sum y = n\sum(x - \bar{x})(y - \bar{y})$$

since

$$n\sum(x - \bar{x})(y - \bar{y}) = n(\sum xy - \bar{x}\sum y + \bar{x}\sum y - \bar{y}\sum x).$$

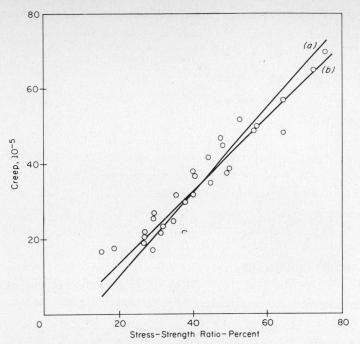

Figure 17.6 Relation between creep of mortar and stress-strength ratio: (a) line of regression of stress-strength ratio upon creep: and (b) line of regression of creep upon stress-strength ratio.

In general,

$$\hat{a} \neq -\frac{\hat{a}'}{\hat{b}'}$$

and

$$\hat{b} \neq \frac{1}{\hat{b}'}$$

but both lines intersect at $(\bar{x}, y)$. An example of the two regression lines is shown in Fig. 17.6. We may note here that it is possible to calculate regression when both variables are subject to error.[4]

The computation of $\hat{a}$ and $\hat{b}$ may be rather laborious and may involve large numbers. The effort can be reduced by taking advantage of the fact that $(\bar{x}, \bar{y})$ is a point on the line. We can, therefore, transform the axes of coordinates to a new origin $(\bar{x}, \bar{y})$. The new coordinates (X, Y) are then

$$\left. \begin{aligned} X &= x - \bar{x} \\ Y &= y - \bar{y} \end{aligned} \right\} . \tag{17.19}$$

[4] See A. Hald, *Statistical Theory with Engineering Applications* (New York: John Wiley & Sons, 1952).

Since the origin of coordinates (X, Y) is at the centroidal point, it follows that

$$\sum X = \sum Y = 0.$$

Therefore, from Eq. (17.14),

$$\hat{a} = 0$$

and from Eq. (17.15),

$$\hat{b} = \frac{\sum XY}{\sum X^2}. \tag{17.20}$$

This is equivalent to writing Eq. (17.15) in the form

$$\hat{b} = \frac{\sum(x - \bar{x})(y - \bar{y})}{\sum(x - \bar{x})^2} \tag{17.21}$$

which is of more theoretical interest.

Using Eq. (17.20), we find that the equation to the line of regression of y on x (or Y on X) becomes

$$\hat{Y} = \frac{\sum XY}{\sum X^2} X. \tag{17.22}$$

The use of (X, Y), of course, requires computing $(x - \bar{x})$ and $(y - \bar{y})$ for all the observations. This may be tedious if $\bar{x}$ or $\bar{y}$ involves several decimal places, and the computation of products and squares may in consequence be more laborious than operation on (x, y) directly when the latter are integers. As an example, computation by both methods is given here.

EXAMPLE

To determine the relation between the normal stress and the shear resistance of soil, a shear-box experiment was performed, giving the following results:

Normal stress, x (kN/m^2)	11	13	15	17	19	21
Shear resistance, y (kN/m^2)	15.2	17.7	19.3	21.5	23.9	25.4

In the test, the value of x is assigned, and y is the derived quantity. The estimated relation between the two is of the form

$$\hat{y} = \hat{a} + \hat{b}x$$

where $\hat{a}$ is the estimate of the cohesion of soil, $\hat{b} = \tan \phi$, and ϕ is the estimate of the angle of friction.

TABLE 17.1

x	y	x^2	xy	$X = x - \bar{x}$	$Y = y - \bar{y}$	XY	X^2
11	15.2	121	167.2	-5	-5.3	26.5	25
13	17.7	169	230.1	-3	-2.8	8.4	9
15	19.3	225	289.5	-1	-1.2	1.2	1
17	21.5	289	365.5	1	1.0	1.0	1
19	23.9	361	454.1	3	3.4	10.2	9
21	25.4	441	533.4	5	4.9	24.5	25
$\sum = 96$	123.0	1606	2039.8	$8 - 8 = 0$	$9.3 - 9.3 = 0$	71.8	70

$$\bar{x} = \frac{\sum x}{n} = \frac{96}{6} = 16.0 \text{ kN/m}^2; \quad \bar{y} = \frac{\sum y}{n} = \frac{123.0}{6} = 20.5 \text{ kN/m}^2.$$

Tabular arrangement is most convenient (see Table 17.1). From Eq. (17.14),

$$\hat{a} = \frac{\sum x^2 \sum y - \sum x \sum xy}{n \sum x^2 - (\sum x)^2}$$

$$= \frac{1606 \times 123 - 96 \times 2039.8}{6 \times 1606 - 96 \times 96}$$

$$= 4.089.$$

From Eq. (17.15),

$$\hat{b} = \frac{n \sum xy - \sum x \sum y}{n \sum x^2 - (\sum x)^2}$$

$$= \frac{6 \times 2039.8 - 96 \times 123}{6 \times 1606 - 96 \times 96}$$

$$= 1.026.$$

Hence, the estimated relation between the normal stress x and the shear resistance y is given by

$$\hat{y} = 4.089 + 1.026x.$$

We can solve the same problem using coordinates (X, Y) referred to the centroidal point; the appropriate values are computed in the right-hand part of the preceding table. From Eq. (17.20),

$$\hat{b} = \frac{\sum XY}{\sum X^2} = \frac{71.8}{70} = 1.026.$$

Substituting in Eq. (17.22), we obtain

$$\hat{Y} = 1.026X.$$

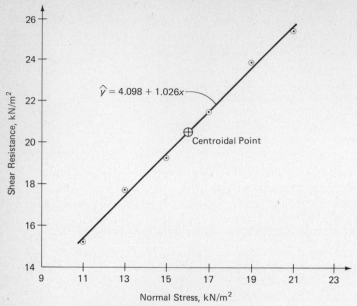

Figure 17.7   Regression line of shear resistance on normal stress for the data of the example on page 374.

Transforming to the original coordinates yields

$$y - 20.5 = 1.026(x - 16.0)$$

whence $$y = 4.089 + 1.026x.$$

In terms of the estimated mean of the conditional probability distribution of y, the above equation is written as

$$\hat{y} = 4.089 + 1.026x \qquad \text{(as before).}$$

The line of regression of y on x, as well as the experimental points, is shown in Fig. 17.7.   ■ ■

LIMITATIONS OF METHOD

It may be worth repeating that the method of least squares is applicable only when the observed values of y_i correspond to assigned (or error-free) values of x_i; furthermore, the error in y (expressed as variance of y, i.e., σ_y^2) must be independent of the level of x. (Of course, x and y are interchangeable.)

For inferences and estimates to be made about regression (but not for the method of least squares), it is also necessary that the population of y corresponding to a given x be normally distributed, with the mean of the distribution, μ, satisfying the true regression equation. Furthermore, the variance of y for a given value of x should be independent of the magnitude of x. In many practical problems this is not the case,[5] and transformation is then necessary; the usual transformations are by taking logarithms, square roots, and so on. The transformation stabilizes the variance of y and makes the distribution closer to normal. This procedure is discussed in Chapters 11 and 14.

CONFIDENCE LIMITS OF REGRESSION ESTIMATES

An estimate of y is given by Eq. (17.3) for any value of x, not necessarily the one at which y was observed but within the range of values for which Eq. (17.16) was established. The question arises: what confidence can we have in our estimate of the "true" equation to the line, that is, the population regression line?

The variance of an estimate enables us to form confidence limits of the estimate. In a manner similar to the variance of a sample (Chapter 4), we shall consider variance about the sample regression line; in this case, the deviations are reckoned from the line instead of from the mean. Thus, the variance of y, estimated by the regression line, is the sum of squares of deviations divided by the number of degrees of freedom, v, available for calculating the sample regression line; that is,

$$s_y^2 = \frac{\sum \epsilon_i^2}{v} \tag{17.23}$$

where ϵ_i is defined by Eq. (17.5). While different y observations come from different conditional distributions and the deviation of any y is reckoned from its own estimated mean $\hat{y}$, that is, ϵ or $(y - \hat{y})$, we still can combine the deviations around $\hat{y}$ since the model we have assumed has the same conditional standard deviation for all the conditional probability distributions. It should be mentioned that s_y^2 is an unbiased estimator for the population variance σ_y^2.

In order to determine v we should remember that two constraints determine the regression line: the centroidal point $(\bar{x}, \bar{y})$ and either slope $\hat{b}$ or intercept $\hat{a}$, or alternatively both $\hat{b}$ and $\hat{a}$. Since these coefficients have been estimated from the sample of size n number of observations (x_i, y_i), there will be two linear restrictions or constraints on the values of ϵ_i as defined by Eq. (17.5). Thus, from the definition of degrees of freedom in Chapter 4, the number of degrees of freedom v for the variance s_y^2 is

$$v = n - 2.$$

Hence,

$$s_y^2 = \frac{\sum \epsilon_i^2}{n - 2}. \tag{17.24}$$

The term s_y^2 in Eq. (17.24) can be more readily calculated from the following expression:

$$s_y^2 = \frac{\sum y_i^2 - \hat{a} \sum y_i - \hat{b} \sum x_i y_i}{n - 2}. \tag{17.24a}$$

[5] For example, the scatter of values of temperature determined by the pyrometer is smaller the higher the temperature, since the source of light is brighter. Contrariwise, the scatter of values of strength of concrete is greater the higher the mean strength.

The estimated variance of $\hat{y}$ at $\bar{x}$, or simply $\bar{y}$ (since $\hat{y}$, at $x = \bar{x}$, is equal to $\bar{y}$), is given in a manner similar to Eq. (6.8) by

$$s_{\bar{y}}^2 = \frac{s_y^2}{n}. \tag{17.25}$$

We can now write the confidence limits for the population mean μ at $x = \bar{x}$. As in the case of the sample mean, we find the value of t for the desired level of significance and the appropriate number of degrees of freedom (Table A.7). We can then state that the true value of $\bar{y}$, that is, μ at $x = \bar{x}$, lies within the interval

$$\bar{y} \pm t s_{\bar{y}}.$$

The probability of our being wrong is equal to the level of significance of the value of t.

Since the regression line must pass through the centroidal point, an error in the value of $\bar{y}$ leads to a constant error in y for all points on the line, the line being translated up or down without a change in slope [Fig. 17.8(a)].

The variance of the slope b is derived as follows. From Eq. (17.20), we have

$$\hat{b} = \frac{\sum XY}{\sum X^2}.$$

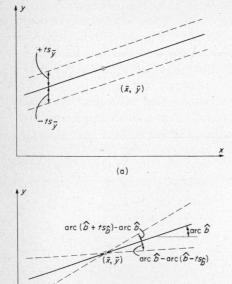

(a)

(b)

Figure 17.8 Confidence bands for (a) μ at $x = \bar{x}$; (b) slope of the population regression line, b.

Thus, using $\hat{b}$ as a point estimator of the population parameter b,

$$\text{variance of } b = \sigma_{\hat{b}}^2 = \text{Var}\left(\frac{\sum XY}{\sum X^2}\right).$$

From the discussion of the propagation of errors (Chapter 16) and recognizing that X has a negligible error and can therefore be assumed to be deterministic, we find that

$$\sigma_{\hat{b}}^2 = \left(\frac{1}{\sum X^2}\right)^2 \text{Var}(\sum XY)$$

$$= \left(\frac{1}{\sum X^2}\right)^2 \sum \text{Var}(XY)$$

$$= \left(\frac{1}{\sum X^2}\right)^2 (X_1^2\sigma_y^2 + X_2^2\sigma_y^2 + X_3^2\sigma_y^2 + \cdots)$$

$$= \frac{\sum X^2}{(\sum X^2)^2}\sigma_y^2 = \frac{\sigma_y^2}{\sum X^2}.$$

An estimate of $\sigma_{\hat{b}}^2$ from the sample would be

$$s_{\hat{b}}^2 = \frac{s_y^2}{\sum X^2}$$

or

$$s_{\hat{b}}^2 = \frac{s_y^2}{\sum (x - \bar{x})^2}. \qquad (17.26)$$

The confidence band for the slope is represented by a double fan-shaped area with slopes of $\hat{b} \pm ts_{\hat{b}}$ and apex at $(\bar{x}, \bar{y})$ [Fig. 17.8(b)].

If we require the confidence limits for the mean of the population of $y(\mu_i)$ at, say, $x = x_i$, then we need the variance of $\sigma_{\hat{y}_i}^2$ of the estimate $\hat{y}_i$. We can estimate this variance from the sample by

$$s_{\hat{y}_i}^2 = s_y^2\left[\frac{1}{n} + \frac{(x_i - \bar{x})^2}{\sum (x - x)^2}\right]. \qquad (17.27)$$

Equation (17.27) is derived in the same manner as Eq. (17.26). From Eqs. (17.3) and (17.12), we can write

$$\hat{y}_i = \bar{y} + \hat{b}(x_i - \bar{x}).$$

Now, with $(x - \bar{x})$ being assumed free from error, using Rules 4 and 7 in Chapter 5, we have

$$\sigma_{\hat{y}_i}^2 = \text{variance of } \bar{y} + (x_i - \bar{x})^2 \text{ variance of } \hat{b},$$

that is,

$$\sigma_{\hat{y}_i}^2 = \sigma_{\bar{y}}^2 + (x_i - \bar{x})^2 \frac{\sigma_y^2}{\sum (x - \bar{x})^2}$$

or

$$\sigma_{\hat{y}_i}^2 = \frac{\sigma_y^2}{n} + \frac{(x_i - \bar{x})^2}{\sum (x - \bar{x})^2}\sigma_y^2.$$

Hence,
$$\sigma_{\hat{y}_i}^2 = \sigma_y^2 \left[\frac{1}{n} + \frac{(x_i - \bar{x})^2}{\sum (x - \bar{x})^2} \right]. \tag{17.28}$$

We can estimate σ_y^2 by s_y^2 from the sample, and $\sigma_{\hat{y}_i}^2$ by $s_{\hat{y}_i}^2$. Thus,

$$s_{\hat{y}_i}^2 = s_y^2 \left[\frac{1}{n} + \frac{(x_i - \bar{x})^2}{\sum (x - \bar{x})^2} \right]. \tag{17.27}$$

It is obvious that if $x_i = \bar{x}$, then $\hat{y}_i$ is at the centroid, that is, $\hat{y}_i$ at $x_i = \bar{x}$ is equal to $\bar{y}$, and hence Eq. (17.27) reduces to Eq. (17.25).

The confidence interval for the mean of a population of y at x_i, that is, μ_i, is then

$$\hat{y}_i \pm t s_{y_i}.$$

For a specified level of significance, we can thus predict the limits within which the population mean, μ_i, will lie with the appropriate probability of error.

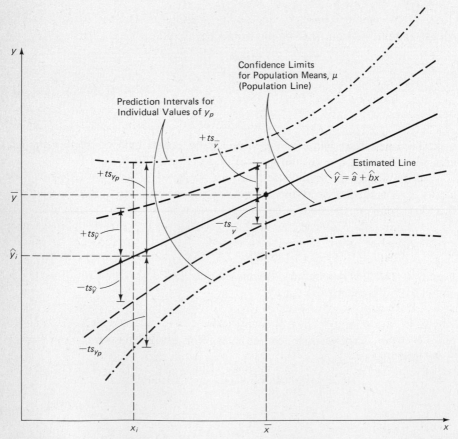

Figure 17.9 Confidence limits for mean μ at $x = \bar{x}$, for mean μ_i (at $x = x_i$), and prediction intervals for individual values of y_p.

The limits are wider the larger the value of $(x_i - \bar{x})$, that is, the further x_i is removed from the centroidal point. This is shown in Fig. 17.9.

If we are interested in predicting the confidence interval of a *single individual value of y at $x = x_i$*, that is, y_p, we have to use the variance of such a single value; this variance is

$$s_{y_p}^2 = s_y^2 \left[1 + \frac{1}{n} + \frac{(x_i - \bar{x})^2}{\sum (x - \bar{x})^2} \right]. \tag{17.29}$$

We can see that such a variance is larger than $s_{\hat{y}_i}^2$ and has two components. The first of these is the sampling error in using $\hat{y}_i$ for estimating μ_i, viz. $s_{\hat{y}_i}^2$; the second component is s_y^2 which is due to the inherent variation, e, in the conditional probability distribution (see Fig. 17.3). Since these two components are independent, the variances can be added. Thus, the estimate for the variance of an individual observation in a population of y at $x = x_i$ is

$$s_{y_p}^2 = s_{\hat{y}_i}^2 + s_y^2 \tag{17.30}$$

and hence Eq. (17.29).

The confidence interval for a single individual value is correspondingly greater, namely,

$$\hat{y}_i \pm t s_{y_p} \tag{17.31}$$

and is shown in Fig. 17.9.

An examination of Fig. 17.9 together with the relevant equation shows:

a. The larger the size of the sample, n, the smaller the estimation intervals. Intuitively, this is expected since larger sample sizes result in a greater precision of estimation.

b. The greater the deviation of x_i from $\bar{x}$, the wider the intervals.

c. A large variance of the conditional probability distributions, σ_y^2 (and hence s_y^2), leads to large intervals, since the more variability in the data the less precise the predictions from these data.

d. Taking more observations at or near the ends (away from the centroid) will increase the value of the term $\sum (x - \bar{x})^2$ and thus decrease the standard error and consequently narrow the intervals.

If we want to use the intercept $\hat{a}$ to define the regression line, we find the variance of $\hat{a}$ as a particular case of the variance of any mean estimated value $\hat{y}_i$. Therefore, we substitute $x_i = 0$ in Eq. (17.27), and the variance of $\hat{a}$ is given by

$$s_{\hat{a}}^2 = s_y^2 \left[\frac{1}{n} + \frac{\bar{x}^2}{\sum (x - \bar{x})^2} \right]. \tag{17.32}$$

For all the confidence intervals of this section, the number of degrees of freedom used in determining t is $v = n - 2$, for the reasons stated on page 377.

It must be emphasized again that the "best-fit" equations apply only within the range of the values of x used in the sample data. They should not be used to estimate the population mean of y, μ_i, or an individual value of y for values of x outside that range unless there are good grounds for doing so as, otherwise, large errors may result.

SIGNIFICANCE TEST FOR SLOPE

In some cases, we have a theoretical value b_0 of the slope b in Eq. (17.1), and we want to determine whether there is a significant difference between b_0 and the value of b given by the population regression line. This is done by means of the t test applied to $|b - b_0|$. This is a two-sided test, with the null hypothesis $H_0 : b = b_0$ versus the alternative hypothesis $H_a : b \neq b_0$, where b is the slope of the population regression line. We recall that $\hat{b}$ is a point estimator of the parameter b.

The standard deviation of $|\hat{b} - b_0|$ is equal to the standard deviation of $\hat{b}$, s_b, because the theoretical value of b is free from error. We find

$$t = \frac{|\hat{b} - b_0|}{s_b} \tag{17.33}$$

and, if the calculated t is greater than t given in Table A.7 for a required level of significance, we conclude that there is a significant difference between b and b_0. The level of significance represents the probability of our drawing an erroneous conclusion.

The number of degrees of freedom for t is equal to $(n - 2)$, where n is the number of observations used in deriving the regression line.

A similar test can be applied to the intercept a. The difference between the value given by regression and the theoretical value a_0 is tested by

$$t = \frac{|\hat{a} - a_0|}{s_{\hat{a}}}. \tag{17.34}$$

The number of degrees of freedom is the same as before.

Sometimes, it is useful to test whether the slope differs significantly from zero. Here, the null hypothesis is $H_0 : b = 0$ versus $H_a : b \neq 0$. We then find

$$t = \frac{\hat{b}}{s_{\hat{b}}} \tag{17.35}$$

and proceed as before. If b does not differ significantly from zero, y is independent of x, and the computation of the regression line is pointless.

EXAMPLE
Referring to the preceding example on the relation between normal stress x and shear resistance of soil y:

a. Check whether the intercept a and slope b are significantly different from zero.
b. Find whether the slope differs significantly from a theoretically predicted slope $b = 1.000$.

TABLE 17.2

x	$\hat{y}$	$\epsilon_i = y_i - \hat{y}_i$	ϵ_i^2
11	15.375	−0.175	0.0306
13	17.427	+0.273	0.0745
15	19.479	−0.179	0.0320
17	21.531	−0.031	0.0010
19	23.583	+0.317	0.1005
21	25.635	−0.235	0.0552
$n = 6$			$\sum \epsilon_i^2 = 0.2938$

   c. Find the 95 percent confidence interval for the estimates of a and b.
   d. Assuming that the regression line can be extrapolated to $x = 25 \text{ kN/m}^2$, find an estimate for the mean value of shear resistance for $x = 25 \text{ kN/m}^2$ and also the 90 percent confidence interval for this estimate.
   e. Find the 95 percent confidence interval for a single individual value of the shear resistance corresponding to $x = 25 \text{ kN/m}^2$.

The regression line of the preceding example gives $\hat{y} = 4.089 + 1.026x$. From this, we compute the estimates $\hat{y}$, and the deviations ($y_i - \hat{y}_i$) for all assigned values of x (see Table 17.2).
   a. From Eq. (17.24),

$$s_y = \sqrt{\frac{\sum \epsilon_i^2}{n-2}} = \sqrt{\frac{0.2938}{6-2}} = 0.271.$$

From Eq. (17.26) and using the value $\sum X^2 = \sum (x - \bar{x})^2 = 70$, we have

$$s_{\hat{b}} = \frac{s_y}{\sqrt{\sum (x - \bar{x})^2}} = \frac{0.271}{\sqrt{70}} = 0.0324.$$

From Eq. (17.32),

$$s_{\hat{a}} = s_y \sqrt{\frac{1}{n} + \frac{\bar{x}^2}{\sum (x - \bar{x})^2}} = 0.271 \sqrt{\frac{1}{6} + \frac{16^2}{70}}$$

$$= 0.5298.$$

To test the significance of $\hat{b}$, we use Eq. (17.35) and find that

$$t = \frac{\hat{b}}{s_{\hat{b}}} = \frac{1.026}{0.0324} = 31.667.$$

For $v = 4$, Table A.7 shows this value of t as significant at better than 0.1 percent. For $\hat{a}$,

$$t = \frac{\hat{a}}{s_{\hat{a}}} = \frac{4.089}{0.5298} = 7.718$$

and this is significant at the 1 percent level.

b. From Eq. (17.33),

$$t = \frac{|\hat{b} - b_0|}{s_{\hat{b}}} = \frac{1.026 - 1}{0.0324} = 0.8025.$$

From Table A.7 for $v = 4$, this value of t is not significant, and we conclude that the observed value of b accords with the predicted value $b_0 = 1.000$.

c. The 95 percent confidence intervals for the estimates of a and b are $\hat{a} \pm ts_{\hat{a}}$ and $\hat{b} \pm ts_{\hat{b}}$, respectively. For $v = 4$, and a 5 percent level of significance, $t = 2.776$. Hence, the required estimates are:

For a:

$$4.089 \pm 2.776 \times 0.5298 = (2.62, 5.56) \text{ kN/m}^2.$$

For b:

$$1.026 \pm 2.776 \times 0.0324 = (0.94, 1.12) \text{ kN/m}^2.$$

d. From the sample regression equation $\hat{y} = a + bx$, for $x = 25$ kN/m^2, the estimate of the mean value of y_i, $\hat{y}_i$, is

$$\hat{y}_i = 4.089 + 1.026 \times 25 = 29.74 \text{ kN/m}^2.$$

The 90 percent confidence interval for this estimate is

$$\hat{y}_i \pm ts_{\hat{y}_i}$$

where $s_{\hat{y}_i}$ is given by Eq. (17.27):

$$s_{\hat{y}_i} = s_y \sqrt{\frac{1}{n} + \frac{(x_i - \bar{x})^2}{\sum(x - \bar{x})^2}}$$

$$= 0.271 \sqrt{\frac{1}{6} + \frac{(25 - 16)^2}{70}}$$

or $s_{\hat{y}} = 0.312$

and for $v = 4$ and a 10 percent level of significance, $t = 2.132$. The confidence interval is, therefore,

$$29.74 \pm 2.132 \times 0.312 = (29.07, 30.40) \text{ kN/m}^2.$$

e. For a single estimated value of y_i, the standard deviation is given by Eq. (17.29):

$$s_{y_p} = 0.271 \sqrt{1 + \frac{1}{6} + \frac{(25 - 16)^2}{70}} = 0.413.$$

For the 5 percent level of significance, $t = 2.776$. Hence, the confidence interval is

$$29.74 \pm 2.776 \times 0.413 = (28.59, 30.88) \text{ kN/m}^2. \qquad \blacksquare \blacksquare$$

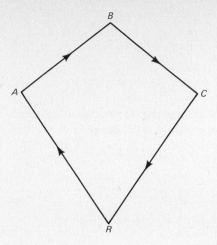

Figure 17.10

TABLE 17.3

Leg	Observed difference in elevation, m	Most probable value	Error	Weight, w
R to A	$\alpha_1 = \quad 94.775$	$\hat{\theta}_1$	$\epsilon_1 = \alpha_1 - \hat{\theta}_1$	4
A to B	$\alpha_2 = -21.739$	$\hat{\theta}_2$	$\epsilon_2 = \alpha_2 - \hat{\theta}_2$	2
B to C	$\alpha_3 = \quad 18.631$	$\hat{\theta}_3$	$\epsilon_3 = \alpha_3 - \hat{\theta}_3$	3
C to R	$\alpha_4 = -91.317$	$\hat{\theta}_4$	$\epsilon_4 = \alpha_4 - \hat{\theta}_4$	4

USE OF THE METHOD OF LEAST SQUARES IN SURVEYING

It may be of interest to mention that the principle of minimizing errors by the method of least squares can be used also in computing most probable values where these have to satisfy a condition different from that of linearity. For example, in surveying operations, we measure angles, lengths, or levels; these may have to satisfy a condition equation of the type $\sum$ angles $= 360°$ or $\sum$ differences in level $= 0$. The procedure is illustrated by the following example.

EXAMPLE

Bench marks at three locations A, B, and C were required. Precise leveling was carried from a known bench mark R, as shown in Fig. 17.10. Due to differences in lengths of lines, number of instrument settings, and so on, the observations were weighted[6] as shown in Table 17.3. Find the most probable values of the elevations of A, B, and C with respect to R.

We denote the most probable value of an elevation by $\hat{\theta}$. Because of the closed circuit of observations, the most probable values must satisfy

---

[6] The "weight" is proportional to our confidence in the observed value.

the condition equation:

$$\hat{\theta}_1 + \hat{\theta}_2 + \hat{\theta}_3 + \hat{\theta}_4 = 0.$$

Hence, we can write

$$\epsilon_4 = \alpha_4 + \hat{\theta}_1 + \hat{\theta}_2 + \hat{\theta}_3.$$

We now apply the principle of least squares to the circuit by minimizing the *weighted* sum of squares of errors, $\sum w\epsilon^2$. Now,

$$\sum w\epsilon^2 = w_1\epsilon_1^2 + w_2\epsilon_2^2 + w_3\epsilon_3^2 + w_4\epsilon_4^2 = P$$

or

$$P = w_1(\alpha_1 - \hat{\theta}_1)^2 + w_2(\alpha_2 - \hat{\theta}_2)^2 \\ + w_3(\alpha_3 - \hat{\theta}_3)^2 + w_4(\alpha_4 + \hat{\theta}_1 + \hat{\theta}_2 + \hat{\theta}_3)^2.$$

This has a minimum value when

$$\frac{\partial P}{\partial \hat{\theta}_1} = \frac{\partial P}{\partial \hat{\theta}_2} = \frac{\partial P}{\partial \hat{\theta}_3} = 0$$

that is, when

$$-2w_1(\alpha_1 - \hat{\theta}_1) + 2w_4(\alpha_4 + \hat{\theta}_1 + \hat{\theta}_2 + \hat{\theta}_3) = 0 \\ -2w_2(\alpha_2 - \hat{\theta}_2) + 2w_4(\alpha_4 + \hat{\theta}_1 + \hat{\theta}_2 + \hat{\theta}_3) = 0 \\ -2w_3(\alpha_3 - \hat{\theta}_3) + 2w_4(\alpha_4 + \hat{\theta}_1 + \hat{\theta}_2 + \hat{\theta}_3) = 0.$$

These are the normal equations. Substituting the values of w and α and simplifying, we obtain

$$8\hat{\theta}_1 + 4\hat{\theta}_2 + 4\hat{\theta}_3 = 744.368 \\ 4\hat{\theta}_1 + 6\hat{\theta}_2 + 4\hat{\theta}_3 = 321.790 \\ 4\hat{\theta}_1 + 4\hat{\theta}_2 + 7\hat{\theta}_3 = 421.161.$$

Solving these three equations by elimination, we obtain

$$\hat{\theta}_1 = +94.709, \qquad \hat{\theta}_2 = -21.870, \qquad \hat{\theta}_3 = +18.543, \qquad \hat{\theta}_4 = -91.382.$$

Hence, the most probable values of elevation with respect to R are $R = 0$ m, $A = 94.709$ m, $B = 72.839$ m, and $C = 91.382$ m.   ■ ■

NONLINEAR RELATIONS

The method of fitting a regression line can be extended to the case where the known, expected, or suspected relation is not in the form of a straight line. The procedure is to write the equation to the curve in its general form, tabulate the deviations of y from the assumed curve, and to find the constants in the equation which satisfy the condition that the sum of the squares of deviations is a minimum.

TABLE 17.4

x	0	1	2	3
Observed value, y_i	0.5	6.5	21.3	48.6
Most probable value, $\hat{y}$	$\hat{a}$	$\hat{a} + \hat{b}$	$\hat{a} + 4\hat{b}$	$\hat{a} + 9\hat{b}$
Deviation $(y_i - \hat{y})$	$0.5 - \hat{a}$	$6.5 - (\hat{a} + \hat{b})$	$21.3 - (\hat{a} + 4\hat{b})$	$48.6 - (\hat{a} + 9\hat{b})$

EXAMPLE

Suppose we observed the values of y for four values of x, x being the assigned variable. (For example, x can be time, and y the measured distance.) Assume further that the general relation between y and x is of the form

$$y = a + bx^2$$

in which a and b are the parameters of the distribution of y. The population of y is estimated from the sample by

$$\hat{y} = \hat{a} + \hat{b}x^2$$

where $\hat{a}$ and $\hat{b}$ are estimates of the parameters a and b, respectively: We can tabulate the results as in Table 17.4. From the table, the sum of squares of deviations is

$$P = (0.5 - \hat{a})^2 + (6.5 - \hat{a} - \hat{b})^2 + (21.3 - \hat{a} - 4\hat{b})^2 + (48.6 - \hat{a} - 9\hat{b})^2.$$

For P to be a minimum, we have to satisfy the conditions:

$$\frac{\partial P}{\partial \hat{a}} = 0 \quad \text{and} \quad \frac{\partial P}{\partial \hat{b}} = 0$$

or

$$(0.5 - \hat{a}) + (6.5 - \hat{a} - \hat{b}) + (21.3 - \hat{a} - 4\hat{b}) + (48.6 - \hat{a} - 9\hat{b}) = 0$$

and

$$(6.5 - \hat{a} - \hat{b}) + 4(21.3 - \hat{a} - 4\hat{b}) + 9(48.6 - \hat{a} - 9\hat{b}) = 0.$$

These reduce to the normal equations:

$$4\hat{a} + 14\hat{b} = 76.9$$
$$14\hat{a} + 98\hat{b} = 529.1.$$

Hence, $\hat{a} = 0.657$ and $\hat{b} = 5.305$.

Thus the equation to the best line of the general form of $y = a + bx^2$ is

$$\hat{y} = 0.657 + 5.305x^2.$$

It should be stressed, however, that a better fit may be obtained with an equation of a different form, for example, $y = a + bx + cx^2$. This can be determined only by trial and error, the procedure depending on the problem in hand, and, in many cases, of course, the search for a "better fit" may not be warranted. ■ ■

RECTIFICATION

The application of the method of least squares to nonlinear relations usually requires a great deal of computational effort. However, in many cases, a non-linear relation can be transformed to a straight-line relation, that is, it can be rectified. This not only simplifies the handling of the data, but also results in a graphical presentation that is more revealing as far as the assessment of scatter is concerned. Extrapolation, if this is warranted (and often it is not), is also easier, and so is the computation of various statistics, such as standard deviation or confidence limits. Clearly, the statistics calculated for rectified variables apply to them and not to the original data. Several straightforward cases will be illustrated. For simplicity in notation, the population, and not the estimate, format is used.

The *exponential function* $y = ab^x$ can be rectified by log transformation, that is, by taking logarithms of both sides of the equation:

$$\log y = \log a + x \log b.$$

This will plot as a straight line if the ordinates give log y (that is, are to a logarithmic scale) while the abscissae are to a linear scale. Log a and log b are the fitting constants of the equation. In other words, log y and x are treated as new (and linear) variables to which the principle of least squares is applied.

The *power function* $y = ax^b$ can be rectified even more simply, again by taking logarithms:

$$\log y = \log a + b \log x.$$

The fitting constants are now log a and b, and the new variables log x and log y are linearly related.

The *hyperbola* $y = a + b/x$ can be rectified by treating $1/x = u$ as the new variable. Then y and u are linearly related.

If the equation is in the form

$$y = \frac{x}{a + bx}$$

we can invert it to

$$\frac{1}{y} = \frac{a}{x} + b.$$

Then $1/x$ and $1/y$ are linearly related. Alternatively, we can multiply both sides of the above equation by x, thus obtaining

$$\frac{x}{y} = a + bx.$$

We then plot x/y versus x. The choice depends on the nature of the case considered.

The *polynomial function* of the form $y = a + bx + cx^2$ is concave up or down, depending on the signs of the coefficients. We differentiate both sides of the equation with respect to x:

$$\frac{dy}{dx} = b + 2cx.$$

A straight-line relation is given by plotting dy/dx versus x.

If no advance information on the shape of the curve fitting the experimental data is available, trial-and-error methods may be necessary. As a first step, the data should be plotted using linear x and y coordinates; a smooth curve is then drawn, and a function likely to fit is chosen from the knowledge of the shapes of curves corresponding to simple algebraic functions. (See scatter diagram discussed on page 366.)

It is important to note that when transformation is used, the deviation minimized is not in y but in the transformed variable. We should remember this when drawing conclusions from an experiment, as in some cases the difference may be significant. If we have reason to believe that, from physical considerations of an experiment, it is the original and not the transformed variable that should have its deviation minimized, then the transformed variable should be weighted in inverse proportion of some function of the error of the original variable. Often, the weight is taken as proportional to $1/(\text{error})^2$.

If the fitting of the straight line is done by eye, the standard error of each point representing a mean of a set of observations can be indicated by a bar, and the curve is then drawn so that the smaller the error associated with a given point the greater the probability of the line passing through this point. This, of course, is often done intuitively when we have reason to believe that readings at, say, low temperatures are less reliable (that is, have a lesser weight) than at high temperatures. In Solved Problem 17-1, the difference between minimizing the deviation of the original variable and of the transformed variable is shown.

Standard computer programs for the fitting of various least square curves are available. For more information on available computer programs, see Chapter 19.

UNCERTAINTY IN GRAPHICAL ANALYSIS

Before ending this chapter, we should note that the use of graphs to find slopes, intercepts, and so on, can add uncertainty to our ever-present error in the sample measurements. In order to minimize this uncertainty in reading off, plotting, and computing from a plotted graph, it is recommended that the smallest division (or least count) of the graph paper should be approximately equal to the probable error (one standard deviation) in our sample data. If the probable error equals, say, 10 of the smallest divisions, then the results will exhibit exaggerated scatter so much so that trends and relationships cannot be fully appreciated [see Fig. 17.11(a)]. On the other hand, if the probable error equals one-tenth of the smallest division, then all scatter will disappear, and evidence of precision will not be clear [see Fig. 17.11(b)]. The plot in Fig. 17.11(c) meets the general rule given above and thus reduces the uncertainty in graphical study.

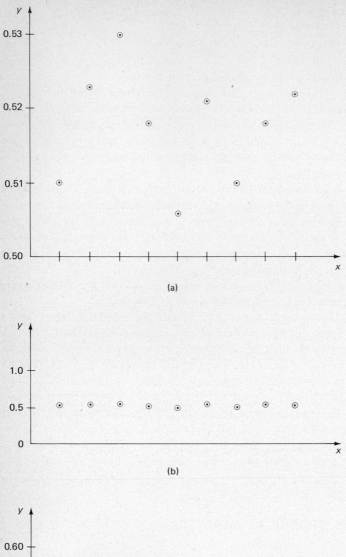

(a)

(b)

(c)

Figure 17.11   Plot of y versus x data, with a probable error of 0.01, using three different y-scale divisions.

SOLVED PROBLEMS

17-1. In an experiment, the volume of a gas was measured at different pressures, the temperature remaining constant. The results were as follows:

Pressure, p (Pa)	20	25	30	35	40
Volume, v (m³)	0.31	0.22	0.18	0.15	0.13

The assumed relation is given by $p = A/v + B$, where A and B are constants (B can be considered as instrument error). Assuming that only v contains errors,

a. Find the best values of A and of B.
b. Plot the relation between p and $1/v$.

Solution. Let us estimate the relation by:

$$p = \frac{\hat{A}}{\hat{v}} + \hat{B}.$$

The *first solution* is by minimizing the deviation of the transformed variable.

a. The problem is to determine the best value for the constant $\hat{A}$ and is best approached by employing a change of variable:

$$v' = \frac{1}{\hat{v}}.$$

Then, $p = \hat{A}\hat{v}' + \hat{B}$, and we have

Pressure, p (Pa)	20	25	30	35	40
v'		3.226	4.545	5.556	6.667	7.692

This approach implies that the error of all $1/v$ values is the same, which may or may not be the case in practice. The centroidal point of the five observations (p, v') is (30, 5.537). When the pressure is, say p_1, the estimated value for v'_1 from the equation is

$$\hat{v}'_1 = \frac{p_1}{\hat{A}} - \frac{\hat{B}}{\hat{A}}.$$

Therefore, the deviation in v'_1, say, is

$$\epsilon_1 = \frac{p_1 - \hat{B}}{\hat{A}} - v'_1.$$

Then,

$$\sum \epsilon^2 = \left(\frac{p_1 - \hat{B}}{\hat{A}} - v'_1\right)^2 + \left(\frac{p_2 - \hat{B}}{\hat{A}} - v'_2\right)^2 + \left(\frac{p_3 - \hat{B}}{\hat{A}} - v'_3\right)^2 + \left(\frac{p_4 - \hat{B}}{\hat{A}} - v'_4\right)^2$$

$$+ \left(\frac{p_5 - \hat{B}}{\hat{A}} - v'_5\right)^2.$$

To obtain the regression line, $\sum \epsilon^2$ is to be a minimum, that is,

$$\frac{\partial (\sum \epsilon^2)}{\partial \hat{A}} = 2\left(\frac{p_1 - \hat{B}}{\hat{A}} - v'_1\right)\left(\frac{-(p_1 - \hat{B})}{\hat{A}^2}\right) + \cdots + 2\left(\frac{p_5 - \hat{B}}{\hat{A}} - v'_5\right)\left(\frac{-(p_5 - \hat{B})}{\hat{A}^2}\right) = 0.$$

Hence,

$$A = \frac{(p_1 - \hat{B})^2 + (p_2 - \hat{B})^2 + (p_3 - \hat{B})^2 + (p_4 - \hat{B})^2 + (p_5 - \hat{B})^2}{v_1'(p_1 - \hat{B}) + v_2'(p_2 - \hat{B}) + v_3'(p_3 - \hat{B}) + v_4'(p_4 - \hat{B}) + v_5'(p_5 - \hat{B})}$$

$$= \frac{p_1^2 + p_2^2 + p_3^2 + p_4^2 + p_5^2 - 2\hat{B}(p_1 + p_2 + p_3 + p_4 + p_5) + 5\hat{B}^2}{v_1'p_1 + v_2'p_2 + v_3'p_3 + v_4'p_4 + v_5'p_5 - \hat{B}(v_1' + v_2' + v_3' + v_4' + v_5')}.$$

By substituting, we find that

$$\hat{A} = \frac{4750 - 300\hat{B} + 5\hat{B}^2}{885.85 - 27.686\hat{B}}.$$

Now, since the regression line must pass through the centroid (30, 5.537), we can write

$$5.537 = \frac{30 - \hat{B}}{\hat{A}}.$$

Eliminating $\hat{A}$, we obtain

$$\frac{30 - \hat{B}}{5.537} = \frac{4750 - 300\hat{B} + 5\hat{B}^2}{885.85 - 27.686\hat{B}}$$

whence

$$55.3\hat{B} = 274.7$$

$$\hat{B} = \frac{274.7}{55.3} = 4.967$$

and

$$\hat{A} = \frac{30 - 4.967}{5.537} = \frac{25.033}{5.537} = 4.521.$$

Thus

$$p = 4.967 + 4.521\hat{v}'.$$

Hence,

$$p = 4.967 + 4.521\left(\frac{1}{\hat{v}}\right)$$

is the equation of the "best" line.

b. Figure 17.12 shows the plot of p versus $1/v$.

We shall now offer a *second solution* by minimizing the deviations of the original variable. In general, assuming that all values of v have equal precision does not mean that the error of all the values $1/v$ is the same. In fact, the values of $v' = 1/v$ will not be of equal precision, and weighting considerations will have to be applied.

Equation (16.33) states that

$$\sigma_Q^2 = \left(\frac{\partial Q}{\partial x_1}\right)^2 \sigma_{x_1}^2 + \left(\frac{\partial Q}{\partial x_2}\right)^2 \sigma_{x_2}^2 + \cdots.$$

With $v' = 1/v$, this gives

$$\sigma_{v'}^2 = \left(-\frac{1}{v^2}\right)^2 \sigma_v^2$$

whence

$$\sigma_{v'} = \frac{\sigma_v}{v^2}.$$

Adopting the well-known criterion that the weight of a value is proportional to (error)$^{-2}$, we can say that the weight of each value of v' is proportional to $(\sigma_v/v^2)^{-2}$.

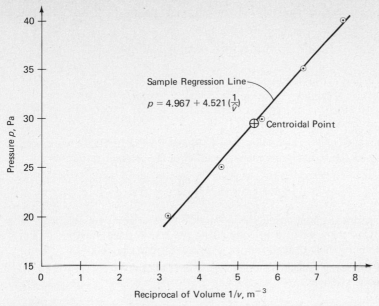

Figure 17.12

TABLE 17.5

Pressure, p (Pa)	20	25	30	35	40
v'		3.226	4.545	5.556	6.667	7.692
Relative weight of v', $w(-v^4 \times 10^4)$		92.35	23.43	10.50	5.06	2.86

Since it is understood that σ_v is constant, it follows that the weight of each value of v' is proportional to v^4 (see Table 17.5).

The weighted centroidal point is found from

$$\bar{p} = \frac{\sum_i w_i p_i}{\sum_i w_i} = 22.647$$

and

$$\bar{v}' = \frac{\sum_i w_i v_i'}{\sum_i w_i} = 3.863.$$

The method of least squares requires that the sum of weighted squares of the errors is a minimum. Thus, we have to differentiate the equation

$$P = \sum_i w_i \epsilon_i^2 = \sum_i w_i \left[\frac{p_i - \hat{B}}{\hat{A}} - v_i' \right]^2$$

which gives

$$\frac{\partial P}{\partial \hat{A}} = -2 \sum_i w_i \left[\frac{p_i - \hat{B}}{\hat{A}^2} \right] \left[\frac{p_i - \hat{B}}{\hat{A}} - v_i' \right] = 0$$

whence

$$\hat{A} = \frac{\sum_i w_i (p_i - \hat{B})^2}{\sum_i w_i v_i'(p_i - \hat{B})} = \frac{71{,}808.25 - 6078.50\hat{B} + 134.20\hat{B}^2}{12{,}431.49 - 518.48\hat{B}}. \tag{17.36}$$

Since the regression line must pass through the centroidal point ($\bar{p} = 22.647$, $\bar{v}' = 3.863$), it follows that

$$\bar{v}' = \frac{\bar{p} - \hat{B}}{\hat{A}}.$$

Substituting for $\bar{p}$ and $\bar{v}'$, we obtain

$$3.863 = \frac{22.647 - \hat{B}}{\hat{A}}. \tag{17.37}$$

From Eqs. (17.36) and (17.37) we find that $\hat{A} = 4.314$ and $\hat{B} = 5.979$. Hence, the equation of the "best" line on the basis of minimum deviation of the original variable is

$$p = 5.979 + 4.314\left(\frac{1}{\bar{v}}\right).$$

It can be seen that minimizing the deviation of the original variable leads to a different result from that obtained by minimizing the transformed variable: which of the two is more appropriate depends on the physical basis to the data.

17-2. The following table gives experimental data obtained from measuring plate current versus plate voltage from a triode with grid voltage held at a certain constant level.

Plate voltage $\times \frac{1}{10} = x$, V	1	2	3	4	5
Plate current $\times \frac{1}{10} = y$, mA	1.7	5.2	8.9	14.2	19.9

It is assumed that y only is subject to error. Find a polynomial of the form $y = Ax + Bx^2$ to fit best the data given.

Solution. The estimated relation is taken as $\hat{y} = \hat{A}x + \hat{B}x^2$. The values of y for $x = 1, 2, \ldots, 5$ from the formula are, respectively,

$$\hat{A} + \hat{B}, \qquad 2\hat{A} + 4\hat{B}, \qquad 3\hat{A} + 9\hat{B}, \qquad 4\hat{A} + 16\hat{B}, \qquad 5\hat{A} + 25\hat{B}.$$

The deviations ϵ of the experimental values of y from the above are, respectively,

$$\hat{A} + \hat{B} - 1.7, \qquad 2\hat{A} + 4\hat{B} - 5.2, \qquad 3\hat{A} + 9\hat{B} - 8.9,$$
$$4\hat{A} + 16\hat{B} - 14.2, \qquad 5\hat{A} + 25\hat{B} - 19.9.$$

Therefore, $\quad \sum \epsilon^2 = (\hat{A} + \hat{B} - 1.7)^2 + (2\hat{A} + 4\hat{B} - 5.2)^2 + (3\hat{A} + 9\hat{B} - 8.9)^2$
$$+ (4\hat{A} + 16\hat{B} - 14.2)^2 + (5\hat{A} + 25\hat{B} - 19.9)^2.$$

Making $\sum \epsilon^2$ a minimum with respect to $\hat{A}$ and $\hat{B}$, we obtain

$$\frac{\partial(\sum \epsilon^2)}{\partial \hat{A}} = 2[(\hat{A} + \hat{B} - 1.7) + 2(2\hat{A} + 4\hat{B} - 5.2) + 3(3\hat{A} + 9\hat{B} - 8.9)$$

$$+ 4(4\hat{A} + 16\hat{B} - 14.2) + 5(5\hat{A} + 25\hat{B} - 19.9)] = 0$$

and $\quad \dfrac{\partial(\sum \epsilon^2)}{\partial \hat{B}} = 2[(\hat{A} + \hat{B} - 1.7) + 4(2\hat{A} + 4\hat{B} - 5.2) + 9(3\hat{A} + 9\hat{B} - 8.9)$

$$+ 16(4\hat{A} + 16\hat{B} - 14.2) + 25(5\hat{A} + 25\hat{B} - 19.9)] = 0.$$

TABLE 17.6

	Weight, w
$\alpha_1 = \quad 75°44'30''$	2
$\alpha_2 = \quad 89°15'40''$	3
$\alpha_3 = 110°27'35''$	2
$\alpha_4 = \quad 84°32'11''$	4

From these two equations, we get the normal equations:

$$55\hat{A} + 225\hat{B} = 195.1$$
$$225\hat{A} + 979\hat{B} = 827.3.$$

Solving for $\hat{A}$ and $\hat{B}$, we find that $\hat{A} = 1.509$ and $\hat{B} - 0.498$. Therefore, the "best" second-degree polynomial is of the form

$$\hat{y} = 1.509x + 0.498x^2.$$

It is now possible to calculate the estimate of the "true" current y for the given voltages x from the above formula, as well as its confidence limits.

17-3. A round of angles α_1, α_2, α_3, and α_4 was observed at a station R. The sum of the four angles was less than $360°$ by $4''$. The angles were measured several times. The average readings and their weights are shown in Table 17.6.

Find the most probable values of the angles $\hat{\theta}_1$, $\hat{\theta}_2$, $\hat{\theta}_3$, and $\hat{\theta}_4$.

Solution. Let ϵ_1, ϵ_2, ϵ_3, and ϵ_4 be the errors in the four angles, respectively. Then

$$\epsilon_1 = \alpha_1 - \hat{\theta}_1, \qquad \epsilon_2 = \alpha_2 - \hat{\theta}_2, \qquad \epsilon_3 = \alpha_3 - \hat{\theta}_3, \qquad \epsilon_4 = \alpha_4 - \hat{\theta}_4.$$

The sum of the squares of the weighted errors is

$$\sum w\epsilon^2 = w_1\epsilon_1^2 + w_2\epsilon_2^2 + w_3\epsilon_3^2 + w_4\epsilon_4^2$$
$$= w_1(\alpha_1 - \hat{\theta}_1)^2 + w_2(\alpha_2 - \hat{\theta}_2)^2 + w_3(\alpha_3 - \hat{\theta}_3)^2 + w_4(\alpha_4 - \hat{\theta}_4)^2.$$

Since $\qquad\qquad \hat{\theta}_4 = 360° - (\hat{\theta}_1 + \hat{\theta}_2 + \hat{\theta}_3)$

we have only three unknowns. By the principle of least squares, $\sum \epsilon^2$ is a minimum when the differential coefficients with respect to $\hat{\theta}_1$, $\hat{\theta}_2$, and $\hat{\theta}_3$ are zero. Thus

$$\frac{\partial(\sum \epsilon^2)}{\partial \hat{\theta}_1} = \frac{\partial(\sum \epsilon^2)}{\partial \hat{\theta}_2} = \frac{\partial(\sum \epsilon^2)}{\partial \hat{\theta}_3} = 0$$

or

$$\frac{\partial(\sum w\epsilon^2)}{\partial \hat{\theta}_1} = -2w_1(\alpha_1 - \hat{\theta}_1) + 2w_4(\alpha_4 - 360° + \hat{\theta}_1 + \hat{\theta}_2 + \hat{\theta}_3) = 0$$

$$\frac{\partial(\sum w\epsilon^2)}{\partial \hat{\theta}_2} = -2w_2(\alpha_2 - \hat{\theta}_2) + 2w_4(\alpha_4 - 360° + \hat{\theta}_1 + \hat{\theta}_2 + \hat{\theta}_3) = 0$$

$$\frac{\partial(\sum w\epsilon^2)}{\partial \hat{\theta}_3} = -2w_3(\alpha_3 - \hat{\theta}_3) + 2w_4(\alpha_4 - 360° + \hat{\theta}_1 + \hat{\theta}_2 + \hat{\theta}_3) = 0.$$

TABLE 17.7

Measured discharge for falling stage in m³/s, y	350	770	1240	1640	1980	2430	3000	3430	4020	4370
Measured discharge for rising stage in m³/s, x	400	800	1300	1680	2010	2500	3050	3510	4050	4450

After substituting the numerical values of w_1, w_2, w_3, w_4, α_1, α_2, α_3, and α_4, the preceding equations reduce to the following normal equations:

$$6\hat{\theta}_1 + 4\hat{\theta}_2 + 4\hat{\theta}_3 = 1253.337778$$
$$4\hat{\theta}_1 + 7\hat{\theta}_2 + 4\hat{\theta}_3 = 1369.637777$$
$$4\hat{\theta}_1 + 4\hat{\theta}_2 + 6\hat{\theta}_3 = 1322.773888.$$

Solving these equations by elimination, we obtain

$$\hat{\theta}_1 = 75°44'31.26''$$
$$\hat{\theta}_2 = 89°15'40.84''$$
$$\hat{\theta}_3 = 110°27'36.27''$$

and
$$\hat{\theta}_4 = 360° - (\hat{\theta}_1 + \hat{\theta}_2 + \hat{\theta}_3) = 84°32'11.63''.$$

17-4. To determine the effects of rising and falling stages on a particular stage discharge curve, the following measurements for falling and rising stages were taken at a constant value of rate of stage change (Table 17.7). The instrument used for the falling stage was new and, therefore, assumed subject to error, while the values for the rising stage are believed to be sensibly free from error.

a. Determine the regression line of discharge for the falling stage upon discharge for the rising stage.

b. Test the hypothesis that the slope of the regression line is 1.00.

c. If the true slope = 1.01, what is the probability of accepting the hypothesis in (b)?

d. Estimate the discharge for the falling stage when the measured discharge for rising stage is 2010 m³/s.

e. Find the 95 percent confidence limits for a single individual value of discharge for falling stage corresponding to a rising stage discharge of 2010 m³/s.

Solution

a. The constants in the sample regression line $\hat{y} = \hat{a} + \hat{b}x$ will be found using Table 17.8.

$$\bar{x} = \frac{\sum x}{n} = \frac{23,750}{10} = 2375 \text{ m}^3/\text{s}$$

$$\bar{y} = \frac{\sum y}{n} = \frac{23,230}{10} = 2323 \text{ m}^3/\text{s}.$$

TABLE 17.8

x	y	$x^2 \times 10^{-4}$	$xy \times 10^{-4}$	$X = x - \bar{x}$	$Y = y - \bar{y}$	$XY \times 10^{-4}$	$X^2 \times 10^{-4}$	$Y^2 \times 10^{-4}$
400	350	16.00	14.00	-1975	-1973	389.668	390.062	389.273
800	770	64.00	61.60	-1575	-1553	244.598	248.063	241.181
1300	1240	169.00	161.20	-1075	-1083	116.423	115.562	117.289
1680	1640	282.24	275.52	-695	-683	47.468	48.303	46.649
2010	1980	404.01	397.98	-365	-343	12.519	13.322	11.765
2500	2430	625.00	607.50	125	107	1.338	1.563	1.145
3050	3000	930.25	915.00	675	677	45.698	45.562	45.833
3510	3430	1232.01	1203.93	1135	1107	125.644	128.823	122.545
4050	4020	1640.25	1628.10	1675	1697	284.247	280.562	287.981
4450	4370	1980.25	1944.65	2075	2047	424.752	430.563	419.021
$\sum = 23{,}750$	23,230	7343.01	7209.48	$5685 - 5685 = 0$	$5635 - 5635 = 0$	1692.355	1702.385	1682.682

From Eqs. (17.12) and (17.13),

$$\hat{a} = \frac{\sum x^2 \sum y - \sum x \sum xy}{n\sum x^2 - (\sum x)^2}$$

$$= \frac{7343.01 \times 23,230 - 23,750 \times 7209.48}{10 \times 7343.01 - (237.5)^2}$$

$$= -38.007$$

and

$$\hat{b} = \frac{n\sum xy - \sum x \sum y}{n\sum x^2 - (\sum x)^2}$$

$$= \frac{10 \times 7209.48 - 237.5 \times 232.3}{10 \times 7343.01 - (237.5)^2}$$

$$= 0.994.$$

Therefore, $\hat{y} = -38.007 + 0.994x$ [with respect to origin $(0,0)$].

Using the XY method

$$\hat{B} = \frac{\sum XY}{\sum X^2} = \frac{1692.355}{1702.385} = 0.994$$

or $\hat{Y} = 0.994X$ [with respect to centroid $(2375, 2323)$ as origin].

b. The sum of the squares of the y residuals $\sum \epsilon^2$ is obtained from Table 17.9. Therefore,

$$s_y = \sqrt{\frac{\sum \epsilon^2}{n-2}} = \sqrt{\frac{2969.858}{8}} = 19.267.$$

To test the hypothesis that $b = 1.00$ versus the alternative hypothesis: $b \neq 1.00$, we calculate

$$s_{\hat{b}} = s_y \sqrt{\frac{1}{\sum X^2}} = \frac{19.267}{100}\sqrt{\frac{1}{1702.385}}$$

$$= 0.00467.$$

Then, $t = \dfrac{|\hat{b} - b|}{s_{\hat{b}}} = \dfrac{1.00 - 0.994}{0.00467} = 1.285.$

TABLE 17.9

x	$\hat{y}$	$\epsilon = \hat{y} - y_{observed}$	ϵ^2
400	359.593	9.593	92.026
800	757.193	−12.807	164.019
1300	1254.193	14.193	201.441
1680	1631.913	−8.087	65.340
2010	1959.933	−20.067	402.684
2500	2446.993	16.993	288.762
3050	2993.693	−6.307	39.778
3510	3450.933	20.933	438.190
4050	3987.693	−32.307	1043.742
4450	4385.293	15.293	233.876
Total			$\sum \epsilon^2 = 2969.858$

From statistical tables, for $v = n - 2 = 10 - 2 = 8$, $t = 1.108$ at a probability level of 30 percent and 1.397 at 20 percent. The difference in slope is, therefore, not significant and the null hypothesis can be considered valid.

  c. Calculate

$$t = \frac{1.01 - 1.00}{s_{\hat{b}}} = \frac{0.01}{0.00467} = 2.141.$$

  For $v = 8$, Table A.7 gives $t = 2.306$ at the 5 percent level of significance. Therefore, the probability of correctly accepting the hypothesis $b = 1.00$ is a little more than 95 percent.

  d. From the equation of the regression line, for $x = 2010$ m^3/s,

$$\hat{y} = 1959.933 \text{ m}^3/\text{s}.$$

  e. The 95 percent confidence limits are

$$1959.933 \pm ts_{y_p}$$

where t is the value at the 5 percent level of significance for 8 degrees of freedom, and

$$s_{y_p} = s_y \sqrt{1 + \frac{1}{n} + \frac{(x_i - \bar{x})^2}{\sum X^2}}.$$

Thus, the limits are

$$1959.933 + 2.306 \times 19.267 \sqrt{1 + \frac{1}{10} + \frac{(2010 - 2375)^2}{17,023,850}}$$

$$= 1959.933 \pm 46.784$$

$$= (1913.1, 2006.7) \text{ m}^3/\text{s}.$$

  17-5. In order to establish bench marks, precise leveling was carried out between four stations A, B, C, and D, as shown in Fig. 17.13. Because of various factors, the results were weighted as indicated in Table 17.10.

  Using the method of least squares, find the most probable values of the differences in level between the various points.

  Solution. Let the most probable values of the differences in levels be $\hat{\theta}_1$, $\hat{\theta}_2$, $\hat{\theta}_3$, $\hat{\theta}_4$, and $\hat{\theta}_5$ for the legs numbered in Fig. 17.13. Considering the two closed circuits $ABCA$ and $ACDA$, with a common link AC, we have

$$\hat{\theta}_1 + \hat{\theta}_2 + \hat{\theta}_5 = 0$$

and
$$\hat{\theta}_3 + \hat{\theta}_4 - \hat{\theta}_5 = 0. \qquad (17.38)$$

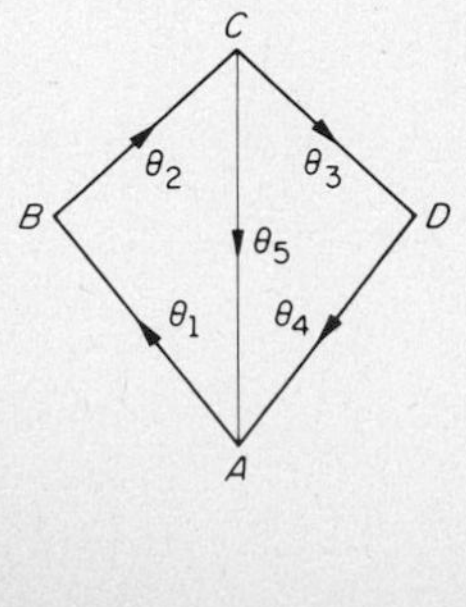

Figure 17.13

TABLE 17.10

Leg	Observed difference in elevation, α, m	Weight, w
A to B	4.912 (rise)	2
B to C	2.638 (rise)	1
C to D	-6.382 (fall)	2
D to A	-1.075 (fall)	3
C to A	-7.450 (fall)	2

If ϵ_1, ϵ_2, ϵ_3, ϵ_4, and ϵ_5 are the errors in levels, then $\epsilon_1 = \alpha_1 - \hat{\theta}_1$, $\epsilon_2 = \alpha_2 - \hat{\theta}_2$, and so on. These errors are not all independent, since they are related by means of Eq. (17.38). Hence, only three errors are independent. Let us assume that ϵ_1 and ϵ_3 are errors dependent on ϵ_2, ϵ_4, and ϵ_5. Then, using Eq. (17.38), we have

$$\epsilon_1 = \alpha_1 + \hat{\theta}_2 + \hat{\theta}_5$$

and

$$\epsilon_3 = \alpha_3 + \hat{\theta}_4 - \hat{\theta}_5. \tag{17.39}$$

The method of least squares requires that the sum of weighted squares of the errors is a minimum, with respect to the independent, most probable differences in levels, $\hat{\theta}_2$, $\hat{\theta}_4$, and $\hat{\theta}_5$. Thus, if

$$P = w_1\epsilon_1^2 + w_2\epsilon_2^2 + w_3\epsilon_3^2 + w_4\epsilon_4^2 + w_5\epsilon_5^2$$

then

$$\frac{\partial P}{\partial \hat{\theta}_2} = \frac{\partial P}{\partial \hat{\theta}_4} = \frac{\partial P}{\partial \hat{\theta}_5} = 0.$$

Writing these in full yields

$$w_1\epsilon_1 \frac{\partial \epsilon_1}{\partial \hat{\theta}_2} + w_2\epsilon_2 \frac{\partial \epsilon_2}{\partial \hat{\theta}_2} + w_3\epsilon_3 \frac{\partial \epsilon_3}{\partial \hat{\theta}_2} + w_4\epsilon_4 \frac{\partial \epsilon_4}{\partial \hat{\theta}_2} + w_5\epsilon_5 \frac{\partial \epsilon_5}{\partial \hat{\theta}_2} = 0$$

$$w_1\epsilon_1 \frac{\partial \epsilon_1}{\partial \hat{\theta}_4} + w_2\epsilon_2 \frac{\partial \epsilon_2}{\partial \hat{\theta}_4} + w_3\epsilon_3 \frac{\partial \epsilon_3}{\partial \hat{\theta}_4} + w_4\epsilon_4 \frac{\partial \epsilon_4}{\partial \hat{\theta}_4} + w_5\epsilon_5 \frac{\partial \epsilon_5}{\partial \hat{\theta}_4} = 0$$

$$w_1\epsilon_1 \frac{\partial \epsilon_1}{\partial \hat{\theta}_5} + w_2\epsilon_2 \frac{\partial \epsilon_2}{\partial \hat{\theta}_5} + w_3\epsilon_3 \frac{\partial \epsilon_3}{\partial \hat{\theta}_5} + w_4\epsilon_4 \frac{\partial \epsilon_4}{\partial \hat{\theta}_5} + w_5\epsilon_5 \frac{\partial \epsilon_5}{\partial \hat{\theta}_5} = 0.$$

Hence, we obtain the following three normal equations:

$$w_1\epsilon_1 - w_2\epsilon_2 = 0$$
$$w_3\epsilon_3 - w_4\epsilon_4 = 0$$
$$w_1\epsilon_1 - w_3\epsilon_3 - w_5\epsilon_5 = 0.$$

Substituting the numerical values of w and expressing ϵ in terms of α and the unknowns $\hat{\theta}_2$, $\hat{\theta}_4$, and $\hat{\theta}_5$, we obtain

$$3\hat{\theta}_2 + 2\hat{\theta}_5 = -7.186$$
$$5\hat{\theta}_4 - 2\hat{\theta}_5 = +9.539$$
$$\hat{\theta}_2 - \hat{\theta}_4 + 3\hat{\theta}_5 = -18.744.$$

The solution of these three simultaneous equations yields

$$\hat{\theta}_2 = 2.584 \text{ m}, \qquad \hat{\theta}_4 = -1.080 \text{ m}, \qquad \hat{\theta}_5 = -7.469 \text{ m}$$

and from Eq. (17.38),

$$\hat{\theta}_1 = 4.885 \text{ m}, \qquad \hat{\theta}_3 = -6.389 \text{ m}.$$

17-6. The design of certain metallic alloys for high temperature is usually based on stress rupture curves. In many cases, the deformation involved is intolerable, and to ensure a life of a given number of hours it is necessary to keep the applied stress below the value that would produce rupture in the same number of hours. An experiment on one such alloy was run at 700°C, and the data listed in Table 17.11 were obtained relating applied stress to rupture time.

a. Estimate the constants in the relation $\log T = a + bf$.

b. Estimate the rupture time by a point estimate corresponding to a stress $f = 65$ MPa.

c. Estimate the predicted rupture time by a 95 percent confidence interval for the stress given in (b).

Solution. The estimated relation can be written as $\log \hat{T} = \hat{a} + \hat{b}f$.

a. Let $y = \log T$ and $x = f$ (see Table 17.12).

From Eqs. (17.14) and (17.15), we obtain

$$\hat{a} = \frac{\sum x^2 \sum y - \sum x \sum xy}{n \sum x^2 - (\sum x)^2} = \frac{17{,}400 \times 8.5320 - 260 \times 525.108}{4 \times 17{,}400 - 260 \times 260}$$

$$= 5.96436$$

and

$$\hat{b} = \frac{n \sum xy - \sum x \sum y}{n \sum x^2 - (\sum x)^2} = \frac{4 \times 525.108 - 260 \times 8.5320}{4 \times 17{,}400 - 260 \times 260}$$

$$= -0.058944.$$

Hence,

$$\log \hat{T} = 5.96436 - 0.058944 f.$$

TABLE 17.11

Stress, f, MPa	Rupture time, T, h
80	22
70	57
60	205
50	1324

TABLE 17.12

T	y	x	x^2	xy
22	1.3424	80	6400	107.392
57	1.7559	70	4900	122.913
205	2.3118	60	3600	138.708
1324	3.1219	50	2500	156.095
$\sum =$	8.5320	260	17,400	525.108

TABLE 17.13

f, MPa	y(= log T)	ŷ(= log T computed)	$\epsilon_i = y_i - \hat{y}_i$	ϵ_i^2
80	1.3424	1.24884	+0.09356	0.00875347
70	1.7559	1.83828	−0.08238	0.00678646
60	2.3118	2.42772	−0.11592	0.01343745
50	3.1219	3.01716	+0.10474	0.01097047
Total				$\sum \epsilon_i^2 = 0.03994785$

b. For $f = 65$ MPa, the above equation for $\hat{T}$ gives

$$\log \hat{T} = 5.96436 - 0.058944 \times 65 = 2.1330$$

whence, $\qquad \hat{T} = 135.8$ h.

c. In order to predict the required confidence interval, the variance of log T, as estimated from the regression line, must be first computed (see Table 17.13). From Eq. (17.24),

$$s_y^2 = \frac{\sum \epsilon_i^2}{n-2} = \frac{0.03994785}{2} = 0.0199739$$

or $\qquad s_y = 0.14133$.

Since the confidence interval is required for $x = 65$, and $\bar{x} = 65$, we have from Eq. (17.29)

$$s_{y_p} = 0.14133 \sqrt{1 + \frac{1}{4}}$$

$$= 0.15799.$$

Hence, the confidence interval for a single individual value is

$$2.1330 \pm t \times 0.15799$$

or $\qquad 2.1330 \pm 4.303 \times 0.15799$

since $t = 4.303$ for $v = 4 - 2$ at the 5 percent probability level. Thus the limits for log T are 2.8128 and 1.4531, and for T, 649.8 and 28.4 h.

PROBLEMS

17-1. In a laboratory experiment, the lateral pressure and failure load were measured, with the following (coded) results:

Pressure, x	0	1	2	3	4	5	8
Failure load, y	10	10.7	12.1	12.6	13.8	16.2	18.9

Obtain the regression equation of y on x, and x on y, and plot these together with the experimental data.

17-2. Tests on the fuel consumption of a vehicle traveling at different speeds yielded the following (coded) results:

Speed, x	20	30	40	50	60	70	80	90
Consumption, y	18.3	18.8	19.1	19.3	19.5	19.7	19.8	20.0

It is believed that the relation between the two variables is of the type $y = a + b/x$. Obtain the equation to the regression line.

17-3. An experimental determination of the relation between x and y yielded the following results:

x	4	5	6	7	8	9	10	11
y	4	6	8	13	18	23	26	31

a. Find the equation to the regression line of y on x.
b. Estimate the 99 percent confidence limits of a predicted single individual observation of y when $x = 8.5$.

17-4. In a study of the linear relation between y and x (believed to be free from error), the following data were obtained: $n = 18$; $\sum(y - \bar{y})^2 = 720$; $\sum(x - \bar{x})^2 = 144$; $\sum(x - \bar{x})(y - \bar{y}) = 288$; and $\bar{x} = 5$; $a = 10$.
a. Obtain the equation to the regression line.
b. Test the hypothesis: $b = 0$. Use $\alpha = 0.05$.
c. Test the hypothesis: $a = 8$. Use $\alpha = 0.05$.
d. Obtain the 95 percent confidence interval for b.
Use the expression

$$(n - 2)s_y^2 = \sum(y - \bar{y})^2 - \frac{[\sum(x - \bar{x})(y - \bar{y})]^2}{\sum(x - \bar{x})^2}.$$

(See Appendix E.)

17-5. Obtain the equation to the regression line of the modulus of elasticity (y) on content of a certain compound (x) in a plastic (see Table 17.14). Hence, calculate the standard deviation of the regression line s_y. If $x = 60$, estimate the expected modulus of elasticity and determine a 95 percent confidence range for the expected modulus at this value of x. Find a prediction interval such that the probability is 95 percent that the value of the modulus of elasticity corresponding to $x = 60$ will lie within the interval.

TABLE 17.14

x	55.8	55.0	54.3	49.9	53.0	50.6	58.3	63.7
y	83.9	66.4	73.1	30.1	36.2	66.7	87.3	135.0
x	67.0	65.0	58.8	57.6	57.5	54.4	54.2	55.8
y	153.1	158.2	65.8	72.1	83.1	72.1	71.3	58.0

TABLE 17.15

Leg	Difference in level, m	Weight
P to Q	6.32 rise	1
Q to S	5.68 rise	2
Q to R	3.15 rise	1
R to S	2.59 rise	1
S to P	12.04 fall	2

TABLE 17.16

Diameter (in 2.54 cm)	2	3	6	8	12	18	24	36
Strength (coded)	108	106	100	96	92	86	84	84

Source: A. M. Neville, "Some Aspects of the Strength of Concrete," Part II, *Civil Engineering* (London), vol. 54, (Nov. 1959), p. 1309.

17-6. Leveling was carried out from a station P at a known elevation of 234.15 m above datum, the weights of the different legs being given in Table 17.15. Find the most probable values of the levels of points Q, R, and S.

17-7. A, B, C, and D form a round of angles at a station such that they add up to $360°$. The observed values are $A = 82°15'35''$; $B = 110°37'45''$; $C = 66°24'40''$; and $D = 100°42'10''$.

The angle $(A + B)$ was measured separately twice, and the average value was found to be $192°53'25''$. If each of the six measurements is of equal reliability (weight), find the most probable values of all the angles.

17-8. The number of bacteria per unit volume found in a tillage after x hours is given in the following table:

Number of hours, x	0	1	2	3	4	5	6	7
Number of bacteria, y	47	64	81	107	151	209	298	841

a. Estimate the constants in the relation $\log y = a + bx$.
b. Estimate the number of bacteria per unit volume by a point estimate corresponding to $x = 4.5$ h.
c. Estimate the 99 percent confidence interval for the predicted number of bacteria per unit volume for $x = 4.5$ h.
d. Plot the data on semilogarithmic graph paper.

17-9. The strengths of concrete cylinders of the same mix proportions, but different size, were recorded as shown in Table 17.16. Obtain an equation to the logarithmic regression line relating the strength (y) and diameter (x).

17-10. The compressive strengths of concrete specimens of three types are given in Table 17.17.

Using the means of each test, obtain equations to the regression lines of: **(a)** 15-cm cubes and 12.7-cm cylinders, and **(b)** 15-cm cubes and 15-cm cylinders. Test the significance of these relations. Test also the hypotheses that the slopes are: for **(a)** 1.00, and for **(b)** 0.85. Use a 10 percent level of significance.

TABLE 17.17

Test number	Strength, MPa		
	15-cm cubes	12.7 cm × 12.7 cm cylinders	15 cm × 30 cm cylinders
1	52.4	49.3	44.3
	52.3	51.0	43.6
	51.9	51.4	43.4
2	44.7	43.1	36.1
	44.2	45.5	37.1
	44.4	43.4	36.1
3	55.3	55.5	46.3
	55.8	55.5	44.4
	53.0	53.8	44.5
4	43.6	42.4	37.6
	43.9	42.7	37.8
	44.3	45.2	39.0
5	42.1	43.1	38.5
	46.1	45.5	38.5
	44.2	43.4	38.3
6	41.2	44.1	37.8
	44.2	40.0	38.3
	45.2	40.7	38.7
7	46.5	47.6	40.7
	45.5	45.2	40.7
	45.2	45.2	39.2
8	49.3	47.6	42.2
	48.8	47.9	42.9
	48.8	45.9	41.7
9	42.4	39.6	37.1
	43.4	39.0	36.6
	43.6	40.3	36.3
10	50.7	50.0	43.4
	—	51.7	43.8
	—	52.4	44.1
11	37.9	40.0	35.9
	42.7	44.8	37.2
	43.1	45.5	38.0
12	44.5	45.2	38.7
	43.6	45.2	38.5
	43.6	45.5	38.5
13	41.0	41.4	34.8
	41.8	42.1	35.2
	42.5	42.7	35.6
14	32.5	31.4	27.7
	32.5	31.0	27.2
	32.4	33.8	28.5
15	22.6	26.5	22.1
	22.3	26.9	22.4
	23.2	26.9	23.8

Source: M. W. Cormack, "Note on Cubes v. Cylinders," *New Zealand Engineering*, vol. 11, no. 3, March 1956, p. 99. The original data were in psi units.

TABLE 17.18

x	y	x	y
667	54	3619	106
727	42	3865	98
823	34	4266	261
1086	75	4299	197
1529	103	4382	106
1941	87	5560	216
2266	53	5955	251
2515	113	6358	347
3187	137	7165	339
3218	114	7910	282

TABLE 17.19

	Approximate distance between stations, km
B 10.714 m higher than A	2.0
A 51.762 m higher than C	1.5
D 32.840 m higher than A	1.0
B 62.463 m higher than C	1.5
D 84.624 m higher than C	1.5

17-11. Experimental measurements of y and x are given in Table 17.18. It is expected that the relation is in the form $y = ax^b$. Fit the constants of the regression line.

17-12. From a certain station, angles A, B, and C are observed a number of times by the method of repetition, with the results, all of equal weight:

$$3A = 172°45'50''$$

$$3A + 3B = 400°25'30''$$

$$A + B + C = 225°46'30''$$

$$2B + 2C = 336°22'10''$$

$$3C = 276°52'50''$$

$$3A + 3C = 449°38'50''$$

$$3B = 227°40'10''.$$

Find to the nearest second the most probable values of A, B, and C.

17-13. In establishing levels of B, C, and D from an ordnance bench mark at A, precise leveling was carried out from A to each point B, C, and D, and in addition between B and C and between C and D with the results given in Table 17.19. Assuming that measurement errors are proportional to the square root of the distance, weight the observations and find the most probable values of the heights of B, C, and D with respect to A.

Chapter 18

Correlation

We should stress the fact that just because we have fitted a straight-line relation to a number of observations, it does not mean that the physical data really follow a straight line. For example, there may be a cyclic (or any other) relation with a general rise of y with x that could be represented by a straight line. An example of this is shown in Fig. 18.1, and it is clear that, although we have fitted a line satisfying the minimum value of the sum of squares of deviations,

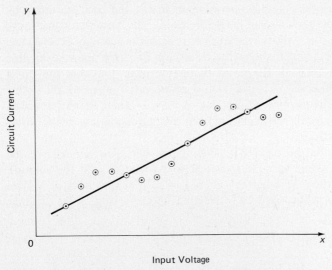

Figure 18.1   Relation between y and x and regression line that would show poor correlation. The experimental points in the form shown would be obtained when a circuit contains resistors with two or more tunnel diodes in series.

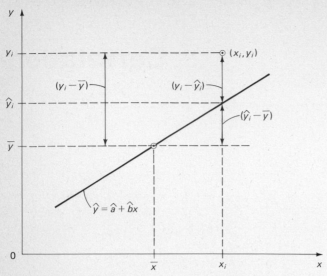

Figure 18.2 Partitioning of the total deviation, $y_i - \bar{y}$, into the "explained" and "unexplained" deviations, $\hat{y}_i - \bar{y}$ and $y_i - \hat{y}_i$, respectively.

their sum is large. We can distinguish thus between the deviations of the y observations from the regression line (this representing the variation about the regression) and the total variation of the y observations about their mean $(\bar{x}, \bar{y})$. The difference between the two variations, expressed in an appropriate mathematical form, gives the amount of variation accounted for by regression, and the higher this amount the better the fit.

It is clear, therefore, that the operation of fitting the best line must be followed by a test of the goodness of fit. Before doing this, however, some more detailed comments on the variation about the regression line may be of value.

Consider Fig. 18.2, which shows the regression line of y upon x; this line must, of course, pass through the point $(\bar{x}, \bar{y})$ (see page 373). Let the point (x_i, y_i) represent an observed value of y_i at a given value of x_i. At this value of x_i, the regression line estimates the value of y as $\hat{y}_i$. Then the difference in ordinates $(y_i - \hat{y}_i)$ represents the deviation from the regression line or the variation that we wish to study.

More generally, the problem is to distinguish between that part of the variation in the dependent variable y_i which is associated with the relation between y and x and the part which is not associated. The deviation of y_i from $\bar{y}$, $(y_i - \bar{y})$, can be seen from Fig. 18.2 to be equal to $(y_i - \hat{y}_i)$ plus the distance $(\hat{y}_i - \bar{y})$. Thus,

$$(y_i - \bar{y}) = (y_i - \hat{y}_i) + (\hat{y}_i - \bar{y}). \tag{18.1}$$

The term $(\hat{y}_i - \bar{y})$ depends on the slope of the regression line, that is, is associated with the relation between y and x; therefore, this part of the deviation can be considered "explained." On the other hand, the term $(y_i - \hat{y}_i)$ represents

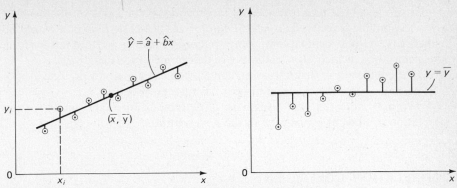

Figure 18.3   Deviations from the line of best fit and from a horizontal line.

that part of the total deviation $(y_i - \bar{y})$ which exists over and above that explained by regression, and is, therefore, "unexplained."

Squaring both sides of Eq. (18.1) and summing for all observed points,
we obtain

$$\sum(y_i - \bar{y})^2 = \sum(y_i - \hat{y}_i)^2 + \sum(\hat{y}_i - \bar{y})^2. \tag{18.2}$$

We should note that the term $2\sum(y_i - \hat{y}_i)(\hat{y}_i - \bar{y})$ does not appear, as it is equal
to zero by virtue of the relation $\hat{y} = \hat{a} + \hat{b}x$, derived by the method of least
squares.[1]

The left-hand side of Eq. (18.2) represents the total variation. Following
the argument given earlier, we can call the first term on the right-hand side the
unexplained variation (or the residual sum of squares), and the second term the
explained variation. Thus the total variation can be partitioned and the ratio
of the explained variation to the total variation gives an indication of how well
the regression line fits the observed data. This ratio is called the *coefficient of
determination*, r^2, given by

$$r^2 = \frac{\sum(\hat{y}_i - \bar{y})^2}{\sum(y_i - \bar{y})^2}. \tag{18.3}$$

The ratio r^2 must lie between zero and unity. This is so because the sum
of squares of the deviations from the straight line of best fit is smaller than
from any other straight line, including the horizontal line through $\bar{y}$ (see
Fig. 18.3). When $r^2 = 1$, all variation has been explained and we have a perfect
fit with all the points lying on the regression line. If the coefficient r^2 is zero,
the regression line does not explain anything; that is, it is horizontal and y is
not a function of x.

---

[1] Since $\hat{y}_i = \hat{a} + \hat{y}x_i$,

$$\sum(y_i - \hat{y}_i)(\hat{y}_i - \bar{y}) = \sum(y_i - \hat{a} - \hat{b}x_i)(\hat{a} + \hat{b}x_i - \bar{y})$$
$$= \hat{a}\sum(y_i - \hat{a} - \hat{b}x_i) + \hat{b}\sum x_i(y_i - \hat{a} - \hat{b}x_i)$$
$$- \bar{y}\sum(y_i - \hat{a} - \hat{b}x_i).$$

This is equal to zero by virtue of the normal equations (17.9) and (17.10).

It can be noted that the value of r^2 depends on the value of the mean, $\bar{y}$; this is reasonable since the best prediction for any general value of y would be $\bar{y}$ since $\bar{y}$ is the best estimator of the population mean μ and the latter is the parameter about which all variations are determined [see Eq. (18.2)].

The coefficient of determination can also be calculated for nonlinear lines of fit as well as for linear and nonlinear multiple correlations.

We may note that the coefficient of determination is the square of the correlation coefficient considered in the next section.

CORRELATION COEFFICIENT

Referring to Eq. (17.16), we can observe that, if there is no correlation between y and x, that is, if y is not a function of x, the coefficient of x (the slope b) is zero and the line plots as a horizontal line, that is,

$$\frac{n\sum xy - \sum x \sum y}{n\sum x^2 - (\sum x)^2} = 0. \tag{18.4}$$

If we consider now the regression of x on y, there is no correlation if x is not a function of y, that is, if the line described by Eq. (17.18) is vertical. Thus, referring the slope to a vertical axis, we obtain

$$\frac{n\sum xy - \sum x \sum y}{n\sum y^2 - (\sum y)^2} = 0 \tag{18.5}$$

and expressing slope in the usual way (y vertical and x horizontal),

$$\frac{n\sum y^2 - (\sum y)^2}{n\sum xy - \sum x \sum y} = \infty. \tag{18.6}$$

If there is no correlation between the two variables being studied, the product of the slopes given by Eqs. (18.4) and (18.5) is zero,

$$\frac{n\sum xy - \sum x \sum y}{n\sum x^2 - (\sum x)^2} \times \frac{n\sum xy - \sum x \sum y}{n\sum y^2 - (\sum y)^2} = 0.$$

Conversely, when there is a perfect correlation, that is, all the points lie exactly on each of the two regression lines, the lines coincide; their slopes are therefore equal, namely,

$$\frac{n\sum xy - \sum x \sum y}{n\sum x^2 - (\sum x)^2} = \frac{n\sum y^2 - (\sum y)^2}{n\sum xy - \sum x \sum y}$$

or $\qquad \dfrac{n\sum xy - \sum x \sum y}{n\sum x^2 - (\sum x)^2} \times \dfrac{n\sum xy - \sum x \sum y}{n\sum y^2 - (\sum y)^2} = 1. \tag{18.7}$

Thus we find that the value of the product on the left-hand side of Eq. (18.7) gives a measure of correlation: when the value is zero, there is no correlation; when it is unity, the correlation is perfect. We call the square root of this product[2] the *correlation coefficient* and denote it by r:

$$r = \frac{n \sum xy - \sum x \sum y}{\sqrt{[n \sum x^2 - (\sum x)^2][n \sum y^2 - (\sum y)^2]}}. \tag{18.8}$$

In terms of the variables X, Y referred to $(\bar{x}, \bar{y})$, r can be written as

$$r = \frac{\sum XY}{\sqrt{\sum X^2 \sum Y^2}}. \tag{18.9}$$

Equation (18.9) can also be derived from the definition of the coefficient of determination (see page 409). The correlation coefficient is then

$$r = \sqrt{\frac{\text{explained variation}}{\text{total variation}}} = \sqrt{\frac{\sum (\hat{y}_i - \bar{y})^2}{\sum (y_i - \bar{y})^2}} \tag{18.10}$$

or, referred to the X, Y coordinate system,

$$r = \sqrt{\frac{\sum \hat{Y}^2}{\sum Y^2}}. \tag{18.11}$$

Using Eqs. (17.20) and (17.22), we can write

$$\hat{Y} = \hat{b}X. \tag{18.12}$$

Now,

$$r^2 = \frac{\sum \hat{Y}^2}{\sum Y^2} = \frac{b^2 \sum X^2}{\sum Y^2}.$$

Substituting for b from Eq. (17.20), we find that

$$r^2 = \frac{(\sum XY)^2}{(\sum X^2)^2} \frac{\sum X^2}{\sum Y^2} = \frac{(\sum XY)^2}{\sum X^2 \sum Y^2}.$$

Hence,

$$r = \frac{\sum XY}{\sqrt{\sum X^2 \sum Y^2}}$$

which is Eq. (18.9). The correlation coefficient r must lie in the range $0 \leqslant |r| \leqslant 1$, but in practice, because of random errors, $0 < |r| < 1$.

We can note that r is symmetrical with respect to x and y so that the correlation coefficient of a line of regression of y on x is the same as that of regression of x on y. Correlation is, in fact, concerned only with the *association* between the variables and not with their dependence or independence.

The sign of r tells us whether y increases with an increase in x (r is positive) or whether y decreases with an increase in x (r is negative). Figure 18.4 shows diagrammatically some of the possible correlations.

The calculation of r should be performed on the actual sampling data and not on averages because in the latter case the random variation is removed and misleadingly high values of r may be obtained.

---

[2] Or the geometric mean of two values.

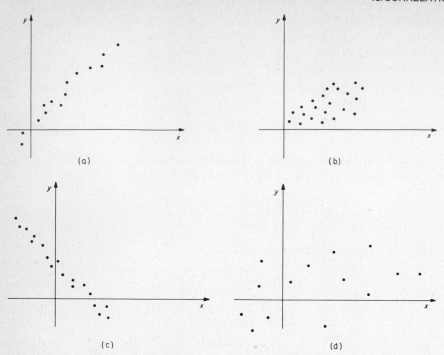

Figure 18.4 Correlations: (a) high positive; (b) low positive; (c) high negative; and (d) none (the variables are independent).

It should be recalled that in the regression analysis in Chapter 17, it was assumed that only y was the random variable with the values of y treated as belonging to a random sample from the conditional probability distribution of y for a given value of x. On the other hand, correlation analysis entails the measure of association between two variables under the following assumptions:

i. Both variables, x and y, are random and normally distributed.
ii. The variance of the y distribution is constant for all values of x and the variance of the x distribution is constant for all values of y. For testing of hypotheses regarding the coefficient of correlation of the population, ρ, it is further assumed that the observed pairs (x, y) are drawn from a bivariate normal distribution.

If these assumptions are not met in a given case, the calculated correlation coefficient may be misleading, and we have to note that many engineering relationships involve *functional dependence*[3] rather than a bivariate normal distribution or else the values of x are preselected. In such cases, the use of the correlation coefficient is inappropriate.

---

[3] When one (dependent) variable U is predicted given any value of another (independent) variable v, then U is said to have a functional dependence on v; for example, force is a function of acceleration, static fluid pressure is a function of fluid density.

DISTRIBUTION OF *r*

The sampling distribution of the correlation coefficient is not normal but depends on the magnitude and sign of the coefficient. The larger the coefficient the more skew the distribution, to the left for positive correlations and vice versa.

It has been shown that the random variable

$$Z = \frac{1}{2} \log_e \frac{1+r}{1-r} \tag{18.13}$$

is approximately normally distributed with mean

$$\mu_Z = \frac{1}{2} \log_e \frac{1+\rho}{1-\rho} \tag{18.14}$$

and variance

$$\sigma_Z^2 = \frac{1}{n-3} \tag{18.15}$$

where *n* is the number of pairs of values determined. For convenience, the conversion of *r* to *Z* is given in Table A.17.

The confidence limits for the correlation coefficient can be written as

$$Z \pm z\sigma_Z \tag{18.16}$$

where *z* is the appropriate value from the normal distribution, Table A.6. The two values of *Z* obtained from the above equation are converted back to the values of *r* using Table A.17. It is clear that, as a consequence of the skew distribution of *r*, the limits of *r* are not symmetrical about the sample value.

TEST OF SIGNIFICANCE

In a correlation analysis, our aim is to make inferences about the population correlation coefficient, ρ. As an estimator of ρ we use the sample correlation coefficient, *r*. To interpret the meaning of *r* calculated by Eq. (18.8) or Eq. (18.9), we use Table A.18. This gives the values of *r* that can be expected at a given level of significance from observations drawn by chance when there is no correlation. In a formal test procedure, we state the null hypothesis as $H_0 : \rho = 0$ versus the alternative hypothesis $H_1 : \rho \neq 0$ at a level of significance α. If the absolute value of the calculated *r* exceeds the tabulated value, we conclude that correlation exists, and the level of significance represents the probability of our having drawn the wrong conclusion; in other words, we reject the null hypothesis that $\rho = 0$ and accept the alternative hypothesis, with a probability of committing a Type I error equal to the level of significance, α.

We may note that *r* is related to *t* by the equation $t = r\sqrt{n-2}/\sqrt{1-r^2}$ when *y* is a function of one independent linear variable *x* (see Appendix E).

Table A.18 is entered with the appropriate number of degrees of freedom and the total number of variables. In the case of regression of the type given by Eq. (17.1), the total number of variables is two and the number of degrees of freedom is $v = n - 2$, where *n* is the total number of observations (readings x_i, y_i).

The test statistic z, based on the normal distribution, is calculated from Eq. (10.17) as

$$z = \frac{Z - \mu_Z}{\sigma_Z} = \frac{2.599 - 0.549}{\sqrt{1/(7 - 3)}} = 4.10.$$

The value of z from Table A.6, for a one-sided test and $\alpha = 0.01$, is $z = 2.33$.

Since $z_{calc} > 2.33$, we can reject the null hypothesis that $\rho = 0.50$ and accept the alternative hypothesis $\rho > 0.50$.

PROBLEMS

18-1. Find the correlation coefficient of the regression of Problem 17-5 and determine the significance of the regression. Use $\alpha = 0.01$.

18-2. Is the correlation between the following values of y and x significant? Use $\alpha = 0.05$.

x	56	58	60	70	72	75	77	77	82	87	92	104	125
y	51	60	69	54	70	65	49	60	63	61	64	84	75

18-3. A correlation coefficient based on a sample of size 16 was calculated to be 0.38. Determine whether we can conclude that the corresponding population correlation differs from zero at a significance level of: **(a)** 5 percent, **(b)** 1 percent. (Use $t = r\sqrt{n - 2}/\sqrt{1 - r^2}$ in Appendix E.)

18-4. Find by a trial method the minimum sample size necessary in order to conclude that a correlation coefficient of 0.38 differs significantly from zero at the 1 percent level.

18-5. The compressive strength of concretes with three different aggregate/cement ratios was measured on four test specimens for each mix (see Table 18.2). Using the mean strength of each mix, obtain the regression line of strength on aggregate/cement ratio, and the correlation coefficient. Test the significance of the slope. Use $\alpha = 0.05$.

18-6. Find the correlation coefficient for the data in Problem 17-2. What are the 95 percent confidence limits for ρ?

TABLE 18.2

Specimen number	Aggregate/cement ratio	4	5	6
	Strength, MPa			
1		40.2	45.4	43.7
2		42.3	42.5	48.5
3		40.8	44.5	48.1
4		40.0	43.9	45.7

Source: P. J. F. Wright, "Statistical Methods in Concrete Research," *Magazine of Concrete Research*, vol. 5, no. 15, March 1954, p. 147. The original data were in psi.

18-7. The sample correlation coefficient between two variables was calculated as $r = 0.76$; the number of pairs in the sample tested was $n = 20$. Test the null hypothesis $H_0:\rho = 0.60$ versus the alternative hypothesis $H_a:\rho > 0.60$. Use $\alpha = 0.05$.

18-8. A linear regression analysis was carried out between the shear strength of a spot weld (y in MPa) and the diameter of the weld (x in 0.001 mm); 10 pairs of measurements were taken. The computed data were as follows:

$$\sum(x - \bar{x})^2 = 1348.715; \qquad \sum(y - \bar{y}) = 1326.147;$$
$$\sum(x - \bar{x})(y - \bar{y}) = 1332.56.$$

a. Calculate the coefficients of determination and correlation.
b. Test $H_0:\rho = 0$ versus $H_a:\rho \neq 0$ at $\alpha = 0.05$.
c. Construct the 95 percent confidence limits for ρ.

Multiple Regression Analysis

In many practical cases, a dependent variable may depend on more than one independent variable. In such a situation, the precision of the association or prediction of the mean of a dependent variable can be improved by multiple regression analysis, which is an extension of the simple regression analysis discussed in Chapter 17. Briefly, the difference between the simple and multiple regression methods lies in the fact that multiple regression establishes the effect of each independent variable with the other independent variables kept constant, while simple regression does not control the other independent variables.

Let us give two examples. In highway pavement design, it is important to predict the frost depth along a particular route. This is done from the knowledge of the mean annual temperature, measured at various stations, as a function of the elevation and latitude of each station along the route. Obviously, if latitude (or elevation) alone is considered as a predictor variable, then the prediction of the mean annual temperature of a locality along the route would not be accurate. On the other hand, the use of the knowledge of the latitude and of the elevation of the locality would lead to a better prediction. Another example of a problem involving multiple regression is afforded by the influence of the temperatures of air and of the coolant on the efficiency of an engine. Because of the influence of the weather, the two temperatures are likely to be low or high at the same time, and a single correlation cannot eliminate the effect of one variable when the effect of the other is measured; it is the multiple correlation that achieves this and establishes the association between efficiency and the two temperatures.

MULTIPLE REGRESSION EQUATION

Let us consider the general case of a relation between the population mean value of the dependent variable y and independent variables $x_1, x_2, \ldots, x_k$; this can be expressed as

$$E(y) = \mu_{y|x_1,\ldots,x_k} = b_0 + b_1 x_1 + b_2 x_2 + \cdots + b_k x_k \qquad (19.1)$$

where b_0 is a constant and $b_1, b_2, \ldots, b_k$ are partial regression coefficients. All of these are the population parameters. The multiple regression model for the distribution of y can be expressed as

$$y = b_0 + b_1 x_1 + b_2 x_2 + \cdots + b_k x_k + e \qquad (19.2)$$

where e is the error or residual.

It is assumed that this model has the following features:

a. The conditional distribution (see Chapter 5) of the population of y for given $x_1, x_2, \ldots, x_k$ is normal, with variance $\sigma_y^2 = \text{Var}(e_i) = $ constant for all values of y.

b. The conditional mean of y is given by Eq. (19.1), that is, $E(e_i) = 0$.

c. The error e is independent, that is, $E(e_i e_j) = \text{Cov}(e_i, e_j) = 0$, when $i \neq j$.[1]

An estimate of Eq. (19.1) can be written as

$$\hat{y} = \hat{b}_0 + \hat{b}_1 x_1 + \cdots + \hat{b}_k x_k \qquad (19.3)$$

where $\hat{b}_0, \hat{b}_1, \ldots, \hat{b}_k$ are point estimators (see Chapter 7) of the population parameters $b_0, b_1, \ldots, b_k$. Equation (19.3) represents a plane in $(k + 1)$ dimensions. It should be mentioned that the variables denoted by the letter x need not be linear or functionally independent, that is, we can, for instance, have a relation of the form

$$\hat{y} = \hat{b}_0 + \hat{b}_1 x_1 + \hat{b}_2 x_2 + \hat{b}_3 x_1^2$$

or a relation containing interaction terms, such as

$$\hat{y} = \hat{b}_0 + \hat{b}_1 x_1 + \hat{b}_2 x_2 + \hat{b}_3 x_1^2 + \hat{b}_4 x_1 x_2.$$

However, the function y should be a linear function[2] of the unknown parameters $\hat{b}_0, \hat{b}_1, \hat{b}_2, \ldots, \hat{b}_k$ as this condition makes it easy to apply the principle of least squares in order to yield the standard error for estimation and prediction.

Up to now, we have assumed that the values of x are quantitative variables. It is possible also for the variable y to be a function of *qualitative* or *dummy* variables which serve to partition the regression model into various components. For example, we can use a model

$$\hat{y} = \hat{b}_0 + \hat{b}_1 x_1 + \hat{b}_2 x_2 + \hat{b}_3 x_3$$

---

[1] For explanation of covariance (Cov) see Eq. (5.34).

[2] That is, involves single terms b only.

with the dummy variable x_1 taking the value of 1 or zero. Thus, if a certain quality is present, $x_1 = 1$, and

$$\hat{y} = (\hat{b}_0 + \hat{b}_1) + \hat{b}_2 x_2 + \hat{b}_3 x_3.$$

If that certain quality is absent, then $x_1 = 0$, and the estimated model becomes

$$\hat{y} = \hat{b}_0 + \hat{b}_2 x_2 + \hat{b}_3 x_3.$$

As shown in Appendix F, the plane represented by Eq. (19.3) passes through the centroid of all the observed values, that is, Eq. (19.3) is satisfied by $(\bar{y}, \bar{x}_1, \bar{x}_2, \ldots, \bar{x}_k)$, where $\bar{y}, \bar{x}_1, \ldots, \bar{x}_k$ are means of all the observed values of $y, x_1, \ldots, x_k$, respectively. Hence,

$$\bar{y} = \hat{b}_0 + \hat{b}_1 \bar{x}_1 + \hat{b}_2 \bar{x}_2 + \cdots + \hat{b}_k \bar{x}_k$$

or $\qquad \hat{b}_0 = \bar{y} - \hat{b}_1 \bar{x}_1 - \hat{b}_2 \bar{x}_2 - \cdots - \hat{b}_k \bar{x}_k.$

Substituting this last equation in Eq. (19.3), we obtain

$$\hat{y} - \bar{y} = \hat{b}_1(x_1 - \bar{x}_1) + \hat{b}_2(x_2 - \bar{x}_2) + \cdots + \hat{b}_k(x_k - \bar{x}_k). \tag{19.4}$$

The coefficients are determined using the method of least squares.

Now, if y_i is the observed value of the dependent variable, then the error in y_i relative to $\hat{y}_i$, which is given by Eq. (19.3), is

$$\epsilon_i = y_i - \hat{y}_i.$$

We can follow the procedure outlined in Chapter 17, and take the partial derivative of $\sum_{i=1}^{n} \epsilon_i^2$ with respect to $\hat{b}_0$ and to each $\hat{b}_j (j = 1, 2, \ldots, k)$ and equate all the partial derivatives to zero. This will yield the following normal equations:

$$n\hat{b}_0 + (\sum x_{1i})\hat{b}_1 + (\sum x_{2i})\hat{b}_2 + \cdots + (\sum x_{ki})\hat{b}_k = \sum y_i$$

$$(\sum x_{1i})\hat{b}_0 + (\sum x_{1i}^2)\hat{b}_1 + (\sum x_{1i}x_{2i})\hat{b}_2 + \cdots + (\sum x_{1i}x_{ki})\hat{b}_k = \sum x_{1i}y_i$$

$$\vdots \qquad \vdots \qquad \qquad \vdots \qquad \qquad \vdots \tag{19.5}$$

$$(\sum x_{ki})\hat{b}_0 + (\sum x_{1i}x_{ki})\hat{b}_1 + \cdots + (\sum x_{(k-1)i}x_{ki})\hat{b}_{k-1} + (\sum x_{ki}^2)\hat{b}_k = \sum x_{ki}y_i$$

where each summation sign indicates summation over all the data points, $i = 1, 2, \ldots, n$. We can note that Eq. (19.5) is a generalization of Eqs. (17.11) and (17.13).

It is useful to point out that the number of predictor variables, that is, the x variables, should not be greater than one-quarter of the sample size n. This ensures a reliable coefficient of determination, r^2.

For simplicity, let us apply Eq. (19.5) to a case of two independent variables only, that is,

$$\hat{y} = \hat{b}_0 + \hat{b}_1 x_1 + \hat{b}_2 x_2$$

with n sets of observations. In each case, the residual is given as

$$\epsilon = y - (\hat{b}_0 + \hat{b}_1 x_1 + \hat{b}_2 x_2) \tag{19.6}$$

and the sum of squares of residuals in the n sets is

$$\sum \epsilon^2 = \sum [y - (\hat{b}_0 + \hat{b}_1 x_1 + \hat{b}_2 x_2)]^2. \tag{19.7}$$

Using the principle of least squares, we minimize $\sum \epsilon^2$, that is, we satisfy the condition that the partial derivatives of $\sum \epsilon^2$ with respect to $\hat{b}_0$, $\hat{b}_1$, and $\hat{b}_2$ are all zero:

$$\frac{\partial(\sum \epsilon^2)}{\partial \hat{b}_0} = -2\sum[y - (\hat{b}_0 + \hat{b}_1 x_1 + \hat{b}_2 x_2)] = 0$$

$$\frac{\partial(\sum \epsilon^2)}{\partial \hat{b}_1} = -2\sum x_1[y - (\hat{b}_0 + \hat{b}_1 x_1 + \hat{b}_2 x_2)] = 0$$

$$\frac{\partial(\sum \epsilon^2)}{\partial \hat{b}_2} = -2\sum x_2[y - (\hat{b}_0 + \hat{b}_1 x_1 + \hat{b}_2 x_2)] = 0.$$

Hence, the normal equations can be written

$$\left.\begin{array}{l} \sum y = n\hat{b}_0 + \hat{b}_1 \sum x_1 + \hat{b}_2 \sum x_2 \\ \sum x_1 y = \hat{b}_0 \sum x_1 + \hat{b}_1 \sum x_1^2 + \hat{b}_2 \sum x_1 x_2 \\ \sum x_2 y = \hat{b}_0 \sum x_2 + \hat{b}_1 \sum x_1 x_2 + \hat{b}_2 \sum x_2^2 \end{array}\right\}. \tag{19.8}$$

The solution of this system of three simultaneous equations gives the values of $\hat{b}_0$, $\hat{b}_1$, and $\hat{b}_2$.

SHORTER COMPUTATION

We can simplify the process of finding the equation to the regression plane by choosing the centroid as origin. Let

$$\hat{Y} = \hat{y} - \bar{y}$$
$$X_1 = x_1 - \bar{x}_1$$
$$\vdots \qquad \vdots \qquad \vdots$$
$$X_k = x_k - \bar{x}_k.$$

Thus, Eq. (19.3) becomes

$$\hat{Y} = \hat{b}_1 X_1 + \hat{b}_2 X_2 + \cdots + \hat{b}_k X_k$$

and the residual

$$\epsilon = Y - (\hat{b}_1 X_1 + \hat{b}_2 X_2 + \cdots + \hat{b}_k X_k).$$

Considering two independent variables X_1 and X_2 only and taking partial derivatives of $\sum \epsilon^2$ with respect to $\hat{b}_1$ and $\hat{b}_2$, we obtain

$$\left.\begin{array}{l} \sum X_1 Y = \hat{b}_1 \sum X_1^2 + \hat{b}_2 \sum X_1 X_2 \\ \sum X_2 Y = \hat{b}_1 \sum X_1 X_2 + \hat{b}_2 \sum X_2^2 \end{array}\right\}. \tag{19.9}$$

The solution of the system of these two equations gives the values of the regression coefficients, and hence the equation to the regression plane.

TABLE 19.1

Water content in percent, y	Percent of lime, x_1	Percent of pozzolan, x_2
27.5	2.0	18.0
28.0	3.5	16.5
28.8	4.5	10.5
29.1	2.5	2.5
30.0	8.5	9.0
31.0	10.5	4.5
32.0	13.5	1.5

EXAMPLE

From an experimental study on the stabilization of a highly plastic clay, molding water content for optimum density was found to be linearly dependent on the percentages of lime and pozzolan mixed with the clay. The results in Table 19.1 were obtained. Fit an equation of the form $\hat{y} = \hat{b}_0 + \hat{b}_1 x_1 + \hat{b}_2 x_2$ to the data in Table 19.1.

The equation can readily be obtained by means of Table 19.2. Using Eq. (19.9), we find that

$$118.21170\hat{b}_1 - 110.54078\hat{b}_2 = 40.99563$$

and $$-110.54078\hat{b}_1 + 258.23270\hat{b}_2 = -53.20647.$$

Solving for $\hat{b}_1$ and $\hat{b}_2$ by elimination, we obtain

$$\hat{b}_1 = 0.257004, \qquad \hat{b}_2 = -0.096026.$$

Now, $$\bar{y} = \hat{b}_0 + \hat{b}_1 \bar{x}_1 + \hat{b}_2 \bar{x}_2.$$

Substituting for $\hat{b}_1$, $\hat{b}_2$, $\bar{y}$, $\bar{x}_1$, and $\bar{x}_2$, we obtain

$$\hat{b}_0 = 28.691.$$

Thus, the required equation is

$$\hat{y} = 28.691 + 0.257x_1 - 0.0960x_2. \qquad \blacksquare\ \blacksquare$$

USE OF MATRICES

As we have seen, multiple linear regression leads to a set of simultaneous equations, which have to be solved. Such simultaneous equations can be represented in the following compact matrix form,

$$[A]\{b\} = [C] \tag{19.10}$$

where $[A]$ and $[C]$ are matrices obtained from the experimental data and $\{b\}$ is the unknown vector (the regression coefficients to be determined). If we re-

TABLE 19.2

y	x_1	x_2	$Y = y - \bar{y}$	$X_1 = x_1 - \bar{x}_1$	$X_2 = x_2 - \bar{x}_2$	YX_1	YX_2	X_1^2	X_2^2	X_1X_2
27.5	2.0	18.0	−1.985	−4.428	9.072	8.78958	−18.00792	19.60718	82.30118	−40.17081
28.0	3.5	16.5	−1.486	−2.929	7.572	4.35239	−11.25199	8.57904	57.33518	−22.17838
28.8	4.5	10.5	−0.686	−1.929	1.571	1.32329	−1.07771	3.72104	2.46804	−3.03046
29.1	2.5	2.5	−0.386	−3.928	−6.429	1.51621	2.48159	15.42918	41.33204	25.25311
30.0	8.5	9.0	0.514	2.071	0.071	1.06449	0.03649	4.28904	0.00504	0.14704
31.0	10.5	4.5	1.514	4.071	−4.429	6.16349	−6.70551	16.57304	19.61604	−18.03046
32.0	13.5	1.5	2.515	7.072	−7.428	17.78608	−18.68142	50.01318	55.17518	−52.53082
$\sum = 206.4$	45.0	62.5	0	0	0	40.99563	−53.20647	118.21170	258.23270	−110.54078

$$\bar{y} = \frac{\sum y}{n} = \frac{206.4}{7} = 29.486$$

$$\bar{x}_1 = \frac{\sum x_1}{n} = \frac{45.0}{7} = 6.429$$

$$\bar{x}_2 = \frac{\sum x_2}{n} = \frac{62.5}{7} = 8.929$$

425

arrange Eq. (19.9) to conform with the above matrix equation, we find that

$$
\left.\begin{aligned}
[A] &= \begin{bmatrix} \sum X_1^2 & \sum X_1 X_2 \\ \sum X_1 X_2 & \sum X_2^2 \end{bmatrix} \\[2mm]
\{b\} &= \begin{bmatrix} b_1 \\ b_2 \end{bmatrix} \\[2mm]
\text{and} \qquad [C] &= \begin{bmatrix} \sum X_1 Y \\ \sum X_2 Y \end{bmatrix}.
\end{aligned}\right\} \tag{19.11}
$$

In many instances, the inverse of matrix $[A]$, denoted by $[A]^{-1}$, is required. The inverse of a matrix is defined by the relation

$$[A]^{-1}[A] = \text{unit matrix.}$$

Writing this in full, and if

$$[A]^{-1} = \begin{bmatrix} e_{11} & e_{12} \\ e_{21} & e_{22} \end{bmatrix} \tag{19.12}$$

then we obtain

$$\begin{bmatrix} e_{11} & e_{12} \\ e_{21} & e_{22} \end{bmatrix}\begin{bmatrix} \sum X_1^2 & \sum X_1 X_2 \\ \sum X_1 X_2 & \sum X_2^2 \end{bmatrix} = \begin{bmatrix} 1 & 0 \\ 0 & 1 \end{bmatrix}. \tag{19.13}$$

The simultaneous equations are

$$
\left.\begin{aligned}
e_{11}\sum X_1^2 + e_{12}\sum X_1 X_2 &= 1 \\
e_{11}\sum X_1 X_2 + e_{12}\sum X_2^2 &= 0 \\
e_{21}\sum X_1^2 + e_{22}\sum X_1 X_2 &= 0 \\
e_{21}\sum X_1 X_2 + e_{22}\sum X_2^2 &= 1
\end{aligned}\right\}. \tag{19.14}
$$

The solution of Eq. (19.14) gives

$$
\left.\begin{aligned}
e_{11} &= \frac{\sum X_2^2}{\sum X_1^2 \sum X_2^2 - (\sum X_1 X_2)^2} \\[2mm]
e_{22} &= \frac{\sum X_1^2}{\sum X_1^2 \sum X_2^2 - (\sum X_1 X_2)^2} \\[2mm]
e_{12} = e_{21} &= \frac{-\sum X_1 X_2}{\sum X_1^2 \sum X_2^2 - (\sum X_1 X_2)^2}
\end{aligned}\right\} \tag{19.15}
$$

provided that the determinant of $[A] \neq 0$, that is, the denominator in Eq. (19.15) is different from zero. Otherwise, values for $e_{11}, e_{22}, e_{12},$ and e_{21} will be undefined.

There are two main uses of finding $[A]^{-1}$ [Eq. (19.12)]. The first is when we want to check whether there is an association between the independent variables that have been used previously and a new dependent variable, for example, between the water–cement ratio of concrete, the specific gravity of aggregate, and the density of the resulting concrete. If there is an association, then the matrix $[A]$ is unchanged and so is $[A]^{-1}$. Thus, the unknown vector $\{b\}$ can easily be found in the following manner. Multiply both sides of $[A]\{b\} = [C]$

by $[A]^{-1}$. Hence,

$$[A]^{-1}[A]\{b\} = [A]^{-1}[C].$$

But $[A]^{-1}[A] = $ unit matrix. Therefore,

$$\{b\} = [A]^{-1}[C].$$

Then,

$$\begin{bmatrix} b_1 \\ b_2 \end{bmatrix} = \begin{bmatrix} e_{11} & e_{12} \\ e_{21} & e_{22} \end{bmatrix} \begin{bmatrix} \sum X_1 Y \\ \sum X_2 Y \end{bmatrix} \qquad (19.16)$$

or

$$\left. \begin{array}{l} b_1 = e_{11} \sum X_1 Y + e_{12} \sum X_2 Y \\ b_2 = e_{21} \sum X_1 Y + e_{22} \sum X_2 Y \end{array} \right\}. \qquad (19.17)$$

The second main use of the inverse matrix $[A]^{-1}$ is in calculating the standard error of the partial regression coefficients, and hence the confidence intervals for such coefficients.

GENERAL PROCEDURE

Before proceeding further, it is instructive to enumerate the steps in the analysis of a multiple regression problem.

Step 1: We specify the model, that is, the equation relating the dependent variable, y, and the independent variables, x_1, $x_2, \ldots$.

Step 2: By means of the method of least squares, we estimate the population parameters $b_0, b_1, b_2, \ldots$.

Step 3: On the basis of the assumptions made on page 421, we estimate the variance of y, σ_y^2, by s_y^2 [see Eq. (19.18)].

Step 4: We check the adequacy of the assumed model by calculating the coefficient of determination, r^2, and testing the significance of r and of each parameter b.

Step 5: If the model is acceptable, we estimate the mean of the population of y, that is, μ, and its confidence limits, as well as prediction intervals for an individual observation, y, if required.

ESTIMATION OF VARIANCE OF
VARIABLE y

Using the assumptions made earlier with regard to the distribution of the population of the variable y, we can estimate σ_y^2, the variance of the error e, from the sample variance, that is, s_y^2. We can write

$$s_y^2 = \frac{\sum \epsilon_i^2}{n - (k + 1)} \qquad (19.18)$$

where ϵ_i = deviation of observed value of y from the value given by the regression plane, that is,

$$\epsilon_i = y - \hat{y}$$

where $\hat{y}$ is the estimate of y from the regression plane, n the number of observations of y, and k the number of independent variables on which y depends.

The denominator term $n - (k + 1)$ is, in fact, the number of degrees of freedom to compute s_y^2, because $(k + 1)$ parameters $(b_0, b_1, \ldots, b_k)$ were estimated from the data to yield the estimate $\hat{y}$. Hence there are $(k + 1)$ constraints in computing ϵ_i in Eq. (19.18).

For two independent variables, x_1 and x_2, the residual variance becomes, after shifting the origin to the centroid $(\bar{y}, \bar{x}_1, \bar{x}_2)$,

$$s_y^2 = \frac{\sum \epsilon_i^2}{n - (k + 1)} = \frac{\sum (Y - \hat{Y})^2}{n - (2 + 1)} = \frac{\sum [Y - (\hat{b}_1 X_1 + \hat{b}_2 X_2)]^2}{n - 3},$$

$\hat{Y}$ being the estimated value given by the regression equation. Expanding the term in the brackets, we find that

$$s_y^2 = \frac{\sum Y^2 - 2\hat{b}_1 \sum YX_1 - 2\hat{b}_2 \sum YX_2 + \hat{b}_1^2 \sum X_1^2 + \hat{b}_2^2 \sum X_2^2 + 2\hat{b}_1 \hat{b}_2 \sum X_1 X_2}{n - 3}.$$

Multiplying the first of Eq. (19.9) by $\hat{b}_1$ and the second by $\hat{b}_2$, and substituting the values of $\hat{b}_1^2 \sum X_1^2$ and $\hat{b}_2^2 \sum X_2^2$ in the above expression, we obtain

$$s_y^2 = \frac{\sum Y^2 - \hat{b}_1 \sum YX_1 - \hat{b}_2 \sum YX_2}{n - 3}. \tag{19.19}$$

MULTIPLE CORRELATION COEFFICIENT

The value of the multiple correlation coefficient, ρ, measures the degree of association between the dependent variable and all of the independent variables $x_1, x_2, \ldots, x_k$ *taken together*. As defined in Chapter 18, the square of the correlation coefficient is equal to the coefficient of determination, ρ^2, which is that fraction of the total variance of y which is contributed by its regression upon the variables $x_1, x_2, \ldots, x_k$. The parameter ρ^2 is estimated by r^2, the coefficient of determination of the sample, representing the population. Thus,

$$r^2 = \frac{\text{sum of squares of deviations in } y \text{ accounted for by regression}}{\text{total sum of squares of deviations in } y \text{ from } \bar{y}}$$

that is,

$$r^2 = \frac{\sum (\bar{y} - \hat{y})^2}{\sum (y - \bar{y})^2}. \tag{19.20}$$

In "shorthand" form,

$$r^2 = \frac{\text{SSR}}{\text{SST}}.$$

As in the case of simple linear regression, when r^2 has a value of zero, there is no correlation between y and the variables $x_1, x_2, \ldots$, whereas a value of 1 means that all the sample points lie exactly on the regression plane (in the case of three independent variables).

To test the significance of r, we use Table A-18, with the total number of variables of $(k + 1)$, and the number of degrees of freedom equal to $v = n - (k + 1)$. We reject the null hypothesis that the population multiple correlation coefficient is zero if $|r|$ exceeds the tabulated value at the specified level of significance. When the hypothesis is rejected, we say that the regression of y on the variables $x_1, x_2, \ldots$ accounts for a significant amount of variation in y.

The degree of association between any two variables can be checked in a manner similar to that described in Chapter 18. Thus,

$$r_{yx_1} = \frac{\sum X_1 Y}{\sqrt{\sum X_1^2 \sum Y^2}}, \qquad r_{yx_2} = \frac{\sum X_2 Y}{\sqrt{\sum X_2^2 \sum Y^2}}$$

$$r_{x_1 x_2} = \frac{\sum X_1 X_2}{\sqrt{\sum X_1^2 \sum X_2^2}}, \qquad \text{and so on.} \tag{19.21}$$

SIGNIFICANCE OF MULTIPLE REGRESSION AS A WHOLE

Sometimes, the assumed regression equation may prove to be statistically not significant. Whether this is so is determined by a comparison of the variance contributed by the regression and the error variance s_y^2, using the F test. In other words, this test indicates the suitability of the assumed model for predicting the population of y values at each setting of the independent variables, x_1, $x_2, \ldots$. The null hypothesis is that all the partial regression coefficients, b_0, $b_1, \ldots, b_k$ are equal to zero, that is, $H_0 : b_0 = b_1 = \cdots = b_k = 0$ versus the alternative hypothesis H_a: at least one of the values of b is nonzero. If H_0 is true, then we would expect the term $\sum (y - \hat{y})^2$, or SSE, to be relatively large and the term $\sum (\bar{y} - \hat{y})^2$, or SSR, to be relatively small. On the other hand, if SSE is not large compared with SSR, then we would reject H_0 and confirm the use of the assumed model. Table 19.3 presents the necessary information, using the notation: $\text{SSR} = \sum (\bar{y} - \hat{y})^2$, $\text{SSE} = \sum (y - \hat{y})^2$, and $\text{SST} = \sum (y - \bar{y})^2 = \text{SSR} + \text{SSE}$.

TABLE 19.3

Source	Sum of squares of deviations, SS	Degrees of freedom, v	Mean square, SS/v
Regression	SSR	k	$\text{SSR}/k = \text{MSR}$
Error	SSE	$n - (k + 1)$	$\text{SSE}/[n - (k + 1)] = \text{MSE}$
Total	SST	$n - 1$	

The appropriate statistic to test the above null hypothesis is given by the ratio of (MSR/MSE) which follows an F distribution (see Chapter 16) with $v_1 = k$ and $v_2 = [n - (k + 1)]$. Thus,

$$F = \frac{SSR/k}{SSE/[n - (k + 1)]} = \frac{MSR}{MSE}.$$ (19.22)

From the definition of r^2 given by Eq. (19.20), it can be readily shown that

$$F = \frac{r^2/k}{(1 - r^2)/[n - (k + 1)]}.$$ (19.23)

We should remember that k is the number of unknown parameters $b_1, b_2, \ldots$, not including b_0.

For three coefficients, $\hat{b}_0$, $\hat{b}_1$, and $\hat{b}_2$ ($k = 2$), the sum of squares of deviations in y accounted for by regression is

$$\sum c^2 = b_1 \sum YX_1 + b_2 \sum YX_2.$$

Therefore, we compute F as

$$F = \frac{(\sum c^2)/k}{s_y^2}$$ (19.24)

with the number of degrees of freedom $v_1 = k = 2$ for the numerator, since there are only two parameters, and $v_2 = n - (k + 1) = n - 3$ for the denominator.

If the computed F is greater than the value tabulated in Table A.14 for the given level of significance, then the hypothesis that all the true partial regression coefficients are equal to zero is rejected.

CONFIDENCE LIMITS OF A PARTIAL REGRESSION COEFFICIENT

After determining that the assumed model is useful in describing the population of y, that is, after rejecting the null hypothesis $H_0: b_1 = b_2 = \cdots = b_k = 0$, we may want to make inferences about a particular parameter b, say b_j, which we consider to have some practical importance. In this case, the null hypothesis is $H_0: b_j = 0$ versus $H_a: b_j > 0$ for a one-sided test, or $H_a: b_j \neq 0$ for a two-sided test. The appropriate statistic to test this null hypothesis is given by the ratio $|b_j - 0|/s_{b_j}$ which follows a t distribution (see Chapter 15) with $v = n - (k + 1)$.

Specifically, the standard deviation of a partial regression coefficient is estimated from the sample as

$$s_{\hat{b}_j} = s_y \sqrt{e_{jj}}$$ (19.25)

where, in the general case, $j = 1, 2, \ldots, k$ and e_{jj} is the corresponding diagonal element of $[A]^{-1}$. Thus, for the two regression coefficients b_1 and b_2, we have

$$s_{\hat{b}_1} = s_y \sqrt{e_{11}}$$

and

$$s_{\hat{b}_2} = s_y \sqrt{e_{22}}.$$ (19.26)

To obtain the standard deviation of the constant $\hat{b}_0$ in Eq. (19.3), but for simplicity taking the terms up to $\hat{b}_2 x_2$ only, we write

$$\hat{b}_0 = \bar{y} - \hat{b}_1 \bar{x}_1 - \hat{b}_2 \bar{x}_2.$$

Hence, the variance of $\hat{b}_0$ is

$$\sigma_{\hat{b}_0}^2 = \sigma_{\bar{y}}^2 + \bar{x}_1^2 \sigma_{\hat{b}_1}^2 + \bar{x}_2^2 \sigma_{\hat{b}_2}^2 + 2\bar{x}_1 \bar{x}_2 \, \text{Cov}(\hat{b}_1 \hat{b}_2)$$

where $\text{Cov}(\hat{b}_1 \hat{b}_2)$ is the covariance of $\hat{b}_1$ and $\hat{b}_2$ and the procedure is based on the argument of Eq. (16.19).

Hence, the standard deviation of the constant $\hat{b}_0$ is estimated from the sample by

$$s_{\hat{b}_0} = s_y \left(\frac{1}{n} + \bar{x}_1^2 e_{11} + \bar{x}_2^2 e_{22} + 2\bar{x}_1 \bar{x}_2 e_{12} \right)^{1/2}. \qquad (19.27)$$

We can now test the significance of the regression coefficients. This is important, since we may have assumed independent variables that do not significantly influence y. The significance of $\hat{b}_1$ is tested by

$$t = \frac{\hat{b}_1}{s_{\hat{b}_1}}. \qquad (19.28)$$

Similar tests are applied to the other coefficients. The number of degrees of freedom is $n - 3$, as 3 constraints were used in fixing the plane, that is, in determining the values of $\bar{y}$, $\hat{b}_1$, and $\hat{b}_2$ (or $\hat{b}_0$, $\hat{b}_1$, and $\hat{b}_2$).

If a regression coefficient is found not to be statistically significant, we have to revise our equation. The independent variable that does not significantly influence the dependent variable is deleted, and new regression coefficients are computed.

If $\hat{b}_1$ is significant, its confidence interval is given by $\hat{b}_1 \pm t s_{\hat{b}_1}$.

If we want to establish whether a regression coefficient $\bar{b}_j$ differs significantly from a value (e.g., a theoretical value) b_j^0, we apply the t test:

$$t = \frac{|\hat{b}_j - \hat{b}_j^0|}{s_{\hat{b}_j}}. \qquad (19.29)$$

The null hypothesis is rejected at the stipulated level of significance if t exceeds the critical value given in Table A.7, with $v = n - (k + 1)$ degrees of freedom.

Estimates for confidence intervals for the population mean, μ, as well as prediction intervals for a particular measurement y can be readily computed, as was shown in Chapter 17. We should note, however, that even if all the statistical tests show that the assumed model is useful in predicting the dependent variable, we *cannot* conclude that such an assumed model is the best predictor model without further data and analysis. Finally, the calculated prediction equation, based on a set of independent variables $(x_1, x_2, \ldots)$ is appropriate only over the range of the sample values of x used in the analysis. Extrapolation beyond this range may lead to errors, as mentioned in Chapter 17.

Multiple regression analysis entails cumbersome calculations which can be more readily handled by a computer. There are many computer software packages which can perform functions that range from plotting a histogram for given data to fitting a regression equation and carrying out tests of significance. The most extensive library of computer programs for statistical analysis of data is the University of California BMDP Biomedical Computer Programs P-Series 1979. A sample of a computer output for an example on multiple regression is given in Solved Problem 19-2.

SOLVED PROBLEMS

19-1. An experiment was conducted at the University of Saskatchewan to determine the relation between the thermal conductivity of sandy textured soils and their moisture content and dry density. The data in Table 19.4 were collected in the field by means of a thermal conductivity probe and a Uhland core sampler (ρ denotes the dry density of soil in kg/m³).

   a. Fit an equation of the form:

$$\hat{K} = \hat{a}_0 + \hat{a}_1 M + \hat{a}_2 e^{0.45\rho}.$$

   b. Use the F test to check whether or not this form of an equation is statistically significant. Use $\alpha = 1$ percent.
   c. Use the t test to check the significance of the partial regression coefficients at the 1 percent level.
   d. Calculate the multiple-correlation coefficient r and test its significance. Use $\alpha = 1$ percent.

Solution

   a. The computation is shown in Table 19.5. Equation (19.9) becomes (*a* being used instead of *b*):

$$52357.08\hat{a}_1 - 1519.01\hat{a}_2 = 169.62$$
$$-1519.01\hat{a}_1 + 136.66\hat{a}_2 = 4.39.$$

TABLE 19.4

Sample number	Thermal conductivity, W·m/m²·°C K	Moisture content, by volume, cm³/m	$e^{0.45\rho}$
1	1.14	96.8	10.80
2	0.97	45.2	14.20
3	1.36	46.8	17.90
4	0.75	70.4	10.80
5	0.68	75.8	8.30
6	1.67	190.3	11.13
7	0.98	157.0	6.48
8	1.14	144.1	6.00
9	0.72	62.9	12.10
10	1.40	255.9	6.87
11	1.85	195.2	11.20
12	1.93	95.2	12.80
13	1.11	150.0	9.65
14	1.66	149.5	12.80

TABLE 19.5

Sample number	$y \equiv K$	$x_1 \equiv M$	$x_2 \equiv e^{0.45\rho}$	$Y = y - \bar{y}$	$X_1 = x_1 - \bar{x}_1$	$X_2 = x_2 - \bar{x}_2$	YX_1	YX_2	X_1^2	X_2^2	X_1X_2	Y^2
1	1.14	96.77	10.80	-0.10	-27.15	0.01	2.72	0.00	737.12	0.00	-0.27	0.01
2	0.97	45.16	14.20	-0.27	-78.76	3.41	21.27	-0.92	6203.14	11.63	-268.57	0.07
3	1.36	46.77	17.90	0.12	-77.15	7.11	-9.26	0.85	5952.12	50.55	-548.54	0.01
4	0.75	70.43	10.80	-0.49	-53.49	0.01	26.21	0.00	2861.18	0.00	-0.53	0.24
5	0.68	75.81	8.3	-0.56	-48.11	-2.49	26.94	1.39	2314.57	6.20	119.79	0.31
6	1.67	190.32	11.13	0.43	66.40	0.34	28.55	0.15	4408.96	0.12	22.58	0.18
7	0.98	156.99	6.48	-0.26	33.07	-4.31	-8.60	1.12	1093.62	18.58	-142.53	0.07
8	1.14	144.09	6.00	-0.10	20.17	-4.79	-2.02	0.48	406.83	22.94	-96.61	0.01
9	0.72	62.90	12.10	-0.52	-61.02	1.31	31.73	-0.68	3723.44	1.72	-79.94	0.27
10	1.40	255.91	6.87	0.16	131.99	-3.92	21.12	-0.63	17421.36	15.37	-517.40	0.03
11	1.85	195.16	11.20	0.61	71.24	0.41	43.46	0.25	5075.14	0.17	29.21	0.37
12	1.93	95.16	12.80	0.69	-28.76	2.01	-19.84	1.39	827.14	4.04	-57.81	0.48
13	1.11	150.00	9.65	-0.13	26.08	-1.14	-3.39	0.15	680.17	1.30	-29.73	0.02
14	1.66	149.46	12.80	0.42	25.54	2.01	10.73	0.84	652.29	4.04	51.34	0.18
$\sum =$	17.36	1734.93	151.03	0	$\simeq 0$	$\simeq 0$	169.62	4.39	52357.08	136.66	-1519.01	2.25

$$\bar{y} = \frac{17.36}{14} = 1.24$$

$$\bar{x}_1 = \frac{1734.93}{14} = 123.92$$

$$\bar{x}_2 = \frac{151.03}{14} = 10.79$$

Solving for $\hat{a}_1$ and $\hat{a}_2$ by elimination, we get $\hat{a}_1 = 0.00616$ and $\hat{a}_2 = 0.101$. Now,

$$\bar{y} = \hat{a}_0 + \hat{a}_1\bar{x}_1 + \hat{a}_2\bar{x}_2$$

or $\qquad\qquad 1.24 = \hat{a}_0 + 0.00616 \times 123.92 + 0.101 \times 10.79.$

Hence $\hat{a}_0 = -0.608$. Therefore, we can write

$$y = -0.608 + 0.00616x_1 + 0.101x_2$$

or $\qquad\qquad K = -0.608 + 0.00616M + 0.101e^{0.45\rho}.$

b. The null hypothesis is $H_0: a_0 = a_1 = a_2 = 0$ versus the alternative hypothesis H_a: at least one of the values a is nonzero.
Compute

$$\sum c^2 = \hat{a}_1 \sum YX_1 + \hat{a}_2 \sum YX_2$$
$$= 0.00616 \times 169.62 + 0.101 \times 4.39$$
$$= 1.48.$$

From Eq. (19.19),

$$s_y^2 = \frac{2.25 - 1.48}{14 - 3} = 0.069.$$

Hence, $\qquad\qquad s_y = 0.26 \text{ W·m/m}^2 \cdot {}^{\circ}\text{C}.$

From Eq. (19.24),

$$F = \frac{\sum c^2/k}{s_y^2} = \frac{1.48/2}{0.069} = 10.7.$$

For $v_1 = 2$, $v_2 = n - 3 = 14 - 3 = 11$, Table A.14 gives $F = 7.20$ at the 1 percent level of significance. Since the calculated $F = 10.7$ is greater than 7.20, we reject the hypothesis that the regression is not significant. The thermal conductivity depends, therefore, on moisture content and dry density.

c. For a_1, the null hypothesis is $H_o: a_1 = 0$ versus $H_a: a_1 \neq 0$. Likewise, for a_2, the null hypothesis is $H_a: a_2 = 0$ versus $H_a: a_2 \neq 0$. Now,

$$\sum X_1^2 \sum X_2^2 - (\sum X_1 X_2)^2 = 52,357.08 \times 136.66 - (-1519.01)^2$$
$$= 4,847,727.2.$$

Using Eq. (19.15), we obtain

$$e_{11} = \frac{136.66}{4,847,727.2} = 0.0000282$$

$$e_{22} = \frac{52,357.08}{4,847,727.2} = 0.0108.$$

Then, from Eq. (19.26),

$$s_{\hat{a}_1} = 0.26 \times \sqrt{0.0000282} = 0.0014$$

$$s_{\hat{a}_2} = 0.26 \times \sqrt{0.0108} = 0.027.$$

From Eq. (19.28), for $\hat{a}_1$,

$$t_{\hat{a}_1} = \frac{|\hat{a}_1|}{s_{\hat{a}_1}} = \frac{0.00616}{0.0014} = 4.40.$$

From Table A.7, for $v = n - (k+1) = 14 - (2+1) = 11$, $t = 3.106$ at the 1 percent level of significance and 4.437 at the 0.1 percent level. Since $t_{\hat{a}_1} > 3.106$, the coefficient $\hat{a}_1$ is significant at the 1 percent level and, indeed, at nearly the 0.1 percent level. Also, for $\hat{a}_2$,

$$t_{\hat{a}_2} = \frac{|\hat{a}_2|}{s_{\hat{a}_2}} = \frac{0.101}{0.027} = 3.67.$$

Again $\hat{a}_2$ is significant at the 1 percent level since $t_{\hat{a}_2} > 3.106$.

    d. Here, the null hypothesis is $H_0 : \rho(=r) = 0$ versus $H_a : \rho \neq 0$. From Eq. (19.20), the square of the multiple correlation coefficient is

$$r^2 = \frac{\sum(\bar{y} - \hat{y})^2}{\sum(y - \bar{y})^2} = \frac{\sum c^2}{\sum Y^2} = \frac{1.48}{2.25}$$

Hence, $\qquad\qquad\qquad\qquad\qquad r = 0.812.$

From Table A.18, with $k+1 = 3$ variables and $v = n - (k+1) = 14 - (2+1) = 11$, we find $r = 0.753$ at the 1 percent level of significance. Since the calculated value is greater than the tabulated one, we conclude that the regression of y on the x variables accounts for a significant amount of variation in y.

    19-2. It is desired to examine the influence on the impact strength of mortar of the following factors: place of manufacture (factory or construction site), length of curing, and age. A sample of 25 specimens was selected at random. The test results, in coded form, are presented in Table 19.6.

    a. Fit an equation of the form

$$\hat{y} = \hat{b}_0 + \hat{b}_1 x_1 + \hat{b}_2 x_2 + \hat{b}_3 x_3.$$

    b. Calculate r^2.

    c. Use the F test to check the statistical significance of the above equation at the $\alpha = 5$ percent level.

    d. Use the t test to check the significance of the partial regression coefficients, b_1, b_2, and b_3 at the 5 percent level.

    Solution. Table 19.7 shows a typical computer output generated by applying a regression-analysis program to the data in Table 19.6. The numerical output from the computer has been rounded off.

    a. The estimated relation can be formulated from the computer results given in Table 19.7 as follows:

$$\hat{y} = 1.414 - 1.174x_1 - 0.151x_2 + 0.040x_3.$$

    b. The coefficient of determination, r^2, is calculated as

$$r^2 = \frac{\text{sum of squares of deviations due to regression, SSR}}{\text{total sum of squares of deviations, SST}}$$

or $\qquad\qquad\qquad\qquad r^2 = \frac{19.98}{31.87} = 0.627,$

as shown by the result for R square in Table 19.7.

TABLE 19.6

Source number	Impact strength, y	Factory or site produced, x_1^a	Length of curing, x_2	Age, x_3
1	0.7	0	15	65
2	0.9	1	10	69
3	1.6	1	12	81
4	2.8	0	16	71
5	3.0	0	6	73
6	3.2	0	6	78
7	3.4	1	6	78
8	3.7	0	12	72
9	0.5	1	16	66
10	0.8	1	9	68
11	1.6	1	12	83
12	2.5	1	8	69
13	3.0	0	9	80
14	3.2	0	10	76
15	3.3	0	4	79
16	3.6	0	12	65
17	3.7	0	6	80
18	0.5	1	14	73
19	0.8	0	16	65
20	1.1	1	12	82
21	2.0	0	10	72
22	2.8	0	12	71
23	3.0	0	6	75
24	3.3	1	6	79
25	3.5	0	9	76

^{a} x_1 is a dummy variable with $x_1 = 1$ if factory produced, and $x_1 = 0$ if not.

TABLE 19.7

Multiple R	0.792
R square	0.627
Standard error of estimate	0.753

	Analysis of variance			
Source	DF (v)	Sum of squares	Mean square	F ratio
Regression (assumed model)	3	19.98 (= SSR)	6.66	11.76
Error (residual)	21	11.89 (= SSE)	0.57	
Total	24	31.87 (= SST)		

Parameter	Estimate	Standard error, s_b	t statistic for H_0:parameter $= 0$
Intercept	1.414	—	—
Factory produced	−1.174	0.314	3.73
Length of curing	−0.151	0.050	3.01
Age	0.040	0.032	1.24

c. In order to test the null hypothesis $H_0: b_1 = b_2 = b_3 = 0$ [or $E(y) = \mu = b_0$] against the alternative hypothesis H_a: at least one of the parameters b_1, b_2, and b_3 is nonzero, we use Eq. (19.23):

$$F_{calc} = \frac{r^2/k}{(1 - r^2)/[n - (k + 1)]} = \frac{(0.627)/3}{(1 - 0.627)/21}$$

$$= 11.76$$

as shown by the computer output in Table 19.7. From Table A.14, for $v_1 = 3$, $v_2 = 21$, and $\alpha = 0.05$,

$$F_{tab} = F_{crit} = 3.07.$$

Since $F_{calc} > F_{tab}$, we reject the null hypothesis and assume that at least one independent variable contributes information for the prediction of y.

d. In order to test the significance of b_1, b_2, and b_3, at $\alpha = 0.05$, we find the tabulated value of t_{crit} in Table A.7 for $v = n - (k + 1) = 21$:

$$t_{crit} = t_{v=21, \alpha=0.05} = 2.080.$$

The computer results are

$$t_{\hat{b}_1} = 3.73, \qquad t_{\hat{b}_2} = 3.01, \qquad \text{and } t_{\hat{b}_3} = 1.24.$$

Thus, testing the null hypothesis $H_0: b_1 = 0$ versus the alternative hypothesis $H_a: b_1 \neq 0$, we have $t_{\hat{b}_1} (= 3.73) > 2.080$; hence the null hypothesis is rejected. Similarly, it is seen that $\hat{b}_2$ is significant, while the null hypothesis for $\hat{b}_3$ cannot be rejected. Thus, we can say that we have sufficient evidence at the 5 percent level of significance that the place of manufacture (factory or construction site) and the length of curing influence the impact strength of mortar but age is not a factor.

PROBLEMS

19-1. It is believed that the extent of a certain reaction (y) depends on the temperature of the ingredient $A(x_1)$, temperature of ingredient $B(x_2)$, and rate of flow (x_3), the relation being of the form $y = a + b_1 x_1 + b_2 x_2 + b_3 x_3$. The test results are as shown in Table 19.8.

TABLE 19.8

x_1	x_2	x_3	y
11	58	11	126
32	21	13	92
15	22	28	107
26	55	27	120
9	41	21	103
31	18	20	84
12	56	20	113
29	40	27	110
13	57	30	104
10	21	12	83
33	40	19	85
31	58	29	104

  a. Determine the constants of the hyperplane in four-dimensional space.
  b. Use the F test to check the significance of this form of regression equation. Use $\alpha = 5$ percent.
  c. Use the t test to check the significance of the partial regression coefficients $\hat{b}_1$, $\hat{b}_2$, and b_3 at the 5 percent level.
  d. Compute the multiple correlation coefficient r and test its significance. Use $\alpha = 5$ percent.
  e. Find the linear correlation coefficients for y and x_1, x_2, and x_3, respectively.

  19-2. Grains used to propel rockets are made by extrusion through a die under pressure. The grain diameter y is dependent not only on the die shape, but also on the powder temperature x_1, the die temperature x_2, and the rate of extrusion x_3. Previous experiments have indicated that there is a relation of the form

$$y = a + b_1 x_1 + b_2 x_2 + b_3 x_3.$$

  An experiment was conducted on a particular type of grain with the coded results shown in Table 19.9.
  a. Find the partial regression coefficients $\hat{a}$, $\hat{b}_1$, $\hat{b}_2$, and $\hat{b}_3$.
  b. Compute the residual variance of the grain diameter y.
  c. Check on the significance of the regression as a whole by means of an F test. Use $\alpha = 5$ percent.
  d. Use the t test to check the significance of the partial regression coefficients $\hat{b}_1$, $\hat{b}_2$, and $\hat{b}_3$ at the 1 percent level of significance.
  e. Calculate the multiple correlation coefficient r and test its significance. Use $\alpha = 5$ percent.

  19-3. A government decides to sell lake lots to potential cottage owners. An engineering inspector develops a model to estimate an equitable selling price for each lot. The model is based on data, recorded from a survey of 20 cottage owners at a neighboring lake, with particulars on: sale price (in $5000 units) ($y$); area of lot ($x_1$); elevation of lot ($x_2$); slope of lot ($x_3$). The inspector fitted a regression-analysis computer program to the gathered data, with the results shown in Table 19.10.

TABLE 19.9

x_1, °C	x_2, °C	x_3, cm/min	y
21	41	12	81
35	29	15	92
31	30	24	105
20	35	21	101
25	31	19	97
37	47	13	93
30	45	16	85
34	31	25	87
29	34	22	102
22	37	9	94
27	28	8	86
33	39	14	84
30	33	17	109
28	38	23	110
23	36	18	103

TABLE 19.10

Multiple R	0.885			
R square	0.784			
Standard error of estimate	0.608			

Analysis of variance				
Source	DF (v)	Sum of squares	Mean square	F ratio
Regression	3	21.41	7.14	19.34
Error (residual)	16	5.90	0.37	
Total	19	27.31		

Parameter	Estimate	Standard error, s_b	t statistic for H_0:parameter $= 0$
Intercept	−2.491	—	—
Area	0.099	0.058	1.71
Elevation	0.029	0.006	4.84
Slope	0.086	0.031	2.77

a. Write the prediction equation for the linear model relating selling price (y) to area, elevation, and slope of a cottage lot.

b. Test the significance of r, at $\alpha = 0.05$.

c. Test, at $\alpha = 0.05$, the hypothesis that none of the independent variables is a useful predictor of y.

d. Indicate the predictor variable which shows the strongest prediction relation to y in the presence of the other variables.

19-4. It is required to investigate the influence of temperature and pressure on the tensile strength of a certain plastic fiber. An experiment was carried out with two temperature levels and two pressure levels. The following relation for the tensile strength is assumed:

$$\hat{y} = \hat{b}_0 + \hat{b}_1 x_1 + \hat{b}_2 x_2 + \hat{b}_3 x_1 x_2$$

in which y = tensile strength in kPa; x_1 = temperature in °C; and x_2 = pressure in kPa.

Results from a sample of $n = 24$ measurements yielded the following estimated regression relation:

$$\hat{y} = 0.920 + 0.015x_1 + 0.005x_2 - 0.002x_1 x_2$$

with
$$s_{\hat{b}_1} = 0.003, \qquad s_{\hat{b}_2} = 0.001, \qquad s_{\hat{b}_3} = 0.001.$$

Test the significance of the partial regression coefficients at $\alpha = 0.05$. Hence, indicate whether there is an interaction between temperature and pressure in their influence on the tensile strength of the plastic fiber.

Chapter 20

Analysis of Variance (ANOVA)

In Chapter 15, we were concerned with comparing the means, μ_1 and μ_2, of two populations by testing, say, the null hypothesis $H_0 : \mu_1 = \mu_2$ versus the alternative hypothesis $H_a : \mu_1 \neq \mu_2$. Examples of such comparisons are: compressive strength of two cements, shear strength of two adhesives, or gasoline mileage (mpg) of two cars. If the samples drawn from the populations being compared are small, or if the variances of the two populations are not known, then the proper test for accepting or rejecting H_0 is based on the t distribution.

In many situations, however, we may be interested in comparing more than two populations; for example, the compressive strength of four cements, shear strength of five adhesives, and mpg of six cars. In such cases, it would be laborious to run t tests on all possible pairs of populations. For example, if we had to compare the mpg of six cars, this would entail t tests on all the possible pairs from a total of six, that is, $_6C_2 = 15$. Furthermore, this procedure could result in one or more false significant differences with a probability much higher than the level of significance α. Let us demonstrate this by considering further the preceding example. Here, all the 15 individual null hypotheses must be accepted if we are to accept the null hypothesis $H_0 : \mu_1 = \mu_2 = \cdots = \mu_6$. Now, if the probability of correctly accepting the null hypothesis for each t test is 0.95, then the probability of correctly accepting the null hypothesis for all 15 tests is $(0.95)^{15} \approx 0.46$. From this we see that we now have a large probability α ($= 1 - 0.46 = 0.54$) of rejecting a true null hypothesis, that is, in effect, we have increased substantially the level of significance α. This can be explained intuitively because the larger the number of pairs the larger the average difference between the smallest and highest observed sample means so that there is a distortion in the level of significance.

In order to avoid these problems we test *simultaneously* the significance of the difference between k $(k > 2)$ population means by using the analysis of variance, known by the acronym ANOVA. This is a general method in which the total variation in a set of data can be partitioned into: variations attributed to certain assignable (controlled) causes called *treatments*[1] and variations attributed to *chance*, encompassing the effect of *all* the uncontrollable factors. This concept was referred to in Chapter 16 where we showed that if a process of manufacture or a system of testing involves a number of independent factors each of which contributes to the scatter of results, and therefore to variance, then the variance for the whole system is equal to the sum of the component variances of the individual factors.

RATIONALE OF USING ANOVA FOR TESTING THE SIGNIFICANCE OF SEVERAL MEANS

First, let us consider a graphic and intuitive explanation of the method of analysis of variance (ANOVA). Figure 20.1 shows the results of six toughness measurements made on each of three different steels, that is, three populations: 1, 2, and 3. In Fig. 20.1(a) we observe that the scatter of the measurements about their mean values ($\bar{y}_1$, $\bar{y}_2$, and $\bar{y}_3$) is about the same. We note also that the means of the three samples appear to have some scatter between them; this scatter is, however, small and is of the same order of magnitude as the scatter in each sample. There is, therefore, no clear evidence, in this case, that the three samples are from different populations. By contrast, Fig. 20.1(b) presents the toughness measurements with the means of the three samples showing a much larger spread between them, compared with the scatter in any one sample. It is clear, in this case, that the samples whose typical values are their means ($\bar{y}_1$, $\bar{y}_2$, and $\bar{y}_3$) are not from the same population. It can be said, therefore, that the greater the variations *between* sample means in comparison with the variations *within* samples the greater the weight of evidence to indicate a difference between the population means μ_1, μ_2, and μ_3. But how much greater? We shall answer this question later on when we discuss the use of the F test in the analysis of variance.

We recall that in Chapter 19 we partitioned the total sum of squares of deviations, SST $[= \sum(y_i - \bar{y})^2]$, into two components: sum of squares of deviations due to regression, SSR, and sum of squares of deviations due to random chance error, SSE. Similarly, the analysis of variance attempts to analyze the variation in a response y so as to apportion this variation to each of an assumed set of independent variables or treatments, SSTr, as shown in Fig. 20.2. Since we rarely can include *all* the independent variables affecting the response y, random variations in the response are inevitable, whence the presence of SSE.

---

[1] This refers to the population we wish to study. For example, in the problem of the four cements mentioned earlier, we can classify each type of cement as a treatment so that we have four treatments.

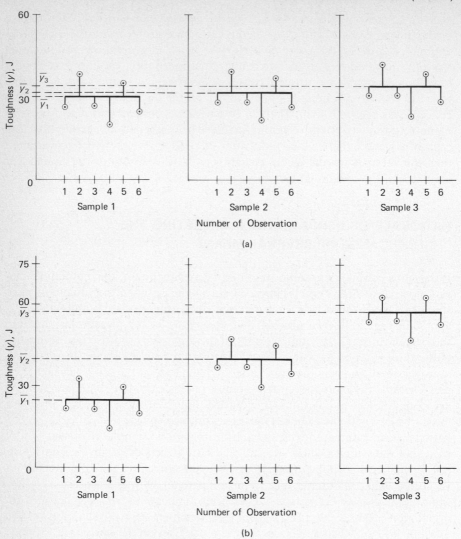

Figure 20.1 Graphical representation of the scatter of the y values (toughness) about their means (the relative scatter within each sample is held constant): (a) no difference between sample means; (b) difference between sample means.

Now, if we divide SSTr by its appropriate number of degrees of freedom, we obtain the between-treatment mean square, MSTr. Similarly, dividing SSE by its number of degrees of freedom gives the within-treatment mean square, MSE.

Using the null hypothesis $H_0: \mu_1 = \mu_2 = \mu_3$ versus an alternative hypothesis H_a: one or more pairs of population means differ, we shall show later that MSE estimates the inherent (unexplained) variability, σ^2, in the data *regardless of whether or not* the treatment means, μ_i, are equal, that is, whether or not the null hypothesis H_0 holds. On the other hand, MSTr estimates σ^2 *only if* H_0

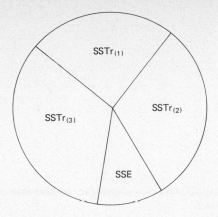

$$\text{SST} = \text{SSTr}_{(1)} + \text{SSTr}_{(2)} + \text{SSTr}_{(3)} + \text{SSE}$$

Figure 20.2 Partitioning of the total sum of squares of deviations (SST).

holds; if H_0 does not hold (i.e., the means are not all equal) then MSTr estimates the sum of two components: (a) σ^2, and (b) an additional component of (explained) variation in the data due to the differences between the treatment means, μ_i [see Eqs. (20.7) and (20.9)]. It follows that if H_a holds, MSTr > MSE since MSTr reflects the variability between the treatment means *as well as* the inherent sampling variability, σ^2. This then is the rationale by which a test of variances is equivalent to a test of the means. Thus, the analysis of variance or ANOVA is a procedure for the *simultaneous* comparison of a number of means. The following example illustrates how we estimate the population variance σ^2 from the deviations within samples as well as from the deviations between samples.

EXAMPLE

Four different air injection systems ($k = 4$) are used, and we want to test whether there is a significant difference between them. We choose $n = 5$ items of each system and measure the efficiency of the injection in each item. The results can be tabulated as shown in Table 20.1. The table gives three estimates of variance. The first is the overall variance, which is based on the total sum of squares of deviations for all $kn = 4 \times 5$ observations and thus represents the variance of all individuals considered as forming a single sample.

The right-hand column of the table gives this sum of squares as 1273 and the number of degrees of freedom is $(4 \times 5) - 1 = 19$. Hence the mean square is $1273/19 = 67.0$.

The second estimate of population variance is obtained from the sum of squares of deviations within the samples and is the sum of values that are obtained in calculating the variance for each group separately, namely,

$$292 + 256 + 216 + 64 = 828.$$

TABLE 20.1

Sample (system)	A	B	C	D	All systems
Efficiency $\bar{y}$	35	21	35	21	112
	24	31	27	17	99
	46	17	39	21	123
	30	37	20	23	110
	40	29	29	28	126
$\sum y$	175	135	150	110	570
$\bar{y}$	35	27	30	22	28.5
$\sum y^2$	6,417	3,901	4,716	2,484	17,518
$\dfrac{(\sum y)^2}{n}$	6,125	3,645	4,500	2,420	16,245
Sum of squares of deviations[a] = $\sum y^2 - \dfrac{(\sum y)^2}{n}$	292	256	216	64	1,273

[a] Since $\sum(y - \bar{y})^2 = \sum y^2 - [(\sum y)^2/n]$ (see Chapter 4).

TABLE 20.2 ONE-WAY ANOVA

Source of variance	Sum of squares, SS	Degrees of freedom, v	Mean square, MS = SS/v
Between samples (systems)	445 (SSTr)	3	148.35 (MSTr)
Within samples (systems)	828 (SSE)	16	51.75 (MSE)
Total	1273 (SST)	19	67.0

The number of degrees of freedom is the sum of the numbers for each sample, that is, $4 \times (5 - 1) = 16$. Hence the mean square is $\frac{828}{16} = 51.75$.

The third and last estimate is obtained from the sample mean. Their deviations from the mean of means, $\bar{y} = 28.5$, are $35 - 28.5$, $27 - 28.5$, $30 - 28.5$, and $22 - 28.5$; that is, $6.5, -1.5, 1.5, -6.5$. The sum of squares of deviations is thus $6.5^2 + 1.5^2 + 1.5^2 + 6.5^2 = 89$. The number of degrees of freedom is one less than the number of samples: 3. Thus the mean square is $\frac{89}{3} = 29.67$. This is an estimate of variance of the mean $s_{\bar{y}}^2$ of $n = 5$ items. This variance is related to the sample variance s^2 by the equation

$$s_{\bar{y}} = \frac{s}{\sqrt{n}} \tag{20.1}$$

so that $s^2 = 29.67 \times 5 = 148.35$. The estimate is based on 3 degrees of freedom so that the sum of squares is $148.35 \times 3 = 445.05$. These results are summarized in Table 20.2.

The row of totals shows that both the total sum of squares and the total number of degrees of freedom have been separated into two parts corresponding to the factors in the variation of the data. The last column gives the *mean squares*, which are ratios of the sum of squares (column 2) to the appropriate number of degrees of freedom (column 3). Table 20.2 is classified as a one-way ANOVA table since we are studying the effect of one controllable factor on the response variable.   ■ ■

USUAL METHOD OF COMPUTATION

The method just outlined explains the analysis of variance but is longer than necessary for routine use. A shorter way of computing the mean squares is to omit the calculations for the individual observations so that only the values of $\sum y$ need be found in the table of the preceding example. We proceed as follows:

a. Find the sum of all observations:

$$\sum y = 175 + 135 + 150 + 110 = 570.$$

b. Find the term[2]:

$$C = \frac{(\sum y)^2}{kn} = \frac{570^2}{4 \times 5} = 16,245.$$

c. Find the sum of squares:

$$\sum y^2 = 35^2 + 24^2 + \quad + 21^2 + 31^2 + \cdots + 23^2 + 28^2 - 17,518.$$

d. Hence obtain the total sum of squares of deviations:

$$\sum y^2 - \frac{(\sum y)^2}{kn} = 17,518 - 16,245 = 1273.$$

e. Compute the sum of squares for sample means:

$$\frac{\sum(\sum y)^2}{n} - \frac{(\sum y)^2}{kn} = \frac{175^2 + 135^2 + 150^2 + 110^2}{5} - 16,245 = 445.$$

We can arrange these results as in Table 20.3, the numbers of degrees of freedom being as before. The values for "within samples" are obtained by subtraction, and the mean squares are calculated by dividing the appropriate sum of squares by the number of degrees of freedom.

Such a computation is quicker, but it does not offer a check on the arithmetic.

We may note that it is usual to arrange the table for the analysis of variance in such a way that the "Totals" appear in the bottom line, that is, the subtraction is made "upward."

---

[2] Known as "correction due to the mean."

TABLE 20.3   ONE-WAY ANOVA

Source of variance	Sum of squares, SS	Degrees of freedom, v	Mean square, MS
Between samples	445 (SSTr)	3	148.35 (MSTr)
Within samples	828 (SSE)	16	51.75 (MSE)
Total	1273 (SST)	19	

SUMS OF SQUARES

In order to prove formally that

$$SST = SSTr + SSE \tag{20.2}$$

or

$$\sum_{i=1}^{k} \sum_{j=1}^{n} (y_{ij} - \bar{y})^2 = n \sum_{i=1}^{k} (\bar{y}_i - \bar{y})^2 + \sum_{i=1}^{k} \sum_{j=1}^{n} (y_{ij} - \bar{y}_i)^2 \tag{20.3}$$

we start by writing

$$(y_{ij} - \bar{y}) = (\bar{y}_i - \bar{y}) + (y_{ij} - \bar{y}_i).$$

Squaring both sides and summing over all values of i and j, we obtain

$$\sum_{i=1}^{k} \sum_{j=1}^{n} (y_{ij} - \bar{y})^2 = \sum_{i=1}^{k} \sum_{j=1}^{n} (\bar{y}_i - \bar{y})^2 + \sum_{i=1}^{k} \sum_{j=1}^{n} (y_{ij} - \bar{y}_i)^2$$

$$+ 2 \sum_{i=1}^{k} \sum_{j=1}^{n} (\bar{y}_i - \bar{y})(y_{ij} - \bar{y}_i).$$

Now,

$$\sum_{i=1}^{k} \sum_{j=1}^{n} (\bar{y}_i - \bar{y})(y_{ij} - \bar{y}_i) = \sum_{i=1}^{k} \left\{ (\bar{y}_i - \bar{y}) \sum_{j=1}^{n} (y_{ij} - \bar{y}_i) \right\} = 0$$

since

$$\sum_{j=1}^{n} (y_{ij} - \bar{y}_i) = 0 \text{ for each } i.$$

Furthermore,

$$\sum_{i=1}^{k} \sum_{j=1}^{n} (\bar{y}_i - \bar{y})^2 = n \sum_{i=1}^{k} (\bar{y}_i - \bar{y})^2$$

and hence the result expressed by Eq. (20.3), which is applicable for samples with a constant size n. Thus, the one-way ANOVA Table 20.3 can be presented in symbols as shown in Table 20.4.

As already stated, Table 20.4 is applicable when the sample size n is the same for each treatment. If, however, the sample size n is not the same for each treatment, then the following values are appropriate:

$$SSTr = \sum_{i=1}^{k} n_i (\bar{y}_i - \bar{y})^2$$

$$\text{number of degrees of freedom for SSE} = v = \sum_{i=1}^{k} n_i - k$$

and

$$\text{number of degrees of freedom for SST} = v = \sum_{i=1}^{k} n_i - 1.$$

TABLE 20.4   GENERAL LAYOUT FOR A ONE-WAY ANOVA

Source of variance	Sum of squares, SS	Degrees of freedom, v	Mean square, SS/v
Between samples (treatments)	$\text{SSTr} = n \sum_{i=1}^{k} (\bar{y}_i - \bar{y})^2$	$k - 1$	$\text{MSTr} = \text{SSTr}/(k-1)$
Within samples	$\text{SSE} = \sum_{i=1}^{k} \sum_{j=1}^{n} (y_{ij} - \bar{y}_i)^2$	$kn - k = k(n-1)$	$\text{MSE} = \text{SSE}/k(n-1)$
Total	$\text{SST} = \sum_{i=1}^{k} \sum_{j=1}^{n} (y_{ij} - \bar{y})^2$	$kn - 1$	

TABLE 20.5   DATA FOR ONE-WAY ANOVA

	Observations	Sample mean	Population mean	Population variance estimated from sample
Treatment 1	$y_{11}, y_{12}, \ldots, y_{1n}$	$\bar{y}_1$	μ_1	s_1^2
Treatment 2	$y_{21}, y_{22}, \ldots, y_{2n}$	$\bar{y}_2$	μ_2	s_2^2
$\vdots$	$\vdots$	$\vdots$	$\vdots$	$\vdots$
Treatment k	$y_{k1}, y_{k2}, \ldots, y_{kn}$	$\bar{y}_k$	μ_k	s_k^2

F TEST IN THE ANALYSIS OF VARIANCE

Let us assume that we have k treatments whose effects on the response variable y are being studied, with n observations taken on each of the k treatments. We assume that the mathematical model for the response y is expressed as

$$Y_{ij} = \mu_i + e_{ij} \tag{20.4}$$

$(i = 1, \ldots, k; j = 1, \ldots, n)$

where Y_{ij} = the response random variable,

μ_i = population mean associated with the ith treatment and estimated by the ith sample mean.

$$\bar{y}_i = \frac{\sum_{j=1}^{n} y_{ij}}{n}, \quad \text{and}$$

e_{ij} = random error variable, normally distributed with a zero mean and a common variance σ^2, that is, $E(e_{ij}) = 0$ and $\text{Var}(e_{ij}) = \sigma^2$ for all i and j.

The resulting data can be presented as shown in Table 20.5.

From Chapter 4, we estimate the variance resulting from variations within a sample i as

$$s_i^2 = \frac{1}{n-1} \sum_{j=1}^{n} (y_{ij} - \bar{y}_i)^2 \qquad (i = 1, \ldots, k). \tag{20.5}$$

An estimate of the population variance σ^2 can be obtained from the average of all values of s_i^2, viz.,

$$\text{MSE} = \frac{\displaystyle\sum_{i=1}^{k} s_i^2}{k} = \frac{\displaystyle\sum_{i=1}^{k} \sum_{j=1}^{n} (y_{ij} - \bar{y}_i)^2}{k(n-1)} \tag{20.6}$$

where MSE is the mean square deviation.

It can be shown[3] that $E(\text{MSE}) = \sigma^2$. We can also estimate σ^2 from the variance of the k sample (treatment) means. We have

$$s_{\bar{y}}^2 = \frac{\displaystyle\sum_{i=1}^{k} (\bar{y}_i - \bar{y})^2}{k-1} \tag{20.7}$$

---

[3] $E(\text{MSE}) = E\left[\dfrac{\displaystyle\sum_{n=1}^{k} \sum_{j=1}^{n} (y_{ij} - \bar{y})^2}{kn-1}\right] = \dfrac{1}{kn-1} E\left[\sum\sum(y_{ij}^2 - 2y_{ij}\bar{y} + \bar{y}^2)\right]$

$\qquad\qquad = \dfrac{1}{kn-1}\left[\sum\sum E(y_{ij}^2) - E\{\sum\sum(2y_{ij}\bar{y} - \bar{y}^2)\}\right].$

Using Eq. (5.35),

$E(\text{MSE}) = \dfrac{1}{kn-1}\left\langle \sum\sum\{\text{variance of } y + [E(y)]^2\} - E[2kn\bar{y}^2 - kn\bar{y}^2]\right\rangle$

$\qquad\qquad = \dfrac{1}{kn-1}\left\langle \sum\sum(\sigma^2 + \mu^2) - knE(\bar{y}^2)\right\rangle.$

Since y_{ij} is assumed to be normally distributed with mean μ and variance σ^2, the variable $\bar{y}_i$ is also normally distributed with mean μ_i and variance σ^2/n. Thus, $E(\bar{y}_i) = \mu_i$, $\text{Var}(\bar{y}_i) = \sigma^2/n$, and $\text{Var}(\bar{y}) = \sigma^2/kn$. Using Eq. (5.35), we can deduce

$$E(\bar{y}_i^2) = \text{Var}(\bar{y}_i) + \mu_i^2 = \frac{\sigma^2}{n} + \mu_i^2$$

and

$$E(\bar{y}^2) = \text{Var}(\bar{y}) + \mu^2 = \frac{\sigma^2}{kn} + \mu^2.$$

Therefore,

$E(\text{MSE}) = \dfrac{1}{kn-1}\left\langle kn(\sigma^2 + \mu^2) - kn[\text{variance of } \bar{y} + \{E(\bar{y})\}^2]\right\rangle$

$\qquad\qquad = \dfrac{1}{kn-1}\left\langle kn(\sigma^2 + \mu^2) - kn\left(\dfrac{\sigma^2}{kn} + \mu^2\right)\right\rangle$

$\qquad\qquad = \dfrac{1}{kn-1}(kn-1)\sigma^2 = \sigma^2.$

where the overall sample mean, $\bar{y}$, is defined by

$$\bar{y} = \frac{\sum_{i=1}^{k} \bar{y}_i}{k} = \frac{1}{k} \sum_{i=1}^{k} \frac{\left(\sum_{j=1}^{n} y_{ij} \right)}{n} = \frac{\sum_{i=1}^{k} \sum_{j=1}^{n} y_{ij}}{kn}.$$

Now, it can be shown[4] that

$$E(S_{\bar{y}}^2) = \frac{\sigma^2}{n} + \frac{\sum_{i=1}^{k} \mu_i^2 - k\mu^2}{k - 1} \tag{20.8}$$

where $\mu = E(\bar{y})$.

If the null hypothesis H_0 is true, that is, $\mu_1 = \mu_2 = \ldots = \mu_k = \mu$, then the term $\sum \mu_i^2 - k\mu^2$ in Eq. (20.8) is zero, and therefore,

$$E(s_{\bar{y}}^2) = \frac{\sigma^2}{n}. \tag{20.9}$$

Thus, the variance between treatments, MSTr, can yield another estimate of σ^2 equal to $ns_{\bar{y}}^2$. Therefore, if H_0 is true, we can say that

$$\text{MSTr} = ns_{\bar{y}}^2 = \frac{n}{k - 1} \sum_{i=1}^{k} (\bar{y}_i - \bar{y})^2 \tag{20.10}$$

is another unbiased estimator of σ^2. Therefore, if H_0 is true, both MSE and MSTr estimate σ^2.

Now, from the definition of the χ^2 statistic given in Chapter 14, we recognize that the variable $(k - 1)(\text{MSTr})/\sigma^2$ has a χ^2 distribution with $(k - 1)$ degrees of freedom, and $k(n - 1)(\text{MSE})/\sigma^2$ also has a χ^2 distribution with $k(n - 1)$ degrees of freedom. Furthermore, we observed in Chapter 16 that the

---

[4] $E(s_{\bar{y}}^2) = \dfrac{1}{k - 1} E\left[\sum_{i=1}^{k} (\bar{y}_i - \bar{y})^2 \right] = \dfrac{1}{k - 1} E\left[\sum_{i=1}^{k} \bar{y}_i^2 - 2\bar{y} \sum_{i=1}^{k} \bar{y}_i + k\bar{y}^2 \right]$

$\qquad = \dfrac{1}{k - 1} E\left[\sum_{i=1}^{k} \bar{y}_i^2 - k\bar{y}^2 \right].$

Therefore,

$$E(s_{\bar{y}}^2) = \frac{1}{k - 1} \left[\sum_{i=1}^{k} \left\{ \frac{\sigma^2}{n} + \mu_i^2 \right\} - k \left\{ \frac{\sigma^2}{kn} + \mu^2 \right\} \right]$$

$$= \frac{1}{k - 1} \left[\frac{k\sigma^2}{n} + \sum_{i=1}^{k} \mu_i^2 - \frac{\sigma^2}{n} - k\mu^2 \right]$$

$$= \frac{1}{k - 1} \left[(k - 1)\frac{\sigma^2}{n} + \sum_{i=1}^{k} \mu_i^2 - k\mu^2 \right].$$

Hence,

$$E(s_{\bar{y}}^2) = \frac{\sigma^2}{n} + \frac{\sum_{i=1}^{k} \mu_i^2 - k\mu^2}{k - 1}.$$

ratio of two independent χ^2 variables, each divided by its number of degrees of freedom, has an F distribution. Therefore,

$$F = \frac{\dfrac{(k-1)(\text{MSTr})}{\sigma^2(k-1)}}{\dfrac{k(n-1)(\text{MSE})}{\sigma^2 k(n-1)}} = \frac{\text{MSTr}}{\text{MSE}} \tag{20.11}$$

with $v_1 = k - 1$ and $v_2 = k(n-1)$. Since it is expected that MSTr will be larger than MSE when H_0 is false, we reject H_0 at a level of significance α when

$$F_{\text{calc}} > F_{(v_1, v_2, \alpha)}$$

the calculated values being given in Table A.13.

Experience has shown that a departure from the conditions of normality and equal variance, mentioned earlier, does not seriously affect the results of ANOVA, provided that the distribution of the response variable is not highly skewed and provided that the sample sizes n are equal for each treatment. This would then make the F test fairly robust to apply to a wide variety of problems.

It should be stressed that if the k treatments constitute the total population of treatments in which we are interested, then the conclusion we reach will apply only to the specific treatments studied; thus, we have a *fixed-effect* model. On the other hand, if the k treatments form a random sample from some larger population of treatments, then we are dealing with a *random-effect* model. As we shall see in a subsequent section (page 452), $E(\text{MSTr})$ for *both* models is equal to the variance σ^2 under the null hypothesis H_0.

It is interesting to show that the F test can be related to the t test when we are comparing two population means, μ_1 and μ_2. For example, if we have two samples of size n_1 and n_2, respectively, taken from the two populations, and s^2 is the pooled estimate of the population variances σ_1^2 and σ_2^2, we test the null hypothesis $H_0 : \mu_1 = \mu_2$ versus $H_a : \mu_1 \neq \mu_2$ by applying Eq. (15.13). Thus, the test statistic is

$$t = \frac{\bar{y}_1 - \bar{y}_2}{\sqrt{s^2 \left(\dfrac{1}{n_1} + \dfrac{1}{n_2} \right)}} \tag{20.12}$$

since $\bar{y}_1$ and $\bar{y}_2$ are point estimators of μ_1 and μ_2, respectively. The t statistic has $[(n_1 - 1) + (n_2 - 1)]$ degrees of freedom. Squaring both sides of Eq. (20.12),

$$t^2 = \frac{(\bar{y}_1 - \bar{y}_2)^2}{s^2 \left(\dfrac{1}{n_1} + \dfrac{1}{n_2} \right)} = \frac{n_1 n_2}{n_1 + n_2} \frac{(\bar{y}_1 - \bar{y}_2)^2}{s^2} = \frac{\text{MSTr}}{\text{MSE}} = F.$$

It follows that we can test H_0 versus H_a by using either the t statistic or the F statistic. Of course, in general, the ANOVA procedure using the F statistic will enable us to compare simultaneously more than two population means.

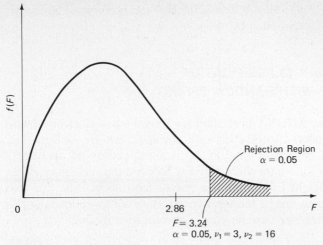

Figure 20.3   The F distribution for the injection systems indicating the critical F value and the rejection region for $\alpha = 0.05$.

TEST ON HOMOGENEITY OF VARIANCES

We return now to the example on the four air injection systems (page 443). Having obtained the two values of mean squares, we test their homogeneity by means of the F test. We state the null hypothesis $H_0 : \mu_A = \mu_B = \mu_C = \mu_D = \mu$ versus the alternative hypothesis H_a: one or more pairs of the population means differ. Thus,

$$F = \frac{\text{MSTr}}{\text{MSE}} = \frac{148.35}{51.75} = 2.86.$$

With 3 degrees of freedom for the numerator and 16 degrees of freedom for the denominator, Table A.14 gives $F = 3.24$ at the 5 percent level of significance. From Fig. 20.3, since $F_{\text{calc}} < F_{\text{tab}}$, we cannot reject the null hypothesis H_0 at $\alpha = 0.05$ level of significance, and conclude, therefore, that the different injection systems do not differ in their efficiency.

We should note that the test which we apply is one sided,[5] as we want to answer the question: is the variance between samples significantly greater than the variance within samples? It cannot be the other way round, as the scatter in any arrangement cannot be less than the random variation between individuals. It is, of course, possible in a particular case for the variance within samples to be greater than the variance between samples, but the difference cannot be significant.

In comparing the means of several populations by ANOVA, we assume that the variances are homogeneous. If it is suspected that the variances might

[5] The F test is a one-sided test.

be significantly different, then Bartlett's test for the homogeneity of variances, considered in Chapter 16, can be applied.

ANOVA FOR ONE-WAY CLASSIFICATION (SINGLE FACTOR) WITH RANDOM EFFECT

We have seen earlier the ANOVA procedure for a one-way classification with a factor that has fixed effects. If the effects are not fixed, but are random (e.g., a sample of operators chosen at random from a population of operators), then the expected mean square for the variations between the various levels (or treatments) will be different from that in a fixed-effect model. The null and alternative hypotheses will not be the same either. In order to understand this difference, let us represent our random-effect problem by a model

$$Y_{ij} = \mu + T_j + e_{ij} \tag{20.13}$$

with $i = 1, 2, \ldots, n_j$ and $j = 1, 2, \ldots, k$.

Here, μ = overall mean, the values of $T_j (= \mu_j - \mu)$ are normally distributed with a mean equal to zero and variance of σ_T^2, and e_{ij} are independent chance errors with identical normal distributions with a mean equal to zero and variance equal to σ^2; both e_{ij} and T_j are independent. For such a model, it can be shown that

$$E(\text{MSTr}) = \sigma^2 + n_0 \sigma_T^2 \tag{20.14}$$

and, as before,

$$E(\text{MSE}) = \sigma^2 \tag{20.15}$$

where

$$n_0 = \frac{N^2 - \sum_j n_j^2}{N(k - 1)}. \tag{20.16}$$

[When the values of n_j are all equal to n, then $n_0 = n$.]

A comparison of the expected mean squares for both fixed- and random-effect models is shown in Table 20.6. Now, if all the k treatments are equal, then $\sigma_T^2 > 0$, and we say that variation exists between the treatments. Thus, for a random-effect model, the null hypothesis of equal treatment means can be expressed as $H_0: \sigma_T^2 = 0$ versus an alternative hypothesis $H_a: \sigma_T^2 > 0$. Hence, if

TABLE 20.6 MEAN SQUARES FOR FIXED- AND RANDOM-EFFECTS MODELS

	Expected mean square, $E(\text{MS})$	
	Fixed model	Random model
Between treatments	$E(\text{MSTr}) = \sigma^2 + \sum_{j=1}^{k} \dfrac{n_j(\mu_j - \mu)^2}{k - 1}$	$E(\text{MSTr}) = \sigma^2 + n_0 \sigma_T^2$
Within treatments	$E(\text{MSE}) = \sigma^2$	$E(\text{MSE}) = \sigma^2$

H_0 is true, then $E(\text{MSTr})$ of both fixed- and random-effect models will be equal to the variance σ^2. The computational procedure for ANOVA is exactly the same for both models for a one-way classification.

As an illustration, let us assume that the injection systems, A, B, C, and D, in the last example, have been selected at random from a large number of such systems. ANOVA will be the same as in the previous case, except that the null hypothesis will be different, that is, $H_0 : \sigma_T^2 = 0$ versus $H_a : \sigma_T^2 > 0$. Then, as before,

$$F = \frac{\text{MSTr}}{\text{MSE}} = \frac{148.35}{51.75} = 2.86$$

which is less than $F_{3,16,0.05} = 3.24$ from Table A.14. We conclude, therefore, that the four injection systems are not statistically different. It should be noted that in a random-effect model we cannot estimate treatment means because the injection systems were selected at random; we can, however, estimate σ_T^2 from

$$\sigma_T^2 = \frac{E(\text{MSTr}) \quad \sigma^2}{n_0} = \frac{148.35 - 51.75}{5} = 19.32$$

where $n_0 = n = 5$. The above calculation for F will be different when dealing with ANOVA for a two-way (or higher) classification. This will be discussed in Chapter 23.

MULTIPLE COMPARISON TEST

When a null hypothesis H_0 has been rejected by applying the method of the analysis of variance, we may quite often want to carry out a follow-up study in order to determine: (i) whether any one treatment mean is much better or much worse than all the other treatment means; and (ii) which treatment means can be grouped as similar, that is, are not significantly different from each other. To answer these questions we perform a comparison test of the treatment means. There are several such tests, for example, Tukey's and Bonferroni's procedures. Here, however, we shall use a method that defines the "least significant difference."

In Chapter 15, we showed that an estimate of the variance of the difference between two treatment means, $\bar{x}_i$ and $\bar{x}_j$, each of sample size n, is

$$s_d^2 = \frac{s_c^2}{n} + \frac{s_c^2}{n} = s_c^2 \left(\frac{2}{n} \right)$$

where s_c^2 is defined as the estimate of the combined (population) variance. In terms of the notation used in ANOVA, this is, in fact, the residual mean square, MSE. Therefore,

$$s_d = \sqrt{(\text{MSE})\left(\frac{2}{n}\right)}.$$

Since the sample size n is relatively small, the least significant difference (LSD) between $\bar{x}_i$ and $\bar{x}_j$ can be determined from the t distribution at the level of significance equal to α as

$$\text{LSD} = t_{\alpha,k(n-1)}s_d$$

or
$$\text{LSD} = t_{\alpha,k(n-1)}\sqrt{(\text{MSE})\left(\frac{2}{n}\right)} \tag{20.17}$$

where the value of $t_{\alpha,k(n-1)}$ is obtained from Table A.7. The procedure is: first, arrange the sample (treatment) means in order of magnitude; next, calculate LSD from Eq. (20.17); then, underline those pairs of means which differ by less than LSD. A pair of sample means not underlined by the same line denotes a pair of population means which are significantly different at the level of significance α. The method is illustrated in Solved Problem 20-3.

SIMPLIFYING THE COMPUTATIONS

In the analysis of variance we are primarily concerned with comparing variances so that reducing the data in a constant proportion does not affect our conclusions. We can, therefore, simplify the data and achieve a considerable saving in computation by the subtraction of a constant number or a division by a constant number, or both. If the actual values of variance are required, the division has to be taken into account. The use of this simplification, known as coding, is illustrated in one of the examples in Chapter 3.

MULTIFACTOR ANALYSIS

The analysis of variance can be extended to cases in which a number of factors affect the observations. As a simple case of three components, we have, say, k different cements, each of which is tested once by n operators. We want to analyze the variance into the components: "between operators," "between cements," and "residual." The variance between operators is that which would be obtained if there were no variation between the individual cements and no inherent variation in the method of test. Similarly, the variance between cements is that which would be obtained if there were no variation between the operators and no inherent variation in the method of test. The residual includes the error variance (which is similar to the variance within samples in the preceding example) and also the effect of interaction between the variables. The latter is the influence of the variation in one variable on another, for example, if the effect of different operators varies with the type of cement. (We can imagine that operator A tends to read "high" when values are high but reads "low" when values are low.) If we want to estimate the error variance free from interactions, it would be necessary to repeat the tests—an operation known as *replication*. This is considered in Chapter 23.

It should be realized that the present chapter is no more than an introduction to the analysis of variance, one of the most powerful methods of statistical analysis.

TABLE 20.7

Low dip	Medium–low dip	Medium dip	Steep dip
$\bar{y}_1 = 0.261$	$\bar{y}_2 = 0.296$	$\bar{y}_3 = 0.312$	$\bar{y}_4 = 0.135$
$s_1 = 0.21$	$s_2 = 0.17$	$s_3 = 0.19$	$s_4 = 0.08$
$n = 44$	$n = 44$	$n = 44$	$n = 44$

SOLVED PROBLEMS

20-1. The influence of angle of dip of strata in a certain area on the form of the drainage basins was investigated. A ridge was divided into segments named "low dip," "medium-low dip," etc. In each segment, the length of stream channels on the ridge flanks was taken from the dip slope. The data on the lengths of streams in kilometers are summarized in Table 20.7. Does the steepness of the dip influence the length of the stream, that is, do the means of all samples belong to the same population? Use $\alpha = 1$ percent.

Solution. We set up a null hypothesis of no significant difference between the means of the four populations, viz., $H_0: \mu_1 = \mu_2 = \mu_3 = \mu_4 = \mu$ versus H_a: one or more pairs of the population means differ. Without setting out an ANOVA table, we calculate

$$F = \frac{\text{variance from sample means}}{\text{average variance within the samples}}.$$

Now,

$$\bar{y} = \frac{0.261 + 0.296 + 0.312 + 0.135}{4} = 0.251.$$

Therefore,

$$s_{\bar{y}}^2 = \frac{(0.261 - 0.251)^2 + (0.296 - 0.251)^2 + (0.312 - 0.251)^2 + (0.135 - 0.251)^2}{4 - 1}$$

$$= 0.00643.$$

But

$$s^2 = n s_{\bar{y}}^2 = 44 \times 0.00643$$

$$= 0.2831.$$

The estimate of variance from the individual measurements within the samples is

$$\frac{\sum (n_i - 1)s_i^2}{\sum n_i - 4} = \frac{43[(0.21)^2 + (0.17)^2 + (0.19)^2 + (0.08)^2]}{4 \times 44 - 4}$$

$$= 0.0289.$$

Therefore,

$$F = \frac{0.2831}{0.0289} = 9.796.$$

For $v_1 = 3$ and $v_2 = 4 \times 44 - 4 = 172$, Table A.14 indicates that the probability for such a value of F occurring by chance is less than 1 percent, that is, the null hypothesis is rejected at $\alpha = 0.01$. Therefore, the difference in means is very significant, and it is concluded that the steepness of the dip influences the length of the stream.

20-2. An experiment was carried out to measure the strain sensitivity of Stresscoat for different curing temperatures, which were applied with no sensible error. We wish to determine at the 1 percent level of significance whether the observed differences in

TABLE 20.8

	80 A	92 B	105 C	118 D	132 E
	Curing temperature, °C				
Strain sensitivity ($\times 10^{-5}$)	83	75	56	50	49
	70	62	59	52	35
	78	70	48	38	48
	71	81	54	42	47
	73	71	61	53	41
	81	79	58	41	38

Note: Number of columns, $k = 5$; sample size in each column $n = 6$; and total number of observations $kn = 30$.

TABLE 20.9

	80 A	92 B	105 C	118 D	132 E	Totals for all temperatures
	Curing temperature, °C					
$\sum y$	456	438	336	276	258	1,764
$\bar{y}$	76	73	56	46	43	$\bar{\bar{y}} = 58.8$
$\sum y^2$	34,804	32,212	18,922	12,902	11,264	110,104
$\dfrac{(\sum y)^2}{n}$	34,656	31,974	18,816	12,696	11,094	103,723.2
$\sum y^2 - \dfrac{(\sum y)^2}{n}$	148	238	106	206	170	6,380.8

the mean values of the strain sensitivity for the different temperatures have been influenced by random sampling errors. The results shown in Tables 20.8 and 20.9 were obtained.

Solution. Denoting the five different curing temperatures (treatments) as A, B, C, D, and E, the null hypothesis can be stated as $H_0: \mu_A = \mu_B = \mu_C = \mu_D = \mu_E = \mu$ versus H_a: at least two treatment means differ.

The total sum of squares of deviations within the samples is

$$148 + 238 + 106 + 206 + 170 = 868$$

with the number of degrees of freedom $v = k(n - 1) = 5(6 - 1) = 25$. Therefore,

$$\text{mean square} = \frac{868}{25} = 34.72.$$

The mean square deviation of sample means from the mean of means is

$$s_{\bar{y}}^2 = \frac{(76 - 58.8)^2 + (73 - 58.8)^2 + (56 - 58.8)^2 + (46 - 58.8)^2 + (43 - 58.8)^2}{5 - 1}$$

$$= \frac{918.80}{4} = 229.7.$$

TABLE 20.10

Source of variance	Sum of squares, SS	Degrees of freedom, v	Mean square, MS
Between samples (treatments)	5512.8 (SSTr)	4	1378.2 (MSTr)
Within samples	868 (SSE)	25	34.72 (MSE)
Total	6380.8 (SST)	29	

Hence,
$$s^2 = s_{\bar{y}}^2 \times n = 229.7 \times 6 = 1378.2.$$

Summarizing, we obtain the results shown in Table 20.10.

The variance ratio is
$$F = \frac{\text{MSTr}}{\text{MSE}} = \frac{1378.2}{34.72} = 39.69.$$

For the degrees of freedom $v_1 = 4$, and $v_2 = 25$, Table A.14 gives, at the 1 percent level of significance, $F = 4.18$. Since the $F_{\text{calc}} \gg 4.18$, we have evidence to reject H_0 and to accept H_a at $\alpha = 0.01$. It can, therefore, be confidently concluded that the curing temperature influences the coating strain sensitivity; that is, the observed difference in the means is not due to random errors.

Using the simplified and more usual method of computation, we obtain the following.

1. The sum of all observations:
$$\sum y = 456 + 438 + 336 + 276 + 258$$
$$= 1764.$$

2. The correction for the mean:
$$C = \frac{(\sum y)^2}{kn} = \frac{(1764)^2}{30} = 103,723.2.$$

3. The total sum of squares:
$$\sum y^2 - \frac{(\sum y)^2}{kn} = 83^2 + 70^2 + \cdots + 38^2 - 103,723.2 = 6380.8.$$

4. The sum of squares for sample means:
$$\frac{\sum(\sum y)^2}{n} - \frac{(\sum y)^2}{kn} = \frac{456^2 + 438^2 + 336^2 + 276^2 + 258^2}{6} - 103,723.2$$
$$= 5512.8.$$

The results are shown in Table 20.11.

Then continue as before. We could have used also Table 20.4 to generate the results.

20-3. The 24-h water absorption (in percent of dry weight) of samples of concrete taken from five different types of precast concrete curbs made with different aggregates is shown in Table 20.12.

TABLE 20.11

Source of variance	Sum of squares, SS	Degrees of freedom, v	Mean square, MS
Between samples	5512.8 (SSTr)	4	1378.2 (MSTr)
Within samples	868.0 (SSE)	25	34.72 (MSE)
Total	6380.8 (SST)	29	

TABLE 20.12

Curb type	A	B	C	D	E	All
	6.7	5.2	4.4	6.7	6.5	
Absorption x,	5.8	4.8	4.9	7.2	5.8	
percent	5.8	5.1	4.6	6.8	4.7	
	5.5	5.3	4.5	6.3	5.9	
$\sum x$	23.8	20.4	18.4	27.0	22.9	112.5

Based on: P. J. F. Wright, "Statistical Methods in Concrete Research," *Magazine of Concrete Research,* vol. 5, no. 15, March 1954.

It is required to determine whether there is a significant difference in the water absorption values of the curbs of different types. Use $\alpha = 1$ percent.

Solution. The null hypothesis is $H_0 : \mu_A = \mu_B = \mu_C = \mu_D = \mu_E = \mu$ versus H_a: at least two treatment means differ.

a. The sum of all observations:

$$\sum y = 112.5.$$

b. Correction due to the mean:

$$C = \frac{(\sum y)^2}{kn} = \frac{(112.5)^2}{20} = 632.81$$

where k is the number of types of curbs and n the sample size.

c. The total sum of squares:

$$\begin{aligned} &= \sum y^2 - C \\ &= 6.7^2 + 5.8^2 + \cdots + 5.9^2 - C \\ &= 646.83 - 632.81 \\ &= 14.02. \end{aligned}$$

d. The sum of squares for sample means:

$$\begin{aligned} &= \frac{\sum (\sum y)^2}{n} - C \\ &= \frac{23.8^2 + 20.4^2 + \cdots + 22.9^2}{4} - C \\ &= 643.64 - 632.81 \\ &= 10.83 \end{aligned}$$

(see Table 20.13).

TABLE 20.13

Source of variance	Sum of squares, SS	Degrees of freedom, v	Mean square, MS
Between samples	10.83 (SSTr)	4	2.71 (MSTr)
Within samples	3.19 (SSE)	15	0.213 (MSE)
Total	14.02 (SST)	19	—

The variance ratio is

$$F = \frac{\text{MSTr}}{\text{MSE}} = \frac{2.79}{0.213} = 12.72.$$

For $v_1 = 4$ and $v_2 = 15$, Table A.14 gives $F = 4.89$ at the 1 percent level of significance. Therefore, the null hypothesis H_0 is rejected and H_a is accepted at $\alpha = 0.01$, and we conclude that the different types of curbs differ significantly in their absorption values.

Now that we have rejected H_0, it is interesting to determine which concrete(s) can be classified as different from the others and which concretes can be grouped as similar. Let us use $\alpha = 0.05$. Since MSE $= 0.213$, then from Eq. (20.17), for $\alpha = 0.05$,

$$\text{LSD} = t_{15,0.05}\sqrt{(0.213)(\tfrac{2}{4})} = 2.131\sqrt{0.106}$$
$$= 0.68.$$

After arranging the five sample means in increasing order, every pair differing by less than 0.68 is underlined as shown below:

$\bar{x}_C$	$\bar{x}_B$	$\bar{x}_E$	$\bar{x}_A$	$\bar{x}_D$
4.60	5.03	5.73	5.95	6.75

It can be observed that concretes type C and B do not differ, neither B and E, nor E and A. While there is evidence that E differs from C, and A differs from both B and C, neither E nor C is shown to be significantly different from B; the same applies to A and B with respect to E. Therefore, concrete types C, B, E, and A can be grouped as similar types with regard to water absorption, and they are different from type D. Thus, it appears that concrete types C, B, E, and A are not dissimilar, while concrete type D has a significantly higher water absorption characteristic than those of the other four concrete types.

20-4. Creep, after a given period of time, was determined on mortar specimens made with 11 cements. It is suggested that creep is a function of the chemical composition of cement in the form

$$y = a_1x_1 + a_2x_2 + a_3x_3 + a_4x_4 + a_5x_5 \tag{20.18}$$

where $y =$ creep, and $x_1, \ldots, x_5$ are the compounds of which the cement consists, expressed as a percentage of weight. Thus the coefficients $a_1, \ldots, a_5$ represent the contribution to creep of 1 percent of the appropriate compound. This type of relationship implies that the same amount of any compound has the same effect, regardless of the total quantity of this or any other compound present. This also means that there is no interaction between the various compounds—an assumption not in disagreement with

TABLE 20.14

Cement number	x_1	x_2	x_3	x_4	x_5	y	$\sum x$
1	42.26	25.31	15.65	6.92	0.75	52	90.89
2	36.63	30.05	15.32	9.10	0.83	50	91.93
3	26.18	28.13	14.97	16.13	0.75	35	86.16
4	37.30	27.29	9.53	10.61	0.65	37	85.68
5	36.62	28.42	14.69	11.14	0.78	49	91.65
6	32.64	28.06	13.88	11.58	0.72	45	86.88
7	34.65	33.28	12.52	5.47	0.56	32	86.48
8	35.11	30.53	10.76	12.10	0.74	47	89.24
9	24.50	36.38	12.14	12.56	0.33	32	85.91
10	41.07	32.04	3.73	13.27	0.54	48	90.65
11	29.09	42.06	5.30	11.30	0.45	42	88.20

our general knowledge of the properties of cement. From physical considerations of the problem, the constant a_0 in the equation relating y to $x_1, x_2, \ldots, x_5$ is zero; that is, the line passes through the origin. If this constraint is not imposed, the sum of squares of residuals is minimized about the mean (see page 422), which from the purely statistical viewpoint is correct, but we must *remember* that the choice of the function should be governed by the physical nature of the problem.

On the basis of the values y and x given in Table 20.14, we want to determine the coefficients in Eq. (20.18) and to establish their significance. Use $\alpha = 1$ percent.

We may remember that in Chapter 19 we tested the significance of the partial regression coefficients of the above equation. The analysis was in a format (e.g., Table 19.3) similar to an ANOVA table. The purpose of solving this problem here is to demonstrate the close relation between ANOVA and regression analysis.

Solution. In the matrix for the least square analysis, the variables are entered in the expected order of importance (x_1, x_5, x_2, x_3, and x_4); this order does not, of course, affect the values of the regression coefficients.

For the sum of squares of residuals to be a minimum, the partial differential coefficients of the sum with respect to the coefficients $a_1, \ldots, a_5$ must all be zero. Hence,

$$\sum yx_1 = a_1 \sum x_1^2 + a_2 \sum x_1x_2 + a_3 \sum x_1x_3 + a_4 \sum x_1x_4 + a_5 \sum x_1x_5$$
$$\vdots$$
$$\sum yx_5 = a_1 \sum x_5x_1 + a_2 \sum x_5x_2 + a_3 \sum x_5x_3 + a_4 \sum x_5x_4 + a_5 \sum x_5^2.$$

This can be written in matrix form as

$$\begin{bmatrix} \sum x_1^2 & \sum x_1x_5 & \sum x_1x_2 & \sum x_1x_3 & \sum x_1x_4 \\ \sum x_5x_1 & \sum x_5^2 & \sum x_5x_2 & \sum x_5x_3 & \sum x_5x_4 \\ \sum x_2x_1 & \sum x_2x_5 & \sum x_2^2 & \sum x_2x_3 & \sum x_2x_4 \\ \sum x_3x_1 & \sum x_3x_5 & \sum x_3x_2 & \sum x_3^2 & \sum x_3x_4 \\ \sum x_4x_1 & \sum x_4x_5 & \sum x_4x_2 & \sum x_4x_3 & \sum x_4^2 \end{bmatrix} \begin{bmatrix} a_1 \\ a_5 \\ a_2 \\ a_3 \\ a_4 \end{bmatrix} = \begin{bmatrix} \sum x_1y \\ \sum x_5y \\ \sum x_2y \\ \sum x_3y \\ \sum x_4y \end{bmatrix}$$

or $AX = Y$, where A is the known matrix on the left, X is the unknown vector, and Y is the known vector on the right. The numerical form of matrix A is shown in Table 20.15.

TABLE 20.15

x_1	x_5	x_2	x_3	x_4	y
13,177.29	246.78	11,537.07	4,377.31	4,025.53	16,324.69
246.78	4.83	214.59	86.71	77.18	309.50
11,537.07	214.59	10,833.43	3,873.86	3,742.25	14,436.63
4,377.31	86.71	3,873.81	1,664.91	1,375.21	5,497.24
4,025.53	77.18	3,742.25	1,375.21	1,399.51	5,096.13

The least squares analysis yields

$$a_1 = 0.6339570$$
$$a_2 = 0.1794424$$
$$a_3 = 0.2073463$$
$$a_4 = -0.2681848$$
$$a_5 = 24.4356348.$$

Thus the expected creep of mortar for the given conditions and range of composition of cements is

$$y = 0.63x_1 + 0.18x_2 + 0.21x_3 - 0.27x_4 + 24.44x_5.$$

The statistical significance of the coefficients of Eq. (20.18) can now be tested by the analysis of variance. For each coefficient in turn, we find the sum of squares accounted for by that coefficient. Thus if $\hat{y}$ is the value of y predicted by

$$\hat{y} = a_1 x_1$$

and since

$$\bar{y} = a_1 \bar{x}$$

we have

$$\hat{y} - \bar{y} = a_1(x_1 - \bar{x}).$$

The total sum of squares is $\sum(y - \bar{y})^2$. This consists of $\sum(\hat{y} - \bar{y})^2$ accounted for by regression and a residual of $\sum(y - \hat{y})^2$, that is,

$$\sum(y - \bar{y})^2 = \sum(\hat{y} - \bar{y})^2 + \sum(y - \hat{y})^2$$

[since $\sum(\hat{y} - \bar{y}) = 0$].
Thus the sum of squares accounted for by x_1 is

$$\sum(\hat{y} - \bar{y})^2 = \frac{[\sum xy - (\sum x \sum y/n)]^2}{\sum(x - \bar{x})^2}.$$

The residual sum of squares is

$$\sum(y - \hat{y})^2 = \sum(y - \bar{y})^2 - \sum(\hat{y} - \bar{y})^2.$$

The F test applied to the ratio of the mean square accounted for by the regression coefficient to the mean square of the residual gives the significance of the regression coefficient (see Table 20.16).

It can be seen that the variables x_1, x_2, and x_5 are significant at the 1 percent level; once these coefficients have been fitted, the variables x_3 and x_4 do not contribute significantly to the regression.

TABLE 20.16

Source of variance	Sum of squares, SS	Degrees of freedom, v	Mean square, MS	Level of significance, in percent
Total (sum of squares of y values)	552.54443	11	—	
Regression on x_1	263.94629	1	263.95	1
Residual after fitting x_1	288.59814	10	28.86	
Reduction on fitting x_5	187.97366	1	187.97	1
Residual after fitting x_1, x_5	100.62448	9	11.18	
Reduction on fitting x_2	69.30536	1	69.31	1
Residual after fitting x_1, x_5, x_2	31.31912	8	3.91	
Reduction on fitting x_3, x_4	11.17663	2	5.59	Not significant
Residual	20.14249 (SSE)	6	3.36	

The regression equation may, therefore, be modified to

$$y = a_1 x_1 + a_2 x_2 + a_5 x_5.$$

The new regression coefficients then become

$$a_1 = 0.6562734$$
$$a_2 = 0.2367266$$
$$a_5 = 20.0406494.$$

Hence, $y = 0.66x_1 + 0.24x_2 + 20.04x_5.$

The 95 percent confidence limits for these coefficients were found to be 0.66 $\pm$ 0.798, 0.24 $\pm$ 1.350, and 20.04 $\pm$ 39.90, respectively. These show that creep cannot be reliably predicted on the basis of the data available. It seems probable, however, that the compounds x_1 and x_2 have a similar influence on creep, and the influence of the compound x_5 is not negligible, even though its percentage content is comparatively low.

From the table of original data, it can be seen that the sum of the values of x_1, x_2, x_3, x_4, and x_5 is approximately constant, and that the values of $(x_1 + x_2)$ and $(x_3 + x_4)$ are complementary; the order of magnitude of the values of x_5 is small compared with the other variables. Hence a high value of $(x_1 + x_2)$ means a low value of $(x_3 + x_4)$, and vice versa, and there is a linear relationship between these two quantities. Thus creep may be a function of either quantity, the other one being looked upon as a complementary filling.

PROBLEMS

20-1. The resistance of wire from six sources was tested by taking five samples from each coil (source) (see Table 20.17). Is there a significant difference between the resistances of the wires from the six sources? Use $\alpha = 1$ percent.

20-2. A student was checking the accuracy of five planimeters of different makes. He conducted his experiment by measuring with each planimeter a definite area four times. The coded results are shown in Table 20.18. Prepare the analysis of variance

TABLE 20.17

	Resistance of sample				
Source	1	2	3	4	5
A	7.9	7.3	7.2	7.5	7.7
B	9.0	8.8	8.8	8.6	8.6
C	9.0	8.3	8.7	8.5	8.7
D	9.6	9.5	9.4	9.4	9.4
E	5.5	5.8	5.7	5.5	5.8
F	8.0	8.4	8.2	8.4	7.6

TABLE 20.18

		Planimeter		
1	2	3	4	5
6.6	5.6	7.5	7.1	5.2
6.0	6.2	5.2	7.0	6.3
6.5	7.1	5.4	6.5	6.8
7.6	5.3	6.8	7.4	7.1

TABLE 20.19

Machine	Strength, kN/m^2			
A	4900	5300	5200	5100
B	5700	5300	5600	5200
C	5200	4800	5100	5000
D	4500	5000	5300	5100

TABLE 20.20

Area A	Area B	Area C
40	43	35
32	47	42
38	40	36
42	41	34

(ANOVA) table and check whether the population means of the five planimeters are homogeneous at the 5 percent level of significance.

20-3. A company manufacturing rubber seals for expansion joints suspected that the tensile strength of their product varied with different machines. The test results are given in Table 20.19. Do the machines have any effect on the tensile strength of the rubber seals? Use a 1 percent level of significance.

20-4. A procedure for measuring runoff was used to determine whether or not the type of terrain has an effect on the measured runoff. The experiment was carried out four times for each type of area with the coded results shown in Table 20.20. Prepare

TABLE 20.21 OUTPUT VOLTAGE, VOLTS

Receiver	Design	
	Vacuum tubes	Transistors
1	20	18
2	22	24
3	21	23
4	23	24

TABLE 20.22

Machine	Weight × 10 g			
I	30.27	30.24	30.25	30.20
II	30.26	30.25	30.22	30.19
III	30.23	30.20	30.23	30.16

the analysis of variance (ANOVA) table. Test at $\alpha = 0.05$ whether the three population runoff means are affected by the type of terrain.

20-5. For the data of Problem 15-11, use the analysis of variance to test whether there is a significant difference between the means of group A, B, and C. Use $\alpha = 5$ percent.

20-6. A manufacturing company of radio receivers wished to ascertain whether or not the use of transistors instead of vacuum tubes had any significant effect on the output voltage. Four receivers were selected at random and operated first with vacuum tubes and then reassembled with transistors and operated. The results are shown in Table 20.21.

Test whether the voltage difference between vacuum tube and transistor designs is significant at $\alpha = 1$ percent. Carry out a 2-sample t test on the same data and compare the result with the value of F.

20-7. Three filling machines in a factory are suspected of malfunction in weighing. Data from a subsequent experiment are shown in Table 20.22.

   a. Prepare the analysis of variance (ANOVA) table.
   b. Test at the 5 percent level of significance whether there is a significant difference between the weight means of machines I, II, and III.
   c. By comparing the mean from machine I with that of machine III, test whether these two machines differ at $\alpha = 0.05$.

Chapter 21

Tolerance and Control Charts

This chapter gives a brief review of some of the graphical methods of presentation of data used mainly in production. Although no fundamental principles of statistics are involved, the use of charts frequently enables us rapidly to assess the behavior of a system and to take appropriate action without delay.

In general terms, the product being controlled may be judged by *attributes* or by *variables*. The former refer to a property that either is or is not possessed, for example, a defect; thus, the products are divided into two categories only. The variables refer to quantities and measurements, and it is with this type of product that we shall deal first.

SPECIFICATION AND
TOLERANCE LIMITS

In design specification, limits on dimensions are usually set in the form of a nominal value and a plus or minus tolerance, for example, 1.000 ± 0.004 cm. (The plus and minus deviations need not be equal.) Such limits ensure that the items manufactured are serviceable and can be assembled together with other parts. These are the *specification limits*. In the actual manufacture of the items, a natural variation in dimensions occurs because of chance errors; from the distribution of these errors, the proportion of items whose dimensions fall within *natural tolerance limits* can be calculated. An understanding of the difference between the two types of limits is of considerable importance.

A process of manufacture is said to be *stable* or *in control* if variations between individuals are caused by chance only. Under such circumstances, the

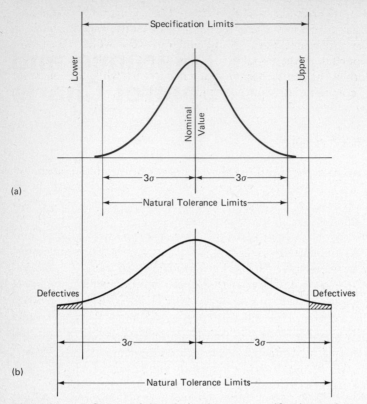

Figure 21.1 Influence of the relation between specification and natural tolerance limits on the proportion of defectives.

data obtained by sampling are consistent with the hypothesis that the observations are random values from a population.

The variability of the process can be described by the population standard deviation σ. Table A.6 shows that, when the variate is normally distributed, all but 0.27 percent of observations will lie within a total range of 6σ. It follows that, if the specification limits are greater than 6σ, the process will produce items with a very small proportion of defectives [Fig. 21.1(a)]. If, on the other hand, the specification limits are narrower than 6σ, then a sensible proportion of defectives will inevitably be manufactured [Fig. 21.1(b)]. Should such a proportion of defectives not be acceptable, the only remedy lies in modifying the process, for example, by using a more precise machine. Before attempting this, it may be wise to see whether the specification limits are not unduly restrictive and cannot be widened without ill effects.

We may also note that, if the natural tolerance limits are considerably narrower than the specification limits, the process of manufacture is "too good" and, therefore, probably unnecessarily costly. In general terms, we should aim at tolerance limits approximately coinciding with the specification limits.

A comment on the fundamental difference between tolerance limits and confidence limits may be helpful. The latter are used to estimate a parameter of the population while tolerance limits are the limits between which we can expect to find a proportion of the population. Thus, as the sample size increases to infinity, the width of the confidence interval tends to zero while the tolerance limits approach the appropriate values for the population.

STABILITY OF A PROCESS

The situation discussed in the preceding section exists when both the mean and the standard deviation remain sensibly constant; we refer to such a situation as *stable*. Conversely, the process is said to be *unstable* or *not in control* when changes either in the mean or in variability take place.

In a general case, the method of manufacture is adjusted until the process becomes stable. To establish this condition, we take samples, preferably all of equal size $n \not< 4$. No fewer than about 25 samples are required.

The reason for the limitations on sample size and number of samples is that the accuracy of an estimate, say of σ, increases and its distribution tends to be normal as the number of samples (or subgroups) increases; this is so by virtue of the central limit theorem (Chapter 6). A sample size of $n = 4$ or 5 is suggested since a larger n may increase the chance of variations within a sample; also, a small sized sample incurs only a small loss of efficiency in estimating σ from the sample ranges.

In the foregoing discussion we assumed that the underlying distribution is normal because the observed distributions of the majority of industrial quality characteristics exhibit normal or near-normal behavior. Even if this is not so, when we deal with sample means, the central limit theorem (Chapter 6) enables us to use the properties of the normal distribution.

The population mean is estimated by the mean of the sample means, $\bar{\bar{x}}$, and the population standard deviation may be estimated from the variance within samples, the average sample standard deviation, or the average sample range $\bar{R}$. The use of the last-mentioned estimate is most common.

WARNING AND ACTION LIMITS

Having established the parameters of the process, we can describe limits which, if exceeded, will tell us that the process is out of control or is in danger of being so.

Two pairs of control limits are used. The first pair represents warning or *inner* limits. These are usually set[1] so that there is a 2.5 percent probability of a sample mean having a value below the lower limit and a 2.5 percent probability

---

[1] Other values may be used, depending on the process.

of its having a value above the upper limit. The warning limits are thus drawn at a distance from the estimated population mean equal to 1.96 × standard deviation of the mean, that is, $\pm 1.96\sigma_{\bar{x}}$.

Action or *outer* limits are usually set[2] so that there is a probability of 0.1 percent of the mean falling above the upper limit and a probability of 0.1 percent of its falling below the lower limit. The distance of the limits from $\bar{\bar{x}}$ is then $\pm 3.09\sigma_{\bar{x}}$.

The values of $1.96\sigma_{\bar{x}}$ and $3.09\sigma_{\bar{x}}$ are obtained from Table A.6 for the normal distribution. We are justified in using this table even if the underlying population is not normally distributed, as we are dealing with sample means. Thus, once again, the central limit theorem (see Chapter 6) has proved of great use.

MEAN CHART

We have defined a process in control as one whose mean and standard deviation do not significantly change. Each of these quantities can be plotted on an appropriate chart on which both the mean value and the warning and action limits are drawn.

Let us first deal with the mean chart. The population mean is estimated from the means of samples, as explained in Chapter 6, and is given by

$$\bar{\bar{x}} = \frac{\bar{x}_1 + \bar{x}_2 + \cdots + \bar{x}_k}{k} \tag{21.1}$$

where $\bar{x}_1, \bar{x}_2, \ldots$ are sample means and k is the number of samples, each of size n.

To establish the warning and action limits for the mean, we require an estimate of the standard deviation of the mean. Not distinguishing between estimates and true values, we can write the standard deviation of the mean as

$$\sigma_{\bar{x}} \simeq \frac{s}{\sqrt{n}} \tag{21.2}$$

where s is the estimate of the population standard deviation and n the sample size. The value s can be estimated from the mean range R, using Eq. (4.14), whence

$$s = \bar{R}d. \tag{21.3}$$

The values of d are given in Table A.1. Hence, the warning limits for the mean (MWL) are given by

$$\bar{\bar{x}} \pm 1.96\sigma_{\bar{x}} \simeq \bar{\bar{x}} \pm \frac{1.96s}{\sqrt{n}}$$

Thus,
$$\text{MWL} = \bar{\bar{x}} \pm \frac{1.96\bar{R}d}{\sqrt{n}}. \tag{21.4}$$

---

[2] A deviation from the mean of $\pm 3\sigma_{\bar{x}}$ is also used.

It is convenient to let

$$A_w = \frac{1.96d}{\sqrt{n}}. \tag{21.5}$$

The values of A_w are given in Table A.19. Hence, the warning limits for the mean become

$$\text{MWL} = \bar{\bar{x}} \pm A_w \bar{R}. \tag{21.6}$$

By a similar argument, the action limits for the mean (MAL) are

$$\bar{\bar{x}} \pm 3.09\sigma_{\bar{x}} \simeq \bar{\bar{x}} \pm \frac{3.09s}{\sqrt{n}}$$

so that

$$\text{MAL} = \bar{\bar{x}} \pm \frac{3.09\bar{R}d}{\sqrt{n}}. \tag{21.7}$$

Let

$$A_A = \frac{3.09d}{\sqrt{n}}. \tag{21.8}$$

The action limits for the mean then become

$$\text{MAL} = \bar{\bar{x}} \pm A_A \bar{R}. \tag{21.9}$$

The values of A_A are given in Table A.19.

If, during the operation, points fall outside the limits, we conclude (with the appropriate probability of being wrong) that the variability between samples is significantly greater than the variability within a sample. The chart gives thus the same result as the analysis of variance for between and within samples.

EXAMPLE

Set up the control limits for the mean chart for the production of steel shafts. The mean of means is $\bar{\bar{x}} = 12.000$ cm, and the mean range has been found to be $\bar{R} = 0.0093$ cm. The samples are of size $n = 5$. From Table A.19 for $n = 5$,

$$A_w = 0.377$$

and

$$A_A = 0.594.$$

Hence, $^{\text{upper}}_{\text{lower}}\text{MWL} = \bar{\bar{x}} \pm A_w\bar{R} = 12.000 \pm 0.377 \times 0.0093$

$$= \left.\begin{matrix} 12.00351 \text{ cm} \\ 11.99649 \text{ cm} \end{matrix}\right\}.$$

Now, $^{\text{upper}}_{\text{lower}}\text{MAL} = \bar{\bar{x}} \pm A_A\bar{R} = 12.000 \pm 0.594 \times 0.0093$

$$= \left.\begin{matrix} 12.00552 \text{ cm} \\ 11.99448 \text{ cm} \end{matrix}\right\}.$$

These should be rounded off using the appropriate number of significant places. If a decision has to be taken on rounding off, the lower limit should be rounded down and the upper limit should be rounded up.

■■

RANGE CHART

As we have said earlier, the mean chart is not sufficient to determine whether the process is stable. The mean of a sample may lie within the limits, and yet individual observations may fall outside these limits. If this happened, it would mean that the standard deviation is changing. For this reason, we have to keep a record of the variability of observations within each sample, and this is best done by plotting the range of each sample on a control chart, known as a range chart.[3] In doing this, we take advantage of the relation between range and standard deviation, given by Eq. (21.3).

In the range chart, we mark warning and action limits in a manner similar to the limits on the mean chart. We may remember, however, that neither the range nor the standard deviation are normally distributed but have probability distributions related to the χ^2 distribution. The limits in the range chart are not symmetrically disposed about the mean range, $\bar{R}$.

We write the range warning limits (RWL):

$$\substack{\text{upper} \\ \text{lower}} \text{RWL} = \left. \begin{array}{l} D_{WU} \times \bar{R} \\ D_{WL} \times \bar{R} \end{array} \right\} \tag{21.10}$$

and the range action limits (RAL):

$$\substack{\text{upper} \\ \text{lower}} \text{RAL} = \left. \begin{array}{l} D_{AU} \times \bar{R} \\ D_{AL} \times \bar{R} \end{array} \right\} \tag{21.11}$$

where the values of the factors D are given in Table A.20.

The coefficients for the range chart are based on normal distribution: however, even if the distribution is not normal, the control limits, especially the action limits, are reliable for most purposes.

We may note that the control limits for range widen as the sample size increases, while the mean chart becomes narrower with an increase in sample size.

EXAMPLE

Find the range control limits for the data of the preceding example.

From Table A.20 for $n = 5$,

$$D_{WU} = 1.81$$
$$D_{WL} = 0.37$$
$$D_{AU} = 2.36$$
$$D_{AL} = 0.16.$$

Hence,
$$\substack{\text{upper} \\ \text{lower}} \text{RWL} = \begin{array}{l} 1.81 \\ 0.37 \end{array} \times 0.0093 = \left. \begin{array}{l} 0.016833 \text{ cm} \\ 0.003441 \text{ cm} \end{array} \right\}$$

and
$$\substack{\text{upper} \\ \text{lower}} \text{RAL} = \begin{array}{l} 2.36 \\ 0.16 \end{array} \times 0.0093 = \left. \begin{array}{l} 0.021948 \text{ cm} \\ 0.001488 \text{ cm} \end{array} \right\}.$$ ■ ■

---

[3] The range chart thus tests the same hypothesis as Bartlett's test (see Chapter 16).

SCHEME OF OPERATION

We can now summarize the steps to be followed in the construction of mean and range charts to be used for the purpose of obtaining a continual check on the stability of a process.

   1. Determine the mean value $\bar{x}$ of the quantity that we are measuring; this is the mean value which the process could be expected to yield if it were functioning perfectly. The symbol $\bar{\bar{x}}$ indicates the mean of means of a large number of random samples during a stable period.

   2. Determine the standard deviation σ of the measured quantity during this stable period. If this is not convenient, find the sample ranges during the same period, calculate the mean range $\bar{R}$, and estimate the standard deviation, using coefficient d of Table A.1.

   3. Find the values of A_w and A_A from Table A.19 for the sample sizes used, and hence establish the warning and action limits $\bar{\bar{x}} \pm A_w\bar{R}$ and $\bar{\bar{x}} \pm A_A\bar{R}$, respectively. Plot these limits on a chart that also shows $\bar{\bar{x}}$. If any future observation falls outside the warning limits, further samples should be carefully watched, and if the trend persists, an investigation of the process should follow. An observation outside the action limits indicates that the process has gone out of control and remedial action is immediately necessary.

   4. Find the upper and lower warning and action limits for range, using the D coefficients of Table A.20. Plot the mean range and the control limits. If any future sample range is found to be outside the action limits, the process is likely to have moved away from a stable position and steps must be taken to find the cause and remedy the situation.

   5. If, in establishing the control limits, we find an occasional value outside the action limits, the value is disregarded and a new mean and new control limits are calculated. There is little theoretical justification for this except that if the process is truly in control, a point outside the limits can be considered as not belonging to the population of items in control. Such a point is then considered to be an outlier and is rejected (cf. Chapter 12).

   In general terms, if a process that was in control becomes unstable, we blame this on "assignable causes of variation," which we seek to remove. Such a cause may be identified as a specific part of the production process, but the possibility of poor sampling should not be ignored. Finally, it may be that the production process has changed (e.g., due to wear of some parts) and new control charts have to be set up.

EXAMPLE

   A manufacturer of a certain type of resistors decided to set up control charts for his product. Twenty-five samples of size $n = 4$ were taken. The mean and range of each sample are shown in Table 21.1. Compute the limits for the mean and range charts for the process and check whether the process is in control. If so, estimate the standard deviation for the process. If the specification limits are 120 ± 8 ohm, is the process able to meet the specification?

TABLE 21.1

| Sample | Resistance in ohms | | Sample | Resistance in ohms | |
	Mean, $\bar{x}$	Range, R		Mean, $\bar{x}$	Range, R
1	122	10	15	120	13
2	126	6	16	125	12
3	118	5	17	118	5
4	121	8	18	119	8
5	126	11	19	124	4
6	125	5	20	121	3
7	119	4	21	125	7
8	121	3	22	121	5
9	124	11	23	120	4
10	125	14	24	121	4
11	123	10	25	119	6
12	124	9		$\sum \bar{x} = 3050$	$\sum R = 185$
13	122	7			
14	121	11			

From Table 21.1,

$$\bar{\bar{x}} = \frac{\sum \bar{x}}{n} = \frac{3050}{25} = 122 \text{ ohm}$$

and

$$\bar{R} = \frac{\sum R}{n} = \frac{185}{25} = 7.4 \text{ ohm.}$$

The trial control limits are computed with the aid of Tables A.19 and A.20 as follows:

For mean chart:

$$^{\text{upper}}_{\text{lower}}\text{warning limits} = \bar{\bar{x}} \pm A_w \bar{R}$$

$$= 122.00 \pm 0.476 \times 7.4$$

$$= \left. \begin{array}{c} 125.52 \\ 118.48 \end{array} \right\} \text{ohm}$$

$$^{\text{upper}}_{\text{lower}}\text{action limits} = \bar{\bar{x}} \pm A_A \bar{R}$$

$$= 122.00 \pm 0.750 \times 7.4$$

$$= \left. \begin{array}{c} 127.55 \\ 116.45 \end{array} \right\} \text{ohm.}$$

For range chart:

$$^{\text{upper}}_{\text{lower}}\text{warning limits} = \left. \begin{array}{l} D_{WU}\bar{R} = 1.93 \times 7.4 = 14.28 \\ D_{WL}\bar{R} = 0.29 \times 7.4 = \ \ 2.15 \end{array} \right\} \text{ohm}$$

$$^{\text{upper}}_{\text{lower}}\text{action limits} = \left. \begin{array}{l} D_{AU}\bar{R} = 2.58 \times 7.4 = 19.09 \\ D_{AL}\bar{R} = 0.10 \times 7.4 = \ \ 0.74 \end{array} \right\} \text{ohm.}$$

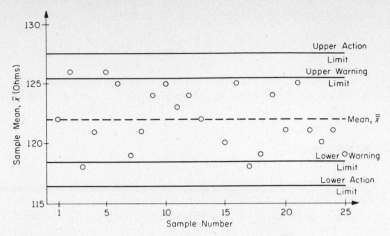

Figure 21.2 Mean chart for the example on page 471.

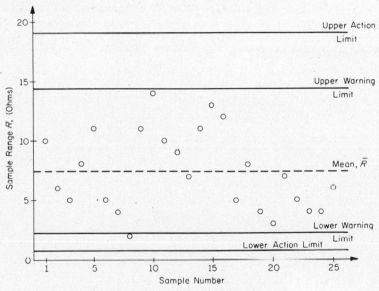

Figure 21.3 Range chart for the example on page 471.

These limits, as well as the appropriate mean values, are shown in Figs. 21.2 and 21.3. The plots of the mean and the range for each sample show that all points fall inside the action limits. Four of the sample means fall outside the warning limits, but the corresponding ranges are inside the warning limits for the range; this indicates that the situation is not serious but has to be watched. Therefore, we can assume for the time being that the process can be brought into control at this level.

To obtain an estimate of the population standard deviation σ, we use Table A.1 for $n = 4$, $d = 0.4857$. Thus,

$$s = \bar{R}d = 7.4 \times 0.4857 = 3.594 \text{ ohm.}$$

The natural tolerance limits are

$$\bar{\bar{x}} \pm 3\sigma \simeq 122 \pm 3 \times 3.594 = \left.\begin{array}{c} 111.22 \\ 132.78 \end{array}\right\} \text{ohm.}$$

The specification limits are 120 ± 8 ohm, that is, 112 to 128 ohm. The process does not, therefore, meet the specification. ■ ■

CUMULATIVE SUM CHART

If we are interested only in changes that are large and, therefore, easily detectable on a control chart, the use of these simple-to-plot charts is adequate. However, if we want to detect at an early stage small changes that may be obscured by residual variation, there is another type of chart which is more efficient and still not laborious to use. This is the cumulative sum chart, often called the *cusum chart*, in which a cumulative sum of the differences between the process variable and the previously accepted mean value is plotted after each observation.

We can call this mean value the target T. Then, at any instant t, the cumulative sum of deviations about T is

$$S_t = \sum_{i=1}^{t} (x_i - T).$$

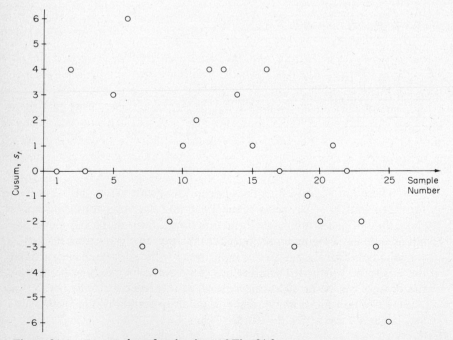

Figure 21.4 Cusum chart for the data of Fig. 21.2.

This value is plotted against time t, as shown in Fig. 21.4 for the data of Fig. 21.2, where, instead of time, successive samples are used. We can see that the slope of the cusum chart indicates the deviation of the process mean from the target, and such a change is visually easier to detect than the variation in the control chart.

Each successive value of S_t is obtained simply by adding the value of $(x - T)$ for the last observation. Now, if we are interested in the change in the mean between the kth and nth observations, we can write the mean value between $(k + 1)$ and n as

$$\bar{x} = \sum_{i=k+1}^{n} \frac{x_i}{n - k}$$

or

$$\bar{x} - T + \frac{\sum_{i=k+1}^{n} (x_i - T)}{n - k}.$$

Hence,

$$\bar{x} = T + \frac{S_n - S_k}{n - k}$$

that is,

$$\bar{x} = T + \frac{\text{change in cusum}}{\text{number of observations made}}.$$

The fraction clearly represents the slope of the cusum, and it is important, therefore, to choose a convenient scale for the desired variation to be readily noticeable.

CHARTS USING ATTRIBUTES

In dealing with attributes, we are concerned with the binomial and Poisson distributions. The former is applicable when we are dealing with *defective* items, the latter when we count the number of *defects* per item.

If p is the mean proportion of defective items, then the mean number of defectives in a sample of size n is np. We may recall from Chapter 8 that the standard deviation of the number of defectives is $\sqrt{npq} = \sqrt{np(1 - p)}$. Since the parameter p is unknown, we estimate it from the k samples by $\hat{p}$ given by

$$\hat{p} = \frac{\text{total number of defectives observed}}{nk} = \frac{\sum_{i=1}^{k} X_i}{nk}.$$

Hence, we can write the action limits for the mean *number* of defectives as

$$\text{MAL} = n\hat{p} \pm 3.09\sqrt{n\hat{p}(1 - \hat{p})}. \tag{21.12}$$

Instead of operating in terms of the number of defectives, we can express the control limits in terms of the *mean proportion* of defectives p. Since

$$E\left(\frac{X_i}{n}\right) = p,$$

and
$$\mathrm{Var}\!\left(\frac{X_i}{n}\right) = \frac{1}{n^2}\,\mathrm{Var}(X_i)$$

$$= \frac{1}{n^2}\,(npq)$$

$$= \frac{pq}{n} = \frac{p(1-p)}{n}$$

the standard deviation of the mean proportion of defectives is

$$\sqrt{\frac{p(1-p)}{n}}.$$

Again, the parameter p is estimated from the sample by $\hat{p}$. Thus, the action limits for the mean proportion of defectives are

$$\text{proportion AL} = \hat{p} \pm 3.09\,\sqrt{\frac{\hat{p}(1-\hat{p})}{n}}. \tag{21.13}$$

If a negative limit is obtained in Eqs. (21.12) and (21.13), it is replaced by zero, as a negative proportion or number of defectives is not possible.

When dealing with an expected number of *defects* in a material, np, the Poisson distribution is applicable. From Eq. (9.6) the standard deviation is $\sqrt{np}$. Thus, in this case, the action limits for the number of defects, in terms of the estimate $\hat{p}$, are

$$\text{number AL} = n\hat{p} \pm 3.09\,\sqrt{n\hat{p}}. \tag{21.14}$$

EXAMPLE

Thirty successive samples, each consisting of 50 machine bolts, were checked by a "go–no-go" gauge. The results are shown in Table 21.2.

Find the mean proportion of defectives and calculate the upper and lower action limits for such a mean proportion. Are any of the plotted points outside these limits? If so, adjust the mean proportion of defectives and the corresponding limits for future production.

The estimated mean proportion of defectives is

$$\hat{p} = \frac{\sum(X/n)}{k} = \frac{0.84}{30} = 0.028.$$

The action limits are given by Eq. (21.13):

$$\text{proportion AL} = \hat{p} \pm 3.09\,\sqrt{\frac{\hat{p}(1-\hat{p})}{n}}$$

or
$$\text{proportion AL} = 0.028 \pm 3.09\,\sqrt{\frac{0.028 \times 0.972}{50}}$$

$$= (-0.044, 0.1001).$$

We substitute zero for the lower limit and write the limits as $(0, 0.1001)$.

TABLE 21.2

Sample	Number defective, X	Proportion defective, X/n	Sample	Number defective, X	Proportion defective, X/n
1	2	0.04	17	0	0.00
2	1	0.02	18	0	0.00
3	5	0.10	19	1	0.02
4	1	0.02	20	3	0.06
5	2	0.04	21	2	0.04
6	1	0.02	22	1	0.02
7	3	0.06	23	1	0.02
8	0	0.00	24	2	0.04
9	1	0.02	25	0	0.00
10	2	0.04	26	0	0.00
11	1	0.02	27	1	0.02
12	0	0.00	28	1	0.02
13	0	0.00	29	2	0.04
14	3	0.06	30	2	0.04
15	2	0.04			
16	2	0.04			$\sum\left(\dfrac{X}{n}\right) = 0.84$

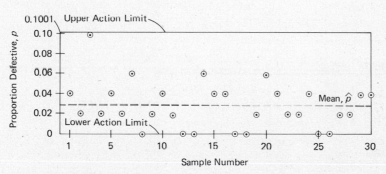

Figure 21.5 Control chart for the proportion defective in the example on page 476.

Figure 21.5 shows the control limits and a plot of the proportion defective in each sample. It can be seen that all the points fall inside the limits; therefore, we can use these limits as control limits for future production. Had some points fallen outside, they could have been eliminated, and a new $\hat{p}$ and new limits should have been calculated from the remaining samples. ■ ■

EXAMPLE
In producing aluminum sheets for a new type of aircraft, it was required to set up control charts for the number of defects per sheet of a certain size. Twenty-five sample sheets were drawn and the number of defects per sheet was recorded. The results are shown in Table 21.3. On the basis of

TABLE 21.3

Sample	Number of defects per sheet	Sample	Number of defects per sheet
1	1	14	1
2	0	15	2
3	2	16	0
4	1	17	0
5	0	18	8
6	0	19	2
7	2	20	0
8	2	21	0
9	0	22	1
10	1	23	0
11	1	24	1
12	2	25	1
13	0		$\Sigma = 28$

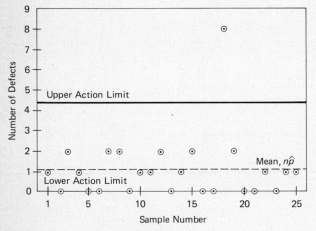

Figure 21.6   Control chart for the number of defects in the example on page 477.

these results, set up control limits for the number of defects for future production.

The estimated number of defects per sheet is

$$n\hat{p} = \frac{28}{25} = 1.12.$$

From Eq. (21.14), the action limits for the number of defects are

$$n\hat{p} \pm 3.09\sqrt{n\hat{p}} = 1.12 \pm 3.09 \times 1.059$$
$$= (-2.15, 4.39).$$

Substituting zero for the negative value, we write the limits as $(0, 4.39)$. A plot of the control limits and of the number of defects in each sample (Fig. 21.6) shows that the 18th sheet falls outside the control limits. In this case, it is best to base future work on a mean of defects $n\hat{p}$ that does not include this particular sheet. We shall now recalculate $n\hat{p}$ and the control limits, ignoring the 18th sheet:

$$\sum \text{number of defects} = 20.$$

Therefore,
$$n\hat{p} = \frac{20}{24} = 0.833.$$

Control limits are

$$0.833 \pm 3.09\sqrt{0.833} = (-1.98, 3.65).$$

Thus the revised control limits are $(0, 3.65)$.   ■ ■

It can be seen by inspection that none of the samples has a number of defects outside these new limits. Thus the new $n\hat{p}$ and control limits can be used in future control work on the number of defects in the production of the aluminum sheets. We may add that these limits do not guarantee that a fixed percentage of the population will lie between them, as the probability of the number of defects falling between these limits depends on the mean estimated number of defects $n\hat{p}$. For large n, $n\hat{p}$ is approximately normally distributed, and hence we can assume that "almost" all the values will fall between the control limits.

ADVANTAGES OF QUALITY CONTROL

The notes on control charts given here are limited to basic principles, and a detailed study of the topic must be sought in one of the numerous books on quality control.

Quality control is used in all manufacturing processes, from pharmaceuticals to concrete products. Its special feature is that it replaces a negative form of inspection—that is, discarding of defective items—by a more positive form. The process is watched continually and systematically so that a departure from a stable condition is diagnosed early; appropriate action can then be taken and the fault can be rectified before an excessive number of defectives has been manufactured. We must remember that quality control accepts the fact that some fraction of the items produced will be defective but makes it possible to ensure that the specified fraction is not exceeded. Moreover, the control limits should usually be set so that the chance of concluding that a process is out of control when, in fact, it is in control is very small. The reason for this is that the consequences of wrongly finding a process to be out of control can be serious and expensive, for example, manufacture could be stopped or products could be discarded.

SOLVED PROBLEMS

21-1. The mean range of shear strength of a certain kind of spot weld was determined from many tests on samples of 6 welds to be $\bar{R} = 35$ kN/m^2. Set up control limits for successive samples of size $n = 6$.

Solution. From Table A.20, the factors for warning limits are $D_{WU} = 1.72$, $D_{WL} = 0.42$. For action limits the factors are $D_{AU} = 2.22$ and $D_{AL} = 0.21$. Hence,

$$\substack{\text{upper}\\\text{lower}}\text{warning limits} = \begin{array}{l} D_{WU}\bar{R} = 1.72 \times 35 = 60.2 \text{ kN/m}^2 \\ D_{WL}\bar{R} = 0.42 \times 35 = 14.7 \text{ kN/m}^2 \end{array}\Big\}$$

$$\substack{\text{upper}\\\text{lower}}\text{action limits} = \begin{array}{l} D_{AU}\bar{R} = 2.22 \times 35 = 77.7 \text{ kN/m}^2 \\ D_{AL}\bar{R} = 0.21 \times 35 = 7.4 \text{ kN/m}^2 \end{array}\Big\}.$$

21-2. Samples of 6 rings are taken at regular intervals from an assembly line for engine pistons. The inside diameters of the rings are measured, and the sample mean $\bar{x}$ and the sample range R are determined. For the first 30 samples, the sums of the means and of the ranges were $\sum \bar{x} = 135.81$ cm and $\sum R = 0.063$ cm.

a. What are the control action limits for the mean and range charts?

b. What are the 3σ natural tolerance limits for the ring diameter, assuming that $\bar{x}$ and $\bar{R}$ can be used to estimate the mean and standard deviation of the population?

c. Is the process able to produce rings with inside diameters within the specification limits of 4.525 ± 0.005 cm?

d. What proportion of rings will fall outside the specification limits if the process is in control with the calculated $\bar{x}$ and derived σ?

Solution

a. Compute

$$\bar{\bar{x}} = \frac{\sum \bar{x}}{n} = \frac{135.81}{30} = 4.527 \text{ cm}$$

$$\bar{R} = \frac{\sum R}{n} = \frac{0.063}{30} = 0.0021 \text{ cm}.$$

From Table A.1, for $n = 6$, $d = 0.3945$. Hence,

$$s = 0.0021 \times 0.3945 = 0.0008293.$$

For the mean chart:

$$\text{action limits} = \bar{\bar{x}} \pm A_A\bar{R}.$$

From Table A.19, for $n = 6$, $A_A = 0.498$. Hence,

$$\text{action limits} = 4.527 \pm 0.498 \times 0.0021$$
$$= 4.52805, 4.52595 \text{ cm}.$$

For the range chart:

$$\substack{\text{upper}\\\text{lower}}\text{action limit} = \begin{array}{l} D_{AU}\bar{R} \\ D_{AL}\bar{R}. \end{array}$$

From Table A.20, for $n = 6$, $D_{AU} = 2.22$ and $D_{AL} = 0.21$. Hence,

$$\text{upper action limit} = 2.22 \times 0.0021$$
$$= 0.00466 \text{ cm}$$

$$\text{lower action limit} = 0.21 \times 0.0021$$
$$= 0.00044 \text{ cm.}$$

b. As instructed, we assume that $\sigma = s$. Hence,

$$\text{natural tolerance limits} = \bar{\bar{x}} \pm 3\sigma$$
$$= 4.527 \pm 3 \times 0.0008293$$
$$= 4.524, 4.529 \text{ cm.}$$

c. The specification limits are $4.525 \pm 0.005 = 4.520, 4.530$ cm. Since the natural tolerance limits fall within the specification, the process is able to meet the specification.

d. We have $\bar{\bar{x}} = 4.527$ cm and $\sigma = 0.0008293$ cm. The specification limits are 4.520 and 4.530 cm. Compute

$$z_1 = \frac{4.530 - 4.527}{0.0008293} = 3.62.$$

From Table A.6, the area under the normal probability curve for such a value of z is approximately 0.49984. Also

$$z_2 = \frac{4.527 - 4.520}{0.0008293} = 8.45.$$

This deviation is so large that the corresponding area under the normal probability curve can be taken as 0.5000. The total area between the specification limits is

$$0.50000 + 0.49984 = 0.99984.$$

Hence the percentage outside these limits is

$$1 - 0.99984 = 0.00016 \quad \text{or} \quad 0.016 \text{ percent}$$

a very small percentage indeed.

21-3. A control chart for a new kind of plastics is to be initiated. Twenty-five samples of 100-m plastic sheets from the assembly line were inspected for flaws during a period of time. The results are given in Table 21.4. Set up the necessary control chart.

Solution. Compute the estimated mean number of flaws

$$n\hat{p} = \frac{\sum \text{flaws}}{25}$$

$$= \frac{141}{25} = 5.64 \text{ flaws per sheet.}$$

The control limits are

$$n\hat{p} \pm 3.09\sqrt{n\hat{p}} = 5.64 \pm 3.09\sqrt{5.64}$$
$$= -1.70, 12.98.$$

TABLE 21.4

Sheet number	Number of flaws per sheet	Sheet number	Number of flaws per sheet
1	2	14	3
2	0	15	2
3	7	16	0
4	8	17	4
5	9	18	5
6	10	19	1
7	10	20	0
8	13	21	2
9	14	22	3
10	16	23	2
11	10	24	5
12	7	25	4
13	4		

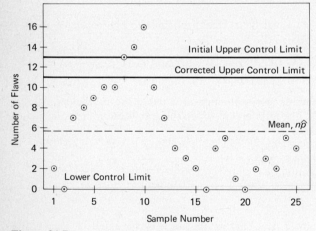

Figure 21.7

Thus the control limits are (0, 12.98). These limits and the mean number of flaws per sheet, as well as the individual number of flaws per sheet, are shown in Fig. 21.7. It can be seen that the samples numbered 8, 9, and 10 fall outside the upper control limit. Removing the value for these samples and recalculating, we get

$$n\hat{p} = \frac{98}{22} = 4.45 \text{ flaws per sheet}$$

$$\text{new control limits} = 4.45 \pm 3.09\sqrt{4.45}$$
$$= -2.07, 10.97$$

that is, the control limits are (0, 10.97). By inspection, it is seen that none of the remaining sheets has flaws outside these limits.

A close look at Fig. 21.7 will show what appears to be an approximately cyclic pattern of variation in the number of flaws in successive sheets. In such cases it is advisable to check the production process before continuing production, since this trend is unlikely to be caused by chance alone.

PROBLEMS

21-1. From numerous tests it has been found that the mean strength and mean range of a certain timber are 3510 and 390 kN/m² respectively. Using these values, set up control limits for the mean chart when the sample size is 5.

21-2. Establish range and mean charts (containing warning and action limits) on the basis of the data for samples of size $n = 3$ in Table 21.5.

21-3. Screws produced by an automatic machine are to be checked. A sample of 60 screws was checked by a go–no-go gauge, and it was found that in 30 successive samples the following defective number of screws was obtained:

5, 4, 3, 1, 2, 0, 0, 0, 1, 2, 0, 1, 2, 1, 0, 1, 1,
0, 1, 0, 0, 1, 2, 0, 1, 0, 1, 0, 0, 1.

a. Is this process in control?
b. Taking the process in its present condition, will it produce screws of which 5 percent or less are defective?

21-4. Thirty 20-m lengths of carpets were inspected, and the average number of defects per unit area was found to be 2.1. Compute the 2.5σ control limits. What are the probability limits corresponding to a probability of 0.3 percent of falling outside the upper control limits?

21-5. For the data on concrete strength given in Problem 4-7:
a. Estimate the standard deviation from the mean range.
b. Construct control charts for the mean and range, and plot the means and the ranges on the respective charts.
c. Are any of the plotted points outside the action limits? If so, adjust the mean of means and the mean range and the corresponding limits for future production.

TABLE 21.5

Sample number	Mean	Range	Sample number	Mean	Range
1	11.97	0.5	13	17.87	8.7
2	14.87	6.3	14	14.97	0.1
3	15.35	7.5	15	14.60	9.8
4	15.72	6.6	16	14.12	7.7
5	11.12	4.9	17	13.21	7.5
6	11.06	6.7	18	12.86	1.2
7	11.97	9.9	19	12.38	9.8
8	12.27	6.9	20	16.99	6.5
9	12.85	0.1	21	18.35	7.6
10	13.23	8.3	22	18.52	4.0
11	16.12	5.1	23	14.13	8.4
12	16.61	3.2	24	14.60	9.8

TABLE 21.6

0.30	0.39	0.36	0.22	0.27	0.29	0.46	0.44	0.35
0.27	0.27	0.23	0.37	0.36	0.58	0.39	0.26	0.38
0.44	0.36	0.30	0.34	0.41	0.69	0.36	0.23	0.27
0.12	0.16	0.22	0.24	0.28	0.33	0.13	0.18	0.35
0.51	0.32	0.50	0.39	0.55	0.66	0.53	0.42	0.42
0.61	0.46	0.65	0.46	0.29	0.29	0.39	0.53	0.46
0.37	0.26	0.22	0.29	0.52	0.54	0.55	0.38	0.39
0.32	0.45	0.46	0.43	0.38	0.30	0.28	0.49	0.29
0.50	0.30	0.47	0.56	0.43	0.45	0.58	0.63	0.27
0.52	0.27	0.51	0.29	0.30	0.38	0.39	0.38	0.53
0.52	0.45	0.39	0.63	0.33	0.37	0.47	0.40	0.39
0.42	0.56	0.46	0.40	0.47	0.49	0.32	0.69	0.49
0.72	0.43	0.75	0.41	0.40	0.49	0.22	0.34	0.51
0.28	0.36	0.41	0.37	0.45	0.42	0.51	0.52	0.13
0.29	0.37	0.45	0.44	0.68	0.28	0.31	0.38	0.42
0.33	0.56	0.31	0.33	0.31	0.46	0.34	0.58	0.22
0.20	0.52	0.38	0.33	0.23	0.21	0.18	0.26	0.36
0.23	0.38	0.33	0.23	0.39	0.38	0.22	0.23	0.28
0.35	0.94	0.23	0.16	0.29	0.46	0.22	0.27	0.18
0.36	0.23	0.20	0.23	0.27	0.35	0.37	0.38	0.37

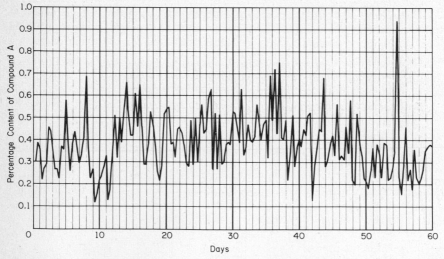

Figure 21.8

21-6. The percentage content of compound A in a product was measured three times a day during 60 days. The 180 measurements, with a mean value of approximately 0.38, were tabulated as shown in Table 21.6 and then plotted in Figure 21.8. Since little can be gleaned from these data, it is proposed to plot a cusum chart using the mean as a reference.

Draw this cusum chart and comment on the pattern of fluctuation. Read the data horizontally.

TABLE 21.7

Sample	Number of defects	Sample	Number of defects
1	2	14	2
2	0	15	0
3	1	16	4
4	3	17	3
5	0	18	1
6	3	19	2
7	5	20	0
8	2	21	7
9	2	22	2
10	6	23	5
11	3	24	1
12	0	25	4
13	2		

21-7. Data for the shear strength of spot welds has been maintained to construct mean and range control charts. From tests on 30 samples each of size $n = 4$, it is found that $\sum \bar{x} = 15{,}450$ N, and $\sum R = 1206$ N. Assuming the process is in control, determine:
  a. the limits for the mean and range charts;
  b. the standard deviation for the process.
  c. If the minimum specifications for the spot weld is 400 N, what percentage of the welds does not meet the minimum specifications?

21-8. The number of defects observed in randomly selected samples of a specific size of glass plate produced daily is shown in Table 21.7.
  Construct the appropriate control chart and determine whether you would adjust the control limits before using them in future production.

21-9. Thirty samples of 1-m² pieces of woolen goods were inspected and the average number of defects per piece was found to be 1.5.
  a. Determine the 3σ control limits.
  b. What are the probability limits corresponding to a probability of 0.002 of falling outside the upper control limit?

21-10. Quality control charts are used for the mean $\bar{x}$ and the range R of resistors. The sample size n is 4. After a long period of testing, the values of $\bar{x}$ and $\bar{R}$ were found to be 8.1 ohm and 0.3 ohm, respectively. Compute the values of the 3σ limits for the $\bar{x}$ chart and the 3.09σ limits for the R chart.
  The specification for the resistors is 8.0 ± 0.01 ohm. Will the process be able to meet this specification?

Chapter 22

Acceptance and Rejection Testing

In the previous chapter, we discussed decision making in a continuous manu-facturing process or other similar situations. We shall now consider specific decisions about acceptance or rejection of *batches* of items on the basis of tests on samples drawn from those batches.

ACCEPTANCE SAMPLING

The issue here is different from that in Chapter 21: we are concerned with the problem of decision about acceptance or rejection of a finite batch, using as a basis for our decision measurements on a sample drawn from that batch. As in Chapter 21, judgment can be exercised on the basis of attributes or of variables. Let us first deal with attributes, that is, when the acceptance is based simply on the basis of the product possessing or not possessing a defect.

The quality of the batch is judged by the proportion, p, of defective items. Generally, *some* defective items are allowable, either because they are virtually unavoidable or because it would be too expensive to produce batches that are entirely defect-free. It follows then that any sample drawn from a batch has to be judged against a prearranged, or agreed, proportion of defective items, say p_0. This is the acceptable quality level, AQL, which means that if the true proportion of defectives is p such that $p \leqslant p_0$, the batch is acceptable. However, our test is limited to a sample from the batch and we use the sample results to test the hypothesis $H_0: p \leqslant p_0$ versus the alternative hypothesis $H_a: p > p_0$.

Let us assume that our test data are based on a sample size n with the observed number of defectives v. Our decision, based on a sample, can of

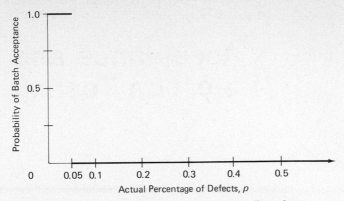

Figure 22.1   The OC curve for a perfect sampling plan.

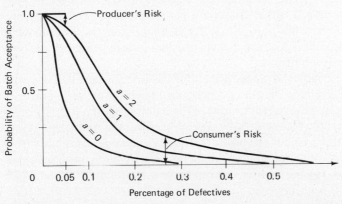

Figure 22.2   The OC curves for samples of size $n = 20$ with acceptance numbers $a = 0$, 1. and 2.

course be wrong as far as the whole batch is concerned. If we reject the batch when, in fact, the proportion of defectives is $p_1 \not> p_0$, we are unfair to the producer, and this is the *producer's risk* or Type I error, α. Conversely, if we accept a batch when, in fact, the proportion of defectives is $p_1 > p_0$, we are unfair to the consumer, and this is the *consumer's risk* or Type II error, β. If there were no risk, we would operate a perfect testing plan such that for all cases $p_1 \leqslant p_0$ the batch is accepted and for all cases $p_1 > p_0$ the batch is rejected. This is illustrated in Fig. 22.1; but alas this can only be achieved when the entire batch is tested—a situation undesirable on account of the cost of testing and, of course, impossible when the test is destructive.

In practice, then, we select for our sample an acceptable number of defectives, a, called the *acceptance number*, and compare v with a. We can see from Fig. 22.2 that the smaller the value of a the smaller the consumer's risk but, of course, for a constant sample size, the larger the producer's risk.

If, instead of dealing with attributes, we effect a measurement for each item tested, we can make our decision to accept or reject a batch on the basis

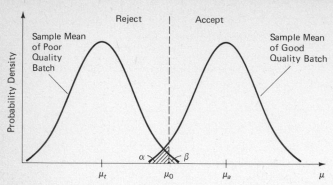

Figure 22.3 Distribution of a sample mean and corresponding producer's and consumer's risk, α and β, respectively.

of the actual measurements rather than on a go–no-go basis. These measurements may afford some insight into the degree of nonconformance of the items tested. Such an approach is known as *sampling by variables*, in contradistinction to sampling by attributes.

Sampling by variables is appropriate, for instance, when dealing with density or moisture content of soils or building materials or with purity of chemicals. Let us assume that a mean value of the batch property, μ_a, represents a quality of the material which should be acceptable from the producer's standpoint and a mean value of μ_t for the batch represents unacceptable quality from the consumer's standpoint. Let α and β be the producer's and consumer's risk, respectively. Our task is to determine a mean value μ_0 and sample size n which will minimize these risks.

We assume that the standard deviation of the variable, σ, is known from past experience. For sample size n, the standard error of the sample mean is $\sigma/\sqrt{n}$. The probability distribution of samples from an acceptable batch with mean μ_a will be as shown by the right-hand side curve in Fig. 22.3. The value of μ_0 should then be such that the area under this curve to the left of μ_0 is α. Likewise, for a batch with a mean μ_t, the area under the probability distribution curve to the right of μ_0 should be β, as shown by the left-hand curve in Fig. 22.3. A solution of the equations

$$F\left(z = \frac{\mu_0 - \mu_a}{\dfrac{\sigma}{\sqrt{n}}}\right) = 0.5 - \alpha$$

and

$$F\left(z = \frac{\mu_t - \mu_0}{\dfrac{\sigma}{\sqrt{n}}}\right) = 0.5 - \beta$$

will give μ_0 and n. If n is undesirably large, we can reduce it but we must simultaneously increase α or β or both. With the values μ_0 and n decided upon, the situation is such that:

In $(1 - \alpha)$ cases, we accept batches with a mean of at least μ_a.

In $(1 - \beta)$ cases, we reject batches with a mean at most μ_t.

Since sampling by variables provides more information than sampling by attributes, the sample size for given risks is smaller in the former case.

EXAMPLE

A certain chemical is supplied on the understanding that it must be accepted if the impurity content is less than 0.1 percent, the probability of wrong rejection being 5 percent. The purchaser insists on rejecting the chemical when the impurity content is 0.25 percent but is willing to accept it wrongfully in 10 percent of cases. From past experience, the standard deviation of the determination of the impurity content is 0.1 percent.

Calculate the critical value of the sample impurity content, μ_0, and the sample size, n.

Solution. We have

$$\mu_a = 0.10; \qquad \mu_t = 0.25; \qquad \alpha = 0.05; \qquad \beta = 0.10;$$
$$\sigma = 0.10 \text{ (see Fig. 22.4).}$$

Substituting in the equations on page 488, we have

$$\text{(a)} \quad F\left(z = \frac{\mu_0 - 0.10}{0.10/\sqrt{n}}\right) = 0.50 - 0.05$$

$$= 0.45$$

and

$$\text{(b)} \quad F\left(z = \frac{\mu_0 - 0.40}{0.10/\sqrt{n}}\right) = 0.50 - 0.10$$

$$= 0.40.$$

From Table A.3, we find for (a):

$$\frac{\mu_0 - 0.10}{0.10/\sqrt{n}} = 1.645$$

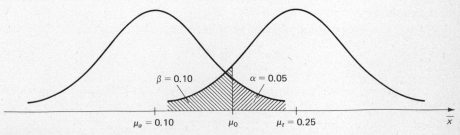

Figure 22.4

and for (b):

$$\frac{0.25 - \mu_0}{0.10/\sqrt{n}} = 1.282.$$

Hence, we obtain $\mu_0 = 0.18$ and $n \simeq 4$.   ■ ■

CHOICE OF SAMPLE SIZE

As we have seen in earlier chapters, our decisions about populations or batches (such as their acceptability under specification) are usually based on tests on samples. A problem that often arises is how many observations should be made so that the risk of making a wrong decision is acceptably small. Some risk is, of course, always present because of the random variation in results, but the risk becomes smaller as the number of observations increases. It is clear, however, that, for reasons of economy of time and effort, the testing should be kept to a minimum consistent with the maximum risk of a wrong decision which we are prepared to accept. In practice, there is thus a certain optimum testing effort. In this book, we cannot evaluate the cost of testing or the economic results of making a wrong decision; therefore, we shall consider our decision making on the basis of a specified risk of being wrong.[1]

We have to admit then that there is no direct answer to the question: how large should the sample size be? On the one hand, the larger the sample size the greater the cost of testing, but on the other hand the greater the amount of the information derived. In other words, the amount of information in the sample affects the measure of goodness of the method of inference, and this has to be decided upon by the experimenter. It is he who knows how accurate his estimate need be, and he should therefore specify the error of estimation which is acceptable.

The information required first of all is the distribution of the true mean value of the measured property of batches of the material.[2] Let us consider, for example, the strength of a plastic, and assume that in the past we received a sequence of batches of the plastic. From each batch, k samples were taken and tested, and the mean of the k values was obtained. The means so obtained differ from one another for two reasons: they are estimates of different (batch) means and they are also affected by the testing error (arising from sampling and measuring).

Any test observation, x_{ij}, can be written as

$$x_{ij} = \mu_0 + \phi_i + e_{ij} \tag{22.1}$$

---

[1] Details of the method described in the following pages and its further development are presented clearly in O. L. Davies, ed., *Statistical Methods in Research and Production* (Edinburgh, Scotland: Oliver & Boyd Ltd., 1958).

[2] Since the tests refer usually to a batch of material, this term will be used in preference to a "finite population."

where $i = 1, \ldots, k$ are batch numbers,

$\qquad j = 1, \ldots, n$ are item numbers,

$\qquad \mu_0 =$ grand mean of all batches,

$\qquad \phi_i =$ variation between the true means of the samples, assumed normally distributed with mean $= 0$ and variance $= \sigma_\phi^2$,

and $\quad e_{ij} =$ variation within samples, assumed normally distributed with mean $= 0$ and variance $= \sigma_T^2$.

Every e is assumed to be independent of every ϕ.

From Eq. (22.1), we can write an expression for the mean strength obtained from tests on batch i, that is, $\bar{x}_i$, as

$$\bar{x}_i = \mu_0 + \phi_i + e_i$$

or $$\bar{x}_i = \mu_i + e_i \qquad (22.2)$$

where $\mu_i = \mu_0 + \phi_i$ is the true mean of sample i.

Since we are dealing with normally distributed variables, by invoking the addition theorem (Chapter 5), we find

$$E(\bar{x}_i) = \mu \quad \text{and} \quad \text{Var}(\bar{x}_i) = \sigma_{\bar{x}}^2 = \sigma_\phi^2 + \frac{\sigma_T^2}{n}.$$

Now, $\sigma_{\bar{x}}^2$ can be estimated from the available test results, and σ_T^2 is the variance of the testing error, assumed known. Hence, σ_ϕ^2 can be readily estimated and the distribution of the underlying strength of the plastic can be determined. Assume that this is as shown in Fig. 22.5(a). Suppose further that the specification calls for a minimum strength of 3000 kN/m². In practice, we obtain n test specimens of the plastic and find their strengths. If the mean strength is greater than 3000 kN/m², we accept the batch of plastic, and, if not, we reject it. The problem is: how large should n be?

To answer this, we have to consider the testing scheme, which is characterized by the *power curve*. This shows the probability of a plastic from a batch of any given strength being accepted as satisfactory; hence, the power curve is related to the testing error. We shall recall from Chapter 15 that when we accept a value as being within a specified range, while in fact it is not, we are committing a Type II error. The power curve gives the probability of not committing this error. Figure 22.5(b) shows the shape of the power curve. An explanation for the distributions shown in Fig. 22.5(c) is given on page 498.

The steepness of the power curve indicates the discriminating power of our testing scheme. The curve becomes steeper as the sample size increases and becomes vertical for $n = \infty$. In practice, we usually compromise between the advantage of increasing the discriminating power of our test and the increased cost of more extensive testing (which may be extremely high if the test is destructive).

The power curve can be used not only with a normal distribution, but also with a t distribution; G. P. Sillito computed the number of observations needed in a t test in order to control the probabilities of Type I and II errors.[3]

[3] See W. Volk, *Applied Statistics for Engineers* (New York: McGraw-Hill, 1958).

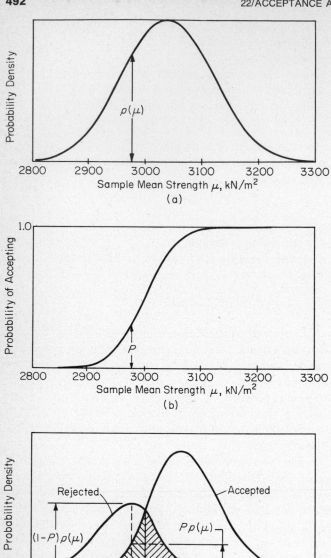

Figure 22.5 (a) Underlying distribution; (b) power curve; and (c) distribution of accepted and rejected batches.

CONSTRUCTION OF THE POWER CURVE

As we have said, the ordinate of the power curve represents the probability P that a batch of any strength μ will be accepted. In our testing scheme, we perform n tests on samples from each batch and make our decision on the basis of whether the mean of our tests, $\bar{x}$, is greater or smaller than 3000 kN/m². The results from the n tests will differ among themselves because of the testing error, which can be considered as the resultant of the sampling and measurement errors. Such testing error can be estimated from the differences among the n determinations.

The underlying distribution of the strength of the plastic is normal, and this in practice must be the case, since we are concerned with the distribution of means $\bar{x}$ (see central limit theorem, Chapter 6). Assuming that the distribution of testing errors is also normal, we can now obtain the probability P that for any given value of mean batch strength μ_0 the sample mean $\bar{x}$ will exceed 3000 and the batch will be accepted. In other words, we are testing the hypothesis $H_0: \mu_0 = 3000$ versus the alternative hypothesis $H_a: \mu_0 < 3000$, noting that we estimate μ_0 by the mean $\bar{x}$ from a sample drawn from the population.

For n observations in a sample, the standard deviation of the sample mean is $\sigma_T/\sqrt{n}$. Therefore, we calculate

$$z = \frac{3000 - \mu_0}{\sigma_T/\sqrt{n}} \tag{22.3}$$

and, using Table A.6, find the probability P of z having at most this value. [This is $0.5 + F(z)$.]

A plot of P against μ gives the power curve [Fig. 22.5(b)]. This curve is descriptive of the testing scheme and depends only on σ_T^2 and n.

It is important to note that the power curve is determined by two points only; this will be illustrated in an example later in this chapter.

From Eq. (22.3), we can see that there is a general relation between the absolute difference between the population mean and the sample mean, the standard deviation of the population, the sample size, and the probability of obtaining a difference not greater than the given one due to chance when in fact it is a "real" difference, that is, of committing the Type II error. Therefore,

$$z = \frac{|\bar{x} - \mu_0|}{\sigma/\sqrt{n}}.$$

It may be useful to consider this argument more fully. We recall that any testing scheme has an associated Type I error. The probability α of committing such an error is generally set at 5 percent or 1 percent, depending on the risk that we wish to take. Having specified the level of committing the Type I error for an acceptable testing scheme, the experimenter is faced with the problem of determining the sample size n for a desirable magnitude of the Type II error.

For a specific sample size, the plot of the probability of wrongly accepting a hypothesis (β) against μ, estimated by the measured quantity $\bar{x}$, results in an *operating characteristic curve* (briefly called an OC curve). Such an OC curve passes through two points: (μ, β) and $(\mu_0, 1 - \alpha)$. The former point arises from the fact that the testing scheme requires that we detect a level of the measured quantity $\bar{x}_1$ with an associated risk, β, of making the wrong decision. The latter point is found when we conclude that the measured quantity is μ_0 when it really is μ, with the risk of a wrong decision in this case being $1 - \alpha$. The construction of the OC curve is illustrated in Fig. 22.6. This figure shows a typical OC curve

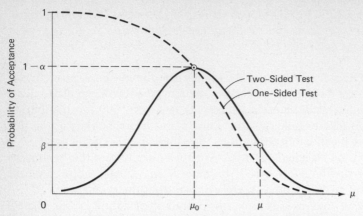

Figure 22.6   The OC curves for one-sided and two-sided tests.

for the test of the hypothesis that the mean of a normal distribution with a known standard deviation σ is μ_0 against one-sided and two-sided alternatives. In a one-sided test, we make the hypothesis that $\mu \leqslant \mu_0$ against the alternative of $\mu > \mu_0$ (or a hypothesis of $\mu \geqslant \mu_0$ against the alternative of $\mu < \mu_0$); in a two-sided test, the hypothesis is $\mu = \mu_0$ against the alternative of $\mu \neq \mu_0$. We should remember that, in an experiment, the sample mean $\bar{x}$ is used as an estimator of μ.

It may be useful to summarize the situation. Ideally, a test of significance should reject a null hypothesis when it is false. The probability of achieving this is called the power of the test. The power is a complex quantity which depends not only on the difference between the two values μ and μ_0 (i.e., the departure from the null hypothesis value), but also on the sample size, the standard deviation, the level of significance of the test, and on whether it is one or two sided. We can view the power in terms of the quantity $(1 - \beta) = (\mu - \mu_0)(\sqrt{n}/\sigma)$ (see page 301). Table 22.1 gives some of the power values

TABLE 22.1   POWER[a] $(1 - \beta)$ OF A TEST OF THE NULL
HYPOTHESIS $\mu = \mu_0$ MADE FROM THE MEAN $\bar{X}$ OF
NORMAL SAMPLE WITH KNOWN σ

Level of test	One-or two-tailed	$(1 - \beta) = (\mu - \mu_0)(\sqrt{n}/\sigma) =$				
		1.5	2	2.5	3	3.5
0.05	One	0.44	0.64	0.80	0.91	0.97
0.05	Two	0.32	0.52	0.71	0.85	0.94
0.01	One	0.20	0.37	0.57	0.75	0.88
0.01	Two	0.14	0.22	0.47	0.61	0.82

[a] Sometimes referred to as a power function.
Source: G. W. Snedecor and W. G. Cochran, *Statistical Methods,*
7th ed. (Iowa State University Press 1980).

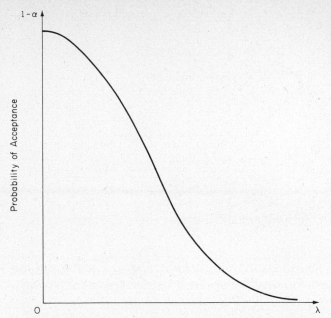

Figure 22.7   Standardized OC curve for a fixed sample size n.

which may be used to decide on the sample size. It has been suggested by Snedecor and Cochran[4] that power can be considered high when the value of $(\mu - \mu)(\sqrt{n}/\sigma)$ is at least 2.5 or 3 for tests at the 5 percent level and 3.5 for tests at the 1 percent level.

    A more useful form of the OC curve is found when the probability of acceptance of the hypothesis is plotted against a dimensionless quantity λ, where $\lambda = |\mu - \mu_0|/\sigma$, as shown in Fig. 22.7. A family of such curves for various values of sample size n is found in Figs. 22.8, 22.9, 22.10, and 22.11. The first two figures are for a two-sided normal test with a level of significance $\alpha = 0.05$ and $\alpha = 0.01$, respectively. Figures 22.10 and 22.11 are for a one-sided normal test with $\alpha = 0.05$ and $\alpha = 0.01$, respectively. For a given level of significance, the required sample size n is obtained by entering the appropriate figure with the point (λ, β) and reading out the value of n corresponding to the OC curve passing through this point. Clearly, the larger the value of n the nearer the sample result to the population value. Of course, here again μ is estimated by the sample mean $\bar{x}$. Other OC curves for the χ^2 test, F test and t test, have been derived by Ferris et al.[5]

    [4] G. W. Snedecor and W. G. Cochran, *Statistical Methods* (Iowa State University Press, 1980).

    [5] C. D. Ferris, F. E. Grubbs and C. L. Weaver, "Operating Characteristics for the Common Statistical Tests of Significance," *Annals of Mathematical Statistics*, vol. 17 (June 1946), p. 178.

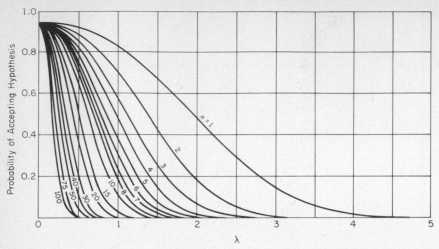

Figure 22.8 The OC curves for different values of *n* for the two-sided normal test for a level of significance $\alpha = 0.05$. [From C. D. Ferris, F. E. Grubbs, and C. L. Weaver, "Operating Characteristics for the Common Statistical Tests of Significance," *Annals of Mathematical Statistics*, vol. 17 (June 1946), p. 178.]

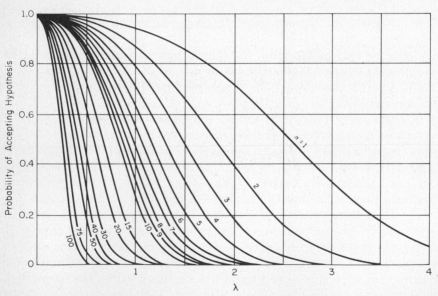

Figure 22.9 The OC curves for different values of *n* for the two-sided normal test for a level of significance $\alpha = 0.01$. [From A. H. Bowker and G. J. Lieberman, *Engineering Statistics* (Englewood Cliffs, N. J., Prentice-Hall, 1959).]

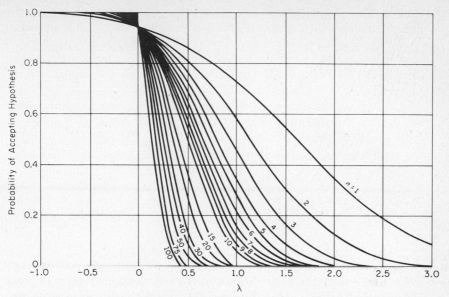

Figure 22.10   The OC curves for different values of *n* for the one-sided normal test for a level of significance $\alpha = 0.05$. [From A. H. Bowker and G. J. Lieberman, *Engineering Statistics* (Englewood Cliffs, N.J., Prentice-Hall 1959).]

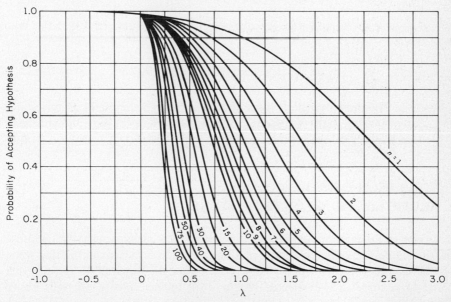

Figure 22.11   The OC curves for different values of *n* for the one-sided normal test for a level of significance $\alpha = 0.01$, [From A. H. Bowker and G. J. Lieberman, *Engineering Statistics* (Englewood Cliffs, N.J., Prentice-Hall 1959).]

EXAMPLE

Past experience with a certain type of rope has shown its breaking strength to be 195 N, with a standard deviation $\sigma = 10$ N. How many ropes do we need to test in order to detect that the actual mean strength of a consignment is 190 N? We are willing to take the risks: $\alpha = 0.05$ and $\beta = 0.10$.

Here, $\mu_0 = 195$ N and $\mu = 190$ N.

It is clear that this is a one-sided test with the null hypothesis H_0: $\mu = \mu_0$ and the alternative hypothesis $H_a : \mu < \mu_0$. Now, the number of ropes needed in a sample is determined by forcing β to be 0.1 if $\mu = 190$ N and simultaneously requiring $\alpha = 0.05$. Therefore, let us calculate λ from

$$\lambda = \frac{|\mu - \mu_0|}{\sigma}$$

$$= \frac{|190 - 195|}{10} = 0.5.$$

Since the test is one-sided with $\alpha = 0.05$, we enter Fig. 22.10 with the point $(\lambda, \beta) = (0.50, 0.10)$ and find that $n = 35$. A value $\bar{x}_c$ between 190 and 195 N becomes critical when we reject the hypothesis for observed values of $\bar{x}$ below it and accept the hypothesis for $\bar{x}$ values above it. This critical value is given by

$$\bar{x}_c = 195 - \frac{z\sigma}{\sqrt{n}}.$$

Now, from Table A.6 for $\alpha = 0.05$ [i.e., $F(z) = 0.45$], $z = 1.645$. Hence,

$$\bar{x}_c = 195 - 1.645 \times \frac{10}{\sqrt{35}} = 192.2 \text{ N}.$$

The decision rule is then: choose a random sample of 35 ropes and if the mean strength of these is less than 192.2 N, reject the null hypothesis that $\mu = 195$ N; otherwise, accept the hypothesis.   ■ ■

DISTRIBUTION OF STRENGTH OF ACCEPTED AND REJECTED BATCHES

Referring to the previous example on the strength of plastic (page 490), because the discrimination of the power curve is not perfect, it is to be expected that some of the accepted batches will actually have a strength below 3000 kN/m², and, conversely, some of the rejected batches will in fact have a strength above 3000 kN/m².

To determine the relative frequency with which batches of a strength μ are offered *and* accepted, we multiply the ordinate $p(\mu)$ of Fig. 22.5(a) by the ordinate P of Fig. 22.5(b). The product $p(\mu)P$ then gives the distribution of strength of the accepted batches. This is plotted against μ in Fig. 22.5(c).

Similarly, the distribution of strength of batches offered and rejected is given by the product $p(\mu)(1 - P)$. A plot of this is also given in Fig. 22.5(c).

The area under the "accepted" curve, as a fraction of the sum of the areas under the two curves, represents the proportion of all the batches that are accepted. The remainder represents the proportion of rejected batches.

The proportion of cases in which we accept a batch of plastic, when in fact its strength is below 3000 kN/m^2, is represented by the area under the "accepted" curve to the left of the abscissa of 3000, as a fraction of the total area under both curves. Similarly, the proportion of cases in which we reject a batch, when in fact its strength exceeds 3000 kN/m^2, is represented by the area under the "rejected" curve to the right of the abscissa of 3000, as a fraction of the total area under both curves.

The acceptable level of the percentage of "wrong decisions" depends on the consequences. Obviously, the level would have to be considerably lower when we are dealing with human life than when we fail to discriminate, for example, between the qualities of two products offered at the same price.

The method outlined here can also be used when full information about the underlying distribution is not available, but this is outside the scope of the present book.[6]

EXAMPLE

We require limestone containing at least 92 percent calcium carbonate. From past experience, the percentage of the carbonate in different batches is known to be normally distributed with a mean of 91 percent and a variance of 5 (percent)^2. The variance due to the testing error (i.e. sampling and measurement errors) obtained from a single test on each batch ($k = 1$) is known to be $\sigma_T^2 = 1$ (percent)^2. [NOTE: To avoid confusion, it is preferable not to work in percentages but in "units."]

Obtain power curves for samples (per batch of the rock) of size $n = 1, 4, 25$, and ∞. Then, for $n = 4$,

    a. Obtain the distribution of the content of calcium carbonate in accepted and rejected batches.
    b. Calculate the percentage of batches accepted.
    c. Calculate the fraction of the accepted batches that, in fact, have a calcium carbonate content below 92 percent.

Solution. We are given that the variance of the batch contents is 5 and that the variance due to testing is 1. Therefore, since k equals 1, the variance of the underlying distribution exclusive of testing error is $5 - 1 = 4$, or the standard deviation is 2.

Thus we can assume that the underlying distribution is normal with mean $= 91$ and $\sigma = 2$. This distribution is plotted in Fig. 22.12(a). To

---

[6] See O. L. Davies, ed., *Statistical Methods in Research and Production* (Edinburgh, Scotland: Oliver & Boyd Ltd., 1958).

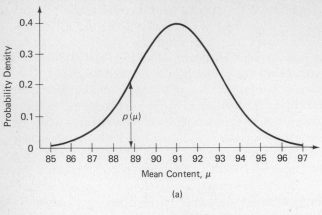

(a)

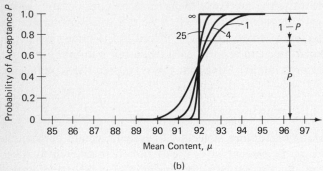

(b)

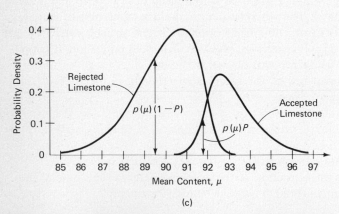

(c)

Figure 22.12 (a) Underlying distribution; (b) power curves for $n = 1, 4, 25$, and ∞; (c) distribution of accepted and rejected batches of samples size $n = 4$.

construct the power curves for $n = 1, 4, 25$, and ∞, we need to calculate P for

$$z = \frac{92 - \mu}{\sigma_T/\sqrt{n}}.$$

Hence,   For $n = 1$: $z = (92 - \mu)$

          For $n = 4$: $z = (92 - \mu) \times 2$

$$\text{For } n = 25: \qquad z = (92 - \mu) \times 5$$
$$\text{For } n = \infty: \qquad z = \infty \text{ for } \mu > 92 \text{ and } \mu < 92.$$

From Table A.6, we can find the probability P of z having at most the preceding values. [This is $0.5 - F(z)$ if $\mu < 92$, and it is $0.5 + F(z)$ for $\mu < 92$.] These values of P for various values of μ are shown in Tables 22.2 to 22.4 for the different values of n.

For $n = \infty$:

$$z = \infty \text{ for any } \mu < 92 \qquad \text{whence } P = 0.0000$$
$$z = -\infty \text{ for any } \mu > 92 \qquad \text{whence } P = 1.0000.$$

TABLE 22.2 FOR $n = 1$

μ	z	P
88.0	4.0	0.0000
88.4	3.6	0.0002
88.8	3.2	0.0007
89.2	2.8	0.0026
89.6	2.4	0.0082
90.0	2.0	0.0228
90.4	1.6	0.0548
90.8	1.2	0.1151
91.2	0.8	0.2119
91.6	0.4	0.3446
92.0	0.0	0.5000
92.4	−0.4	0.6554
92.8	−0.8	0.7881
93.2	−1.2	0.8849
93.6	−1.6	0.9452
94.0	−2.0	0.9772
94.4	−2.4	0.9918
94.8	−2.8	0.9974
95.2	−3.2	0.9993
95.6	−3.6	0.9998
96.0	−4.0	1.0000

TABLE 22.3 FOR $n = 4$

μ	z	P
90.0	4.0	0.0000
90.4	3.2	0.0007
90.8	2.4	0.0082
91.2	1.6	0.0548
91.6	0.8	0.2119
92.0	0.0	0.5000
92.4	−0.8	0.7881
92.8	−1.6	0.9452
93.2	−2.4	0.9918
93.6	−3.2	0.9993
94.0	−4.0	1.0000

TABLE 22.4   FOR $n = 25$

μ	z	P
91.0	5.0	0.0000
91.2	4.0	0.0000
91.4	3.0	0.0013
91.6	2.0	0.0228
91.8	1.0	0.1587
92.0	0.0	0.5000
92.2	−1.0	0.8413
92.4	−2.0	0.9772
92.6	−3.0	0.9987
92.8	−4.0	1.0000
93.0	−5.0	1.0000

TABLE 22.5

μ	$p(\mu)$	P	$p(\mu)P$	$p(\mu)(1 - P)$
85.0	0.0044	0.0000	0.0000	0.0044
85.4	0.0079	0.0000	0.0000	0.0079
85.8	0.0136	0.0000	0.0000	0.0136
86.2	0.0224	0.0000	0.0000	0.0224
86.6	0.0355	0.0000	0.0000	0.0355
87.0	0.0540	0.0000	0.0000	0.0540
87.4	0.0790	0.0000	0.0000	0.0790
87.8	0.1109	0.0000	0.0000	0.1109
88.2	0.1497	0.0000	0.0000	0.1497
88.6	0.1942	0.0000	0.0000	0.1942
89.0	0.2420	0.0000	0.0000	0.2420
89.4	0.2897	0.0000	0.0000	0.2897
89.8	0.3332	0.0000	0.0000	0.3332
90.2	0.3683	0.0002	0.0001	0.3682
90.6	0.3910	0.0026	0.0010	0.3900
91.0	0.3989	0.0228	0.0091	0.3898
91.4	0.3910	0.1151	0.0450	0.3460
91.8	0.3683	0.3446	0.1269	0.2414
92.2	0.3332	0.6554	0.2184	0.1148
92.6	0.2897	0.8849	0.2564	0.0333
93.0	0.2420	0.9772	0.2365	0.0055
93.4	0.1942	0.9974	0.1937	0.0005
93.8	0.1497	0.9998	0.1497	0.0000
94.2	0.1109	1.0000	0.1109	0.0000
94.6	0.0790	1.0000	0.0790	0.0000
95.0	0.0540	1.0000	0.0540	0.0000
95.4	0.0355	1.0000	0.0355	0.0000
95.8	0.0224	1.0000	0.0224	0.0000
96.2	0.0136	1.0000	0.0136	0.0000
96.6	0.0079	1.0000	0.0079	0.0000
97.0	0.0044	1.0000	0.0044	0.0000
97.4	0.0024	1.0000	0.0024	0.0000
97.8	0.0012	1.0000	0.0012	0.0000
98.2	0.0006	1.0000	0.0006	0.0000
$\sum =$	4.9947		1.5687	3.4260

The plot of P versus μ gives the power curve. These curves are shown in Fig. 22.12(b) for $n = 1, 4, 25$, and ∞. The power curve for $n = \infty$ is sometimes called the *ideal* power curve.

a. To obtain the distribution of the content of calcium carbonate in accepted and rejected batches, we have to find $p(\mu)P$ and $p(\mu)(1 - P)$ for various values of μ, corresponding to $n = 4$. These values are given in Table 22.5.

The plots of $p(\mu)P$ and $p(\mu)(1 - P)$ versus μ give the required distributions. These are shown in Fig. 22.12(c).

b. The percentage of batches accepted is obtained from the ratio:

$$\frac{\sum p(\mu)P}{\sum p(\mu)} = \frac{1.5687}{4.9947} = 31.4 \text{ percent.}$$

c. The fraction of the accepted batches that, in fact, have a calcium carbonate content below 92 percent is obtained by summing up the column $p(\mu)P$ from $\mu = 85.0$ to $\mu = 91.8$ (just below $\mu = 92$). This sum $- 0.1821$. Therefore, the required fraction $= 0.1821/1.5687 = 11.6$ percent. This is equivalent to 3.64 percent of all the accepted and rejected batches. From Fig. 22.12(c) it can be observed that the mean content of calcium carbonate in rejected batches is 90.8 percent and, in accepted batches, equals 92.6 percent. ■ ■

SIMPLIFIED CASE

In some cases, a simpler approach to deciding on the size of the sample can be adopted. For example, this is so in testing concrete, where we may be concerned with the maximum error of the mean strength determined by tests on a sample.

The t statistic of Chapter 15 can be written as

$$t = \frac{|\mu - \bar{x}|}{s_{\bar{x}}}$$

where μ is the population mean, $\bar{x}$ the sample mean, and $s_{\bar{x}}$ the standard deviation of the sample mean.

The value of t for the largest value of $|\mu - \bar{x}|$ corresponding to different levels of significance and numbers of degrees of freedom is given in Table A.7.

Now, $s_{\bar{x}} = s/\sqrt{n}$, where s is the estimate of the population standard deviation from the sample and n the sample size.

In tests on the compressive strength of concrete, the coefficient of variation within a sample is under many circumstances $V = 5$ percent.[7] Hence,

$$s = \frac{V}{100}\mu = 0.05\mu.$$

[7] W. A. Cordon, "Size and Number of Samples and Statistical Considerations in Sampling." ASTM, Special Technical Publication No. 169, 1955.

Expressing $|\mu - \bar{x}|$ as a percentage of the population mean, we put

$$E = \frac{\mu - \bar{x}}{\mu} \times 100.$$

Then,

$$t = \frac{\mu E \sqrt{n}}{V\mu}$$

whence

$$E = \frac{Vt}{\sqrt{n}}. \qquad (22.4)$$

Working at the 10 percent level of significance,[8] and using a sample size $n = 3$, we have, from Table A.7, $t = 2.920$ for $v = 3 - 1 = 2$. Then,

$$E = \frac{0.05 \times 2.920}{\sqrt{3}} \times 100 = 8.5 \text{ percent.}$$

Thus, for a sample of three specimens, the error of the mean will exceed 8.5 percent in 10 percent of the cases.

If V is based on a large number of tests, we reach in the limit t for an infinite number of degrees of freedom (cf. z of Chapter 15); at the 10 percent level of significance, we have $t = 1.645$. Then,

$$E = \frac{0.05 \times 1.645}{\sqrt{3}} \times 100 = 4.8 \text{ percent.}$$

Thus the mean of three specimens will indicate the *average* strength of concrete with an "error" of 4.8 percent of the mean, exceeded in 10 percent of the cases.

We can now consider the problem of determining the size of the sample n when the "error" in the estimated strength of concrete is not to exceed 5 percent in 90 percent of our tests. The coefficient of variation is assumed to be 5 percent. From Eq. (22.4),

$$n = \left(\frac{Vt}{E}\right)^2 = \left(\frac{0.05 \times 1.645}{0.05}\right)^2 = 2.7. \qquad (22.5)$$

The next higher integer is 3 so that we require a sample of three specimens. This is, indeed, the number commonly used.

SAMPLING OF ATTRIBUTES

A sampling plan similar to that outlined in the earlier part of this chapter can be used with attributes, such as defective items. In fact, our case of distribution of strength can be considered as that of the sampling of attributes, since each test can be classified as success (strength at least 3000 kN/m^2) or failure (strength smaller than 3000 kN/m^2). In the general case, we expect a small number of

---

[8] Ibid.

failures, or defectives; therefore, we can use the Poisson distribution as a sufficiently good approximation. (This is justified when the proportion of defectives does not exceed 0.1.)

Suppose that to inspect a batch we draw a sample of 100 and accept the batch if the number of defectives does not exceed 2 but reject it if it does. Knowing the average number of defectives in the sample,[9] we can determine from the Poisson distribution (Fig. 9.1) the probability of our sample containing 0, 1, 2, 3 . . . defectives. Conversely, from batches with different proportions of defectives (this being reflected in the average number of defectives in the samples), we can draw samples containing a specified number of defectives with a probability determined by the Poisson distribution. For example, if the batch being inspected contains 1.5 percent of defectives ($np = 1.5$), the probability of drawing a sample containing at least 3 defectives is 0.20 (from Fig. 9.1). Thus, one sample out of five will contain 3 or more defectives. We might use a sample with at least 3 defectives as a basis for rejection of the batch. We know, however, that the percentage of defectives is 1.5 percent so that we are wrong in our decision to reject in 20 percent of the cases.

Let us consider Fig. 9.1 further. We can observe that not more than 2 defectives in a sample would be obtained with a probability of 0.2 when the average number of defectives is as high as 4.3. We thus run a risk of 0.2 of accepting a batch containing 4.3 percent of defectives.

We can see that there is a definite probability of wrongly rejecting a batch and also of wrongly accepting a batch. These are, of course, the Type I and Type II errors, respectively. The former is simply the confidence level α, and the latter, β, determines the power curve associated with any sampling plan; see Chapter 15.

Instead of specifying the sample size and the acceptable number of defectives in it, we can define the curve by two points, (p_1, α) and (p_2, β), where α is the probability of rejecting a batch in which the proportion of defectives is p_1, β is the probability of accepting a batch in which the proportion of defectives is p_2, and $p_2 > p_1$.

We can plot the power curve as shown in Fig. 22.5(b), from which we read off the probabilities of accepting batches of different qualities.

The risk of a Type I error can be made as small as we wish by increasing the acceptance interval, that is, by increasing the acceptable number of defectives. We therefore usually fix this risk, and to compare procedures we compare the Type II errors.

It is important to realize that the tacit assumption underlying the procedures outlined here is that a small number of defectives is admissible; otherwise, of course, a 100 percent inspection would be necessary, and there would be no question of sampling procedure.

We should further stress that the power curve alone provides no information about the quality of the material but only gives the probability of accepting a batch containing a specified proportion of defectives. To know the qualities

---

[9] This is directly related to the proportion of defectives in the material tested.

of accepted and rejected material, we must know the underlying distribution of the material as manufactured [see Fig. 22.5(a)].

Finally, we should observe that information obtained from a sample of size n depends on the sample size only and is in no way related to the size of the batch from which the sample was drawn. Thus, provided that the batches are homogeneous, it is more economical to test large batches than small ones.

EXAMPLE

a. Construct the power curve for a sampling plan such that the risk of rejecting a batch containing not more than the specified proportion of defectives p is 0.1, when the sample size $n = 50$, and we accept samples when the number of defectives per sample is $r \leqslant 2$.

b. For approximately the same risk of wrong rejection, establish the decision rule when the sample size $n = 150$ and construct the power curve for this sampling plan.

Solution

a. Figure 9.1 shows that for the probability of 0.1 of rejecting a batch with the average number of defectives per sample np, the number r of observed defectives which is *exceeded* is as follows:

r	0	1	2	3	4	5
np	0.1	0.53	1.10	1.54	2.4	3.1

Thus, if we reject samples with $r > 2$, $np = 1.10$, whence the proportion of defectives in the batch is 0.022. Since the probability of accepting a batch is then 0.9, we have a point on the power curve $(0.022, 0.9)$.

To find a second point, consider, for example, $p = 0.08$. Then $np = 4$, and for our decision rule $r \leqslant 2$, Fig. 9.1 gives the probability of accepting a batch containing this proportion of defectives as 0.24. Therefore, the second point on the power curve is $(0.08, 0.24)$.

Some of the other points are (from Fig. 9.1):

np	6	5	3	2	1	0
Proportion of defectives in batch p	0.12	0.10	0.06	0.04	0.02	0.0
Probability of accepting the batch	0.06	0.12	0.41	0.67	0.92	1.0

b. When $n = 150$ and p is still 0.022, the average number of defects in a sample is $np = 150 \times 0.022 = 3.3$. However, bearing in mind that the actual number of defectives in a sample used as our decision rule must be an integer, we choose the nearest value of r, namely $r \leqslant 5$. For $np = 3.3$, this gives a probability of 0.12 of rejecting a batch containing not more than the specified proportion of defectives (i.e., a wrong rejection).

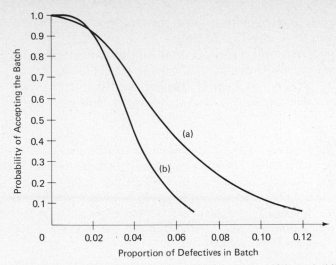

Figure 22.13   Power curves for example on page 506; probability of wrongful rejection of 0.10. (a) Decision rule: accept batch when a sample of 50 contains not more than 2 defectives. (b) Decision rule: accept batch when a sample of 150 contains not more than 5 defectives.

The power curve thus passes through the point $(0.022, 0.88)$. From Fig. 9.1, the probability of accepting a batch containing a proportion of defectives $p = 0.06$ $(np - 9)$ on the basis of our decision rule $r \leqslant 5$ is 0.12. Thus the second point on the power curve is $(0.06, 0.12)$.

Some of the other points (from Fig. 9.1) are

np	10	7.5	6	4.5	2.4	1.5	0
Proportion of defectives in batch p	0.067	0.05	0.04	0.03	0.016	0.01	0.0
Probability of accepting the batch	0.070	0.25	0.44	0.70	0.962	0.995	1.0

The two power curves are shown in Fig. 22.13. We can see that, although the risk of wrongly rejecting a batch is nearly the same with either sampling plan, the use of the larger sample ensures a better discrimination against acceptance of batches containing too great a proportion of defectives.   ■ ■

SOLVED PROBLEM

22-1. The breaking strength of a fabric has been determined from numerous tests to be 250 N, with a standard deviation due to testing of 18 N. Recently, a new manufacturing process X was introduced, which seems to increase the strength of the fabric.

    a. Find the criterion for rejecting the old manufacturing process A at a 1 percent level of significance when 36 specimens of the fabric are tested.

    b. Using the criterion found in (a), and assuming that the standard deviation remains as a result of testing at 18 N, find the probability of accepting process

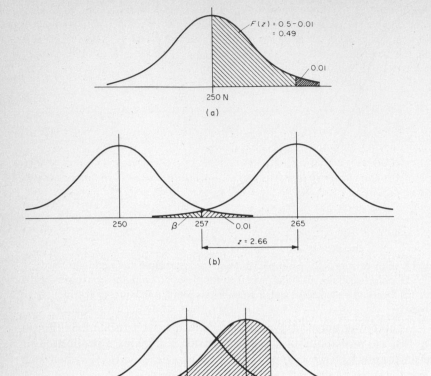

Figure 22.14

  A when process X has, in fact, improved on the mean strength to the value of
  265 N.
  c. Construct a power curve for the test of the hypothesis and interpret the graph.

Solution.   Here, $\mu_0 = 250$ N, and μ is estimated by $\bar{x}$.
  a. From Table A.6, for a one-tailed test, at a 1 percent level of significance [see
Fig. 22.14(a)], the value of z corresponding to $F(z) = 0.49$ is $z = 2.33$. But,

$$z = \frac{\bar{x} - 250}{\sigma_T/\sqrt{n}} = \frac{\bar{x} - 250}{18/\sqrt{36}} = \frac{\bar{x} - 250}{3}$$

$$= 2.33.$$

Hence, $\bar{x} = 250 + 3 \times 2.33$

$$= 257 \text{ N}.$$

Therefore, the criterion is: Reject the hypothesis that process X is the same as process
A if the mean breaking strength of 36 fabric specimens > 257 N. Otherwise, accept the
hypothesis.

b. Figure 22.14(b) shows the two normal distributions corresponding to means of 250 and 265 N. The probability of accepting process A when the new mean breaking strength is actually 265 N (Type II error) is represented by the region marked β. To calculate the probability of committing a Type II error, we proceed as follows: Deviation of 265 from 257 in terms of $\sigma_{\bar{x}}$ is

$$\frac{265 - 257}{\sigma_T/\sqrt{n}} = \frac{8}{18/6} = 2.66.$$

Hence, using Table A.6, β = area under the right-hand normal curve to the left of $z = 2.66$, i.e. $0.5 - 0.4961 = 0.0039$ (small indeed).

c. In order to draw the power curve, we have to find β for various breaking strengths of the fabric manufactured by the new process X. Thus, if the breaking strength by the new process X is, say, 255 N, then its deviation from 257 N in terms of $\sigma_{\bar{x}}$ is

$$\frac{257 - 255}{18/\sqrt{36}} = 0.67.$$

Using Table A.6, β = shaded area in Fig. 22.14(c), that is, 0.5 + the area under the right-hand normal curve between $z - 0$ and $z = 0.67$. Hence,

$$\beta = 0.5 + 0.2486 = 0.7486.$$

Following the above procedure, we can compile the following table for β corresponding to the mean breaking strength μ.

μ	240	245	250	255	260	265	270
β	1.0000	1.0000	0.9901	0.7486	0.1587	0.0039	0.0000

Plotting μ versus $(1 - \beta)$ yields the power curve shown in Fig. 22.15. This curve indicates the power of the test to reject a false hypothesis. We notice from this curve

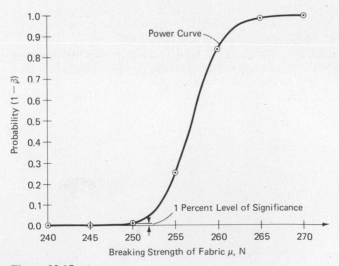

Figure 22.15

that the probability of rejecting process A if the new breaking strength is less than 250 N is practically nil. On the other hand, we see that the curve rises sharply so that it is with almost a certainty that we reject the hypothesis of maintaining process A when the mean breaking strength is greater than 265 N. Note the point of inflection on the power curve at $\mu = 257$ N and $(1 - \beta) = 0.5$.

PROBLEMS

22-1. From previous data it was found that a certain chemical process produced a mean yield of 10 units with a standard deviation $\sigma_T = 0.3$. It is believed that by a newly developed process the mean yield can be increased.

    a. If it is agreed to run 36 tests, design a decision rule for rejecting the old process at the 1 percent level of significance.

    b. Following this decision rule, what is the probability of accepting the old process, when in fact the new process has increased the yield to 10.8? Assume the same standard deviation as before.

    c. Construct the power curve for the process with $\sigma_T = 0.3$.

    d. What sample size is necessary if the power of the test is to be 98 percent?

22-2. A project requires the use of components whose density has a coded value of at least 100. It is known from past experience that the standard deviation due to testing is 11. It is decided that the probability of accepting components with a density of 94 is to be 0.1, and the probability of rejecting those with a density of 112 is to be 0.1. Find a sample size n in order to avoid having either risk exceed the desired value. Hence draw a power curve for these decision rules.

22-3. A steel company manufactures a particular steel with an average ultimate strength of 356 MPa and a standard deviation of 4.8 MPa. The manufacturer wishes to investigate whether a change in the composition of the steel alloy increases the strength. The company will take a 10 percent risk of not detecting an increase in the strength by as much as 3.4 MPa; furthermore, it wants to reach the conclusion of no change in the strength with 0.99 probability ($\alpha = 0.01$). Note that the particular change in the steel alloy is assumed not to influence the standard deviation, nor to cause a decrease in the strength.

    a. Find the required sample size n from the appropriate OC curve.

    b. If the mean strength from the sample in (a) is found to be 361 MPa, test the hypothesis that the strength is unaffected by the change in the steel alloy composition.

Chapter 23

Introduction to the Design of Experiments

The statistical methods discussed in the preceding chapters are generally used in the interpretation of experimental results. In some cases, the planning of the experiment, in the broad sense of the word, may be outside our control, but in others we may be able to decide the procedure and details of the tests. This should be done in the light of the statistical analysis which will be subsequently applied; more information can then be extracted from a given experimental effort than when the statistical aspects of the program are considered only *a posteriori*.

The design of experiments is therefore of considerable importance. In general, we require some advance knowledge of the variability of results. Such information may be available from previous work or alternatively should be obtained from pilot tests.

Broadly speaking, in designing an experiment we aim at providing specific information with reasonable statistical precision and at minimum cost. In order to achieve this objective, the experimenter must consider the following design phases of his project:

1. Define the problem. This includes: proper selection of the response to be measured; selection of the independent variables or factors (treatments) that influence the response: these may be quantitative (such as temperature or pressure) or qualitative (such as days or operators); determination of the levels of these factors; and decision as to whether to use factors that are fixed or specific (such as a given pressure) or random, that is, selected at random from some larger population of treatments.

2. Determine the number of observations to be taken, that is, the size of the sample (see Chapter 22); the random order of experimentation in order to average out the effect of all unforeseen or uncontrollable variables; and the mathematical model relating the response variable to the independent factors.

3. Finally, determine the methods of data collection, tabulation, and computation of test statistics; and make decisions about the influence of the various factors (treatments) on the measured response.

Generally, it is desirable to choose as simple an experimental design as possible, consistent with the above requirements. Using such an approach, even with a small sample size, designs of experiments have been found to be both efficient and economical.

We shall now consider the design of experiments involving several variables but, clearly, no more than an introduction to the subject can be given.

TWO-WAY CLASSIFICATION ANALYSIS OF VARIANCE (ANOVA)

In Chapter 20, we considered a one-way classification analysis of variance, ANOVA, by which we studied the variations in the response variable Y_{ij} with respect to one controllable factor (or set of treatments); there, we partitioned the total variation in the data into within-treatment variation and between-treatment variation. In this section, we shall deal with an analysis of variance involving two controllable factors (or two sets of treatments).

Let us assume that the response Y_{ij} is influenced by a treatment A, having a number of levels, and by treatment B, having b number of levels, and is modeled as

$$Y_{ijk} = \mu + \alpha_i + \beta_j + (\alpha\beta)_{ij} + e_{ijk} \tag{23.1}$$

where
$i = 1, 2, \ldots, a;$
$j = 1, 2, \ldots, b;$
$k = 1, 2, \ldots, n;$
$n =$ the number of observations per level or cell, that is, the number of repetitions or replications of the experiment;
$\mu =$ overall or grand mean;
$\alpha_i = \mu_{i..} - \mu =$ deviation of ith row mean from the overall mean, or the effect of factor A at level i;
$\beta_j = \mu_{.j.} - \mu =$ deviation of the jth column mean from the overall mean, or the effect of factor B at level j;
$(\alpha\beta)_{ij} = \mu_{ij.} - (\mu + \alpha_i + \beta_j) =$ the remainder term giving a measure of the interaction between the ith row and the jth column. (Interaction exists between factors A and B if the joint effect of the two taken simultaneously is different from the sum of their separate effects.)

For the experimental data, the observations are best arranged in tabular form as shown in Table 23.1. As before, we shall assume that the errors e_{ijk} are

TABLE 23.1   LAYOUT FOR A TWO-WAY CLASSIFICATION ANOVA, n OBSERVATIONS PER CELL

Factor A	Factor B						Totals	Row means
	Level 1	Level 2	$\cdots$	Level j	$\cdots$	Level b		
Level 1	y_{111} $\cdots$ y_{11n}	y_{121} $\cdots$ y_{12n}	$\cdots$	y_{1j1} $\cdots$ y_{1jn}	$\cdots$	y_{1b1} $\cdots$ y_{1bn}	$T_{1..}$	$\bar{y}_{1..}$
Level 2	y_{211} $\cdots$ y_{21n}	y_{221} $\cdots$ y_{22n}		y_{2j1} $\cdots$ y_{2jn}		y_{2b1} $\cdots$ y_{2bn}	$T_{2..}$	$\bar{y}_{2..}$
$\cdots$	$\cdots$	$\cdots$		$\cdots$		$\cdots$	$\cdots$	$\cdots$
Level i	y_{i11} $\cdots$ y_{i1n}	y_{i21} $\cdots$ y_{i2n}	Sum of all observations in cell (ij) = $T_{ij.}*$	y_{ij1} $\cdots$ y_{ijn}	$\cdots$	y_{ib1} $\cdots$ y_{ibn}	$T_{i..}*$	$\bar{y}_{i..}$
$\cdots$	$\cdots$	$\cdots$		$\cdots$		$\cdots$	$\cdots$	$\cdots$
Level a	y_{a11} $\cdots$ y_{a1n}	y_{a21} $\cdots$ y_{a2n}	$\cdots$	y_{aj1} $\cdots$ y_{ajn}	$\cdots$	y_{ab1} $\cdots$ y_{abn}	$T_{a..}$	$\bar{y}_{a..}$
Totals	$T_{.1.}$	$T_{.2.}$	$\cdots$	$T_{.j.}$	$\cdots$	$T_{.b.}$	$T_{...}$	$\bar{y}_{...}$
Column means	$\bar{y}_{.1.}$	$\bar{y}_{.2.}$	$\cdots$	$\bar{y}_{.j.}$	$\cdots$	$\bar{y}_{.b.}$		

$$*T_{ij.} = \sum_{k=1}^{n} y_{ijk}; \quad T_{i..} = \sum_{j=1}^{b} \sum_{k=1}^{n} y_{ijk}; \quad T_{.j.} = \sum_{i=1}^{a} \sum_{k=1}^{n} y_{ijk};$$

$$T_{...} = \sum_{i=1}^{a} T_{i..} = \sum_{j=1}^{b} T_{.j.} = \sum_{i=1}^{a} \sum_{j=1}^{b} \sum_{k=1}^{n} y_{ijk}$$

TABLE 23.2

	a	b	c	d
a′	2	4	0	1
b′	4	6	2	3
c′	5	7	3	4

mutually independent and normally distributed random variables with zero means and a common variance σ^2. We shall further assume, without loss of generality, that

$$\sum_{i=1}^{a} \alpha_i = \sum_{j=1}^{b} \beta_j = \sum_{i=1}^{a} (\alpha\beta)_{ij} = \sum_{j=1}^{b} (\alpha\beta)_{ij} = 0. \tag{23.2}$$

These constraints allow us to estimate uniquely the parameters μ, α_i, β_j and $(\alpha\beta)_{ij}$.

It is appropriate at this stage to explain the concept of interaction between factors A and B. Let us consider the numbers in Table 23.2. An examination of the numbers in the three rows reveals that the difference between any two rows is constant from column to column; similarly, the difference between any two columns is constant from row to row; such data do not exhibit any interaction between columns and rows. We can say, therefore, that interaction arises from variations in row differences from column to column, or in column differences from row to row. A graphical interpretation of interaction is shown on page 543.

We can derive point estimates of the parameters in Eq. (23.1) from our sample data; thus, we calculate the sample mean in the (i, j)th cell, the sample mean of row i, the sample mean of column j, and the overall mean, respectively, as follows:

$$\text{sample mean of } (i, j)\text{th cell} = \bar{y}_{ij\cdot} = \frac{\sum_{k=1}^{n} y_{ijk}}{n} \tag{23.3}$$

$$\text{sample mean of row } i = \bar{y}_{i\cdot\cdot} = \frac{\sum_{j=1}^{b} \sum_{k=1}^{n} y_{ijk}}{bn} = \frac{\sum_{j=1}^{b} \bar{y}_{ij\cdot}}{b} \tag{23.4}$$

$$\text{sample mean of column } j = \bar{y}_{\cdot j\cdot} = \frac{\sum_{i=1}^{a} \sum_{k=1}^{n} y_{ijk}}{an} = \frac{\sum_{i=1}^{a} \bar{y}_{ij\cdot}}{a} \tag{23.5}$$

and

$$\text{overall mean} = \bar{y}_{\cdot\cdot\cdot} = \frac{\sum_{i=1}^{a} \sum_{j=1}^{b} \sum_{k=1}^{n} y_{ijk}}{abn} = \frac{\sum_{i=1}^{a} \bar{y}_{i\cdot\cdot}}{a} = \frac{\sum_{j=1}^{b} \bar{y}_{\cdot j\cdot}}{b}. \tag{23.6}$$

Thus, from Chapter 7, the best unbiased estimates of the model parameters in Eq. (23.1) are

$$\hat{\mu} = \bar{y}_{...} = \frac{T_{...}}{N}; \qquad \hat{\alpha}_i = \bar{y}_{i..} - \bar{y}_{...}, \hat{\beta}_j = \bar{y}_{.j.} - \bar{y}_{...},$$

and

$$(\hat{\alpha}\hat{\beta})_{ij} = \bar{y}_{ij.} - \bar{y}_{i..} - \bar{y}_{.j.} + \bar{y}_{...} \tag{23.7}$$

PARTITIONING THE TOTAL VARIATION

As in the one-way classification of Chapter 20, the total sum of squares of the deviations from the overall mean, that is,

$$\sum_{i=1}^{a} \sum_{j=1}^{b} \sum_{k=1}^{n} (y_{ijk} - \bar{y}_{...})^2,$$

can be partitioned as follows. Given the identity

$$y_{ijk} - \bar{y}_{...} = (\bar{y}_{i..} - \bar{y}_{...}) + (\bar{y}_{.j.} - \bar{y}_{...})$$
$$+ (\bar{y}_{ij.} - \bar{y}_{i..} - \bar{y}_{.j.} + \bar{y}_{...}) + (y_{ijk} - \bar{y}_{ij.})$$

we square both sides and sum over $i, j,$ and k with the result

$$\sum_{i=1}^{a} \sum_{j=1}^{b} \sum_{k=1}^{n} (y_{ijk} - \bar{y}_{...})^2 = bn \sum_{i=1}^{a} (\bar{y}_{i..} - \bar{y}_{...})^2 + an \sum (\bar{y}_{.j.} - \bar{y}_{...})^2$$

$$+ n \sum_{i=1}^{a} \sum_{j=1}^{b} (\bar{y}_{ij.} - \bar{y}_{i..} - \bar{y}_{.j.} + \bar{y}_{...})^2$$

$$+ \sum_{i=1}^{a} \sum_{j=1}^{b} \sum_{k=1}^{n} (y_{ijk} - \bar{y}_{ij.})^2. \tag{23.8}$$

Using the notation of Chapter 20, we can write Eq. (23.8) as

$$\text{SST} = \text{SS}A + \text{SS}B + \text{SS}AB + \text{SSE} \tag{23.9}$$

where SST = total sum of squares, SSA = sum of squares of variations due to factor (or treatment) A, SSB = sum of squares of variations due to factor B, SSAB = sum of squares of variations due to interaction between factors A and B, and SSE = sum of squares of variations due to experimental (chance) error. The various components of Eq. (23.9) can be expressed as follows:

$$\text{SST} = \sum_{i=1}^{a} \sum_{j=1}^{b} \sum_{k=1}^{n} (y_{ijk} - \bar{y}_{...})^2 = \sum_{i=1}^{a} \sum_{j=1}^{b} \sum_{k=1}^{n} y_{ijk}^2 - \frac{T_{...}^2}{N} \tag{23.10}$$

$$\text{SS}A = \frac{\displaystyle\sum_{i=1}^{a} T_{i..}^2}{bn} - \frac{T_{...}^2}{N} \tag{23.11}$$

and

$$\text{SS}B = \frac{\displaystyle\sum_{j=1}^{b} T_{.j.}^2}{an} - \frac{T_{...}^2}{N}. \tag{23.12}$$

The interaction sum of squares, $SSAB$, is calculated in two steps. We first calculate the sum of squares of variations between the ab treatment combinations, referred to as the sum of squares among cell means:

$$SS_{\text{cell means}} = \sum_{i=1}^{a} \sum_{j=1}^{b} \frac{T_{ij.}^2}{n} - \frac{T_{...}^2}{N}. \tag{23.13}$$

It can be shown also that

$$SSA + SSB + SSAB = n \sum_{i=1}^{a} \sum_{j=1}^{b} (\bar{y}_{ij.} - \bar{y}_{...})^2$$

$$= SS_{\text{cell means}}.$$

Therefore, $SSAB = SS_{\text{cell means}} - SSA - SSB. \tag{23.14}$

The various totals, $T_{i..}$, $T_{.j.}$, $T_{...}$ are shown in Table 23.1. We have marked there the total $T_{ij.}$, which is the sum of the observations in the (ij)th cell, that is,

$$T_{ij.} = \sum_{k=1}^{n} y_{ijk}. \tag{23.15}$$

Thus, the procedure to evaluate the first term on the right-hand side of Eq. (23.13) is as follows: (a) sum all observations for each cell, (b) square each sum, (c) divide each of the squares by the number of observations in the respective cell, and (d) sum for all cells. Once SST, SSA, SSB, and $SSAB$ have been computed from the above formulae, SSE is derived from Eq. (23.9) as

$$SSE = SST - SSA - SSB - SSAB. \tag{23.16}$$

It can be demonstrated that the total number of degrees of freedom (v) is also partitioned, that is,

$$N - 1 = (a - 1) + (b - 1) + (a - 1)(b - 1) + (N - ab)$$

v for: SST   SSA   SSB   SSAB   SSE.

TEST OF HYPOTHESES

In Chapter 20, we defined the mean square (MS) for each source of variation as the sum of squares (SS) divided by its degrees of freedom, v. Thus, for a two-way classification ANOVA, we have

$$MSA = \frac{SSA}{(a-1)}; \quad MSB = \frac{SSB}{(b-1)}; \quad MSAB = \frac{SSAB}{(a-1)(b-1)}; \quad \text{and}$$

$$MSE = \frac{SSE}{(N-ab)}.$$

Following some cumbersome algebra and manipulation, it can be shown that the expected values of the above mean squares are (see procedure in Chapter 20)

$$
\left.\begin{aligned}
E(MSA) &= \sigma^2 + \frac{bn \sum\limits_{i=1}^{a} \alpha_i^2}{(a-1)} \\[2em]
E(MSB) &= \sigma^2 + \frac{an \sum\limits_{j=1}^{b} \beta_j^2}{(b-1)} \\[2em]
E(MSAB) &= \sigma^2 + \frac{n \sum\limits_{i=1}^{a} \sum\limits_{j=1}^{b} (\alpha\beta)_{ij}^2}{(a-1)(b-1)} \\[2em]
\text{and} \qquad E(MSE) &= \sigma^2.
\end{aligned}\right\} \tag{23.17}
$$

For the model defined by Eq. (23.1), there are three basic hypotheses to be tested:

$$
\left.\begin{aligned}
&H_0 : \alpha_1 = \alpha_2 = \cdots = \alpha_a = 0 \\
&H_a : \text{not all values of } \alpha_i \text{ are zero}
\end{aligned}\right\} \tag{23.18}
$$

$$
\left.\begin{aligned}
&H_0 : \beta_1 = \beta_2 = \cdots = \beta_b = 0 \\
&H_a : \text{not all values of } \beta_j \text{ are zero}
\end{aligned}\right\} \tag{23.19}
$$

$$
\left.\begin{aligned}
&H_0 : (\alpha\beta)_{11} = (\alpha\beta)_{12} = \cdots = (\alpha\beta)_{ab} = 0 \\
&H_a : \text{not all values of } (\alpha\beta)_{ij} \text{ are zero}
\end{aligned}\right\} \tag{23.20}
$$

Based on our assumption that the error e_{ijk} is normally distributed with a zero mean and constant variance σ^2, it is clear that the variable SST/σ^2 has a χ^2 distribution with $v = N - 1$. Also, under the null hypotheses of Eqs. (23.18), (23.19), and (23.20), each mean square, given by Eq. (23.17), is another unbiased estimator of σ^2. Therefore, by following the procedure of Chapter 20, we find that

$$
(a-1)(MSA)/\sigma^2 \text{ has a } \chi^2 \text{ distribution with } v = a - 1,
$$

$$
(b-1)(MSB)/\sigma^2 \text{ has a } \chi^2 \text{ distribution with } v = b - 1,
$$

$$
(a-1)(b-1)(MSAB)/\sigma^2 \text{ has a } \chi^2 \text{ distribution with } v = (a-1)(b-1),
$$

and $\qquad (N-ab)(MSE)/\sigma^2$ has a χ^2 distribution with $v = (N-ab)$.

All these χ^2 random variables are independent. Thus, from the definition of the F statistic (see Chapter 16), we can write, for factor A,

$$
F_{calc} = \frac{\dfrac{(a-1)(MSA)}{\sigma^2(a-1)}}{\dfrac{(N-ab)(MSE)}{\sigma^2(N-ab)}} = \frac{MSA}{MSE}
$$

with $v_1 = (a - 1)$ and $v_2 = (N - ab)$. Since it is expected that MSA will be greater than MSE when H_0 [Eq. (23.18)] is false, we reject H_0 at a specified level of significance α when

$$F_{calc} > F_{v_1, v_2, \alpha}.$$

The latter is given in Table A.14. Similarly, we calculate the F statistics for factor B and interaction (AB) as follows.

For factor B,

$$F = \frac{MSB}{MSE}$$

with $v_1 = (b - 1)$, $v_2 = N - ab$.

For interaction (AB),

$$F = \frac{MSAB}{MSE}$$

with $v_1 = (a - 1)(b - 1)$, $v_2 = N - ab$.

The tabulated form of a two-way ANOVA with interaction is shown in Table 23.3. It should be recalled that both factors, A and B, were assumed to be fixed, that is, we have a *fixed-effect model*. In some cases, the factors (or treatments) are randomly chosen from all possible factors; they are then considered as random samples with variance σ_A^2 and σ_B^2, say. These factors can be, for example, concrete batches, days, operators, and they often are a small sample of all possible concrete batches, days, or operators. Here, then, we are concerned with the effect of the magnitude of σ_A^2 and of σ_B^2 on the variability of the test data.

It should be stressed that the decision whether the levels of the factors should be fixed or random must be made prior to the running of the experiment. When all levels are chosen at random, we say that we have a *random-effect model*; sometimes, one or more factors are at fixed levels while the other factor(s) is at random levels, thus producing a *mixed-effect model*. Table 23.3 shows the expected MS and the appropriate ratios for the F statistic for fixed-, random-, and mixed-effect models with a two-way classification. It should be emphasized that in the case of the random- and mixed-effect models, the null hypotheses to be tested are different from those of the fixed-effect model. For example, in a two-way classification ANOVA for a random-effect model, the null hypotheses are

$$\text{for } A, \quad H_0 : \sigma_A^2 = 0;$$
$$\text{for } B, \quad H_0 : \sigma_B^2 = 0; \quad \text{and}$$
$$\text{for interaction } (AB), \quad H_0 : \sigma_{AB}^2 = 0.$$

On the other hand, in a mixed-effect model, with A fixed and B random, the null hypotheses are

$$\text{for } A, \quad H_0 : \alpha_i = 0 \text{ for all } i;$$
$$\text{for } B, \quad H_0 : \sigma_B^2 = 0; \quad \text{and}$$
$$\text{for interaction } (AB), \quad H_0 : \sigma_{AB}^2 = 0.$$

TABLE 23.3 ANOVA FOR TWO-WAY CLASSIFICATION, n OBSERVATIONS PER CELL

Source of variation	Sum of squares, SS	Degrees of freedom, ν	Mean square, MS = SS/ν	Model with effects A and B fixed — Expected mean square	Model with effects A and B fixed — Test statistic	Model with effects A and B random — Expected mean square	Model with effects A and B random — Test statistic	Model with effect A fixed, B random — Expected mean square	Model with effect A fixed, B random — Test statistic
Factor (treatments) A	SSA	$(a-1)$	MSA	$\sigma^2 + \dfrac{bn\sum_{i=1}^{a}\alpha_i^2}{a-1}$	$F=\dfrac{MSA}{MSE}$	$\sigma^2 + nb\sigma_\alpha^2 + n\sigma_{\alpha\beta}^2$	$F=\dfrac{MSA}{MSAB}$	$\sigma^2 + n\sigma_{\alpha\beta}^2 + \dfrac{bn\sum_{i=1}^{a}\alpha_i^2}{a-1}$	$F=\dfrac{MSA}{MSAB}$
Factor (treatments) B	SSB	$(b-1)$	MSB	$\sigma^2 + \dfrac{an\sum_{j=1}^{b}\beta_j^2}{b-1}$	$F=\dfrac{MSB}{MSE}$	$\sigma^2 + na\sigma_\beta^2 + n\sigma_{\alpha\beta}^2$	$F=\dfrac{MSB}{MSAB}$	$\sigma^2 + na\sigma_\beta^2$	$F=\dfrac{MSB}{MSE}$
Interaction	$SSAB$	$(a-1)(b-1)$	MSAB	$\sigma^2 + \dfrac{n\sum_{i=1}^{a}\sum_{j=1}^{b}(\alpha\beta)_{ij}^2}{(a-1)(b-1)}$	$F=\dfrac{MSAB}{MSE}$	$\sigma^2 + n\sigma_{\alpha\beta}^2$	$F=\dfrac{MSAB}{MSE}$	$\sigma^2 + n\sigma_{\alpha\beta}^2$	$F=\dfrac{MSAB}{MSE}$
Residual error	SSE	$(N-ab)=abn-ab$	MSE	σ^2	—	σ^2	—	σ^2	—
Total	SST	$(N-1)$							

TABLE 23.4 ANOVA for two-way classification, one observation per cell

Source of variation	Sum of squares, SS	Degrees of freedom, ν	Mean square, $MS = SS/\nu$	Model with effects A and B fixed		Model with effects A and B random		Model with effect A fixed, B random	
				Expected mean square	Test statistic	Expected mean square	Test statistic	Expected mean square	Test statistic
Factor (treatments) A	SSA	$(a-1)$	MSA	$\sigma^2 + \dfrac{b\sum\limits_{i=1}^{a}\alpha_i^2}{a-1}$	$F = \dfrac{\text{MS}A}{\text{MSE}}$	$\sigma^2 + b\sigma_\alpha^2$	$F = \dfrac{\text{MS}A}{\text{MSE}}$	$\sigma^2 + \dfrac{b\sum\limits_{i=1}^{a}\alpha_i^2}{a-1}$	$F = \dfrac{\text{MS}A}{\text{MSE}}$
Factor (treatments) B	SSB	$(b-1)$	MSB	$\sigma^2 + \dfrac{a\sum\limits_{j=1}^{b}\beta_j^2}{b-1}$	$F = \dfrac{\text{MS}B}{\text{MSE}}$	$\sigma^2 + a\sigma_\beta^2$	$F = \dfrac{\text{MS}B}{\text{MSE}}$	$\sigma^2 + a\sigma_\beta^2$	$F = \dfrac{\text{MS}B}{\text{MSE}}$
Residual error including interaction	SSE	$(a-1)(b-1)$	MSE	σ^2	—	σ^2	—	σ^2	—
Total	SST	$(N-1) = (ab-1)$							

The appropriate F ratios for each model are shown in Table 23.3. The calculation procedures for the SS columns are exactly the same as those for the fixed-effect model, presented earlier by Eqs. (23.10) to (23.16).

In practice, we test the significance of the interaction first; if the hypothesis is rejected, that is, significant interaction exists, then the tests for significance of the main factors A and B become irrelevant. In that case, we can still test whether the set of levels of factor A differs for a *given* level of factor B by means of a one-way ANOVA (Chapter 20). If it is justified to assume, before performing the experiment, that interaction is zero, then, in the case where there is more than one observation in a cell, $SSAB$ and SSE can be combined into a new value denoted by SSE' with $v = (a - 1)(b - 1) + ab(n - 1)$. The revised MSE then becomes

$$\text{MSE}' = \frac{\text{SSE}'}{[(a - 1)(b - 1) + ab(n - 1)]}.$$

This value of MSE' is used in the denominator of the F ratios in order to test the significance of the main factors A and B.

The ANOVA for a two-way classification where there is only *one* observation per cell, that is, there are no replications, can be deduced from Table 23.3 by putting $n = 1$; the result is shown in Table 23.4. From this table it can be seen that we postulate that no interaction exists between factors A and B, since we have no estimate of error against which we can test any possible interaction. Therefore, it is assumed here that the interaction term is zero and the model for this case can be represented by

$$y_{ij} = \mu + \alpha_i + \beta_j + e_{ij}.$$

The assumption of no interaction is often made on the basis of some strong prior information about the physical problem at hand. However, if we are not sure about the absence of interaction, we must take more than one observation per cell (i.e., replicate) and test the hypothesis of no interaction.

EXAMPLE

A steel company wishes to investigate the influence of the type of paint and of the drying time on the surface finish of their rolled sections. Three drying times, 20, 30, and 40 min, are chosen and two types of paint are selected randomly from the many types (population) that are available on the market. The company conducts the experiment by measuring the degree of abrasion on three samples for each combination of drying time and paint. The data are shown in Table 23.5.

Derive the ANOVA table. Using a 5 percent level of significance, check the effect of:

a. interaction between paint type (random effect) and drying time (fixed effect); and

b. paint type and drying time factors on the surface finish.

TABLE 23.5 DEGREE OF ABRASION (CODED DATA)

Paint (A)	Drying time(B), min		
	20 (B1)	30 (B2)	40 (B3)
A1	4	9	5
	5	6	8
	6	4	10
A2	8	9	11
	7	8	9
	6	8	8

TABLE 23.6

	B1	B2	B3	Row total
A1	4	9	5	
	5	6	8	
	6	4	10	$T_{1..} = 57$
	$\overline{15} = T_{11}$	$\overline{19} = T_{12}$	$\overline{23} = T_{13}$	
A2	8	9	11	
	7	8	9	
	6	8	8	$T_{2..} = 74$
	$\overline{21} = T_{21}$	$\overline{25} = T_{22}$	$\overline{28} = T_{23}$	
Column total	$T_{.1.} = 36$	$T_{.2.} = 44$	$T_{.3.} = 51$	$T_{...} = 131$

Solution. From the data in Table 23.5, we calculate the various required totals, as shown in Table 23.6. In this example, $a = 2$, $b = 3$, and $n = 3$. Hence, from Eqs. (23.10) to (23.16):

$$SST = 4^2 + 5^2 + \cdots + 9^2 + 8^2 - \frac{131^2}{18} = 69.61$$

$$SSA = \frac{57^2 + 74^2}{(3 \times 3)} - \frac{131^2}{18} = 16.05$$

$$SSB = \frac{36^2 + 44^2 + 51^2}{(2 \times 3)} - \frac{131^2}{18} = 18.77$$

$$SSAB = \frac{15^2 + 19^2 + 23^2 + 21^2 + 25^2 + 28^2}{3} - \frac{131^2}{18} - 16.05 - 18.77$$

$$= 0.12$$

and

$$SSE = SST - SSA - SSB - SSAB = 36.67.$$

The above values are entered in the ANOVA Table 23.7.

We can now check the significance of the interaction (AB) by calculating the F ratio as

$$F = \frac{MSAB}{MSE} = \frac{0.06}{3.05} = 0.02 < 1.$$

TABLE 23.7 ANOVA FOR EXAMPLE ON PAGE 521

Source of variation	Sum of squares, SS	v	Mean square, MS	F
Paint (A)	16.05	1	$16.05 = \text{MS}A$	267.5
Drying time (B)	18.77	2	$9.38 = \text{MS}B$	3.07
Interaction (AB)	0.12	2	$0.06 = \text{MS}AB$	<1
Error	36.67	12	$3.05 = \text{MSE}$	
Total	69.61	17		

Therefore, interaction is not significant. Also, since the two paints were selected at random from many paints on the market, the F ratio for the main factor "paint" is calculated as

$$F = \frac{\text{MS}A}{\text{MS}AB} = \frac{16.05}{0.06} = 267.50.$$

From Table A.14, the critical value of F for $\alpha = 0.05$, $v_1 = 1$, and $v_2 = 2$, is $F = 18.51 < 267.50$. Therefore, paint type affects the surface finish. Similarly, for the main factor of drying time (fixed effect), the F ratio is

$$F = \frac{\text{MS}B}{\text{MSE}} = \frac{9.38}{3.05} = 3.07.$$

The critical value of F from Table A.14, for $\alpha = 0.05$, $v_1 = 2$, and $v_2 = 12$, is $F = 3.87 > 3.07$. Therefore, drying time used in the experiment does not appear to affect the surface finish.

The above example deals with a mixed-effect model. If the steel company investigated the influence of two *particular* paints, then we would have a fixed-effect model. In such a case, the calculated F ratio for the paint type is

$$F = \frac{\text{MS}A}{\text{MSE}} = \frac{16.05}{3.05} = 5.26.$$

The critical F value from Table A.14, for $\alpha = 0.05$, $v_1 = 1$, and $v_2 = 12$ is $F = 4.75 < 5.26$. Therefore, the paint type affects the surface finish in this case, too. ■ ■

ADVANTAGES OF A TWO-WAY OVER A ONE-WAY ANALYSIS OF VARIANCE (ANOVA)

A two-way ANOVA design is much more efficient than a one-way ANOVA design, discussed in Chapter 20. Let us demonstrate this by considering the preceding example on the surface finish of steel. If we carried out a one-way ANOVA design, we would fix, in one experiment, the drying time at a certain level and measure the surface finish for the two types of paint. This experiment would be followed by another one to examine the effects of the second drying time, and so on. Under these circumstances, it is very difficult to duplicate the *same* conditions for *all* the required experiments; in consequence, the experimental error would be very large. Furthermore, in a one-way ANOVA design, we *cannot* discern the presence of interaction, if any, between the two main factors, for example, paint type and drying time.

Summarizing, we can list the following advantages of a two-way ANOVA design over a one-way ANOVA design.

1. We are able to test simultaneously the effects of two factors on the measured variable, thus saving time and experimental effort.
2. We can determine whether there is any interaction between the two main factors.
3. Since the effect of one factor can be estimated at several levels of the second factor, our conclusions are applicable over a wide range of situations.

RANDOMIZED BLOCKS

The first requirements of a properly designed experiment are that an unbiased estimate of error can be obtained and that the error be at a minimum. This can be achieved by the use of a randomized-block design.

Suppose that we wish to compare four methods of molding a plastic, and further that the material arrives in batches large enough only to permit four tests per batch. From our knowledge of engineering materials, we expect the batches to vary from one another. In statistical terminology of design of experiments, a unit such as our batch would be called a *block*.

The term has its origin in agricultural experiments, where it denoted a strip of land consisting of adjacent plots believed to be more similar to one another than plots chosen at random. This greater homogeneity of units within the block than of those chosen at random is the essential feature of a block.[1] However, the homogeneity must be related to the measurements of the dependent variable, and blocks should not be formed on the basis of irrelevant or unrelated variables. For this reason, blocks are normally formed on the basis of prior information about the units, but when dealing with random units, we can use blocks to control some sources of variation not associated with the units. For example, if we suspect a day-to-day variation in laboratory conditions, we may consider all the units tested the same day as a block. In the analysis of variance, the day-to-day variation would be eliminated from the estimate of error.

Suppose further that we are going to use each method of molding, which we shall call treatment, four times, that is, replicate four times. The question is: How should we arrange the tests?

---

[1] If all subjects are homogeneous, nothing is gained by the use of blocks.

It does not require any knowledge of statistics to realize that to assign each block to one treatment would be purposeless, for the observed differences might be those between blocks and not between treatments; we would have no information on the basis of which to decide which is the case. It is obvious, then, that the blocks have to be distributed between the treatments.

The distribution could be made at random, for example, by assigning a letter A, B, C, or D to the four treatments, and writing A on four cards, B on another four cards, and so on, putting all 16 cards in a hat, and withdrawing four for each block. We would thus determine the treatment to which the four components of each block should be subjected. An actual drawing from a hat has produced the data in Table 23.8.

This procedure would enable us to estimate the difference between the treatments, but the error of the mean value for each treatment would include the differences between blocks. Specifically, treatment D would be applied only to blocks 1 and 3, and no treatment would be applied to specimens from all four blocks. It is obvious, therefore, that we should apply each treatment to each block so that the mean value for each treatment is independent of the differences between the blocks. Our test program might therefore be as shown in Table 23.9.

It is possible, however, that some uncontrolled variables are acting, and these could influence our results. For example, if only four treatments can be performed in a day, treatment A would be applied first, and, say, with a lower temperature of the machine, we might obtain a consistently "low" reading. Or, the last treatment might be done in a hurry, and the reading could be "high." To remove such a bias, we should randomize the treatments by determining the order for each block by drawing letters A, B, C, and D from a hat. As an example, the results in Table 23.10 have been obtained. This, then, is the randomized block.

TABLE 23.8

Block	Treatment			
1	D	C	A	A
2	B	A	C	C
3	D	D	B	D
4	B	B	A	C

TABLE 23.9

Block	Treatment			
1	A	B	C	D
2	A	B	C	D
3	A	B	C	D
4	A	B	C	D

TABLE 23.10

Block	Treatment			
1	*D*	*C*	*A*	*B*
2	*A*	*D*	*B*	*C*
3	*A*	*B*	*C*	*D*
4	*C*	*B*	*A*	*D*

Since the units in each block are more homogeneous than units selected at random, the differences between blocks can be taken into account in the analysis of variance, with the result that the estimate of experimental error will be smaller than if randomized selection had been used.

We should note that the number of blocks for any treatment must be the same so that all the observations in the testing program as designed are necessary. Should one be missing (through mishap, breakdown, etc.) it has to be replaced by an estimate; this will be treated later in this chapter. On the other hand, with a completely randomized design, the analysis of variance can be applied for unequal numbers of experiments for each treatment, as was shown in Chapter 20.

To summarize then, in *completely randomized design*, the samples are assumed to have been randomly selected from k populations in an independent manner; these populations (whose means, $\mu_1, \mu_2, \ldots, \mu_k$ are to be compared) are assumed to be normally distributed with equal variances σ^2. On the other hand, in *randomized block design* comparisons are made between sets of treatments within blocks of relatively homogeneous material. An example of this is a test to compare three brands of tires in 10 cars, where each car would be driven by the same driver over the same terrain and distance and fitted by one brand of tires, the brand being assigned in a random sequence; in this manner, the car to car variation is eliminated by using the cars as blocks. With this design, 10 cars only are required to acquire the data (the 10 treadwear measurements per tire brand). Using a completely randomized design would have required 30 cars to achieve the same results. The randomized block design implies the presence of two independent variables, "blocks" and "treatments"; hence the total sum of squares SST can be divided into SSBl, SSTr, and SSE, calculated by Eqs. (23.10) to (23.12) with $n = k = 1$ and therefore no interaction term. The analysis of variance of the results of a randomized block experiment is best illustrated by means of an example.

EXAMPLE

In order to establish the temperature of complete melting of cadmium and tin alloys with various percentages of cadmium, a large piece from each of five different alloys was obtained and was cut into four smaller pieces, each of which was tested for the complete melting state. Find the influence of the content of cadmium on the melting state of the alloys. What can be said about the homogeneity of each individual large piece of alloy? The data are given in Table 23.11. Use $\alpha = 0.01$.

TABLE 23.11

| Block t (percent cadmium) | Melting point, °C | | | | |
| | Replications (pieces), r | | | | |
	1	2	3	4	Totals
40	201	185	182	179	747
50	200	195	220	199	814
60	257	240	224	225	946
70	252	228	275	250	1005
80	280	275	277	260	1092
Totals	1190	1123	1178	1113	$G = 4604$

Solution. Following Eq. (23.1) and with no interaction, the response Y_{ij} (melting point) can be modeled as

$$Y_{ij} = \mu + \alpha_i + \beta_j + e_{ij}$$

and the hypotheses to be tested are those expressed by Eqs. (23.18) and (23.19). The procedure is as follows:

a. Compute the row, column, and the grand totals as shown in Table 23.11.

b. Obtain the correction factor:

$$C = \frac{G^2}{tr} = \frac{(4604)^2}{5 \times 4} = 1,059,840.80.$$

c. Square every measurement and add:

$$(201)^2 + (185)^2 + \cdots + (277)^2 + (260)^2 = 1,082,234.00.$$

Hence, the total sum of squares is

$$\text{SST} = 1,082,234.00 - C = 22,393.20.$$

d. Replications. Square the totals of each column, sum these squares, and divide by the number of measurements in each column:

$$\frac{(1190)^2 + (1123)^2 + (1178)^2 + (1113)^2}{5} = 1,060,736.40.$$

Hence, $\text{SSRep} = 1,060,736.40 - C = 895.60.$

e. Blocks. Square the totals of each row, sum these squares, and divide by the number of measurements in each row:

$$\frac{(747)^2 + (814)^2 + (946)^2 + (1005)^2 + (1092)^2}{4} = 1,079,502.50$$

Hence, $\text{SSBl} = 1,079,502.50 - C = 19,661.70.$

TABLE 23.12

Source of variation	Sum of squares, SS	Degrees of freedom, v	Mean square, MS
Replications	(SSRep) = 895.60	$r - 1 = 3$	298.53
Blocks	(SSBl) = 19,661.70	$t - 1 = 4$	4,915.43
Error	(SSE) = 1,835.90	$(r - 1)(t - 1) = 12$	152.99
Totals	(SST) = 22,393.20	$rt - 1 = 19$	

The analysis of variance is shown in Table 23.12. The same results would be deduced from Eqs. (23.10) to (23.12) recognizing that no interaction exists (since there is only one observation per cell, i.e., $n = k = 1$) and that the correction factor C is $T^2 ./N$.

The number of degrees of freedom associated with replications is $(r - 1)$, since this is the number of classifications that can arbitrarily be assigned; similarly, there are $(t - 1)$ degrees of freedom associated with the blocks. The number of degrees of freedom associated with the residual error is obtained from the assumption that blocks and replications are independent. In other words, the variations present in the data are attributable to chance and unaccountable factors. Therefore, as explained in Chapters 14 and 20, the number of degrees of freedom in this case will be

$$rt - 1 - (r - 1) - (t - 1) = rt - t - r + 1 = (r - 1)(t - 1).$$

We calculate

$$SSE = SST - SSRep - SSBl$$
$$= 22,393.20 - 895.60 - 19,661.70$$
$$= 1835.90.$$

The value of F for blocks $= \dfrac{4915.43}{152.99} = 32.13.$

Referring to Table A.14, for $v_1 = 4$ and $v_2 = 12$, $F = 5.41$ at the 1 percent level of significance. We conclude, therefore, that the block effect is significant at that level, that is, the cadmium content affects the melting state of the alloy. The value of F for replications $= 298.53/152.99 = 1.95$, which is not significant at the 5 percent level ($v_1 = 3$ and $v_2 = 12$). Therefore, we can state that there is no evidence of each of the large pieces of alloy being nonhomogeneous. ■ ■

LATIN SQUARES

Let us now consider the situation in which we have, say, five treatments to be compared. We have 25 specimens but only 5 can be tested in any one day. We have no prior information about the specimens that would enable us to arrange

TABLE 23.13

Day	Part of the day				
	1	2	3	4	5
1	A	B	C	D	E
2	E	A	B	C	D
3	D	E	A	B	C
4	C	D	E	A	B
5	B	C	D	E	A

them in blocks. We might suspect, however, that there may be some variation between observations made on different days, and, to eliminate this effect, we would consider a group of 5 specimens tested on the same day as a block. We would, therefore, assign the specimens at random to each day, and, of the day's block, we would subject one to each treatment, A, B, C, D, and E. The procedure would be, for example, to number cards corresponding to the specimens as 1 to 25 and to make cards with letters A to E. We could then draw one number card and one letter card at a time, and this would determine which specimens are to be tested on the first day, and in what order. The letter card would then be replaced, and a further draw would determine the tests for the second day, and so on.

The analysis of variance of these results would be the same as for the randomized blocks, and the day-to-day variation would be removed from the estimate of the experimental error.

It is possible, however, that the time of the day affects the results. To remove this error, we would arrange our testing program so that each treatment occurs not only once every day but also once at a particular time of the day. Denoting the five parts of a working day by numbers 1, 2, 3, 4, and 5, we would arrange the test program so that each treatment occurs once and only once in each row and each column, as shown in Table 23.13.

Such an arrangement is known as a Latin square. Since it is a square, the number of observations (specimens) must be equal to the square of the number of treatments. Thus, with a large number of treatments, the total testing effort is high, but a high reduction in errors is achieved as every row and every column is a complete replication. The experiment should be designed so that the differences among rows and columns represent major sources of variation.

EXAMPLE

It is desired to know whether the rate of flow of fuels through different types of nozzles is affected by temperature. An experiment was carried out by six operators, A, B, ..., F, chosen at random, at six different temperatures on six different types of nozzles. The coded results are shown in Table 23.14. Use $\alpha = 1$ percent for temperature effects and $\alpha = 5$ percent for both nozzle and operator effects.

Solution. Here, there are three main factors, namely: temperature (α), nozzle (β), and operator (γ). Therefore, the response Y_{ijl} (volume of fuel)

TABLE 23.14

Temperature, °C	Volume of fuel through nozzle						
	Nozzle type						
	1	2	3	4	5	6	Totals
0	A 24	D 20	E 22	C 17	F 12	B 18	113
5	E 20	A 15	C 18	F 11	B 19	D 10	93
10	D 16	C 22	B 24	E 18	A 13	F 15	108
20	C 24	E 32	F 27	B 22	D 30	A 24	159
40	B 26	F 29	D 28	A 32	E 30	C 27	172
80	F 33	B 34	A 30	D 28	C 29	E 33	187
Totals	143	152	149	128	133	127	G = 832

Operator	A	B	C	D	E	F	Total
Totals for operators	138	143	137	132	155	127	832

can be modeled as

$$Y_{ijl} = \mu + \alpha_i + \beta_j + \gamma_l + e_{ijl}.$$

The hypotheses to be tested are those expressed by Eqs. (23.18) and (23.19) and that for the factor operator (γ), viz., $H_0 : \gamma_1 = \gamma_2 = \cdots = \gamma_6 = 0$ versus H_a: not all values of γ are zero. The procedure is as follows.

First, the totals for each row, column, operator, and the grand total G are computed as shown in Table 23.14.

Second, the correction factor C is calculated:

$$C = \frac{G^2}{r^2} = \frac{(832)^2}{(6)^2} = 19,228.44.$$

a. The sum of the squares of all measurements is then obtained:

$$(24)^2 + (20)^2 + (22)^2 + \cdots + (29)^2 + (33)^2 = 20,884.$$

$$\text{SST} = 20,884.00 - C = 1655.56.$$

b. The sum of squares of row totals is obtained and then divided by the number of measurements in each row, viz., 6:

$$\frac{(113)^2 + (93)^2 + (108)^2 + (159)^2 + (172)^2 + (187)^2}{6} = 20,486.00.$$

$$\text{SSTemp} = 20,486.00 - C = 1257.56.$$

c. Similarly, for the columns:

$$\frac{(143)^2 + (152)^2 + (149)^2 + (128)^2 + (133)^2 + (127)^2}{6} = 19,326.00.$$

$$\text{SSNoz} = 19,326.00 - C = 97.56.$$

TABLE 23.15

Source of variation	Sums of squares, SS	Degrees of freedom, v	Mean square, MS
Temperature (rows)	(SSTemp) = 1257.56	$r - 1 = 5$	251.51
Nozzle type (columns)	(SSNoz) = 97.56	$r - 1 = 5$	19.51
Operators (treatments)	(SSOp) = 78.23	$r - 1 = 5$	15.65
Residual error	(SSE) = 222.21	$(r - 1)(r - 2) = 20$	11.11
Totals	(SST) = 1655.56	$r^2 - 1 = 35$	

d. Similarly, for the operators:

$$\frac{(138)^2 + (143)^2 + (137)^2 + (132)^2 + (155)^2 + (127)^2}{6} = 19{,}306.67.$$

$$\text{SSOp} = 19{,}306.67 - C = 78.23.$$

We can now form the table of the analysis of variance (Table 23.15). The number of degrees of freedom v associated with temperature, nozzle type, and operators is obviously $r - 1$, all three variables having the same number of classifications, namely 6. The number of degrees of freedom for the sum of squares of the residual error is, in this case, $(r)(r) - 1 - (r - 1) - (r - 1) - (r - 1) = r^2 - 3r + 2 = (r - 1)(r - 2)$.

The residual error of the sum of squares is

$$\text{SSE} = \text{SST} - \text{SSTemp} - \text{SSNoz} - \text{SSOp}$$
$$= 1655.56 - 1257.56 - 97.56 - 78.23$$
$$= 222.21.$$

Each mean square is obtained by dividing the sums of squares by the corresponding number of degrees of freedom v. The variance ratio F is then computed for the different effects.

Temperature:

$$F = \frac{\text{mean square of temperature variation}}{\text{mean square of residual error}} = \frac{251.51}{11.11} = 22.64.$$

Nozzle type:

$$F = \frac{19.51}{11.11} = 1.76.$$

Operator:

$$F = \frac{15.65}{11.11} = 1.41.$$

From Table A.14, for $v_1 = 5$ and $v_2 = 20$, the F values are 4.10 at the 1 percent level of significance, 2.71 at the 5 percent level of significance, and 2.16 at the 10 percent level of significance.

We conclude that the temperature effect is significant at the 1 percent level of significance (in fact, it passes the 0.1 percent level).[2] However, both the nozzle type and the operator effects do not reach the 10 percent level of significance. (They fall between the 10 percent and the 20 percent level.)[3] Therefore, we can state that no definite effect on the volume of fuel because of different nozzles or operators is established.

Let us pursue further the effect of temperature on the volume of fuel. The mean volumes for the various temperatures are:

0°C	5°C	10°C	20°C	40°C	80°C
18.83	15.50	18.00	26.50	28.67	31.17

The estimated standard error of each of such means is $s_{\bar{y}} = \sqrt{s^2/n}$, where s^2 = residual error mean square = 11.11, and $n = r = 6$. Hence, the estimated error of each mean, $s_{\bar{y}} = \sqrt{11.11/6} = 1.361$. For testing the difference between a pair of means, the standard error is

$$\sqrt{2}\, s_{\bar{y}} = \sqrt{2} \times 1.361 = 1.924.$$

From Table A.7, the value of t at the 5 percent level of significance, for $v = 20$, is $t = 2.086$. Hence, we have for the 95 percent confidence limits: $\pm(2.086)(1.924) = \pm 4.01$; that is, the difference between two means must be at least ± 4.01 in order to reach significance at this level.

Now,

$$\text{mean volume} = \frac{832}{6 \times 6} = 23.11$$

and the 95 percent confidence interval = $23.11 \pm 4.01 = (27.12, 19.10)$.

By comparing the mean volumes for the various temperatures, we may be led to suspect that the temperature effects fall into 3 sets: $(0°C, 5°C, 10°C)$, $(20°C, 40°C)$, and $(80°C)$, but further study of the problem is outside the scope of this book. ∎ ∎

BALANCED INCOMPLETE BLOCKS

The above procedure is simple but can be applied only if each block is large enough to include all the treatments. Suppose, however, that each batch is large enough only to make four specimens, but we want to compare five treatments.

The most efficient procedure is to use five batches of four and to replicate each of the five treatments four times, the arrangement being that of a balanced incomplete block (see Table 23.16).

[2] See R. A. Fisher and F. Yates, *Statistical Tables for Biological and Medical Research* (Edinburgh, Scotland: Oliver & Boyd Ltd., 1963).

[3] *Ibid.*

TABLE 23.16

		Batch number			
	1	2	3	4	5
Treatment	A	A	A	A	B
	B	B	B	C	C
	C	C	D	D	D
	D	E	E	E	E

We can note that:

1. Each treatment occurs once and only once in four of the batches.
2. Any specified pair of treatments occurs in three of the batches (e.g., *A* and *B* can be compared in batches 1, 2, and 3).
3. The two batches in which a direct comparison of treatments (e.g., *A* and *B* in batches 4 and 5) is not possible can provide a means of comparison because they each contain the remaining three treatments, *C*, *D*, and *E*. The average of these three can be considered as a "standard" against which the difference between *A* and *B* can be assessed.

Thus, although the blocks are incomplete, for none of them contains the full number of treatments, they are balanced because each treatment occurs to the same extent. The disadvantage of this method is that the number of replications necessary may be large, generally *t* treatments requiring $(\sqrt{t} + 1)$ replications.

MULTIPLE FACTOR EXPERIMENTS

The various blocks considered up to now are applicable only to experiments containing one independent variable, which we termed treatment. In many practical cases, we may have several independent variables. This problem is often approached by keeping all independent variables but one constant in each series of tests. Although this may appear to be a reasonable approach, it is not always the best one, for the variables (referred to as factors) must necessarily be kept constant at an arbitrary value. The influence on some property of a variation in the factor *A* when the factor *B* is kept constant at value B_1 may be different from the influence when $B = B_2$. To detect this type of behavior, we may use the *factorial design* of experiments,[4] which has the additional advantage of giving the greatest amount of information about the given system of variables for the given amount of work. Specifically, information can be obtained about the interaction of the variables, that is, the

---

[4] An excellent treatment of this topic is given by K. A. Brownlee, *Industrial Experimentation* (London: H.M.S.O., 1960).

TABLE 23.17

Test number	Water/cement ratio	Type of aggregate	Type of admixture
1	0.4	Normal weight	Variable
2	Variable	Lightweight	A
3	0.7	Variable	B

dependence of the effect of one factor on the value of another. This may be of considerable importance in many engineering applications. As a simple example, let us consider tests on the durability of concrete, in which we may vary the water/cement ratio, the type of aggregate, and the type of admixture. Suppose that the tests shown in Table 23.17 have been made.

Test 1 may tell us which admixture is best from the standpoint of durability, but this finding may not be true when we use lightweight instead of normal aggregate or a water/cement ratio of 0.7 instead of 0.4. The same may apply to the influence of aggregate when different admixtures or water/cement ratios are used. Of course, none of these variables may interact, admixture A being better than B whatever the other factors, and if we *know* this to be the case we need not worry about interaction. If, however, the assumption is unwarranted, ignoring the interaction may lead to completely erroneous conclusions.

In some cases, we may choose deliberately to sacrifice the precision of the estimates of interactions, especially those of higher order, and reduce the size of the block, and achieve an increase in the precision with which the average effects of the factors are estimated. This is the principle of *confounding*.

It is important to note that factorial experiments can be applied only when the dependent variable is a function of the sums of the functions of the independent variables, namely,

$$S = F_1(x) + F_2(y) + F_3(z) + \cdots. \tag{23.21}$$

This limitation is not as restrictive as it might appear at first, because transformation can often reduce other forms to that of Eq. (23.21). For example,

$$S = x^b(\sin y)e^{fz}$$

can be transformed to

$$\log S = b \log x + \log \sin y + fz.$$

CLASSICAL THREE-FACTOR EXPERIMENT

Let us consider the problem of the durability of concrete and denote a measure of this dependent variable by x, and the three independent variables by P, Q, and R. We assume that all the variables can be expressed quantitatively, e.g. the type of aggregate can be measured by its density, etc.

Suppose that we have in hand data on the durability of concrete when P, Q, and R have values P_1, Q_1, and R_1, respectively. We now want to find the effect of changing the values to P_2, Q_2, and R_2; we are therefore concerned with only two levels of each variable.

Let us denote the effect on x of changing P from P_1 to P_2 by $(P_1 - P_2)_x$. To determine this, we observe, say, the value of x for P_1, Q_1, R_1 [denoted by $(P_1 Q_1 R_1)_x$] and the value of x for P_2, Q_1, R_1, i.e. $(P_2 Q_1 R_1)_x$. We have thus

$$(P_1 - P_2)_x = (P_1 Q_1 R_1)_x - (P_2 Q_1 R_1)_x.$$

This tells us nothing about $(P_1 - P_2)_x$ when $R = R_2$, and to determine this we would have to find

$$(P_1 - P_2)_x = (P_1 Q_1 R_2)_x - (P_2 Q_1 R_2)_x.$$

The procedure would be similar for $Q = Q_2$, and the appropriate combinations of the different values of Q and R.

The second important observation concerns the experimental error. If we make only one observation at P_1, Q_1, R_1 and one at P_2, Q_1, R_1, we cannot tell whether the difference between the observed values of x is real or is caused by the errors of sampling, testing, etc. To make an estimate of the experimental error, at least two replications of each experiment are necessary. Therefore, in order to determine $(P_1 - P_2)_x$, $(Q_1 - Q_2)_x$, and $(R_1 - R_2)_x$, each at *one* level of the other two factors, we have to perform, for example, each of the following experiments twice: P_1, Q_1, R_1; P_2, Q_1, R_1; P_1, Q_2, R_1; and P_1, Q_1, R_2. This is a total of eight observations.

FACTORIAL THREE-FACTOR EXPERIMENT

Let us now consider the factorial design of the experiment. Here, we need to perform experiments for all the possible combinations of the three factors, namely, P_1, Q_1, R_1; P_1, Q_2, R_1; P_1, Q_1, R_2; P_2, Q_1, R_1; P_2, Q_2, R_1; P_2, Q_1, R_2; P_2, Q_2, R_2; and P_1, Q_2, R_2. The number required is thus eight, which is the same as in the classical case.

Brownlee[5] represents the above combinations as coordinates of points on a system of axes P, Q, and R, with P_1, Q_1, R_1 as origin (Fig. 23.1). Then, $(P_1 - P_2)$, $(Q_1 - Q_2)$, and $(R_1 - R_2)$ are the edges of a rectangular parallelepiped. This enables us to visualize how to obtain an estimate of $(P_1 - P_2)_x$ for the various levels of the other two factors. Consider the plane containing the four points whose P coordinate is P_1. The average value of the dependent variable for these points characterizes P_1. Likewise, the average value for the plane containing the points for which $P = P_2$ characterizes P_2. The difference of the two averages is $(P_1 - P_2)_x$, that is, the effect on the dependent variable of changing the value of P from P_1 to P_2.

Although the effects of the other two factors cancel out only approximately, the accuracy of our determination is twice as high as in the classical design, since each value is a mean of four observations instead of the two in

[5] *Ibid.*

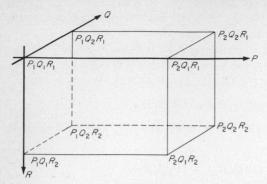

Figure 23.1   Graphical representation of a three-factor experiment.

the classical case (for the same total number of experiments). The full number of observations enters every comparison, even though each treatment contains only a limited number of observations.

We should note that the main advantage of factorial design lies in the fact that it enables us to estimate the interactions between the factors. For example, in order to estimate the interaction between Q and R, we average the values of the dependent variable for the pairs of points differing in P only. These are

$$(Q_1R_1)_x^P \qquad (Q_2R_1)_x^P$$
$$(Q_1R_2)_x^P \qquad (Q_2R_2)_x^P.$$

The top line gives $(Q_1 - Q_2)_x$ at $R = R_1$, and the bottom line gives $(Q_1 - Q_2)_x$ at $R = R_2$. Since each value is an average of two results, we can estimate the experimental error and hence determine whether $(Q_1 - Q_2)_x$ at $R = R_1$ is significantly different from $(Q_1 - Q_2)_x$ at $R = R_2$. If the difference is significant, there is interaction between Q and R. The same procedure can be used to determine the other interactions, and this gives us additional information on how each factor operates.

If the interactions are not significant, our results provide a better basis for generalized statements about the effects of each factor than if each factor had been tested with the others held at constant and arbitrary levels.

EXAMPLE

An experiment was conducted to determine the pull-off force in newtons on glued parts of a piece of furniture. The completely randomized experiment was carried out by two operators at two temperatures and two humidities. There were $n = 10$ observations for each treatment. The data are shown in Table 23.18. Use $\alpha = 0.01$.

Solution.   Total the columns as shown. Then,

   a. Calculate the correction factor:

$$C = \frac{G^2}{8n} = \frac{(2359)^2}{80} = 69,561.01.$$

TABLE 23.18

				Pull-off force, N (coded)			
Temperature, cold (A_1)				Temperature, hot (A_2)			
Humidity, 50 percent (B_1)		Humidity, 90 percent (B_2)		Humidity, 50 percent (B_1)		Humidity, 90 percent (B_2)	
Operator C_1	Operator C_2	Operator C_1	Operator C_2	Operator C_1	Operator C_2	Operator C_1	Operator C_2
9	20	27	31	35	41	42	50
16	22	28	30	39	40	40	43
20	16	19	26	32	35	35	47
18	21	15	20	28	39	30	52
24	15	17	27	25	29	21	30
12	14	14	29	40	34	36	39
15	22	27	17	33	28	47	54
16	21	29	18	32	41	49	29
14	19	25	27	28	45	50	45
13	17	23	28	29	42	53	51
$\sum = 157$	187	224	253	321	374	403	440 $G = 2359$

b. Sum the squares of all observations:

$$(9)^2 + (16)^2 + \cdots + (45)^2 + (51)^2 = 80{,}151.00.$$

c. Sum the squares of the totals of each column, and divide this sum by the number of individual observations, that is, $n = 10$:

$$\frac{(157)^2 + (187)^2 + \cdots + (440)^2}{10} = 77{,}272.90.$$

To test whether the treatment means differ significantly, we proceed as follows:

$$\text{sum of squares for total SST} = 80{,}151.00 - C$$
$$= 10{,}589.99$$

and $$\text{sum of squares for treatments SSTr} = 77{,}272.90 - C$$
$$= 7711.89$$

(see Table 23.19).

The number of degrees of freedom associated with treatments is clearly $(t - 1)$. To obtain the number for within-treatment variation, we first reckon the total number of observations, tn. Now, for each treatment (column) the sum of the deviations about the column mean must be zero, which introduces a constraint. There are t columns and hence t constraints. Therefore, by definition of the number of degrees of freedom, $tn - t$ or $t(n - 1)$ is the number of degrees of freedom associated with

TABLE 23.19

Source of variation	Sum of squares, SS	v	Mean square, MS
Between treatments (SSTr)	7,711.89	$t - 1 = 7$	1,101.7
Within treatments (SSE)	2,878.10	$t(n - 1) = 72$	39.97
Total (SST)	10,589.99	79	

within-treatment variation. Now,

$$\text{within-treatments sum of squares} = \text{SST} - \text{SSTr}$$
$$= 2878.10.$$

Testing the treatments mean square for significance, we have

$$F = \frac{1101.7}{39.97} = 27.6$$

which is much greater than the value of F for $v_1 = 7$ and $v_2 = 72$, from Table A.14 at the 1 percent level of significance. We conclude, therefore, that the treatment means differ very significantly.

Now, we can investigate the effects of the three main factors and their interactions (since there is more than one observation per cell) on the random variable response (pull-off force). This response, $Y_{ijl(k)}$, is a function of the main factors: temperature (α), humidity (β), operator (γ), and of their interactions: ($\alpha\beta$), ($\alpha\gamma$), ($\beta\gamma$), and ($\alpha\beta\gamma$). Therefore, we can write

$$Y_{ijl(k)} = \mu + \alpha_i + \beta_j + \gamma_l + (\alpha\beta)_{ij} + (\alpha\gamma)_{il} + (\beta\gamma)_{jl} + (\alpha\beta\gamma)_{ijl} + e_{ijl(k)}.$$

The hypotheses which we are testing are as follows:
For temperature,

$$H_0: \alpha_1 = \alpha_2 = 0, \text{ versus } H_a: \text{ not both values of } \alpha \text{ are zero;}$$

For humidity,

$$H_0: \beta_1 = \beta_2 = 0, \text{ versus } H_a: \text{ not both values of } \beta \text{ are zero;}$$

For operator,

$$H_0: \gamma_1 = \gamma_2 = 0, \text{ versus } H_a: \text{ not both values of } \gamma \text{ are zero;}$$

For interaction between temperature and humidity,

$$H_0: (\alpha\beta)_{11} = (\alpha\beta)_{12} = (\alpha\beta)_{21} = (\alpha\beta)_{22} = 0, \text{ versus}$$
$$H_a: \text{ not all values of } (\alpha\beta)_{ij} \text{ are zero;}$$

similarly for the other interactions.   ■ ■

PARTITIONING THE TREATMENTS SUM OF SQUARES

The treatments sum of squares, having 7 degrees of freedom, can be divided into 7 components, each with 1 degree of freedom, viz.

1. Sum of squares for A, the temperature effect.
2. Sum of squares for B, the humidity effect.
3. Sum of squares for C, the operator effect.
4. Interaction between the temperature effect and humidity effect, $A \times B$.
5. Interaction between the temperature effect and operator effect, $A \times C$.
6. Interaction between the humidity effect and operator effect, $B \times C$.
7. Interaction among the temperature, humidity, and operator effects, $A \times B \times C$.

THE MAIN EFFECTS *A*, *B*, AND *C*

To compare A_1 with A_2, we have the sum of pull-off forces:

$$\text{for } A_1 = 157 + 187 + 224 + 253 = 821 \text{ N}$$
$$\text{for } A_2 = 321 + 374 + 403 + 440 = 1538 \text{ N}.$$

For each of these, the sum is based upon $4 \times 10 = 40$ measurements. Thus

$$\text{sum of squares for } A = \frac{(821)^2 + (1538)^2}{40} - C$$

$$= 75{,}987.13 - 69{,}561.01 = 6426.12.$$

Similarly, to compare B_1 with B_2, we have the sum of pull-off forces:

$$\text{for } B_1 = 157 + 187 + 321 + 374 = 1039 \text{ N}$$
$$\text{for } B_2 = 224 + 253 + 403 + 440 = 1320 \text{ N}$$

$$\text{sum of squares for } B = \frac{(1039)^2 + (1320)^2}{40} - C$$

$$= 70{,}548.03 - 69{,}561.01 = 987.02.$$

To compare C_1 with C_2, we take the sum of pull-off forces:

$$\text{for } C_1 = 157 + 224 + 321 + 403 = 1105 \text{ N}$$
$$\text{for } C_2 = 187 + 253 + 374 + 440 = 1254 \text{ N}$$

$$\text{sum of squares for } C = \frac{(1105)^2 + (1254)^2}{40} - C$$

$$= 69{,}838.53 - 69{,}561.01 = 277.52.$$

THE INTERACTIONS $A \times B$, $B \times C$, $A \times C$, $A \times B \times C$

The interactions sum of squares may be obtained from the formula

$$A \times B \text{ interaction sum of squares} = \frac{[(a + d) - (b + c)]^2}{(4)(n_1)}$$

where the factors a, b, c, and d are sums corresponding to the arrangement shown in the following table:

	B_1	B_2
A_1	a	b
A_2	c	d

and n_1 is the number of observations contributing to each of the above sums; that is, $2 \times 10 = 20$ observations in our case. Similarly, the tables for interactions $A \times C$ and $B \times C$ are as follows:

	C_1	C_2
A_1	a	b
A_2	c	d

	C_1	C_2
B_1	a	b
B_2	c	d

Thus, the sum for:

$$A_1 B_1 = a = 157 + 187 = 344$$
$$A_1 B_2 = b = 224 + 253 = 477$$
$$A_2 B_1 = c = 321 + 374 = 695$$
$$A_2 B_2 = d = 403 + 440 = 843.$$

Similarly, the sum for:

$$A_1 C_1 = a = 157 + 224 = 381$$
$$A_1 C_2 = b = 187 + 253 = 440$$
$$A_2 C_1 = c = 321 + 403 = 724$$
$$A_2 C_2 = d = 374 + 440 = 814.$$

Finally, the sum for:

$$B_1 C_1 = a = 157 + 321 = 478$$
$$B_1 C_2 = b = 187 + 374 = 561$$
$$B_2 C_1 = c = 224 + 403 = 627$$
$$B_2 C_2 = d = 253 + 440 = 693.$$

See Table 23.20.

TABLE 23.20

	B_1	B_2	$\sum =$		C_1	C_2	$\sum =$		C_1	C_2	$\sum =$
A_1	344	477	821	A_1	381	440	821	B_1	478	561	1039
A_2	695	843	1538	A_2	724	814	1538	B_2	627	693	1320
$\sum =$	1039	1320	2359	$\sum =$	1105	1254	2359	$\sum =$	1105	1254	2359

Substituting the numerical values of a, b, c, and d in the formula, we obtain for:

$$A \times B \text{ interaction sum of squares} = \frac{[(344 + 843) - (477 + 695)]^2}{(4)(20)}$$

$$= 2.81$$

$$A \times C \text{ interaction sum of squares} = \frac{[(381 + 814) - (440 + 724)]^2}{(4)(20)}$$

$$= 12.01$$

$$B \times C \text{ interaction sum of squares} = \frac{[(478 + 693) - (561 + 627)]^2}{(4)(20)}$$

$$= 3.61.$$

The number of degrees of freedom associated with any interaction sum of squares equals the product of the degrees of freedom associated with the factors for which the interaction is being calculated; for instance, the number of degrees of freedom for $A \times B$ interaction sum of squares is the number of degrees of freedom for factor A times the number of degrees of freedom for factor B, namely, $1 \times 1 = 1$. Thus, the number of degrees of freedom for each of $A \times B$, $A \times C$, $B \times C$, $A \times B \times C$ interaction sums of squares is 1.

Since the treatments sum of squares is known, then

$A \times B \times C$ interaction sum of squares

$\quad$ = treatment sum of squares — (sum of the sums of squares for A, B, C, $A \times B$, $A \times C$, and $B \times C$)

$\quad = 7711.89 - (6426.12 + 987.02 + 277.52 + 2.81 + 12.01 + 3.61)$

$\quad = 2.80.$

The summary of the complete analysis of variance is given in Table 23.21.

The values of F were obtained by dividing each of the mean squares by the error mean square, 39.97. Since the four interaction mean squares were less than the error mean square, the F values for these were not calculated, and we can say that the four interactions are not significant.

From Table A.14, we find that for $v_1 = 1$ and $v_2 = 72$, $F = 7.00$ approximately, at the 1 percent level of significance. Thus the main effects, A and B, are highly significant. The effect of C is almost significant at the 1 percent level. It is definitely significant at the 5 percent level, where $F = 3.98$, approximately.

TABLE 23.21

	Source of variation	Sum of squares		v	Mean square	F
A	Temperature	SSA	= 6,426.12	1	6,426.12	160.77
B	Humidity	SSB	= 987.02	1	987.02	24.69
C	Operator	SSC	= 277.52	1	277.52	6.94
$A \times B$	Temperature × humidity	SSAB	= 2.81	1	2.81	
$A \times C$	Temperature × operator	SSAC	= 12.01	1	12.01	
$B \times C$	Humidity × operator	SSBC	= 3.61	1	3.61	
$A \times B \times C$	Temperature × humidity × operator	SSABC	= 2.80	1	2.80	
Error	Within treatments	SSE	= 2,878.10	72	39.97	
Totals		SST	= 10,589.99	79		

MEANING OF THE MAIN AND INTERACTION EFFECTS

The main effect of A represents a comparison between the means of force for cold temperature A_1 and for the hot temperature A_2, averaged over the two levels of B and the two levels of C. The mean for A_1 is obtained from the original data and is equal to $821/40 = 20.525$ N. The mean for $A_2 = 1538/40 = 38.45$ N. Since the A mean square is significant, we can conclude that the two corresponding population means differ significantly; that is, glued parts of a furniture piece become stronger with increase in temperature within the range of the experiment. Similarly, for the humidity effect B, the mean force for $B_1 = 1039/40 = 25.975$ N, and the mean force for $B_2 = 1320/40 = 33.00$ N. Since the analysis of variance showed the mean square for B to be significant, we can state that the population means of forces for B_1 and B_2 differ significantly; that is, the glued parts of the furniture become stronger with an increase in humidity, in the range of the experiment. The same procedure can be followed in comparing the means of force, $1105/40$ and $1254/40$, for the two operators C_1 and C_2, respectively. The difference in population means is significant at the 5 percent level but not quite significant at the 1 percent level.

The meaning of the interaction effects being nonsignificant is that the difference between the population means due to a main effect for one level is not significantly different from the difference between the population means due to the same effect at a higher level. For example, the statement that the $A \times C$ interaction mean square is not significant is interpreted to mean that the difference between population means of force due to A_1 and A_2 for the first level of C is not significantly different from the difference between the population means of force due to A_1 and A_2 for the second level of C. With a nonsignificant $A \times C$ interaction, we can state that the A effect, that is, the difference between the effect of A_1 and A_2 on the force, is independent of C; in other words, we have approximately the same difference between the effect of A_1 and A_2 on the force regardless of the level of C. Similar explanations can be made of the nonsignificance of $A \times B$, $B \times C$, and $A \times B \times C$.

GRAPHICAL INTERPRETATION

We can also examine interaction effects, say $A \times B$, by taking factor B for the x-axis and plotting the means of force for each level of A; that is, corresponding to B_1:

$$\text{mean for } A_1 = \tfrac{344}{20} = 17.2 \text{ N}$$
$$\text{mean for } A_2 = \tfrac{695}{20} = 34.75 \text{ N}$$

and corresponding to B_2:

$$\text{mean for } A_1 = \tfrac{477}{20} = 23.85 \text{ N}$$
$$\text{mean for } A_2 = \tfrac{843}{20} = 42.15 \text{ N.}$$

These values are plotted in Fig. 23.2(a). If the lines for A_1 and A_2 were exactly parallel, the $A \times B$ interaction would be zero. In fact, the lines are very nearly parallel (within the limits of random sampling), which shows that the $A \times B$ interaction is not significant. Similar graphical representation of the $A \times C$ and $B \times C$ interactions can be given.

For the nature of the $A \times B \times C$ interaction, we consider the $A \times B$ interaction separately for each level of C, as shown in Table 23.22. This table shows the means of force due to A and B for each level of C, as obtained from the original data.

The graphs for A_1 and A_2 versus B for levels C_1 and C_2, respectively, are shown in Fig. 23.2(b). We notice that the forms of these graphs are similar,

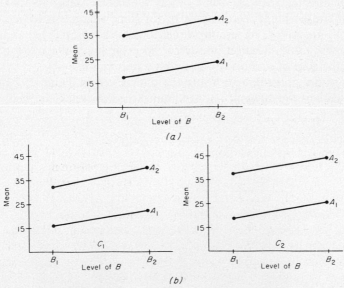

Figure 23.2 Graphical representation of the results of example on page 536. (a) Means for levels of A at each level of B; (b) means for levels of A at each level of B for C_1 and C_2, respectively.

TABLE 23.22

	C_1		C_2	
	B_1	B_2	B_1	B_2
A_1	15.7	22.4	18.7	25.3
A_2	32.1	40.3	37.4	44.0

which confirms our finding of the nonsignificance of the $A \times B \times C$ interaction mean square. In other words, this nonsignificance means that the $A \times C$ interactions for the separate levels of B are of the same form, the $A \times B$ interactions for the separate levels of C are of the same form, and the $B \times C$ interactions for the separate levels of A are of the same form.

ANOVA TABLE WITH MISSING VALUES

Frequently, an engineer or scientist meets a situation where one or more observations are missing from the ANOVA table. For example, in the previously described test to measure the loss in tread thickness in a tire, a particular tire may have ruptured before completing a certain specified distance. If the experiment is set up to deal with only a single factor (i.e., a one-way ANOVA), no difficulty is encountered since we can apply the method of ANOVA to samples of unequal size. However, for a problem with a two-way (or more) classification, if an observation is missing, then for some blocks (effects of factor A, say), $\sum_{j=1}^{b} \beta_j$ and $\sum_{j=1}^{b} \hat{\beta}_j$ are no longer zero; similarly, for some treatments (effects of factor B, say), $\sum_{i=1}^{a} \alpha_i$ and $\sum_{i=1}^{a} \hat{\alpha}_i$ are not equal to zero. See Eqs. (23.2) and (23.7). In order to rectify this situation, we derive an estimate of the missing value(s) by making the sum of squares of the errors a minimum.

Let us illustrate the procedure by using the data given in Table 23.23. The variable in the table is the difference in maximum tread thickness (in milli-

TABLE 23.23   TWO-WAY CLASSIFICATION ANOVA WITH A MISSING VALUE
[LOSS IN TREAD THICKNESS (CODED), mm]

Car	Tire brand				Total, $T_{i.}$
	A	B	C	D	
I	4	1	-1	0	4
II	1	1	-1	-2	-1
III	0	0	y	-2	$y - 2$
IV	0	-5	-4	-4	-13
Total, $T_{.j}$	5	-3	$(y - 6)$	-8	Grand total, $T_{..} = (y - 12)$

Source: Fundamental Concepts in the Design of Experiments, by Charles R. Hicks. Copyright © 1964 by Holt, Rinehart and Winston. Reprinted by permission of Holt, Rinehart and Winston, CBS College Publishing.

meters) on a tire between the time when it is mounted and the time when it has completed 20,000 miles. Four cars were used with four different brands of tires. Note that the variable y is used to denote the missing observation.

We know that

$$SST = SSTr + SSBl + SSE$$

or, for $n = 1$,

$$\sum_i \sum_j y_{ij}^2 - \frac{T^2}{ab} = \frac{\sum_j T_j^2}{a} - \frac{T^2}{ab} + \frac{\sum_i T_i^2}{b} - \frac{T^2}{ab} + SSE.$$

Therefore,

$$SSE = \sum_i \sum_j y_{ij}^2 - \frac{\sum_i T_i^2}{b} - \frac{\sum_j T_j^2}{a} + \frac{T^2}{ab}.$$

Thus, for the data in Table 23.23, we have

$$SSE = 4^2 + 1^2 + \cdots + y^2 + \cdots + (-4)^2$$
$$- \frac{[5^2 + (-3)^2 + (y - 6)^2 + (-8)^2]}{4}$$
$$- \frac{[4^2 + (-1)^2 + (y - 2)^2 + (-13)^2]}{4}$$
$$+ \frac{(y - 12)^2}{16}.$$

We minimize SSE by putting

$$\frac{d}{dy} SSE = 0.$$

Thus, $$\frac{d}{dy} SSE = 2y - \frac{2}{4}(y - 6) - \frac{2}{4}(y - 2) + \frac{2}{16}(y - 12) = 0$$

or, $$9y = -20.$$

Therefore, $$y = -2.2.$$

Inserting this value in Table 23.23, we can proceed with ANOVA in the usual manner, noting that the degrees of freedom for the error term are reduced by one, since there are only 15 actual measurements from which y is determined. If there are more missing observations than one, say $y_1, y_2, \ldots$, they can be determined by differentiating SSE partially with respect to each of the missing observations and equating the derivatives to zero, that is,

$$\frac{\partial(SSE)}{\partial y_1} = 0, \qquad \frac{\partial(SSE)}{\partial y_2} = 0,$$

and so on.

If $T_{i.}$ and $T_{.j}$ denote the totals, respectively, of the ith and jth column containing the missing value, then it can be shown that, for one missing value, y_{ij},

$$y_{ij} = \frac{aT_{i.} + bT_{.j} - T_{..}}{(a-1)(b-1)} \tag{23.22}$$

where $T_{..}$ is the grand total excluding the missing value. For the above example, using Table 23.23,

$$y_{ij} = y_{33} = \frac{4 \times (-2) + 4 \times (-6) - (-12)}{(4-1) \times (4-1)}$$

$$= -2.2$$

as before.

ANALYSIS OF RESIDUALS

In order to ascertain that the assumed model is reasonably accurate, we should attempt to check the assumptions on which the model is based; this applies regardless of whether we are dealing with a regression problem (Chapters 17 and 19) or with an ANOVA problem (Chapters 20 and 23). The check on the assumptions can be performed by studying the behavior of the residuals (a residual is the difference between an observation and the fitted value). A plot in the form of a dot diagram of the overall residuals (sum of all residuals due to the various factors or parameters), or plots of residuals for each factor, should have roughly the appearance of a sample from a normal distribution, with center at zero. When one or more residuals is very much larger (or smaller) than any of the others, this indicates an arithmetic error and the data should then be checked and corrected. Furthermore, a plot of residuals on a normal probability paper (see Chapter 11) which shows serious deviations of the data from a straight line would indicate either an error in our assumptions for the model, or an outlier (see Chapter 12).

Another possible check on the size of residuals is to examine whether there is a drift. This could be, for example, due to the diminishing skills of the experimenter with time (he might be getting tired with time) or vice versa (he might be getting better or more skilled with time). In such a case, plots of residuals versus time will not appear random. The causes of the lack of randomness should be found and, if possible, corrected.

RANDOM NUMBERS

On several occasions we have achieved randomization by drawing numbered cards "from a hat." With a large number of items involved, this becomes tedious, and it may be more convenient to use a table of random numbers, such as Table A.21.

Numerous methods of using the table exist. For example, in order to arrange the numbers 1 to 13 in a random order, we can select any row, column, or diagonal in the table, and record the numbers 1 to 13 as they occur.

It may be quicker to read all the numbers in order and to divide each by 13, recording the remainder. Any remainder that has already been obtained is rejected. Since the remainders will be between 0 and 12 inclusive, we consider 0 as 13. We should note that since the highest possible two-digit multiple of 13 is 91, the remainders 1, 2, . . . , 8 have a higher chance of occurring than others. To remove this bias, we ignore the numbers 92, 93, . . . , 99.

As an alternative, we can use the divisor 20 instead of 13, rejecting any number that gives 0, 14, 15, 16, 17, 18, 19. Thus, using the fifth column of Table A.21, we record: 7, 14, 6, 9, 6, 9, 2, 9, 15, 11, 6, 19, 2, 0 , 6, 15, 4, 17, 14, 10, 1, 6, 11, 19, 4, 16, 3, 8, 0, 5, 19, 12, 13; that is, 7, 6, 9, 2, 4, 10, 1, 11, 3, 8, 5, 12, 13.

PROBLEMS

23-1. To check the variation of gauge blocks and of the sensitive devices measuring them, the manufacturer chose at random five gauge blocks and five micrometers and asked five quality control engineers, A, B, C, D, and E to carry out the experiment. The 1-cm gauge blocks were used with the coded results given in Table 23.24. Assume there is no interaction present.

    a. Estimate the component of the variance due to micrometers.

    b. Estimate the component of the variance due to gauge blocks.

    c. Estimate the component of the variance due to engineers.

    d. Test for micrometer and gauge block effects at the 1 percent level of significance.

    e. Test for engineer effects at the 5 percent level of significance.

23-2. A car manufacturing company wishes to determine whether or not the time to perform a certain assembly operation is influenced by either the operator or the time-study engineer. The company has three time-study engineers. The four operators on this job were timed to perform the operation in question by each of the three time-study engineers. The data (in seconds) are given in Table 23.25.

    a. Establish the ANOVA table.

    b. Test the significance of the effects of "operator" and "time-study engineer" on the time necessary to perform the assembly operation. Use $\alpha = 0.05$.

    c. Estimate the variabilities in the above two factors.

TABLE 23.24

Gauge blocks	Micrometer				
	1	2	3	4	5
1	B 95	E 101	D 109	C 99	A 95
2	C 97	A 104	B 104	E 98	D 105
3	D 98	B 99	C 105	A 95	E 99
4	E 101	C 98	A 99	D 102	B 97
5	A 100	D 102	E 97	B 103	C 101

TABLE 23.25

| | Time-study engineer (B) | | |
Operator (A)	B1	B2	B3
A1	134	140	152
A2	143	138	144
A3	138	138	146
A4	144	142	149

TABLE 23.26

| | Kilometers per gallon | | |
| | Car (B) | | |
Brand of gasoline (A)	B1	B2	B3
A1	36.0	27.2	30.7
	36.4	27.8	31.1
A2	33.3	31.0	32.4
	32.7	31.4	32.2
A3	34.4	30.0	34.0
	35.0	30.2	34.2

TABLE 23.27

| | Shift | | | |
Year	12 P.M.–6 A.M.	6 A.M.–12 noon	12 noon–6 P.M.	6 P.M.–12 P.M.
1	9.8	12.1	15.8	11.7
2	9.5	11.8	15.5	11.7
3	11.8	15.5	17.2	13.6
4	13.9	15.4	17.2	14.6

23-3. Kilometer-per-gallon tests were required for three imported cars. In order to obtain these, three brands of gasoline were investigated by having a customer drive twice each car with 1 gal of each brand of gasoline. The numbers of kilometers recorded in the experiments are given in Table 23.26.

    a. Establish the ANOVA table; using $\alpha = 0.05$, check for interaction effects.

    b. Is there a brand-of-gasoline effect?

    c. Check for car effects.

    d. Estimate the variability of the random error in this experiment.

    23-4. For the data in Problem 23-3, suppose that the cars and brands of gasoline were chosen at random from their respective populations. Assuming no interaction, establish an ANOVA table. How do your conclusions differ, if at all, from the conclusions of Problem 23-3?

TABLE 23.28

Process	Source I	II	III	Process	Source I	II	III
	9	11	16		13	11	16
	12	13	15		15	13	17
A	13	13	17	B	17	14	15
	16	15	16		12	13	18
	15	16	16		15	16	18

23-5. The average production figures for four shifts measured during four years are as shown in Table 23.27. Establish the production trends within the working day and over the years. Use $\alpha = 0.01$.

23-6. In order to decide on the choice of a clay for the manufacture of artificial aggregate, samples were obtained from three sources and were treated by two processes. The coded results of the performance of the clay are shown in Table 23.28. Test whether the performance depends on the source of clay or the process by which it was treated. The 5 percent level of significance is suggested as a basis for making decisions.

Bessel's Correction

Consider a sample of size n drawn from a population with a mean μ and standard deviation σ.

Let x_i be an observation in the sample. Then,

$$x_i - \mu = (x_i - \bar{x}) + (\bar{x} - \mu)$$
$$- (x_i - \bar{x}) - \epsilon$$

where $\epsilon = \mu - \bar{x}$ is the "error" or deviation of the sample mean, $\bar{x}$. Squaring, we obtain

$$(x_i - \mu)^2 = (x_i - \bar{x})^2 + \epsilon^2 - 2\epsilon(x_i - \bar{x}).$$

For all the observations in the sample, we sum for i from 1 to n and obtain

$$\sum(x_i - \mu)^2 = \sum(x_i - \bar{x})^2 + n\epsilon^2 - 2\epsilon\sum(x_i - \bar{x}).$$

But $$\sum(x_i - \bar{x}) = 0 \text{ by definition of } \bar{x}.$$

Therefore, $$\sum(x_i - \mu)^2 = \sum(x_i - x)^2 + n\epsilon^2.$$

If we repeat this calculation for a large number of samples, the mean value of the left-hand side of the above equation will (by definition of σ^2) tend to $n\sigma^2$. Similarly, the mean value of $n\epsilon^2 = n(\mu - \bar{x})^2$ will tend to n times the variance of $\bar{x}$, since ϵ represents the deviation of the sample mean from the population mean. Thus

$$n\epsilon^2 \to n\left(\frac{\sigma^2}{n}\right)$$

whence $$n\sigma^2 \to \sum(x_i - \bar{x})^2 + \sigma^2$$

or $$\sum(x_i - \bar{x})^2 \to (n - 1)\sigma^2.$$

Thus, $$\frac{\sum(x_i - \bar{x})^2}{n - 1} \to \sigma^2.$$

In other words, for a large number of random samples, the mean value of

$$\frac{\sum(x_i - \bar{x})^2}{n - 1}$$

tends to σ^2, that is, it is an unbiased estimate of the variance of the population. The estimate is denoted by s^2. Thus

$$s^2 = \frac{\sum(x_i - \bar{x})^2}{n - 1}.$$ [4.3]

Since for a sample which has a mean $\bar{x}$,

$$\text{variance of sample} = \frac{\sum(x_i - \bar{x})^2}{n}$$ [4.2]

Bessel's correction is

$$\frac{s^2}{\text{variance of sample}} = \frac{n}{n - 1}.$$

Derivation of $P_r = e^{-\mu}\mu^r/r!$ from the Poisson Process

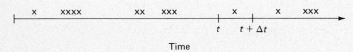

Time

Figure B.1

Figure B.1 shows the random occurrence of events marked by x on a time scale. Let there be λ events on average in a unit time interval; then there will be on average λt events in a time interval of length t.

It is assumed that (a) the probability of observing one event in a very small interval of time Δt is $\lambda \, \Delta t$; (b) the probability of more than one event occurring in Δt is comparatively very small and, therefore, can be neglected; and (c) events in nonoverlapping time intervals are independent. Let

$P_r(t) =$ probability of observing exactly r events in a time
interval from zero to time t, denoted $(0, t)$.

Consider the time interval $(0, t + \Delta t)$ as split into two adjacent and nonoverlapping intervals $(0, t)$ and $(t, t + \Delta t)$. Now, r events can occur within the interval $(0, t + \Delta t)$ in any of the following ways:

r events occur in $(0, t)$ and 0 events occur in $(t, t + \Delta t)$,

$r - 1$ events occur in $(0, t)$ and 1 event occurs in $(t, t + \Delta t)$,

$r - 2$ events occur in $(0, t)$ and 2 events occur in $(t, t + \Delta t)$, and so on. It follows, then, that for $r \geqslant 1$

$$P_r(t + \Delta t) = P_r(t) \times \text{probability of no event in } (t, t + \Delta t)$$
$$+ P_{r-1}(t) \times \text{probability of 1 event in } (t, t + \Delta t)$$
$$+ P_{r-2}(t) \times \text{probability of 2 events in } (t, t + \Delta t)$$
$$\vdots \qquad \vdots \quad \vdots \qquad \qquad \vdots$$
$$+ P_0(t) \times \text{probability of } r \text{ events in } (t, t + \Delta t).$$

From the assumptions made earlier, we then have

$$P_r(t + \Delta t) = P_r(t) \times (1 - \lambda \Delta t) + P_{r-1}(t) \times \lambda \Delta t + 0 \cdots .$$

Rearranging yields

$$\frac{P_r(t + \Delta t) - P_r(t)}{\Delta t} = -\lambda [P_r(t) - P_{r-1}(t)].$$

In the limit, as $\Delta t \to 0$, we obtain

$$\frac{d}{dt}[P_r(t)] = -\lambda[P_r(t) - P_{r-1}(t)]. \tag{a}$$

It can rigorously be shown[1] that the solution of the above differential equation, for $r = 1, 2, \ldots$, is

$$P_r(t) = \frac{e^{-\lambda t}(\lambda t)^r}{r!} \tag{b}$$

using the initial condition that $P_r(0) = 0$. It can easily be verified by substitution that Eq. (b) is the solution of Eq. (a).

For $r = 0$ we can show by similar reasoning that

$$P_0(t + \Delta t) = P_0(t) \times (1 - \lambda \Delta t) + 0$$

from which

$$\frac{dP_0(t)}{P_0(t)} = -\lambda \, dt.$$

Integrating and using the initial condition that $P_0(0) = 1$,

$$P_0(t) = e^{-\lambda t}. \tag{c}$$

Using the definition that $0! = 1$, we can combine Eqs. (b) and (c) to write

$$P_r(t) = \frac{e^{-\lambda t}(\lambda t)^r}{r!}.$$

for $r = 0, 1, 2, \ldots$. Putting the average $\lambda t = \mu$, we find that

$$P_r = \frac{e^{-\mu}\mu^r}{r!}. \tag{9.1}$$

---

[1] T. C. Fry, *Probability and Its Engineering Uses* (New York: Van Nostrand Reinhold Company, 1965), p. 217.

Mean and Standard Deviation of Terms of Expansion of $(\frac{1}{2} + \frac{1}{2})^{2n}$

Let the abscissae for which the expansion gives the ordinates vary in steps of Δx. We can then tabulate the values as shown in Table C.1. Hence,

$$\text{mean} = \mu = \frac{\sum f_i x_i}{\sum f_i} = 2np\,\Delta x.$$

Since $p = \frac{1}{2}$,

$$\mu = n\,\Delta x. \qquad [10.6]$$

Now,

$$\sum[f_i x_i^2 - f_i x_i(\Delta x)] = \sum f_i x_i^2 - (\Delta x)\sum f_i x_i.$$

Hence,

$$\sum f_i x_i^2 = (\Delta x)\sum f_i x_i + (2n - 1)(2n)(\Delta x)^2 p^2 (q + p)^{2n-2}$$
$$= 2np(\Delta x)^2 + (2n - 1)(2n)(\Delta x)^2 p^2.$$

Since $p = q = \frac{1}{2}$,

$$\sum f_i x_i^2 = n(\Delta x)^2 - \frac{n}{2}(\Delta x)^2 + n^2(\Delta x)^2$$

$$= \mu^2 + \frac{n}{2}(\Delta x)^2.$$

From Eq. (4.6),

$$\sigma^2 = \frac{\sum f_i x_i^2}{\sum f_i} - \mu^2$$

$$= \mu^2 + \frac{n}{2}(\Delta x)^2 - \mu^2$$

or

$$\sigma^2 = \frac{n}{2}(\Delta x)^2. \qquad [10.7]$$

TABLE C.1

x_i	Probability, f_i	$f_i x_i$	$f_i x_i^2$	$f_i x_i^2 - f_i x_i(\Delta x)$
0	q^{2n}	0	0	0
Δx	$2nq^{2n-1}p$	$2n\,\Delta x\,q^{2n-1}p$	$2n(\Delta x)^2 q^{2n-1}p$	0
$2\Delta x$	$\dfrac{2n(2n-1)}{2!}q^{2n-2}p^2$	$2n\,\Delta x(2n-1)q^{2n-2}p^2$	$4n(\Delta x)^2(2n-1)q^{2n-2}p^2$	$2n(\Delta x)^2(2n-1)q^{2n-2}p^2$
$\cdots$	$\cdots$	$\cdots$	$\cdots$	$\cdots$
$(2n-1)\Delta x$	$2nqp^{2n-1}$	$(2n-1)\Delta x(2n)qp^{2n-1}$	$(2n-1)^2(\Delta x)^2(2n)qp^{2n-1}$	$(2n-2)(2n)(\Delta x)^2(2n-1)qp^{2n-1}$
$2n\Delta x$	p^{2n}	$2n\,\Delta x\,p^{2n}$	$4n^2(\Delta x)^2 p^{2n}$	$2n(\Delta x)^2(2n-1)p^{2n}$
	$\overline{\sum f_i = (q+p)^{2n} = 1}$	$\overline{\begin{array}{c}\sum f_i x_i = 2np\,\Delta x(q+p)^{2n-1}\\ = 2np\,\Delta x\end{array}}$		$\overline{\begin{array}{c}\sum[f_i x_i^2 - f_i x_i(\Delta x)]\\ = (2n-1)(2n)(\Delta x)^2 p^2(q+p)^{2n-2}\end{array}}$

Evaluation of

$$\int_{-\infty}^{+\infty} e^{-(X^2/2\sigma^2)}dX$$

To evaluate the integral

$$I = \int_{-\infty}^{+\infty} e^{-(X^2/2\sigma^2)}\,dX$$

let

$$I_1 = \int_{-a}^{+a} e^{-(X^2/2\sigma^2)}\,dX.$$

Using an arbitrary variable y, we can also write

$$I_1 = \int_{-a}^{+a} e^{-(y^2/2\sigma^2)}\,dy.$$

Hence,

$$I_1^2 = \int_{-a}^{+a}\int_{-a}^{+a} e^{-(X^2+y^2)/2\sigma^2}\,dX\,dy.$$

As a physical interpretation of this integral, we can imagine that it represents the volume under a surface of height $e^{-(X^2+y^2)/2\sigma^2}$ on a square base of side $2a$ (Fig. D.1).

Let the square be $ABCD$ as shown in the figure. If we inscribe and circumscribe the square $ABCD$ by two circles, then the integral I_1^2 will be intermediate in value between the integrals I_3 and I_4, corresponding, respectively, to the volumes with the two circles as a base. Using polar coordinates, we find that

$$I_3 = \int_0^{+a}\int_0^{2\pi} e^{-r^2/2\sigma^2} r\,d\theta\,dr$$

and

$$I_4 = \int_0^{a\sqrt{2}}\int_0^{2\pi} e^{-r^2/2\sigma^2} r\,d\theta\,dr.$$

Hence,

$$\int_0^{2\pi} d\theta \int_0^{a} re^{-r^2/2\sigma^2}\,dr < I_1^2 < \int_0^{2\pi} d\theta \int_0^{a\sqrt{2}} re^{-r^2/2\sigma^2}\,dr.$$

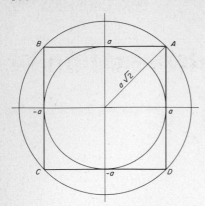

Figure D.1

However, as $a \to \infty$, the integrals on the right-hand side and the left-hand side converge to

$$2\pi \int_0^\infty \sigma^2 \frac{r}{\sigma^2} e^{-r^2/2\sigma^2}\, dr = 2\pi\sigma^2 [-e^{-r^2/2\sigma^2}]_0^\infty$$

$$= 2\pi\sigma^2.$$

Hence,

$$I^2 = \lim_{a \to \infty} I_1^2 = 2\pi\sigma^2$$

or

$$\int_{-\infty}^{+\infty} e^{-X^2/2\sigma^2}\, dX = \sigma\sqrt{2\pi}. \qquad\qquad [10.12]$$

Relation between *t* and *r*

Equation (17.35) gives the test for the significance of slope as

$$t = \frac{\hat{b}}{s_{\hat{b}}}.$$

The correlation coefficient is given by Eq. (18.9) as

$$r = \frac{\sum XY}{\sqrt{\sum X^2 \sum Y^2}}.$$

Now, from Eq. (17.20),

$$\hat{b} = \frac{\sum XY}{\sum X^2}$$

and from Eq. (17.26),

$$s_{\hat{b}}^2 = \frac{s_y^2}{\sum X^2}.$$

Also, from Eq. (17.24),

$$s_y^2 = \frac{\sum \epsilon_j^2}{n-2}$$

$$= \frac{\sum (Y - \hat{Y})^2}{n-2}.$$

Since

$$\hat{Y} = \hat{b}X$$

we can expand:

$$\sum(Y - \hat{Y})^2 = \sum Y^2 - 2\hat{b}\sum XY + \hat{b}^2 \sum X^2$$

$$= (\sum Y^2)\left[1 + \frac{\hat{b}(\hat{b}\sum X^2 - 2\sum XY)}{\sum Y^2}\right]$$

$$= (\sum Y^2)\left[1 + \frac{(\sum XY)(\sum XY - 2\sum XY)}{\sum X^2 \sum Y^2}\right]$$

$$= (\sum Y^2)\left[1 - \frac{(\sum XY)^2}{\sum X^2 \sum Y^2}\right].$$

Hence,
$$s_b^2 = \frac{\sum Y^2}{(n-2)\sum X^2}\left[1 - \frac{(\sum XY)^2}{\sum X^2 \sum Y^2}\right]$$

and
$$t = \frac{\sum XY(n-2)^{1/2}(\sum X^2)^{1/2}}{(\sum X^2)\left\{\sum Y^2\left[1 - \frac{(\sum XY)^2}{\sum X^2 \sum Y^2}\right]\right\}^{1/2}}$$

or
$$t = \frac{r\sqrt{n-2}}{\sqrt{1-r^2}}.$$

Proof That the Regression Plane Contains the Centroidal Point

Let $(\bar{y}, \bar{x}_1, \bar{x}_2)$ be the centroid of all observations. Dividing the first part of Eq. (19.8) by n, we obtain

$$\hat{b}_0 + \hat{b}_1 \frac{\sum x_1}{n} + \hat{b}_2 \frac{\sum x_2}{n} = \frac{\sum y}{n}.$$

Hence, by the definition of centroid

$$\hat{b}_0 + \hat{b}_1 \bar{x}_1 + \hat{b}_2 \bar{x}_2 = \bar{y}$$

which proves that $(\bar{y}, \bar{x}_1, \bar{x}_2)$ lies on the plane.

Tables in Appendix

TABLE A.1 RANGE COEFFICIENT d

Number of observations, n	Coefficient, d	Number of observations, n	Coefficient, d
2	0.8862	14	0.2935
3	0.5908	15	0.2880
4	0.4857	16	0.2831
5	0.4299	17	0.2787
6	0.3945	18	0.2747
7	0.3698	19	0.2711
8	0.3512	20	0.2677
9	0.3367	24	0.2567
10	0.3249	50	0.2223
11	0.3152	100	0.1994
12	0.3069	1000	0.1543
13	0.2998		

This table gives values of d in equation $s = \bar{R}d$ for the estimate of the standard deviation from mean range $\bar{R}$. This method of estimating s is valid only when the underlying variate is approximately normally distributed.

This table is reproduced by permission of the author and the publishers from a paper "On the Extreme Individuals and the Range of Samples Taken from a Normal Population," by L. H. C. Tippett, *Biometrika*, vol. 17, 1925, pp. 364–387 and from Table 22 of *Biometrika Tables for Statisticians*, vol. 1 (London: Cambridge University Press, 1954).

TABLE A.2 CUMULATIVE TERMS OF BINOMIAL DISTRIBUTION

						p					
n	r'	.05	.10	.15	.20	.25	.30	.35	.40	.45	.50
2	1	.0975	.1900	.2775	.3600	.4375	.5100	.5775	.6400	.6975	.7500
	2	.0025	.0100	.0225	.0400	.0625	.0900	.1225	.1600	.2025	.2500
3	1	.1426	.2710	.3859	.4880	.5781	.6570	.7254	.7840	.8336	.8750
	2	.0072	.0280	.0608	.1040	.1562	.2160	.2818	.3520	.4252	.5000
	3	.0001	.0010	.0034	.0080	.0156	.0270	.0429	.0640	.0911	.1250
4	1	.1855	.3439	.4780	.5904	.6836	.7599	.8215	.8704	.9085	.9375
	2	.0140	.0523	.1095	.1808	.2617	.3483	.4370	.5248	.6090	.6875
	3	.0005	.0037	.0120	.0272	.0508	.0837	.1265	.1792	.2415	.3125
	4	.0000	.0001	.0005	.0016	.0039	.0081	.0150	.0256	.0410	.0625
5	1	.2262	.4095	.5563	.6723	.7627	.8319	.8840	.9222	.9497	.9688
	2	.0226	.0815	.1648	.2627	.3672	.4718	.5716	.6630	.7438	.8125
	3	.0012	.0086	.0266	.0579	.1035	.1631	.2352	.3174	.4069	.5000
	4	.0000	.0005	.0022	.0067	.0156	.0308	.0540	.0870	.1312	.1875
	5	.0000	.0000	.0001	.0003	.0010	.0024	.0053	.0102	.0185	.0312
6	1	.2649	.4686	.6229	.7379	.8220	.8824	.9246	.9533	.9723	.9844
	2	.0328	.1143	.2235	.3447	.4661	.5798	.6809	.7667	.8364	.8906
	3	.0022	.0158	.0473	.0989	.1694	.2557	.3529	.4557	.5585	.6562
	4	.0001	.0013	.0059	.0170	.0376	.0705	.1174	.1792	.2553	.3438
	5	.0000	.0001	.0004	.0016	.0046	.0109	.0223	.0410	.0692	.1094
	6	.0000	.0000	.0000	.0001	.0002	.0007	.0018	.0041	.0083	.0156
7	1	.3017	.5217	.6794	.7903	.8665	.9176	.9510	.9720	.9848	.9922
	2	.0444	.1497	.2834	.4233	.5551	.6706	.7662	.8414	.8976	.9375
	3	.0038	.0257	.0738	.1480	.2436	.3529	.4677	.5801	.6836	.7734
	4	.0002	.0027	.0121	.0333	.0706	.1260	.1998	.2898	.3917	.5000
	5	.0000	.0002	.0012	.0047	.0129	.0288	.0556	.0963	.1529	.2266
	6	.0000	.0000	.0001	.0004	.0013	.0038	.0090	.0188	.0357	.0625
	7	.0000	.0000	.0000	.0000	.0001	.0002	.0006	.0016	.0037	.0078
8	1	.3366	.5695	.7275	.8322	.8999	.9424	.9681	.9832	.9916	.9961
	2	.0572	.1869	.3428	.4967	.6329	.7447	.8309	.8936	.9368	.9648
	3	.0058	.0381	.1052	.2031	.3215	.4482	.5722	.6846	.7799	.8555
	4	.0004	.0050	.0214	.0563	.1138	.1941	.2936	.4059	.5230	.6367
	5	.0000	.0004	.0029	.0104	.0273	.0580	.1061	.1737	.2604	.3633
	6	.0000	.0000	.0002	.0012	.0042	.0113	.0253	.0498	.0885	.1445
	7	.0000	.0000	.0000	.0001	.0004	.0013	.0036	.0085	.0181	.0352
	8	.0000	.0000	.0000	.0000	.0000	.0001	.0002	.0007	.0017	.0039
9	1	.3698	.6126	.7684	.8658	.9249	.9596	.9793	.9899	.9954	.9980
	2	.0712	.2252	.4005	.5638	.6997	.8040	.8789	.9295	.9615	.9805
	3	.0084	.0530	.1409	.2618	.3993	.5372	.6627	.7682	.8505	.9102
	4	.0006	.0083	.0339	.0856	.1657	.2703	.3911	.5174	.6386	.7461
	5	.0000	.0009	.0056	.0196	.0489	.0988	.1717	.2666	.3786	.5000
	6	.0000	.0001	.0006	.0031	.0100	.0253	.0536	.0994	.1658	.2539
	7	.0000	.0000	.0000	.0003	.0013	.0043	.0112	.0250	.0498	.0898
	8	.0000	.0000	.0000	.0000	.0001	.0004	.0014	.0038	.0091	.0195
	9	.0000	.0000	.0000	.0000	.0000	.0000	.0001	.0003	.0008	.0020
10	1	.4013	.6513	.8031	.8926	.9437	.9718	.9865	.9940	.9975	.9990
	2	.0861	.2639	.4557	.6242	.7560	.8507	.9140	.9536	.9767	.9893
	3	.0115	.0702	.1798	.3222	.4744	.6172	.7384	.8327	.9004	.9453
	4	.0010	.0128	.0500	.1209	.2241	.3504	.4862	.6177	.7340	.8281
	5	.0001	.0016	.0099	.0328	.0781	.1503	.2485	.3669	.4956	.6230
	6	.0000	.0001	.0014	.0064	.0197	.0473	.0949	.1662	.2616	.3770
	7	.0000	.0000	.0001	.0009	.0035	.0106	.0260	.0548	.1020	.1719
	8	.0000	.0000	.0000	.0001	.0004	.0016	.0048	.0123	.0274	.0547
	9	.0000	.0000	.0000	.0000	.0000	.0001	.0005	.0017	.0045	.0107
	10	.0000	.0000	.0000	.0000	.0000	.0000	.0000	.0001	.0003	.0010

(*continued*)

TABLE A.2 (CONTINUED)

n	r'	.05	.10	.15	.20	.25	.30	.35	.40	.45	.50
						p					
12	1	.4596	.7176	.8578	.9313	.9683	.9862	.9943	.9978	.9992	.9998
	2	.1184	.3410	.5565	.7251	.8416	.9150	.9576	.9804	.9917	.9968
	3	.0196	.1109	.2642	.4417	.6093	.7472	.8487	.9166	.9579	.9807
	4	.0022	.0256	.0922	.2054	.3512	.5075	.6533	.7747	.8655	.9270
	5	.0002	.0043	.0239	.0726	.1576	.2763	.4167	.5618	.6956	.8062
	6	.0000	.0005	.0046	.0194	.0544	.1178	.2127	.3348	.4731	.6128
	7	.0000	.0001	.0007	.0039	.0143	.0386	.0846	.1582	.2607	.3872
	8	.0000	.0000	.0001	.0006	.0028	.0095	.0255	.0573	.1117	.1938
	9	.0000	.0000	.0000	.0001	.0004	.0017	.0056	.0153	.0356	.0730
	10	.0000	.0000	.0000	.0000	.0000	.0002	.0008	.0028	.0079	.0193
	11	.0000	.0000	.0000	.0000	.0000	.0000	.0001	.0003	.0011	.0032
	12	.0000	.0000	.0000	.0000	.0000	.0000	.0000	.0000	.0001	.0002
15	1	.5367	.7941	.9126	.9648	.9866	.9953	.9984	.9995	.9999	1.0000
	2	.1710	.4510	.6814	.8329	.9198	.9647	.9858	.9948	.9983	.9995
	3	.0362	.1841	.3958	.6020	.7639	.8732	.9383	.9729	.9893	.9963
	4	.0055	.0556	.1773	.3518	.5387	.7031	.8273	.9095	.9576	.9824
	5	.0006	.0127	.0617	.1642	.3135	.4845	.6481	.7827	.8796	.9408
	6	.0001	.0022	.0168	.0611	.1484	.2784	.4357	.5968	.7392	.8491
	7	.0000	.0003	.0036	.0181	.0566	.1311	.2452	.3902	.5478	.6964
	8	.0000	.0000	.0006	.0042	.0173	.0500	.1132	.2131	.3465	.5000
	9	.0000	.0000	.0001	.0008	.0042	.0152	.0422	.0950	.1818	.3036
	10	.0000	.0000	.0000	.0001	.0008	.0037	.0124	.0338	.0769	.1509
	11	.0000	.0000	.0000	.0000	.0001	.0007	.0028	.0093	.0255	.0592
	12	.0000	.0000	.0000	.0000	.0000	.0001	.0005	.0019	.0063	.0176
	13	.0000	.0000	.0000	.0000	.0000	.0000	.0001	.0003	.0011	.0037
	14	.0000	.0000	.0000	.0000	.0000	.0000	.0000	.0000	.0001	.0005
	15	.0000	.0000	.0000	.0000	.0000	.0000	.0000	.0000	.0000	.0000
20	1	.6415	.8784	.9612	.9885	.9968	.9992	.9998	1.0000	1.0000	1.0000
	2	.2642	.6083	.8244	.9308	.9757	.9924	.9979	.9995	.9999	1.0000
	3	.0755	.3231	.5951	.7939	.9087	.9645	.9879	.9964	.9991	.9998
	4	.0159	.1330	.3523	.5886	.7748	.8929	.9556	.9840	.9951	.9987
	5	.0026	.0432	.1702	.3704	.5852	.7625	.8818	.9490	.9811	.9941
	6	.0003	.0113	.0673	.1958	.3828	.5836	.7546	.8744	.9447	.9793
	7	.0000	.0024	.0219	.0867	.2142	.3920	.5834	.7500	.8701	.9423
	8	.0000	.0004	.0059	.0321	.1018	.2277	.3990	.5841	.7480	.8684
	9	.0000	.0001	.0013	.0100	.0409	.1133	.2376	.4044	.5857	.7483
	10	.0000	.0000	.0002	.0026	.0139	.0480	.1218	.2447	.4086	.5881
	11	.0000	.0000	.0000	.0006	.0039	.0171	.0532	.1275	.2493	.4119
	12	.0000	.0000	.0000	.0001	.0009	.0051	.0196	.0565	.1308	.2517
	13	.0000	.0000	.0000	.0000	.0002	.0013	.0060	.0210	.0580	.1316
	14	.0000	.0000	.0000	.0000	.0000	.0003	.0015	.0065	.0214	.0577
	15	.0000	.0000	.0000	.0000	.0000	.0000	.0003	.0016	.0064	.0207
	16	.0000	.0000	.0000	.0000	.0000	.0000	.0000	.0003	.0015	.0059
	17	.0000	.0000	.0000	.0000	.0000	.0000	.0000	.0000	.0003	.0013
	18	.0000	.0000	.0000	.0000	.0000	.0000	.0000	.0000	.0000	.0002
	19	.0000	.0000	.0000	.0000	.0000	.0000	.0000	.0000	.0000	.0000
	20	.0000	.0000	.0000	.0000	.0000	.0000	.0000	.0000	.0000	.0000

This table gives the probability of an event succeeding at least r' times out of n trials, when the probability of success in each trial is p. Linear interpolation will be accurate at most to two decimal places.

The table is reproduced in condensed form by permission of the publishers CRC Handbook of Tables for Applied Engineering Science, 2nd ed. (Cleveland: The Chemical Rubber Co., 1972).

TABLE A.3   VALUES OF $e^{-\mu}$

μ	0.00	0.01	0.02	0.03	0.04	0.05	0.06	0.07	0.08	0.09
0.0	1.000	0.990	0.980	0.970	0.961	0.951	0.942	0.932	0.923	0.914

μ	0.0	0.1	0.2	0.3	0.4	0.5	0.6	0.7	0.8	0.9
0.0	1.000	0.905	0.819	0.741	0.670	0.607	0.549	0.497	0.449	0.407
1.0	0.368	0.333	0.301	0.273	0.247	0.223	0.202	0.183	0.165	0.150
2.0	0.135	0.122	0.111	0.100	0.091	0.082	0.074	0.067	0.061	0.055
3.0	0.050	0.045	0.041	0.037	0.033	0.030	0.027	0.025	0.022	0.020
4.0	0.018	0.017	0.015	0.014	0.012	0.011	0.010	0.0091	0.0082	0.0074
5.0	0.0067									

Intermediate values of $e^{-\mu}$ can be obtained by making use of the values in the upper part of the table. For example, the value of $e^{-1.11} = e^{-1.1} \times e^{-0.01} = 0.333 \times 0.990 = 0.330$.

TABLE A.4   CUMULATIVE TERMS OF POISSON DISTRIBUTION

					np					
r'	0.1	0.2	0.3	0.4	0.5	0.6	0.7	0.8	0.9	1.0
0	1.0000	1.0000	1.0000	1.0000	1.0000	1.0000	1.0000	1.0000	1.0000	1.0000
1	.0952	.1813	.2592	.3297	.3935	.4512	.5034	.5507	.5934	.6321
2	.0047	.0175	.0369	.0616	.0902	.1219	.1558	.1912	.2275	.2642
3	.0002	.0011	.0036	.0079	.0144	.0231	.0341	.0474	.0629	.0803
4	.0000	.0001	.0003	.0008	.0018	.0034	.0058	.0091	.0135	.0190
5	.0000	.0000	.0000	.0001	.0002	.0004	.0008	.0014	.0023	.0037
6	.0000	.0000 ·	.0000	.0000	.0000	.0000	.0001	.0002	.0003	.0006
7	.0000	.0000	.0000	.0000	.0000	.0000	.0000	.0000	.0000	.0001

					np					
r'	1.1	1.2	1.3	1.4	1.5	1.6	1.7	1.8	1.9	2.0
0	1.0000	1.0000	1.0000	1.0000	1.0000	1.0000	1.0000	1.0000	1.0000	1.0000
1	.6671	.6988	.7275	.7534	.7769	.7981	.8173	.8347	.8504	.8647
2	.3010	.3374	.3732	.4082	.4422	.4751	.5068	.5372	.5663	.5940
3	.0996	.1205	.1429	.1665	.1912	.2166	.2428	.2694	.2963	.3233
4	.0257	.0338	.0431	.0537	.0656	.0788	.0932	.1087	.1253	.1429
5	.0054	.0077	.0107	.0143	.0186	.0237	.0296	.0364	.0441	.0527
6	.0010	.0015	.0022	.0032	.0045	.0060	.0080	.0104	.0132	.0166
7	.0001	.0003	.0004	.0006	.0009	.0013	.0019	.0026	.0034	.0045
8	.0000	.0000	.0001	.0001	.0002	.0003	.0004	.0006	.0008	.0011
9	.0000	.0000	.0000	.0000	.0000	.0000	.0001	.0001	.0002	.0002

(continued)

TABLE A.4 (CONTINUED)

					np					
r'	2.1	2.2	2.3	2.4	2.5	2.6	2.7	2.8	2.9	3.0
0	1.0000	1.0000	1.0000	1.0000	1.0000	1.0000	1.0000	1.0000	1.0000	1.0000
1	.8775	.8892	.8997	.9093	.9179	.9257	.9328	.9392	.9450	.9502
2	.6204	.6454	.6691	.6916	.7127	.7326	.7513	.7689	.7854	.8009
3	.3504	.3773	.4040	.4303	.4562	.4816	.5064	.5305	.5540	.5768
4	.1614	.1806	.2007	.2213	.2424	.2640	.2859	.3081	.3304	.3528
5	.0621	.0725	.0838	.0959	.1088	.1226	.1371	.1523	.1682	.1847
6	.0204	.0249	.0300	.0357	.0420	.0490	.0567	.0651	.0742	.0839
7	.0059	.0075	.0094	.0116	.0142	.0172	.0206	.0244	.0287	.0335
8	.0015	.0020	.0026	.0033	.0042	.0053	.0066	.0081	.0099	.0119
9	.0003	.0005	.0006	.0009	.0011	.0015	.0019	.0024	.0031	.0038
10	.0001	.0001	.0001	.0002	.0003	.0004	.0005	.0007	.0009	.0011
11	.0000	.0000	.0000	.0000	.0001	.0001	.0001	.0002	.0002	.0003
12	.0000	.0000	.0000	.0000	.0000	.0000	.0000	.0000	.0001	.0001

					np					
r'	3.1	3.2	3.3	3.4	3.5	3.6	3.7	3.8	3.9	4.0
0	1.0000	1.0000	1.0000	1.0000	1.0000	1.0000	1.0000	1.0000	1.0000	1.0000
1	.9550	.9592	.9631	.9666	.9698	.9727	.9753	.9776	.9798	.9817
2	.8153	.8288	.8414	.8532	.8641	.8743	.8838	.8926	.9008	.9084
3	.5988	.6201	.6406	.6603	.6792	.6973	.7146	.7311	.7469	.7619
4	.3752	.3975	.4197	.4416	.4634	.4848	.5058	.5265	.5468	.5665
5	.2018	.2194	.2374	.2558	.2746	.2936	.3128	.3322	.3516	.3712
6	.0943	.1054	.1171	.1295	.1424	.1559	.1699	.1844	.1994	.2149
7	.0388	.0446	.0510	.0579	.0653	.0733	.0818	.0909	.1005	.1107
8	.0142	.0168	.0198	.0231	.0267	.0308	.0352	.0401	.0454	.0511
9	.0047	.0057	.0069	.0083	.0099	.0117	.0137	.0160	.0185	.0214
10	.0014	.0018	.0022	.0027	.0033	.0040	.0048	.0058	.0069	.0081
11	.0004	.0005	.0006	.0008	.0010	.0013	.0016	.0019	.0023	.0028
12	.0001	.0001	.0002	.0002	.0003	.0004	.0005	.0006	.0007	.0009
13	.0000	.0000	.0000	.0001	.0001	.0001	.0001	.0002	.0002	.0003
14	.0000	.0000	.0000	.0000	.0000	.0000	.0000	.0000	.0001	.0001

(continued)

TABLE A.4 (CONTINUED)

					np					
r'	4.1	4.2	4.3	4.4	4.5	4.6	4.7	4.8	4.9	5.0
0	1.0000	1.0000	1.0000	1.0000	1.0000	1.0000	1.0000	1.0000	1.0000	1.0000
1	.9834	.9850	.9864	.9877	.9889	.9899	.9909	.9918	.9926	.9933
2	.9155	.9220	.9281	.9337	.9389	.9437	.9482	.9523	.9561	.9596
3	.7762	.7898	.8026	.8149	.8264	.8374	.8477	.8575	.8667	.8753
4	.5858	.6046	.6228	.6406	.6577	.6743	.6903	.7058	.7207	.7350
5	.3907	.4102	.4296	.4488	.4679	.4868	.5054	.5237	.5418	.5595
6	.2307	.2469	.2633	.2801	.2971	.3142	.3316	.3490	.3665	.3840
7	.1214	.1325	.1442	.1564	.1689	.1820	.1954	.2092	.2233	.2378
8	.0573	.0639	.0710	.0786	.0866	.0951	.1040	.1133	.1231	.1334
9	.0245	.0279	.0317	.0358	.0403	.0451	.0503	.0558	.0618	.0681
10	.0095	.0111	.0129	.0149	.0171	.0195	.0222	.0251	.0283	.0318
11	.0034	.0041	.0048	.0057	.0067	.0078	.0090	.0104	.0120	.0137
12	.0011	.0014	.0017	.0020	.0024	.0029	.0034	.0040	.0047	.0055
13	.0003	.0004	.0005	.0007	.0008	.0010	.0012	.0014	.0017	.0020
14	.0001	.0001	.0002	.0002	.0003	.0003	.0004	.0005	.0006	.0007
15	.0000	.0000	.0000	.0001	.0001	.0001	.0001	.0001	.0002	.0002
16	.0000	.0000	.0000	.0000	.0000	.0000	.0000	.0000	.0001	.0001

					np					
r'	5.1	5.2	5.3	5.4	5.5	5.6	5.7	5.8	5.9	6.0
0	1.0000	1.0000	1.0000	1.0000	1.0000	1.0000	1.0000	1.0000	1.0000	1.0000
1	.9939	.9945	.9950	.9955	.9959	.9963	.9967	.9970	.9973	.9975
2	.9628	.9658	.9686	.9711	.9734	.9756	.9776	.9794	.9811	.9826
3	.8835	.8912	.8984	.9052	.9116	.9176	.9232	.9285	.9334	.9380
4	.7487	.7619	.7746	.7867	.7983	.8094	.8200	.8300	.8396	.8488
5	.5769	.5939	.6105	.6267	.6425	.6579	.6728	.6873	.7013	.7149
6	.4016	.4191	.4365	.4539	.4711	.4881	.5050	.5217	.5381	.5543
7	.2526	.2676	.2829	.2983	.3140	.3297	.3456	.3616	.3776	.3937
8	.1440	.1551	.1665	.1783	.1905	.2030	.2159	.2290	.2424	.2560
9	.0748	.0819	.0894	.0974	.1056	.1143	.1234	.1328	.1426	.1528
10	.0356	.0397	.0441	.0488	.0538	.0591	.0648	.0708	.0772	.0839
11	.0156	.0177	.0200	.0225	.0253	.0282	.0314	.0349	.0386	.0426
12	.0063	.0073	.0084	.0096	.0110	.0125	.0141	.0160	.0179	.0201
13	.0024	.0028	.0033	.0038	.0045	.0051	.0059	.0068	.0078	.0088
14	.0008	.0010	.0012	.0014	.0017	.0020	.0023	.0027	.0031	.0036
15	.0003	.0003	.0004	.0005	.0006	.0007	.0009	.0010	.0012	.0014
16	.0001	.0001	.0001	.0002	.0002	.0002	.0003	.0004	.0004	.0005
17	.0000	.0000	.0000	.0001	.0001	.0001	.0001	.0001	.0001	.0002
18	.0000	.0000	.0000	.0000	.0000	.0000	.0000	.0000	.0000	.0001

(continued)

TABLE A.4   (CONTINUED)

					np					
r'	6.1	6.2	6.3	6.4	6.5	6.6	6.7	6.8	6.9	7.0
0	1.0000	1.0000	1.0000	1.0000	1.0000	1.0000	1.0000	1.0000	1.0000	1.0000
1	.9978	.9980	.9982	.9983	.9985	.9986	.9988	.9989	.9990	.9991
2	.9841	.9854	.9866	.9877	.9887	.9897	.9905	.9913	.9920	.9927
3	.9423	.9464	.9502	.9537	.9570	.9600	.9629	.9656	.9680	.9704
4	.8575	.8658	.8736	.8811	.8882	.8948	.9012	.9072	.9129	.9182
5	.7281	.7408	.7531	.7649	.7763	.7873	.7978	.8080	.8177	.8270
6	.5702	.5859	.6012	.6163	.6310	.6453	.6594	.6730	.6863	.6993
7	.4098	.4258	.4418	.4577	.4735	.4892	.5047	.5201	.5353	.5503
8	.2699	.2840	.2983	.3127	.3272	.3419	.3567	.3715	.3864	.4013
9	.1633	.1741	.1852	.1967	.2084	.2204	.2327	.2452	.2580	.2709
10	.0910	.0984	.1061	.1142	.1226	.1314	.1404	.1498	.1505	.1695
11	.0469	.0514	.0563	.0614	.0668	.0726	.0786	.0849	.0916	.0985
12	.0224	.0250	.0277	.0307	.0339	.0373	.0409	.0448	.0490	.0534
13	.0100	.0113	.0127	.0143	.0160	.0179	.0199	.0221	.0245	.0270
14	.0042	.0048	.0055	.0063	.0071	.0080	.0091	.0102	.0115	.0128
15	.0016	.0019	.0022	.0026	.0030	.0034	.0039	.0044	.0050	.0057
16	.0006	.0007	.0008	.0010	.0012	.0014	.0016	.0018	.0021	.0024
17	.0002	.0003	.0003	.0004	.0004	.0005	.0006	.0007	.0008	.0010
18	.0001	.0001	.0001	.0001	.0002	.0002	.0002	.0003	.0003	.0004
19	.0000	.0000	.0000	.0000	.0001	.0001	.0001	.0001	.0001	.0001

					np					
r'	7.1	7.2	7.3	7.4	7.5	7.6	7.7	7.8	7.9	8.0
0	1.0000	1.0000	1.0000	1.0000	1.0000	1.0000	1.0000	1.0000	1.0000	1.0000
1	.9992	.9993	.9993	.9994	.9994	.9995	.9995	.9996	.9996	.9997
2	.9933	.9939	.9944	.9949	.9953	.9957	.9961	.9964	.9967	.9970
3	.9725	.9745	.9764	.9781	.9797	.9812	.9826	.9839	.9851	.9862
4	.9233	.9281	.9326	.9368	.9409	.9446	.9482	.9515	.9547	.9576
5	.8359	.8445	.8527	.8605	.8679	.8751	.8819	.8883	.8945	.9004
6	.7119	.7241	.7360	.7474	.7586	.7693	.7797	.7897	.7994	.8088
7	.5651	.5796	.5940	.6080	.6218	.6354	.6486	.6616	.6743	.6866
8	.4162	.4311	.4459	.4607	.4754	.4900	.5044	.5188	.5330	.5470
9	.2840	.2973	.3108	.3243	.3380	.3518	.3657	.3796	.3935	.4075
10	.1798	.1904	.2012	.2123	.2236	.2351	.2469	.2589	.2710	.2834
11	.1058	.1133	.1212	.1293	.1378	.1465	.1555	.1648	.1743	.1841
12	.0580	.0629	.0681	.0735	.0792	.0852	.0915	.0980	.1048	.1119
13	.0297	.0327	.0358	.0391	.0427	.0464	.0504	.0546	.0591	.0638
14	.0143	.0159	.0176	.0195	.0216	.0238	.0261	.0286	.0313	.0342
15	.0065	.0073	.0082	.0092	.0103	.0114	.0127	.0141	.0156	.0173
16	.0028	.0031	.0036	.0041	.0046	.0052	.0059	.0066	.0074	.0082
17	.0011	.0013	.0015	.0017	.0020	.0022	.0026	.0029	.0033	.0037
18	.0004	.0005	.0006	.0007	.0008	.0009	.0011	.0012	.0014	.0016
19	.0002	.0002	.0002	.0003	.0003	.0004	.0004	.0005	.0006	.0006
20	.0001	.0001	.0001	.0001	.0001	.0001	.0002	.0002	.0002	.0003
21	.0000	.0000	.0000	.0000	.0000	.0000	.0001	.0001	.0001	.0001

(continued)

TABLE A.4   (CONTINUED)

r'					np					
	8.1	8.2	8.3	8.4	8.5	8.6	8.7	8.8	8.9	9.0
0	1.0000	1.0000	1.0000	1.0000	1.0000	1.0000	1.0000	1.0000	1.0000	1.0000
1	.9997	.9997	.9998	.9998	.9998	.9998	.9998	.9998	.9999	.9999
2	.9972	.9975	.9977	.9979	.9981	.9982	.9984	.9985	.9987	.9988
3	.9873	.9882	.9891	.9900	.9907	.9914	.9921	.9927	.9932	.9938
4	.9604	.9630	.9654	.9677	.9699	.9719	.9738	.9756	.9772	.9788
5	.9060	.9113	.9163	.9211	.9256	.9299	.9340	.9379	.9416	.9450
6	.8178	.8264	.8347	.8427	.8504	.8578	.8648	.8716	.8781	.8843
7	.6987	.7104	.7219	.7330	.7438	.7543	.7645	.7744	.7840	.7932
8	.5609	.5746	.5881	.6013	.6144	.6272	.6398	.6522	.6643	.6761
9	.4214	.4353	.4493	.4631	.4769	.4906	.5042	.5177	.5311	.5443
10	.2959	.3085	.3212	.3341	.3470	.3600	.3731	.3863	.3994	.4126
11	.1942	.2045	.2150	.2257	.2366	.2478	.2591	.2706	.2822	.2940
12	.1193	.1269	.1348	.1429	.1513	.1600	.1689	.1780	.1874	.1970
13	.0687	.0739	.0793	.0850	.0909	.0971	.1035	.1102	.1171	.1242
14	.0372	.0405	.0439	.0476	.0514	.0555	.0597	.0642	.0689	.0739
15	.0190	.0209	.0229	.0251	.0274	.0299	.0325	.0353	.0383	.0415
16	.0092	.0102	.0113	.0125	.0138	.0152	.0168	.0184	.0202	.0220
17	.0042	.0047	.0053	.0059	.0066	.0074	.0082	.0091	.0101	.0111
18	.0018	.0021	.0023	.0027	.0030	.0034	.0038	.0043	.0048	.0053
19	.0008	.0009	.0010	.0011	.0013	.0015	.0017	.0019	.0022	.0024
20	.0003	.0003	.0004	.0005	.0005	.0006	.0007	.0008	.0009	.0011
21	.0001	.0001	.0002	.0002	.0002	.0002	.0003	.0003	.0004	.0004
22	.0000	.0000	.0001	.0001	.0001	.0001	.0001	.0001	.0002	.0002
23	.0000	.0000	.0000	.0000	.0000	.0000	.0000	.0000	.0001	.0001

(*continued*)

TABLE A.4 (CONTINUED)

					np					
r'	9.1	9.2	9.3	9.4	9.5	9.6	9.7	9.8	9.9	10
0	1.0000	1.0000	1.0000	1.0000	1.0000	1.0000	1.0000	1.0000	1.0000	1.0000
1	.9999	.9999	.9999	.9999	.9999	.9999	.9999	.9999	1.0000	1.0000
2	.9989	.9990	.9991	.9991	.9992	.9993	.9993	.9994	.9995	.9995
3	.9942	.9947	.9951	.9955	.9958	.9962	.9965	.9967	.9970	.9972
4	.9802	.9816	.9828	.9840	.9851	.9862	.9871	.9880	.9889	.9897
5	.9483	.9514	.9544	.9571	.9597	.9622	.9645	.9667	.9688	.9707
6	.8902	.8959	.9014	.9065	.9115	.9162	.9207	.9250	.9290	.9329
7	.8022	.8108	.8192	.8273	.8351	.8426	.8498	.8567	.8634	.8699
8	.6877	.6990	.7101	.7208	.7313	.7416	.7515	.7612	.7706	.7798
9	.5574	.5704	.5832	.5958	.6082	.6204	.6324	.6442	.6558	.6672
10	.4258	.4389	.4521	.4651	.4782	.4911	.5040	.5168	.5295	.5421
11	.3059	.3180	.3301	.3424	.3547	.3671	.3795	.3920	.4045	.4170
12	.2068	.2168	.2270	.2374	.2480	.2588	.2697	.2807	.2919	.3032
13	.1316	.1393	.1471	.1552	.1636	.1721	.1809	.1899	.1991	.2084
14	.0790	.0844	.0900	.0958	.1019	.1081	.1147	.1214	.1284	.1355
15	.0448	.0483	.0520	.0559	.0600	.0643	.0688	.0735	.0784	.0835
16	.0240	.0262	.0285	.0309	.0335	.0362	.0391	.0421	.0454	.0487
17	.0122	.0135	.0148	.0162	.0177	.0194	.0211	.0230	.0249	.0270
18	.0059	.0066	.0073	.0081	.0089	.0098	.0108	.0119	.0130	.0143
19	.0027	.0031	.0034	.0038	.0043	.0048	.0053	.0059	.0065	.0072
20	.0012	.0014	.0015	.0017	.0020	.0022	.0025	.0028	.0031	.0035
21	.0005	.0006	.0007	.0008	.0009	.0010	.0011	.0013	.0014	.0016
22	.0002	.0002	.0003	.0003	.0004	.0004	.0005	.0005	.0006	.0007
23	.0001	.0001	.0001	.0001	.0001	.0002	.0002	.0002	.0003	.0003
24	.0000	.0000	.0000	.0000	.0001	.0001	.0001	.0001	.0001	.0001

This table gives the probability of an event occurring at least *r'* times when *np* is the mean number of occurrences of the event per unit time (or space). The tabulated values are thus:

$$\sum_{r=r'}^{\infty} \frac{(np)^r e^{-np}}{r!}$$

The table is reproduced by permission of the publishers, *CRC Handbook of Tables for Mathematics*, 3rd ed. (Cleveland: The Chemical Rubber Co., 1972).

TABLE A.5 ORDINATES OF THE NORMAL CURVE, $f(z) = \dfrac{1}{\sqrt{2\pi}} e^{-z^2/2}$

z	.00	.01	.02	.03	.04	.05	.06	.07	.08	.09
.0	.3989	.3989	.3989	.3988	.3986	.3984	.3982	.3980	.3977	.3973
.1	.3970	.3965	.3961	.3956	.3951	.3945	.3939	.3932	.3925	.3918
.2	.3910	.3902	.3894	.3885	.3876	.3867	.3857	.3847	.3836	.3825
.3	.3814	.3802	.3790	.3778	.3765	.3752	.3739	.3725	.3712	.3697
.4	.3683	.3668	.3653	.3637	.3621	.3605	.3589	.3572	.3555	.3538
.5	.3521	.3503	.3485	.3467	.3448	.3429	.3410	.3391	.3372	.3352
.6	.3332	.3312	.3292	.3271	.3251	.3230	.3209	.3187	.3166	.3144
.7	.3123	.3101	.3079	.3056	.3034	.3011	.2989	.2966	.2943	.2920
.8	.2897	.2874	.2850	.2827	.2803	.2780	.2756	.2732	.2709	.2685
.9	.2661	.2637	.2613	.2589	.2565	.2541	.2516	.2492	.2468	.2444
1.0	.2420	.2396	.2371	.2347	.2323	.2299	.2275	.2251	.2227	.2203
1.1	.2179	.2155	.2131	.2107	.2083	.2059	.2036	.2012	.1989	.1965
1.2	.1942	.1919	.1895	.1872	.1849	.1826	.1804	.1781	.1758	.1736
1.3	.1714	.1691	.1669	.1647	.1626	.1604	.1582	.1561	.1539	.1518
1.4	.1497	.1476	.1456	.1435	.1415	.1394	.1374	.1354	.1334	.1315
1.5	.1295	.1276	.1257	.1238	.1219	.1200	.1182	.1163	.1145	.1127
1.6	.1109	.1092	.1074	.1057	.1040	.1023	.1006	.0989	.0973	.0957
1.7	.0940	.0925	.0909	.0893	.0878	.0863	.0848	.0833	.0818	.0804
1.8	.0790	.0775	.0761	.0748	.0734	.0721	.0707	.0694	.0681	.0669
1.9	.0656	.0644	.0632	.0620	.0608	.0596	.0584	.0573	.0562	.0551
2.0	.0540	.0529	.0519	.0508	.0498	.0488	.0478	.0468	.0459	.0449
2.1	.0440	.0431	.0422	.0413	.0404	.0396	.0387	.0379	.0371	.0363
2.2	.0355	.0347	.0339	.0332	.0325	.0317	.0310	.0303	.0297	.0290
2.3	.0283	.0277	.0270	.0264	.0258	.0252	.0246	.0241	.0235	.0229
2.4	.0224	.0219	.0213	.0208	.0203	.0198	.0194	.0189	.0184	.0180
2.5	.0175	.0171	.0167	.0163	.0158	.0154	.0151	.0147	.0143	.0139
2.6	.0136	.0132	.0129	.0126	.0122	.0119	.0116	.0113	.0110	.0107
2.7	.0104	.0101	.0099	.0096	.0093	.0091	.0088	.0086	.0084	.0081
2.8	.0079	.0077	.0075	.0073	.0071	.0069	.0067	.0065	.0063	.0061
2.9	.0060	.0058	.0056	.0055	.0053	.0051	.0050	.0048	.0047	.0046
3.0	.0044	.0043	.0042	.0041	.0039	.0038	.0037	.0036	.0035	.0034
3.1	.0033	.0032	.0031	.0030	.0029	.0028	.0027	.0026	.0025	.0025
3.2	.0024	.0023	.0022	.0022	.0021	.0020	.0020	.0019	.0018	.0018
3.3	.0017	.0017	.0016	.0016	.0015	.0015	.0014	.0014	.0013	.0013
3.4	.0012	.0012	.0012	.0011	.0011	.0010	.0010	.0010	.0009	.0009
3.5	.0009									
3.6	.0006									
3.7	.0004									
3.8	.0003									
3.9	.0002									

The above ordinates give the probability density for $z = (x - \mu)/\sigma$ deviations from the mean μ (i.e., $z = 0$). To fit a normal frequency curve to observed data consisting of n observations, multiply the ordinate from the table for any value of z by n/σ. To fit a normal probability curve, multiply the ordinate by $1/\sigma$.

The values for z up to 3.0 are taken from Table II of Fisher and Yates: *Statistical Tables for Biological, Agricultural, and Medical Research*, published by Oliver & Boyd Ltd., Edinburgh, Scotland, by permission of the authors and publishers. The values for the range $z = 3.1$ to $z = 3.9$ are reproduced by permission of the author and publishers from Table A.2 of *Methods of Statistical Analysis* by Cyril H. Goulden, 2nd ed. (New York: John Wiley & Sons, 1960).

TABLE A.6 AREAS UNDER THE NORMAL CURVE, $F(z) = \int_0^z \dfrac{1}{\sqrt{2\pi}}\, e^{-z^2/2}\, dz$

z	.00	.01	.02	.03	.04	.05	.06	.07	.08	.09
.0	.0000	.0040	.0080	.0120	.0159	.0199	.0239	.0279	.0319	.0359
.1	.0398	.0438	.0478	.0517	.0557	.0596	.0636	.0675	.0714	.0753
.2	.0793	.0832	.0871	.0910	.0948	.0987	.1026	.1064	.1103	.1141
.3	.1179	.1217	.1255	.1293	.1331	.1368	.1406	.1443	.1480	.1517
.4	.1554	.1591	.1628	.1664	.1700	.1736	.1772	.1808	.1844	.1879
.5	.1915	.1950	.1985	.2019	.2054	.2088	.2123	.2157	.2190	.2224
.6	.2257	.2291	.2324	.2357	.2389	.2422	.2454	.2486	.2518	.2549
.7	.2580	.2611	.2642	.2673	.2704	.2734	.2764	.2794	.2823	.2852
.8	.2881	.2910	.2939	.2967	.2995	.3023	.3051	.3078	.3106	.3133
.9	.3159	.3186	.3212	.3238	.3264	.3289	.3315	.3340	.3365	.3389
1.0	.3413	.3438	.3461	.3485	.3508	.3531	.3554	.3577	.3599	.3621
1.1	.3643	.3665	.3686	.3708	.3729	.3749	.3770	.3790	.3810	.3830
1.2	.3849	.3869	.3888	.3907	.3925	.3944	.3962	.3980	.3997	.4015
1.3	.4032	.4049	.4066	.4082	.4099	.4115	.4131	.4147	.4162	.4177
1.4	.4192	.4207	.4222	.4236	.4251	.4265	.4279	.4292	.4306	.4319
1.5	.4332	.4345	.4357	.4370	.4382	.4394	.4406	.4418	.4430	.4441
1.6	.4452	.4463	.4474	.4485	.4495	.4505	.4515	.4525	.4535	.4545
1.7	.4554	.4564	.4573	.4582	.4591	.4599	.4608	.4616	.4625	.4633
1.8	.4641	.4649	.4656	.4664	.4671	.4678	.4686	.4693	.4699	.4706
1.9	.4713	.4719	.4726	.4732	.4738	.4744	.4750	.4756	.4762	.4767
2.0	.4772	.4778	.4783	.4788	.4793	.4798	.4803	.4808	.4812	.4817
2.1	.4821	.4826	.4830	.4834	.4838	.4842	.4846	.4850	.4854	.4857
2.2	.4861	.4865	.4868	.4871	.4875	.4878	.4881	.4884	.4887	.4890
2.3	.4893	.4896	.4898	.4901	.4904	.4906	.4909	.4911	.4913	.4916
2.4	.4918	.4920	.4922	.4925	.4927	.4929	.4931	.4932	.4934	.4936
2.5	.4938	.4940	.4941	.4943	.4945	.4946	.4948	.4949	.4951	.4952
2.6	.4953	.4955	.4956	.4957	.4959	.4960	.4961	.4962	.4963	.4964
2.7	.4965	.4966	.4967	.4968	.4969	.4970	.4971	.4972	.4973	.4974
2.8	.4974	.4975	.4976	.4977	.4977	.4978	.4979	.4980	.4980	.4981
2.9	.4981	.4982	.4983	.4983	.4984	.4984	.4985	.4985	.4986	.4986
3.0	.4987	.4987	.4987	.4988	.4988	.4989	.4989	.4989	.4990	.4990
3.1	.4990	.4991	.4991	.4991	.4992	.4992	.4992	.4992	.4993	.4993
3.2	.4993	.4993	.4994	.4994	.4994	.4994	.4994	.4995	.4995	.4995
3.3	.4995	.4995	.4996	.4996	.4996	.4996	.4996	.4996	.4996	.4997
3.4	.4997	.4997	.4997	.4997	.4997	.4997	.4997	.4997	.4998	.4998
⋮	⋮									
4.0	.499968									
5.0	.4999997									

This table gives the probability of a random value of a normal variate falling *in* the range $z = 0$ to $z = z$ (in the *shaded area in the figure*). The probability of the same variate having a deviation greater than z is given by 0.5 − probability from the table for the given z. The table refers to a single tail of the normal distribution; therefore, the probability of a normal variate falling in the range $\pm z = 2 \times$ probability from the table for the given z. The probability of a variate falling outside the range $\pm z$ is $1 - 2 \times$ probability from the table for given z.

The values in this table were obtained by permission of authors and publishers from C. E. Weatherburn, *Mathematical Statistics* (London: Cambridge University Press, 1957) (for $z = 0$ to $z = 3.1$); C. H. Richardson, *An Introduction to Statistical Analysis* (New York: Harcourt Brace & Jovanovich, 1944) (for $z = 3.2$ to $z = 3.4$); A. H. Bowker and G. J. Lieberman, *Engineering Statistics* (Englewood Cliffs. N.J.: Prentice-Hall, 1959) (for $z = 4.0$ and 5.0).

TABLE A.7   DISTRIBUTION OF t

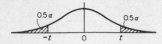

Degrees of freedom, v	Probability, α			
	0.10	0.05	0.01	0.001
1	6.314	12.706	63.657	636.619
2	2.920	4.303	9.925	31.598
3	2.353	3.182	5.841	12.941
4	2.132	2.776	4.604	8.610
5	2.015	2.571	4.032	6.859
6	1.943	2.447	3.707	5.959
7	1.895	2.365	3.499	5.405
8	1.860	2.306	3.355	5.041
9	1.833	2.262	3.250	4.781
10	1.812	2.228	3.169	4.587
11	1.796	2.201	3.106	4.437
12	1.782	2.179	3.055	4.318
13	1.771	2.160	3.012	4.221
14	1.761	2.145	2.977	4.140
15	1.753	2.131	2.947	4.073
16	1.746	2.120	2.921	4.015
17	1.740	2.110	2.898	3.965
18	1.734	2.101	2.878	3.922
19	1.729	2.093	2.861	3.883
20	1.725	2.086	2.845	3.850
21	1.721	2.080	2.831	3.819
22	1.717	2.074	2.819	3.792
23	1.714	2.069	2.807	3.767
24	1.711	2.064	2.797	3.745
25	1.708	2.060	2.787	3.725
26	1.706	2.056	2.779	3.707
27	1.703	2.052	2.771	3.690
28	1.701	2.048	2.763	3.674
29	1.699	2.045	2.756	3.659
30	1.697	2.042	2.750	3.646
40	1.684	2.021	2.704	3.551
60	1.671	2.000	2.660	3.460
120	1.658	1.980	2.617	3.373
∞	1.645	1.960	2.576	3.291

This table gives the values of t corresponding to various values of the probability α (level of significance) of a random variable falling inside the shaded areas in the figure, for a given number of degrees of freedom v available for the estimation of error. For a one-sided test the confidence limits are obtained for 2α.

This table is taken from Table III of Fisher and Yates, *Statistical Tables for Biological, Agricultural, and Medical Research*, published by Oliver & Boyd Ltd., Edinburgh, Scotland, by permission of the authors and publishers.

TABLE A.8 VALUES OF EXTREME DEVIATE $\dfrac{|x_m - \bar{x}|}{s_e}$

see p. 235

NOT REJECTED AS AN OUTLIER

n	5 percent level						
v	3	4	5	6	7	8	9
10	2.02	2.29	2.49	2.63	2.75	2.85	2.93
11	1.99	2.26	2.44	2.58	2.70	2.79	2.87
12	1.97	2.22	2.40	2.54	2.65	2.75	2.83
13	1.95	2.20	2.38	2.51	2.62	2.71	2.79
14	1.93	2.18	2.35	2.48	2.59	2.68	2.76
15	1.92	2.16	2.33	2.46	2.56	2.65	2.73
16	1.90	2.14	2.31	2.44	2.54	2.63	2.70
17	1.89	2.13	2.30	2.42	2.52	2.61	2.68
18	1.88	2.12	2.28	2.41	2.51	2.59	2.66
19	1.87	2.11	2.27	2.39	2.49	2.58	2.65
20	1.87	2.10	2.26	2.38	2.48	2.56	2.63
24	1.84	2.07	2.23	2.35	2.44	2.52	2.59
30	1.82	2.04	2.20	2.31	2.40	2.48	2.55
40	1.80	2.02	2.17	2.28	2.37	2.44	2.51
60	1.78	1.99	2.14	2.25	2.33	2.41	2.47
120	1.76	1.97	2.11	2.21	2.30	2.37	2.43
∞	1.74	1.94	2.08	2.18	2.27	2.33	2.39
	1 percent level						
10	2.76	3.05	3.25	3.39	3.50	3.59	3.67
11	2.71	3.00	3.19	3.33	3.44	3.53	3.61
12	2.67	2.95	3.14	3.28	3.39	3.48	3.55
13	2.63	2.91	3.10	3.24	3.34	3.43	3.51
14	2.60	2.87	3.06	3.20	3.30	3.39	3.47
15	2.57	2.84	3.02	3.16	3.27	3.35	3.43
16	2.55	2.81	3.00	3.13	3.24	3.32	3.39
17	2.52	2.79	2.97	3.10	3.21	3.29	3.36
18	2.50	2.77	2.95	3.08	3.18	3.27	3.34
19	2.49	2.75	2.92	3.06	3.16	3.24	3.31
20	2.47	2.73	2.91	3.04	3.14	3.22	3.29
24	2.43	2.68	2.85	2.97	3.07	3.15	3.22
30	2.38	2.62	2.79	2.91	3.01	3.08	3.15
40	2.34	2.57	2.73	2.85	2.94	3.02	3.08
60	2.30	2.52	2.68	2.79	2.88	2.95	3.01
120	2.25	2.48	2.62	2.73	2.82	2.89	2.95
∞	2.22	2.43	2.57	2.68	2.76	2.83	2.88

(continued)

TABLE A.8   (CONTINUED)

v \ n	0.1 percent level						
	3	4	5	6	7	8	9
10	3.54	3.84	4.04	4.17	4.28	4.35	4.40
11	3.49	3.80	3.99	4.12	4.23	4.30	4.36
12	3.45	3.75	3.94	4.07	4.19	4.26	4.31
13	3.41	3.71	3.90	4.03	4.14	4.22	4.28
14	3.38	3.67	3.86	4.00	4.10	4.18	4.24
15	3.35	3.64	3.83	3.96	4.06	4.15	4.21
16	3.32	3.61	3.80	3.93	4.03	4.12	4.18
17	3.29	3.58	3.77	3.90	4.00	4.09	4.15
18	3.27	3.55	3.74	3.88	3.98	4.06	4.12
19	3.25	3.53	3.72	3.85	3.95	4.03	4.10
20	3.23	3.51	3.70	3.83	3.93	4.01	4.08
24	3.16	3.44	3.62	3.75	3.85	3.93	4.00
30	3.08	3.36	3.53	3.66	3.76	3.84	3.90
40	3.01	3.27	3.44	3.57	3.66	3.74	3.81
60	2.93	3.19	3.35	3.47	3.56	3.64	3.70
120	2.85	3.10	3.26	3.37	3.46	3.53	3.59
∞	2.78	3.01	3.17	3.28	3.36	3.43	3.48

An outlier is rejected if its value exceeds the tabulated value at the requisite level of significance.

x_m = greatest or smallest value that can be expected in a sample of size n at the given level of significance.

s_e = estimate of standard deviation from a sample with v degrees of freedom.

This table is adapted by permission of the author and publishers from a paper "Tables of Percentage Points of the 'Studentized' Extreme Deviate from the Sample Mean" by K. R. Nair, *Biometrika*, vol. 39, 1952, pp. 189–191.

A slight revision of the above values has been suggested by H. A. David in a paper "Revised Upper Percentage Points of the Extreme Studentized Deviate from the Sample Mean," *Biometrika*, vol. 43, 1956, pp. 449–451.

TABLE A.9   CHAUVENET'S CRITERION FOR REJECTION OF OUTLIERS

Sample size, n	$\dfrac{\lvert x_m - \bar{x}\rvert}{s}$	Sample size, n	$\dfrac{\lvert x_m - \bar{x}\rvert}{s}$
2	1.15	20	2.24
3	1.38	25	2.33
4	1.53	30	2.39
5	1.64	40	2.50
6	1.73	50	2.58
7	1.80	60	2.64
8	1.86	80	2.74
9	1.91	100	2.81
10	1.96	150	2.94
11	2.00	200	3.02
12	2.04	300	3.14
13	2.07	400	3.23
14	2.10	500	3.29
16	2.15	600	3.34
18	2.20	1000	3.48

An outlier may be rejected if the actual value of $\lvert x_m - \bar{x}\rvert/s$ exceeds the tabulated value.

x_m = value of outlier, $\bar{x}$ = sample mean, s^2 = estimate of variance from sample, and n = sample size.

TABLE A.10   CRITICAL VALUES FOR THE DIXON-TYPE TESTS FOR OUTLIERS

p.237

Sample size, n	Critical value for the test, $\dfrac{x_n - x_{n-1}}{x_n - x_1}$ or $\dfrac{x_2 - x_1}{x_n - x_1}$		Critical value for the test, $\dfrac{x_n - x_{n-2}}{x_n - x_1}$	
	Level of significance		Level of significance	
	5 percent	1 percent	5 percent	1 percent
3	0.941	0.988		
4	0.765	0.889	0.967	0.992
5	0.642	0.780	0.845	0.929
6	0.560	0.698	0.736	0.836
7	0.507	0.637	0.661	0.778
8	0.468	0.590	0.607	0.710
9	0.437	0.555	0.565	0.667
10	0.412	0.527	0.531	0.632
12	0.376	0.482	0.481	0.579
14	0.349	0.450	0.445	0.538
16	0.329	0.426	0.418	0.508
18	0.313	0.407	0.397	0.484
20	0.300	0.391	0.372	0.464
25	0.277	0.362	0.343	0.428
30	0.260	0.341	0.322	0.402

An outlier is rejected if the value of the statistic calculated by the quotients given above exceeds the tabulated value at the requisite level of significance.

Source: V. Barnett and T. Lewis, *Outliers in Statistical Data* (New York: John Wiley & Sons, 1978). Reprinted by permission of the authors and publishers.

TABLE A.11 DISTRIBUTION OF χ^2

Degrees of freedom, ν	\multicolumn{12}{c}{Probability of a deviation greater than χ^2}
	0.99	0.95	0.90	0.80	0.70	0.50	0.30	0.20	0.10	0.05	0.01	0.001
1	.000157	.00393	.0158	.0642	.148	.455	1.074	1.642	2.706	3.841	6.635	10.827
2	.0201	.103	.211	.446	.713	1.386	2.408	3.219	4.605	5.991	9.210	13.815
3	.115	.352	.584	1.005	1.424	2.366	3.665	4.642	6.251	7.815	11.345	16.268
4	.297	.711	1.064	1.649	2.195	3.357	4.878	5.989	7.779	9.488	13.277	18.465
5	.554	1.145	1.610	2.343	3.000	4.351	6.064	7.289	9.236	11.070	15.086	20.517
6	.872	1.635	2.204	3.070	3.828	5.348	7.231	8.558	10.645	12.592	16.812	22.457
7	1.239	2.167	2.833	3.822	4.671	6.346	8.383	9.803	12.017	14.067	18.475	24.322
8	1.646	2.733	3.490	4.594	5.527	7.344	9.524	11.030	13.362	15.507	20.090	26.125
9	2.088	3.325	4.168	5.380	6.393	8.343	10.656	12.242	14.684	16.919	21.666	27.877
10	2.558	3.940	4.865	6.179	7.267	9.342	11.781	13.442	15.987	18.307	23.209	29.588
11	3.053	4.575	5.578	6.989	8.148	10.341	12.899	14.631	17.275	19.675	24.725	31.264
12	3.571	5.226	6.304	7.807	9.034	11.340	14.011	15.812	18.549	21.026	26.217	32.909
13	4.107	5.892	7.042	8.634	9.926	12.340	15.119	16.985	19.812	22.362	27.688	34.528

14	4.660	6.571	7.790	9.467	10.821	13.339	16.222	18.151	21.064	23.685	29.141	36.123
15	5.229	7.261	8.547	10.307	11.721	14.339	17.322	19.311	22.307	24.996	30.578	37.697
16	5.812	7.962	9.312	11.152	12.624	15.338	18.418	20.465	23.542	26.296	32.000	39.252
17	6.408	8.672	10.085	12.002	13.531	16.338	19.511	21.615	24.769	27.587	33.409	40.790
18	7.015	9.390	10.865	12.857	14.440	17.338	20.601	22.760	25.989	28.869	34.805	42.312
19	7.633	10.117	11.651	13.716	15.352	18.338	21.689	23.900	27.204	30.144	36.191	43.820
20	8.260	10.851	12.443	14.578	16.266	19.377	22.775	25.038	28.412	31.410	37.566	45.315
21	8.897	11.501	13.240	15.445	17.182	20.377	23.858	26.171	29.615	32.671	38.932	46.797
22	9.542	12.338	14.041	16.314	18.101	21.337	24.939	27.301	30.813	33.924	40.289	48.268
23	10.196	13.091	14.848	17.187	19.021	22.337	26.018	28.429	32.007	35.172	41.638	49.728
24	10.856	13.848	15.659	18.062	19.943	23.337	27.096	29.553	33.196	36.415	42.980	51.179
25	11.524	14.611	16.473	18.940	20.867	24.337	28.172	30.675	34.382	37.652	44.314	52.620
26	12.198	15.379	17.292	19.820	21.792	25.336	29.246	31.795	35.563	38.885	45.642	54.052
27	12.879	16.151	18.114	20.703	22.719	26.336	30.319	32.912	36.741	40.113	46.963	55.476
28	13.565	16.928	18.939	21.588	23.647	27.336	31.391	34.027	37.916	41.337	48.278	56.893
29	14.256	17.708	19.768	22.475	24.577	28.336	32.461	35.139	39.087	42.557	49.588	58.302
30	14.953	18.493	20.599	23.364	25.508	29.336	33.530	36.250	40.256	43.773	50.892	59.703

This table gives the probability α of a variate falling in the shaded area of the figure, that is, outside the range 0 to χ^2 for a given number of degrees of freedom ν. For larger values of ν, the expression $\sqrt{2\chi^2} - \sqrt{2\nu - 1}$ may be used as a normal deviate with unit standard deviation, remembering that the probability for χ^2 corresponds to that of a single tail of the normal curve. For example, let $\chi^2 = 147.92$, $\nu = 113$; then $z = \sqrt{295.84} - \sqrt{225} = 2.2$, corresponding to an area $= 0.4861$ from Table A.2. Therefore, the probability of a variate exceeding z is $0.5000 - 0.4861 = 0.0139$, which is highly significant.

This table is taken from Table IV of Fisher and Yates. *Statistical Tables for Biological, Agricultural, and Medical Research*, published by Oliver & Boyd, Ltd., Edinburgh, Scotland, by permission of the authors and publishers.

TABLE A.12 CRITICAL STATISTIC D FOR THE KOLMOGOROV–SMIRNOV (K–S) TEST FOR GOODNESS OF FIT

Sample size, n	Level of significance, α		
	0.10	0.05	0.01
5	0.51	0.56	0.67
8	0.41	0.46	0.54
10	0.37	0.41	0.49
13	0.32	0.36	0.43
15	0.30	0.34	0.40
18	0.28	0.31	0.37
20	0.26	0.29	0.36
25	0.24	0.27	0.32
30	0.22	0.24	0.29
35	0.21	0.23	0.27
40	0.19	0.21	0.25
50	0.17	0.19	0.23
Large n	$1.22/\sqrt{n}$	$1.36/\sqrt{n}$	$1.63/\sqrt{n}$

Source: B. W. Lindgren, *Statistical Theory* (New York: Macmillan, 1962). Table reproduced by permission of the author and publisher.

TABLE A.13 SIGNIFICANCE OF A DIFFERENCE BETWEEN TWO MEANS WITH DIFFERENCE VARIANCES

	v_1	θ						
		0°	15°	30°	45°	60°	75°	90°
5 percent level	6	2.447	2.440	2.435	2.435	2.435	2.440	2.447
	8	2.447	2.430	2.398	2.364	2.331	2.310	2.306
$v_2 = 6$	12	2.447	2.423	2.367	2.301	2.239	2.193	2.179
	24	2.447	2.418	2.342	2.247	2.156	2.088	2.064
	∞	2.447	2.413	2.322	2.201	2.082	1.993	1.960
	6	2.306	2.310	2.331	2.364	2.398	2.430	2.447
	8	2.306	2.300	2.294	2.292	2.294	2.300	2.306
$v_2 = 8$	12	2.306	2.292	2.262	2.229	2.201	2.183	2.179
	24	2.306	2.286	2.236	2.175	2.118	2.077	2.064
	∞	2.306	2.281	2.215	2.128	2.044	1.982	1.960
	6	2.179	2.193	2.239	2.301	2.367	2.423	2.447
	8	2.179	2.183	2.201	2.229	2.262	2.292	2.306
$v_2 - 12$	12	2.179	2.175	2.169	2.167	2.169	2.175	2.179
	24	2.179	2.168	2.142	2.112	2.085	2.069	2.064
	∞	2.179	2.163	2.120	2.064	2.011	1.973	1.960
	6	2.064	2.088	2.156	2.247	2.342	2.418	2.447
	8	2.064	2.077	2.118	2.175	2.236	2.286	2.306
$v_2 = 24$	12	2.064	2.069	2.085	2.112	2.142	2.168	2.179
	24	2.064	2.062	2.058	2.056	2.058	2.062	2.064
	∞	2.064	2.056	2.035	2.009	1.983	1.966	1.960
	6	1.960	1.993	2.082	2.201	2.322	2.413	2.447
	8	1.960	1.982	2.044	2.128	2.215	2.281	2.306
$v_2 = \infty$	12	1.960	1.973	2.011	2.064	2.120	2.163	2.179
	24	1.960	1.966	1.983	2.009	2.035	2.056	2.064
	∞	1.960	1.960	1.960	1.960	1.960	1.960	1.960
1 percent level	6	3.707	3.654	3.557	3.514	3.557	3.654	3.707
	8	3.707	3.643	3.495	3.363	3.307	3.328	3.355
$v_2 - 6$	12	3.707	3.636	3.453	3.246	3.104	3.053	3.055
	24	3.707	3.631	3.424	3.158	2.938	2.822	2.797
	∞	3.707	3.626	3.402	3.093	2.804	2.627	2.576
	6	3.355	3.328	3.307	3.363	3.495	3.643	3.707
	8	3.355	3.316	3.239	3.206	3.239	3.316	3.355
$v_2 = 8$	12	3.355	3.307	3.192	3.083	3.032	3.039	3.055
	24	3.355	3.301	3.158	2.988	2.862	2.805	2.797
	∞	3.355	3.295	3.132	2.916	2.723	2.608	2.576
	6	3.055	3.053	3.104	3.246	3.453	3.636	3.707
	8	3.055	3.039	3.032	3.083	3.192	3.307	3.355
$v_2 = 12$	12	3.055	3.029	2.978	2.954	2.978	3.029	3.055
	24	3.055	3.020	2.938	2.853	2.803	2.793	2.797
	∞	3.055	3.014	2.909	2.775	2.661	2.595	2.576
	6	2.797	2.822	2.938	3.158	3.424	3.631	3.707
	8	2.797	2.805	2.862	2.988	3.158	3.301	3.355
$v_2 = 24$	12	2.797	2.793	2.803	2.853	2.938	3.020	3.055
	24	2.797	2.785	2.759	2.747	2.759	2.785	2.797
	∞	2.797	2.777	2.726	2.664	2.613	2.585	2.576
	6	2.576	2.627	2.804	3.093	3.402	3.626	3.707
	8	2.576	2.608	2.723	2.916	3.132	3.295	3.355
$v_2 = \infty$	12	2.576	2.595	2.661	2.775	2.909	3.014	3.055
	24	2.576	2.585	2.613	2.664	2.726	2.777	2.797
	∞	2.576	2.576	2.576	2.576	2.576	2.576	2.576

This table gives values of d for known values of v_1, v_2, and θ, where $\tan \theta = s_1/s_2$, and v_1 and v_2 are the corresponding numbers of degrees of freedom. If the difference of means exceeds $d\sqrt{s_1^2 + s_2^2}$, then it is significant at the specified level.

This table is taken from Table VI of Fisher and Yates, *Statistical Tables for Biological, Agricultural, and Medical Research*, published by Oliver & Boyd Ltd., Edinburgh, Scotland, by permission of the authors and publishers.

TABLE A.14 DISTRIBUTION OF VARIANCE RATIO F

5 Percent Level of Significance

$P(F)$

v_2 \ v_1	1	2	3	4	5	6	7	8	9	10	12	15	20	24	30	40	60	120	∞
1	161.45	199.50	215.71	224.58	230.16	233.99	236.77	238.88	240.54	241.88	243.91	245.95	248.01	249.05	250.09	251.14	252.20	253.25	254.32
2	18.51	19.00	19.16	19.25	19.30	19.33	19.35	19.37	19.38	19.40	19.41	19.43	19.45	19.45	19.46	19.47	19.48	19.49	19.50
3	10.13	9.55	9.28	9.12	9.01	8.94	8.89	8.85	8.81	8.79	8.74	8.70	8.66	8.64	8.62	8.59	8.57	8.55	8.53
4	7.71	6.94	6.59	6.39	6.26	6.16	6.09	6.04	6.00	5.96	5.91	5.86	5.80	5.77	5.75	5.72	5.69	5.66	5.63
5	6.61	5.79	5.41	5.19	5.05	4.95	4.88	4.82	4.77	4.74	4.68	4.62	4.56	4.53	4.50	4.46	4.43	4.40	4.36
6	5.99	5.14	4.76	4.53	4.39	4.28	4.21	4.15	4.10	4.06	4.00	3.94	3.87	3.84	3.81	3.77	3.74	3.70	3.67
7	5.59	4.74	4.35	4.12	3.97	3.87	3.79	3.73	3.68	3.64	3.57	3.51	3.44	3.41	3.38	3.34	3.30	3.27	3.23
8	5.32	4.46	4.07	3.84	3.69	3.58	3.50	3.44	3.39	3.35	3.28	3.22	3.15	3.12	3.08	3.04	3.01	2.97	2.93
9	5.12	4.26	3.86	3.63	3.48	3.37	3.29	3.23	3.18	3.14	3.07	3.01	2.94	2.90	2.86	2.83	2.79	2.75	2.71
10	4.96	4.10	3.71	3.48	3.33	3.22	3.14	3.07	3.02	2.98	2.91	2.84	2.77	2.74	2.70	2.66	2.62	2.58	2.54
11	4.84	3.98	3.59	3.36	3.20	3.09	3.01	2.95	2.90	2.85	2.79	2.72	2.65	2.61	2.57	2.53	2.49	2.45	2.40
12	4.75	3.89	3.49	3.26	3.11	3.00	2.91	2.85	2.80	2.75	2.69	2.62	2.54	2.51	2.47	2.43	2.38	2.34	2.30
13	4.67	3.81	3.41	3.18	3.03	2.92	2.83	2.77	2.71	2.67	2.60	2.53	2.46	2.42	2.38	2.34	2.30	2.25	2.21
14	4.60	3.74	3.34	3.11	2.96	2.85	2.76	2.70	2.65	2.60	2.53	2.46	2.39	2.35	2.31	2.27	2.22	2.18	2.13
15	4.54	3.68	3.29	3.06	2.90	2.79	2.71	2.64	2.59	2.54	2.48	2.40	2.33	2.29	2.25	2.20	2.16	2.11	2.07
16	4.49	3.63	3.24	3.01	2.85	2.74	2.66	2.59	2.54	2.49	2.42	2.35	2.28	2.24	2.19	2.15	2.11	2.06	2.01
17	4.45	3.59	3.20	2.96	2.81	2.70	2.61	2.55	2.49	2.45	2.38	2.31	2.23	2.19	2.15	2.10	2.06	2.01	1.96
18	4.41	3.55	3.16	2.93	2.77	2.66	2.58	2.51	2.46	2.41	2.34	2.27	2.19	2.15	2.11	2.06	2.02	1.97	1.92
19	4.38	3.52	3.13	2.90	2.74	2.63	2.54	2.48	2.42	2.38	2.31	2.23	2.16	2.11	2.07	2.03	1.98	1.93	1.88
20	4.35	3.49	3.10	2.87	2.71	2.60	2.51	2.45	2.39	2.35	2.28	2.20	2.12	2.08	2.04	1.99	1.95	1.90	1.84
21	4.32	3.47	3.07	2.84	2.68	2.57	2.49	2.42	2.37	2.32	2.25	2.18	2.10	2.05	2.01	1.96	1.92	1.87	1.81
22	4.30	3.44	3.05	2.82	2.66	2.55	2.46	2.40	2.34	2.30	2.23	2.15	2.07	2.03	1.98	1.94	1.89	1.84	1.78
23	4.28	3.42	3.03	2.80	2.64	2.53	2.44	2.37	2.32	2.27	2.20	2.13	2.05	2.00	1.96	1.91	1.86	1.81	1.76
24	4.26	3.40	3.01	2.78	2.62	2.51	2.42	2.36	2.30	2.25	2.18	2.11	2.03	1.98	1.94	1.89	1.84	1.79	1.73
25	4.24	3.39	2.99	2.76	2.60	2.49	2.40	2.34	2.28	2.24	2.16	2.09	2.01	1.96	1.92	1.87	1.82	1.77	1.71
26	4.23	3.37	2.98	2.74	2.59	2.47	2.39	2.32	2.27	2.22	2.15	2.07	1.99	1.95	1.90	1.85	1.80	1.75	1.69
27	4.21	3.35	2.96	2.73	2.57	2.46	2.37	2.31	2.25	2.20	2.13	2.06	1.97	1.93	1.88	1.84	1.79	1.73	1.67
28	4.20	3.34	2.95	2.71	2.56	2.45	2.36	2.29	2.24	2.19	2.12	2.04	1.96	1.91	1.87	1.82	1.77	1.71	1.65
29	4.18	3.33	2.93	2.70	2.55	2.43	2.35	2.28	2.22	2.18	2.10	2.03	1.94	1.90	1.85	1.81	1.75	1.70	1.64
30	4.17	3.32	2.92	2.69	2.53	2.42	2.33	2.27	2.21	2.16	2.09	2.01	1.93	1.89	1.84	1.79	1.74	1.68	1.62
40	4.08	3.23	2.84	2.61	2.45	2.34	2.25	2.18	2.12	2.08	2.00	1.92	1.84	1.79	1.74	1.69	1.64	1.58	1.51
60	4.00	3.15	2.76	2.53	2.37	2.25	2.17	2.10	2.04	1.99	1.92	1.84	1.75	1.70	1.65	1.59	1.53	1.47	1.39
120	3.92	3.07	2.68	2.45	2.29	2.18	2.09	2.02	1.96	1.91	1.83	1.75	1.66	1.61	1.55	1.50	1.43	1.35	1.25
∞	3.84	3.00	2.60	2.37	2.21	2.10	2.01	1.94	1.88	1.83	1.75	1.67	1.57	1.52	1.46	1.39	1.32	1.22	1.00

TABLE A.14 (CONTINUED)

1 Percent Level of Significance

ν_2 \ ν_1	1	2	3	4	5	6	7	8	9	10	12	15	20	24	30	40	60	120	∞
1	4,052.4	4,999.5	5,403.3	5,624.6	5,763.7	5,859.0	5,928.3	5,981.6	6,022.5	6,055.8	6,106.3	6,157.3	6,208.7	6,234.6	6,260.7	6,286.8	6,313.0	6,339.4	6,366.0
2	98.50	99.00	99.17	99.25	99.30	99.33	99.36	99.37	99.39	99.40	99.42	99.43	99.45	99.46	99.47	99.47	99.48	99.49	99.50
3	34.12	30.82	29.46	28.71	28.24	27.91	27.67	27.49	27.34	27.23	27.05	26.87	26.69	26.60	26.50	26.41	26.32	26.22	26.12
4	21.20	18.00	16.69	15.98	15.52	15.21	14.98	14.80	14.66	14.55	14.37	14.20	14.02	13.93	13.84	13.74	13.65	13.56	13.46
5	16.26	13.27	12.06	11.39	10.97	10.67	10.46	10.29	10.16	10.05	9.89	9.72	9.55	9.47	9.38	9.29	9.20	9.11	9.02
6	13.74	10.92	9.78	9.15	8.75	8.47	8.26	8.10	7.98	7.87	7.72	7.56	7.40	7.31	7.23	7.14	7.06	6.97	6.88
7	12.25	9.55	8.45	7.85	7.46	7.19	6.99	6.84	6.72	6.62	6.47	6.31	6.16	6.07	5.99	5.91	5.82	5.74	5.65
8	11.26	8.65	7.59	7.01	6.63	6.37	6.18	6.03	5.91	5.81	5.67	5.52	5.36	5.28	5.20	5.12	5.03	4.95	4.86
9	10.56	8.02	6.99	6.42	6.06	5.80	5.61	5.47	5.35	5.26	5.11	4.96	4.81	4.73	4.65	4.57	4.48	4.40	4.31
10	10.04	7.56	6.55	5.99	5.64	5.39	5.20	5.06	4.94	4.85	4.71	4.56	4.41	4.33	4.25	4.17	4.08	4.00	3.91
11	9.65	7.21	6.22	5.67	5.32	5.07	4.89	4.74	4.63	4.54	4.40	4.25	4.10	4.02	3.94	3.86	3.78	3.69	3.60
12	9.33	6.93	5.95	5.41	5.06	4.82	4.64	4.50	4.39	4.30	4.16	4.01	3.86	3.78	3.70	3.62	3.54	3.45	3.36
13	9.07	6.70	5.74	5.21	4.86	4.62	4.44	4.30	4.19	4.10	3.96	3.82	3.66	3.59	3.51	3.43	3.34	3.25	3.17
14	8.86	6.51	5.56	5.04	4.70	4.46	4.28	4.14	4.03	3.94	3.80	3.66	3.51	3.43	3.35	3.27	3.18	3.09	3.00
15	8.68	6.36	5.42	4.89	4.56	4.32	4.14	4.00	3.89	3.80	3.67	3.52	3.37	3.29	3.21	3.13	3.05	2.96	2.87
16	8.53	6.23	5.29	4.77	4.44	4.20	4.03	3.89	3.78	3.69	3.55	3.41	3.26	3.18	3.10	3.02	2.93	2.84	2.75
17	8.40	6.11	5.18	4.67	4.34	4.10	3.93	3.79	3.68	3.59	3.46	3.31	3.16	3.08	3.00	2.92	2.83	2.75	2.65
18	8.29	6.01	5.09	4.58	4.25	4.01	3.84	3.71	3.60	3.51	3.37	3.23	3.08	3.00	2.92	2.84	2.75	2.66	2.57
19	8.18	5.93	5.01	4.50	4.17	3.94	3.77	3.63	3.52	3.43	3.30	3.15	3.00	2.92	2.84	2.76	2.67	2.58	2.49
20	8.10	5.85	4.94	4.43	4.10	3.87	3.70	3.56	3.46	3.37	3.23	3.09	2.94	2.86	2.78	2.69	2.61	2.52	2.42
21	8.02	5.78	4.87	4.37	4.04	3.81	3.64	3.51	3.40	3.31	3.17	3.03	2.88	2.80	2.72	2.64	2.55	2.46	2.36
22	7.95	5.72	4.82	4.31	3.99	3.76	3.59	3.45	3.35	3.26	3.12	2.98	2.83	2.75	2.67	2.58	2.50	2.40	2.31
23	7.88	5.66	4.76	4.26	3.94	3.71	3.54	3.41	3.30	3.21	3.07	2.93	2.78	2.70	2.62	2.54	2.45	2.35	2.26
24	7.82	5.61	4.72	4.22	3.90	3.67	3.50	3.36	3.26	3.17	3.03	2.89	2.74	2.66	2.58	2.49	2.40	2.31	2.21
25	7.77	5.57	4.68	4.18	3.86	3.63	3.46	3.32	3.22	3.13	2.99	2.85	2.70	2.62	2.54	2.45	2.36	2.27	2.17
26	7.72	5.53	4.64	4.14	3.82	3.59	3.42	3.29	3.18	3.09	2.96	2.82	2.66	2.58	2.50	2.42	2.33	2.23	2.13
27	7.68	5.49	4.60	4.11	3.78	3.56	3.39	3.26	3.15	3.06	2.93	2.78	2.63	2.55	2.47	2.38	2.29	2.20	2.10
28	7.64	5.45	4.57	4.07	3.75	3.53	3.36	3.23	3.12	3.03	2.90	2.75	2.60	2.52	2.44	2.35	2.26	2.17	2.06
29	7.60	5.42	4.54	4.04	3.73	3.50	3.33	3.20	3.09	3.00	2.87	2.73	2.57	2.49	2.41	2.33	2.23	2.14	2.03
30	7.56	5.39	4.51	4.02	3.70	3.47	3.30	3.17	3.07	2.98	2.84	2.70	2.55	2.47	2.39	2.30	2.21	2.11	2.01
40	7.31	5.18	4.31	3.83	3.51	3.29	3.12	2.99	2.89	2.80	2.66	2.52	2.37	2.29	2.20	2.11	2.02	1.92	1.80
60	7.08	4.98	4.13	3.65	3.34	3.12	2.95	2.82	2.72	2.63	2.50	2.35	2.20	2.12	2.03	1.94	1.84	1.73	1.60
120	6.85	4.79	3.95	3.48	3.17	2.96	2.79	2.66	2.56	2.47	2.34	2.19	2.03	1.95	1.86	1.76	1.66	1.53	1.38
∞	6.63	4.61	3.78	3.32	3.02	2.80	2.64	2.51	2.41	2.32	2.18	2.04	1.88	1.79	1.70	1.59	1.47	1.32	1.00

If the computed statistic $F = s_1^2/s_2^2$, with the larger s in the numerator, exceeds the tabulated value of F at the specified level with ν_1, ν_2 degrees of freedom, we reject the null hypothesis that $\sigma_1 = \sigma_2$ (see the figure).

Table adapted by permission of authors and publishers from E. L. Crow, F. A. Davis, and M. W. Maxfield, *Statistics Manual* (New York: Dover Publications, Inc., 1960).

TABLE A.15 SIGNIFICANCE POINTS FOR THE ABSOLUTE VALUE OF THE SMALLER SUM OF SIGNED RANKS (R) OBTAINED FROM PAIRED OBSERVATIONS

n	5 Percent	2 Percent	1 Percent
6	0	—	—
7	2	0	—
8	4	2	0
9	6	3	2
10	8	5	3
11	11	7	5
12	14	10	7
13	17	13	10
14	21	16	13
15	25	20	16
16	30	24	20
17	35	28	23
18	40	33	28
19	46	38	32
20	52	43	38
21	59	49	43
22	66	56	49
23	73	62	55
24	81	69	61
25	89	77	68

The values in this table were obtained by kind permission of the American Cyanamid Company.

TABLE A.16 5 PERCENT CRITICAL POINTS OF RANK SUMS (T)

n_2 \ n_1	2	3	4	5	6	7	8	9	10	11	12	13	14	15
4			10											
5		6	11	17										
6		7	12	18	26									
7		7	13	20	27	36								
8	3	8	14	21	29	38	49							
9	3	8	15	22	31	40	51	63						
10	3	9	15	23	32	42	53	65	78					
11	4	9	16	24	34	44	55	68	81	96				
12	4	10	17	26	35	46	58	71	85	99	115			
13	4	10	18	27	37	48	60	73	88	103	119	137		
14	4	11	19	28	38	50	63	76	91	106	123	141	160	
15	4	11	20	29	40	52	65	79	94	110	127	145	164	185
16	4	12	21	31	42	54	67	82	97	114	131	150	169	
17	5	12	21	32	43	56	70	84	100	117	135	154		
18	5	13	22	33	45	58	72	87	103	121	139			
19	5	13	23	34	46	60	74	90	107	124				
20	5	14	24	35	48	62	77	93	110					
21	6	14	25	37	50	64	79	95						
22	6	15	26	38	51	66	82							
23	6	15	27	39	53	68								
24	6	16	28	40	55									
25	6	16	28	42										
26	7	17	29											
27	7	17												
28	7													

The values in this table were obtained by permission from Colin White, "The Use of Ranks in a Test of Significance for Comparing Two Treatments," *Biometrics*, vol. 8, 1952, p. 37.

TABLE A.17 FISHER'S Z TRANSFORMATION FOR CORRELATION COEFFICIENT r

r	Z	r	Z	r	Z	r	Z	r	Z
.000	.000	.200	.203	.400	.424	.600	.693	.800	1.099
.005	.005	.205	.208	.405	.430	.605	.701	.805	1.113
.010	.101	.210	.213	.410	.436	.610	.709	.810	1.127
.015	.015	.215	.218	.415	.442	.615	.717	.815	1.142
.020	.020	.220	.224	.420	.448	.620	.725	.820	1.157
.025	.025	.225	.229	.425	.454	.625	.733	.825	1.172
.030	.030	.230	.234	.430	.460	.630	.741	.830	1.188
.035	.035	.235	.239	.435	.466	.635	.750	.835	1.204
.040	.040	.240	.245	.440	.472	.640	.758	.840	1.221
.045	.045	.245	.250	.445	.478	.645	.767	.845	1.238
.050	.050	.250	.255	.450	.485	.650	.775	.850	1.256
.055	.055	.255	.261	.455	.491	.655	.784	.855	1.274
.060	.060	.260	.266	.460	.497	.660	.793	.860	1.293
.065	.065	.265	.271	.465	.504	.665	.802	.865	1.313
.070	.070	.270	.277	.470	.510	.670	.811	.870	1.333
.075	.075	.275	.282	.475	.517	.675	.820	.875	1.354
.080	.080	.280	.288	.480	.523	.680	.829	.880	1.376
.085	.085	.285	.293	.485	.530	.685	.838	.885	1.398
.090	.090	.290	.299	.490	.536	.690	.848	.890	1.422
.095	.095	.295	.304	.495	.543	.695	.858	.895	1.447
.100	.100	.300	.310	.500	.549	.700	.867	.900	1.472
.105	.105	.305	.315	.505	.556	.705	.877	.905	1.499
.110	.110	.310	.321	.510	.563	.710	.887	.910	1.528
.115	.115	.315	.326	.515	.570	.715	.897	.915	1.557
.120	.121	.320	.332	.520	.576	.720	.908	.920	1.589
.125	.126	.325	.337	.525	.583	.725	.918	.925	1.623
.130	.131	.330	.343	.530	.590	.730	.929	.930	1.658
.135	.136	.335	.348	.535	.597	.735	.940	.935	1.697
.140	.141	.340	.354	.540	.604	.740	.950	.940	1.738
.145	.146	.345	.360	.545	.611	.745	.962	.945	1.783
.150	.151	.350	.365	.550	.618	.750	.973	.950	1.832
.155	.156	.355	.371	.555	.626	.755	.984	.955	1.886
.160	.161	.360	.377	.560	.633	.760	.996	.960	1.946
.165	.167	.365	.383	.565	.640	.765	1.008	.965	2.014
.170	.172	.370	.388	.570	.648	.770	1.020	.970	2.092
.175	.177	.375	.394	.575	.655	.775	1.033	.975	2.185
.180	.182	.380	.400	.580	.662	.780	1.045	.980	2.298
.185	.187	.385	.406	.585	.670	.785	1.058	.985	2.443
.190	.192	.390	.412	.590	.678	.790	1.071	.990	2.647
.195	.198	.395	.418	.595	.685	.795	1.085	.995	2.994

Source: A. L. Edwards, *Statistical Methods*, 2nd ed. (New York: Holt, Rinehart & Winston, 1967), p. 427. Reproduced by permission of the author.

TABLE A.18   VALUES OF CORRELATION COEFFICIENT r

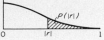

	5 Percent level of significance				1 percent level of significance				
	Total number of variables				Total number of variables				
v	2	3	4	5	2	3	4	5	v
1	.997	.999	.999	.999	1.000	1.000	1.000	1.000	1
2	.950	.975	.983	.987	.990	.995	.997	.998	2
3	.878	.930	.950	.961	.959	.976	.983	.987	3
4	.811	.881	.912	.930	.917	.949	.962	.970	4
5	.754	.836	.874	.898	.874	.917	.937	.949	5
6	.707	.795	.839	.867	.834	.886	.911	.927	6
7	.666	.758	.807	.838	.798	.855	.885	.904	7
8	.632	.726	.777	.811	.765	.827	.860	.882	8
9	.602	.697	.750	.786	.735	.800	.836	.861	9
10	.576	.671	.726	.763	.708	.776	.814	.840	10
11	.553	.648	.703	.741	.684	.753	.793	.821	11
12	.532	.627	.683	.722	.661	.732	.773	.802	12
13	.514	.608	.664	.703	.641	.712	.755	785	13
14	.497	.590	.646	.686	.623	.694	.737	.768	14
15	.482	.574	.630	.670	.606	.677	.721	.752	15
16	.468	.559	.615	.655	.590	.662	.706	.738	16
17	.456	.545	.601	.641	.575	.647	.691	.724	17
18	.444	.532	.587	.628	.561	.633	.678	.710	18
19	.433	.520	.575	.615	.549	.620	.665	.698	19
20	.423	.509	.563	.604	.537	.608	.652	.685	20
21	.413	.498	.552	.592	.526	.596	.641	.674	21
22	.404	.488	.542	.582	.515	.585	.630	.663	22
23	.396	.479	.532	.572	.505	.574	.619	.652	23
24	.388	.470	.523	.562	.496	.565	.609	.642	24
25	.381	.462	.514	.553	.487	.555	.600	.633	25
26	.374	.454	.506	.545	.478	.546	.590	.624	26
27	.367	.446	.498	.536	.470	.538	.582	.615	27
28	.361	.439	.490	.529	.463	.530	.573	.606	28
29	.355	.432	.482	.521	.456	.522	.565	.598	29
30	.349	.426	.476	.514	.449	.514	.558	.591	30
35	.325	.397	.445	.482	.418	.481	.523	.556	35
40	.304	.373	.419	.455	.393	.454	.494	.526	40
45	.288	.353	.397	.432	.372	.430	.470	.501	45
50	.273	.336	.379	.412	.354	.410	.449	.479	50

(*continued*)

TABLE A.18   (CONTINUED)

| | 5 Percent level of significance | | | | 1 percent level of significance | | | | |
| | Total number of variables | | | | Total number of variables | | | | |
v	2	3	4	5	2	3	4	5	v
60	.250	.308	.348	.380	.325	.377	.414	.442	60
70	.232	.286	.324	.354	.302	.351	.386	.413	70
80	.217	.269	.304	.332	.283	.330	.362	.389	80
90	.205	.254	.288	.315	.267	.312	.343	.368	90
100	.195	.241	.274	.300	.254	.297	.327	.351	100
125	.174	.216	.246	.269	.228	.266	.294	.316	125
150	.159	.198	.225	.247	.208	.244	.270	.290	150
200	.138	.172	.196	.215	.181	.212	.234	.253	200
300	.113	.141	.160	.176	.148	.174	.192	.208	300
400	.098	.122	.139	.153	.128	.151	.167	.180	400
500	.088	.109	.124	.137	.115	.135	.150	.162	500
1000	.062	.077	.088	.097	.081	.096	.106	.116	1000

The critical value of r at a given level of significance, total number of variables, and degrees of freedom v, is read from the table. If the computed $|r|$ exceeds the critical value, then the null hypothesis that there is no association between the variables is rejected at the given level. The test is an equal-tails test, since we are usually interested in either positive or negative correlation. The shaded portion of the figure is the stipulated probability as a level of significance.

Table reproduced with the permission of the authors and publisher from E. L. Crow, F. A. Davis, and M. W. Maxfield, *Statistical Manual* (New York: Dover Publications, Inc., 1960).

TABLE A.19 CONTROL CHART LIMITS FOR MEAN
[Factor A_w corresponds to 95 percent probability ($z = 1.96$);
factor A_A corresponds to 99.8 percent probability ($z = 3.09$)]

Sample size, n	2	3	4	5	6	7	8	9	10	11	12
Warning factor, A_w	1.229	0.668	0.476	0.377	0.316	0.274	0.244	0.220	0.202	0.186	0.174
Action factor, A_A	1.937	1.054	0.750	0.594	0.498	0.432	0.384	0.347	0.317	0.294	0.274

To obtain limits for a given sample size n, multiply the mean range $\bar{R}$ by the appropriate value of A_w and A_A; then add to and subtract from mean x.

Table adapted from Table G of O. L. Davies, ed., *Statistical Methods in Research and Production* (Edinburgh, Scotland, Oliver & Boyd Ltd., 1958), by permission of the Imperial Chemical Industries, Ltd., and the publishers.

TABLE A.20 CONTROL CHART LIMITS FOR RANGE
[Factors D_{WU} and D_{WL} correspond to 95 percent probability;
factors D_{AU} and D_{AL} correspond to 99.8 percent probability]

Sample size, n	2	3	4	5	6	7	8	9	10	11	12
Upper warning factor, D_{WU}	2.81	2.17	1.93	1.81	1.72	1.66	1.62	1.58	1.56	1.53	1.51
Lower warning factor, D_{WL}	0.04	0.18	0.29	0.37	0.42	0.46	0.50	0.52	0.54	0.56	0.58
Upper action factor, D_{AU}	4.12	2.99	2.58	2.36	2.22	2.12	2.04	1.99	1.94	1.90	1.87
Lower action factor, D_{AL}	0.00	0.04	0.10	0.16	0.21	0.26	0.29	0.32	0.35	0.38	0.40

To obtain limits, multiply mean range $\bar{R}$ by the appropriate value of D.

Table adapted from Table G of O. L. Davies, ed., *Statistical Methods in Research and Production* (Edinburgh, Scotland, Oliver & Boyd Ltd., 1958), by permission of the Imperial Chemical Industries, Ltd., and the publishers.

TABLE A.21   RANDOM NUMBERS

53 74 23 99 67	61 32 28 69 84	94 62 67 86 24	98 33 41 19 95	47 53 53 38 09
63 38 06 86 54	99 00 65 26 94	02 82 90 23 07	79 62 67 80 60	75 91 12 81 19
35 30 58 21 46	06 72 17 10 94	25 21 31 75 96	49 28 24 00 49	55 65 79 78 07
63 43 36 82 69	65 51 18 37 88	61 38 44 12 45	32 92 85 88 65	54 34 81 85 35
98 25 37 55 26	01 91 82 81 46	74 71 12 94 97	24 02 71 37 07	03 92 18 66 75
02 63 21 17 69	71 50 80 89 56	38 15 70 11 48	43 40 45 86 98	00 83 26 91 03
64 55 22 21 82	48 22 28 06 00	61 54 13 43 91	82 78 12 23 29	06 66 24 12 27
85 07 26 13 89	01 10 07 82 04	59 63 69 36 03	69 11 15 83 80	13 29 54 19 28
58 54 16 24 15	51 54 44 82 00	62 61 65 04 69	38 18 65 18 97	85 72 13 49 21
34 85 27 84 87	61 48 64 56 26	90 18 48 13 26	37 70 15 42 57	65 65 80 39 07
03 92 18 27 46	57 99 16 96 56	30 33 72 85 22	84 64 38 56 98	99 01 30 98 64
62 95 30 27 59	37 75 41 66 48	86 97 80 61 45	23 53 04 01 63	45 76 08 64 27
08 45 93 15 22	60 21 75 46 91	98 77 27 85 42	28 88 61 08 84	69 62 03 42 73
07 08 55 18 40	45 44 75 13 90	24 94 96 61 02	57 55 66 83 15	73 42 37 11 61
01 85 89 95 66	51 10 19 34 88	15 84 97 19 75	12 76 39 43 78	64 63 91 08 25
72 84 71 14 35	19 11 58 49 26	50 11 17 17 76	86 31 57 20 18	95 60 78 46 75
88 78 28 16 84	13 52 53 94 53	75 45 69 30 96	73 89 65 70 31	99 17 43 48 76
45 17 75 65 57	28 40 19 72 12	25 12 74 75 67	60 40 60 81 19	24 62 01 61 16
96 76 28 12 54	22 01 11 94 25	71 96 16 16 88	68 64 36 74 45	19 59 50 88 92
43 31 67 72 30	24 02 94 08 63	38 32 36 66 02	69 36 38 25 39	48 03 45 15 22
50 44 66 44 21	66 06 58 05 62	68 15 54 35 02	42 35 48 96 32	14 52 41 52 48
22 66 22 15 86	26 63 75 41 99	58 42 36 72 24	58 37 52 18 51	03 37 18 39 11
96 24 40 14 51	23 22 30 88 57	95 67 47 29 83	94 69 40 06 07	18 16 36 78 86
31 73 91 61 19	60 20 72 93 48	98 57 07 23 69	65 95 39 69 58	56 80 30 19 44
78 60 73 99 84	43 89 94 36 45	56 69 47 07 41	90 22 91 07 12	78 35 34 08 72
84 37 90 61 56	70 10 23 98 05	85 11 34 76 60	76 48 45 34 60	01 64 18 39 96
36 67 10 08 23	98 93 35 08 86	99 29 76 29 81	33 34 91 58 93	63 14 52 32 52
07 28 59 07 48	89 64 58 89 75	83 85 62 27 89	30 14 78 56 27	86 63 59 80 02
10 15 83 87 60	79 24 31 66 56	21 48 24 06 93	91 98 94 05 49	01 47 59 38 00
55 19 68 97 65	03 73 52 16 56	00 53 55 90 27	33 42 29 38 87	22 13 88 83 34
53 81 29 13 39	35 01 20 71 34	62 33 74 82 14	53 73 19 09 03	56 54 29 56 93
51 86 32 68 92	33 98 74 66 99	40 14 71 94 58	45 94 19 38 81	14 44 99 81 07
35 91 70 29 13	80 03 54 07 27	96 94 78 32 66	50 95 52 74 33	13 80 55 62 54
37 71 67 95 13	20 02 44 95 94	64 85 04 05 72	01 32 90 76 14	53 89 74 60 41
93 66 13 83 27	92 79 64 64 72	28 54 96 53 84	48 14 52 98 94	56 07 93 89 30
02 96 08 45 65	13 05 00 41 84	93 07 54 72 59	21 45 57 09 77	19 48 56 27 44
49 83 43 48 35	82 88 33 69 96	72 36 04 19 76	47 45 15 18 60	82 11 08 95 97
84 60 71 62 46	40 80 81 30 37	34 39 23 05 38	25 15 35 71 30	88 12 57 21 77
18 17 30 88 71	44 91 14 88 47	89 23 30 63 15	56 34 20 47 89	99 82 93 24 98
79 69 10 61 78	71 32 76 95 62	87 00 22 58 40	92 54 01 75 25	43 11 71 99 31
75 93 36 57 83	56 20 14 82 11	74 21 97 90 65	96 42 68 63 86	74 54 13 26 94
38 30 92 29 03	06 28 81 39 38	62 25 06 84 63	61 29 08 93 67	04 32 92 08 09
51 28 50 10 34	31 57 75 95 80	51 97 02 74 77	76 15 48 49 44	18 55 63 77 09
21 31 38 86 24	37 79 81 53 74	73 24 16 10 33	52 83 90 94 76	70 47 14 54 36
29 01 23 87 88	58 02 39 37 67	42 10 14 20 92	16 55 23 42 45	54 96 09 11 06
95 33 95 22 00	18 74 72 00 18	38 79 58 69 32	81 76 80 26 92	82 80 84 25 39
90 84 60 79 80	24 36 59 87 38	82 07 53 89 35	96 35 23 79 18	05 98 90 07 35
46 40 62 98 82	54 97 20 56 95	15 74 80 08 32	16 46 70 50 80	67 72 16 42 79
20 31 89 03 43	38 46 82 68 72	32 14 82 99 70	80 60 47 18 97	63 49 30 21 30
71 59 73 05 50	08 22 23 71 77	91 01 93 20 49	82 96 59 26 94	66 39 67 98 60

This table is taken from Table XXXIII of Fisher and Yates: *Statistical Tables for Biological, Agricultural, and Medical Research*, published by Oliver & Boyd Ltd., Edinburgh, Scotland, by permission of the authors and publishers.

TABLE A.22   FACTORS FOR CONVERTING TO IMPERIAL (AMERICAN) UNITS

SI	Imperial	SI	Imperial
Length		*Force*	
1 millimeter (mm)	0.0394 inch (in)	1 newton (N)	0.225 pound force (lbf)
1 meter (m)	3.28 feet (ft)	*Pressure, stress*	
1 kilometer (km)	0.621 mile (mile)	1 N/m^2	0.0209 lbf/ft^2
Area		(= pascal, Pa)	
1 square millimeter (mm^2)	1.55×10^{-3} square inch (in^2)	1 N/mm^2 (= 1 MPa)	145 lbf/in^2 (p.s.i.)
1 square meter (m^2)	10.76 square feet (ft^2)	1 N/mm^2	295 in. Hg
1 hectare (ha)	2.47 acres (acre)	1 millibar (mb)	0.0295 in. Hg
Volume		*Work, energy*	
1 cubic millimeter (mm^3)	0.0610×10^{-3} cubic inches (in^3)	1 joule (J)	0.738 ft·lbf
1 cubic meter (m^3)	35.3 cubic feet (ft^3)	*Moment, torque*	
		1 N·m	0.738 lbf·ft
1 liter (dm^3)	0.220 gallons (gal)	*Power*	
	0.264 U.S. gallons (gal)	1 watt (W) (= 1 J/s)	1.34×10^{-3} horsepower (hp)
Mass			
1 gram (g)	0.0353 ounce (oz)	*Heat quantity*	
1 kilogram (kg)	2.20 pounds (lb)	1 joule (J)	0.948×10^{-3} (Btu)
1 ton (t) (1000 kg)	2.20 kips (kip)	1 watt (W)	3.41 Btu/h
Density		*Conductivity and*	
1 kg/m^3	0.0624 lb/ft^3	*U value*	
1 t/m^3	0.0361 lb/in^3	*(Transmittance)*	
Flexural		1 W/m°C	6.93 Btu·in/ft^2 h°F
stiffness		1 W/m^2°C	0.176 Btu/ft^2 h°F
1 N·mm^2	$0.348 + 10^{-3}$ lbf·in^2	*Flow*	
Second moment		1 l/s	2.12 ft^3/min
of area		*Viscosity*	
1 mm^4	2.40×10^{-6} in^4	*(kinematic)*	
Velocity		1 cm^2/s (= 1 stoke, St)	1.076×10^{-3} ft^2/s
1 m/s	3.28 ft/s		
1 km/h	0.911 ft/s	*Concrete Mixes*	
	0.621 mile/h (m.p.h.)	1 kg/m^3	1.69 lb/yd^3

Answers to Problems

CHAPTER 2

2-1 (d) 21 years, 15 years.

2-2. (b) 33.8 percent. **(c)** 71 percent.

2-4. (a) 0.75 percent. **(b)** 0.885. **(c)** 0, 1, 2, . . . , 12.

2-5. (c) 46.7 percent for class width of 0.002 cm starting at 1.724 cm.

2-6. (b) 52.5 percent.

CHAPTER 3

3-1. 978, 1152; the set has no mode.

3-2. (c) 0.5354 cm.

3-3. (a) 13.75 cm. **(b)** 13.80 cm; the error is $\simeq 0.34$ percent.

3-4. 10.3 percent.

3-5. 10.56 percent, 10.5 percent, 10.6 percent, 10.66 percent.

3-6. (b) 231.1 hours, 186.25 hours, 50 hours.

3-7. 2.53, 1, 2.

CHAPTER 4

4-1. 1403.2 N, 13.68 N, 42 N.

4-2. 133,884, 365.9, 37.4 percent. One cannot estimate the standard deviation from the range since it is not possible to calculate the mean range, $\bar{R}$, and the given values are far from being normally distributed.

4-3. 0.022 cm.   **(a)** 0.00525 cm, $V = 0.982$ percent.
(b) 0.00529 cm, $V = 0.989$ percent, s from mean range = 0.00542 cm.

4-4. 176.8 hours, 31,249.9, 22.7 percent.

4-5. (a) 2.93, 1.04.   **(b)** 2.16.

4-6. 23.45 MPa, 16.8 MPa, 2.59 MPa, 3.44 MPa, 14.7 percent. Specification requirements are satisfied since only 1 out of 50 samples has a strength less than 17 MPa.

4-7. 23.82 MPa, 2.6 MPa, 10.9 percent.

4-8. $s = 2.835$ MPa.

4-9. By adopting a class width of 1.4 MPa, a cumulative frequency diagram gives a strength of 20.7 MPa exceeded by 90 percent of tests.

4-10. (a) 1073°C.   **(b)** 1197; 34.6°C; 3.225 percent.

CHAPTER 5

5-1. (a) 0.0867.   **(b)** 0.0433.   **(c)** 0.0625.

5-2. 1.575×10^{-12}.

5-3. $(\frac{3}{4})^4$.

5-4. (a) $\frac{11}{36}$.   **(b)** $\frac{1}{3}$.

5-5. 3.6288×10^6.

5-6. 3^{14}.

5-7. (a) 0.06.   **(b)** 0.56.   **(c)** 0.38.

5-8. (a) 0.56.   **(b)** 0.8064.

5-9. 0.72.

5-10. No need to build new bridge.

5-11. The components function independently.

5-12. (a) $\frac{1}{12}$.   **(b)** $\frac{1}{2}$.

5-13. $\frac{4}{3}$; $\frac{8}{9}$.

5-14. 0.8571.

5-15. $\dfrac{(x^2 - 600^2)}{x^2}$; 0.36; 1200 hours.

5-16. 0.93; 0.81; 0.9.

5-17. $E(C) = 100 + 3E(A) + 5E(B)$; $\text{Var}(C) = 9\,\text{Var}(A) + 25\,\text{Var}(B)$.

5-18. (a) 55 percent.   **(b)** 221 to 579 transmissions.

5-19. 0.60.

5-20. (a) 0.9981.   **(b)** 0.902.

CHAPTER 6

6-1. 0.000748 cm.

6-2. 4.57 N, 1.41.

6-3. (a) 16.2.   **(b)** 2.64.   **(c)** 16.2.   **(d)** 1.62.

6-4. 0.43 cm.

6-5. $s = 0.0437$ kg, $s_{\bar{x}} = 0.0219$ kg.

6-6. 60.06 s, 0.324 s, 0.09 s, 0.272 s, 0.54 percent.

6-7. **(a)** 3455. **(b)** 2.8. **(c)** 0.08 percent. **(d)** 1.1. **(e)** 1.1.

6-8. **(i)** Normal. **(ii)** None listed. **(iii)** Normal. **(iv)** None listed. **(v)** None listed. **(vi)** χ^2. **(vii)** t. **(viii)** None listed. **(ix)** t.

CHAPTER 8

8-1. **(a)** 0.349. **(b)** 0.387. **(c)** 0.930. **(d)** 0.264.

8-2. 0.091.

8-3. Consignment is not suspect.

8-4. **(a)** 0.096. **(b)** 0.904. **(c)** 0.1, 0.315.

8-5. 0.294, 0.010.

8-7. **(a)** 0.579. **(b)** 0.209. **(c)** 0.194.

8-8. Hypothesis is rejected.

8-9. The bridge should be strengthened.

8-10. **(a)** 5. **(b)** New nozzle did not solve the problem.

CHAPTER 9

9-1. Distribution is Poisson.

9-2. 0.0039.

9-3. True.

9-4. Reject the consignment.

9-5. 0.647.

9-6. The failures follow a Poisson distribution.

9-7. **(a)** 1.442. **(b)** 1.201. **(c)** 0.764.

9-8. Yes.

CHAPTER 10

10-1. **(a)** 95.4 percent. **(b)** 36.8 percent. **(c)** 93.3 percent.

10-2. 6578 N, 1111 N.

10-3. **(a)** 0.1893. **(b)** 0.5773.

10-4. **(a)** 0.0055. **(b)** 0.7794. **(c)** 109.

10-5. 23,805 pairs, 142,193 pairs.

10-6. 2715 hours, 199 hours.

10-7. 0.0019 ohm^{-1}.

10-8. 13.

CHAPTER 11

11-1. (a) $20 \ \mu\Omega$, $17.3 \ (\mu\Omega)^2$.   (b) $1.04 \ \mu\Omega$.   (c) $(22.7, 17.3)$.

11-2. The numbers are not equally distributed.

11-3. (a) 42.4 percent.   (b) 26.4 percent.

11-4. (a) 50 percent.   (b) 43.2 percent.   (c) 1.27 percent.

11-5. 32.

11-6. (a) 159, 2.79 ± 0.026 cm, 10.   (b) 4.56 percent.   (c) 4 or more.

11-7. $y = \dfrac{57}{3.262\sqrt{2\pi}} \ e^{[-(13.798-x)^2/2 \times 3.262^2]}$.

The histogram and fitted normal curve are in fair agreement.

11-8. $p(x) = 0.3989e^{-0.250x^2}$, $y = 12.45e^{-0.250x^2}$, 10.7 percent, 1.45 percent. Good agreement is shown with the values previously calculated.

11-9. (a) 54.71 ± 4.55 (based on 10 readings taken at random).

   (b) $y = \dfrac{64}{2.43\sqrt{2\pi}} \ e^{[-(54.13-x)^2/2 \times 2.43^2]}$.

   (c) From a plot on normal probability paper, mean is 54.1 and s is 2.4. Good agreement.

11-10. $y = \dfrac{24.64}{\sqrt{2\pi}} \ e^{[-(23.28-x)^2/2 \times 3.45^2]}$; 3.9 percent.

11-11. 32.98 MPa, 37.33 MPa.

11-12. (a) $h = 0.954$ s/kg.   (b) 2.5 or 3; $h = 1.335$ s/kg.

11-13. 503.57 to 498.43 m, 503.63 to 498.37 m.

11-14. (a) $n = 7$.   (b) Yes.

CHAPTER 12

12-1. 5.92 is an outlier.

12-2. $\bar{x} = 3.55$.   (a) No outliers at 5 percent level of significance.
   (b) 4.6 is an outlier; new mean is 3.34 cm.

12-3. (a) 8.92 should be discarded.   (b) 9.01 cm, original mean $= 9.00$ cm.

12-4. 620 is an outlier.

12-5. 620 is an outlier; no, since s_e is not available.

CHAPTER 13

13-1. 0.982.

13-2. 0.916.

13-3. 120 years.

13-4. (a) 0.302.   (b) 0.301.   (c) 8.33 years.

13-5. $m = 2.43$ and $\gamma = 4.6 \times 10^{-7}$, 53 percent.

13-6. $m = 1.92$ and $\gamma = 1.035 \times 10^{-4}$. χ^2 for the Weibull distribution is 10.97. χ^2 for the normal distribution is 9.25.

13-7. **(b)** 4080 m³/s, 2076 m³/s.   **(c)** 4.2 years, 2.3 years.
(d) 7330 m³/s, 8100 m³/s, 9100 m³/s.

13-8. $X = 800 - 94y$.

CHAPTER 14

14-1. χ^2_{calc} is 10.316. Consignment is suspect at 1 percent level of significance.

14-2. χ^2_{calc} is 0.946. Distribution does not differ significantly from Poisson distribution.

14-3. χ^2_{calc} is 2.531. There is no justification in rejecting the goodness of fit.

14-4. χ^2_{calc} is 8.552. Class B receives better instruction at 1 percent level of significance.

14-5. χ^2_{calc} is 191. There is a significant difference between the machines, type A leading to "less trouble," at 0.1 percent level of significance.

14-6. χ^2_{calc} is 11.492. There is a significant difference at the 0.1 percent level.

14-7. χ^2_{calc} is 9.389. There is a significant difference at the 1 percent level.

14-8. χ^2_{calc} is 7.081.   **(a)** Significant difference at 5 percent level.
(b) No significant difference at 1 percent level.

14-9. χ^2_{calc} is 4.002. There is a significant difference at the 5 percent level.

14-10. The data conform to the theoretical binomial distribution.

CHAPTER 15

15-1. t_{calc} is 0.64. No significant difference at the 10 percent level of significance.

15-2. t_{calc} is 2.146. No significant difference at the 5 percent level of significance.

15-3. t_{calc} is 1.84. No significant difference at the 5 percent level of significance.

15-4. t_{calc} is 1.135. No significant difference.

15-5. t_{calc} is 2.236. No significant difference at the 5 percent level of significance.

15-6. t_{calc} is 3.345. Significant difference at the 1 percent level of significance.

15-7. t_{calc} is 1.88. No significant difference.

15-8. t_{calc} is 0.735. No evidence that angle is becoming smaller.

15-9. t_{calc} is 6.852. Significant difference at the 1 percent level of significance.

15-10. t_{calc} is 3.02. Significant difference at the 5 percent level of significance.

15-11. By using normal probability we cannot say that group A and group B are significantly different. There is a difference between groups B and C.

15-12. t_{calc} is 0.39. No significant difference at 10 percent level of significance.

15-13. 1. No significant difference.
2. No significant difference.
3. There is a significant difference.

CHAPTER 16

16-1. (a) σ_A^2 does not differ significantly from σ_B^2 at the 10 percent level. (b) σ_A^2 does not differ significantly from $1.75\sigma_B^2$ at the 10 percent level. (c) σ_A^2 is not significantly greater than σ_B^2 at the 5 percent level.

16-2. No significant difference.

16-3. No significant difference.

16-4. No significant difference.

16-5. No significant difference.

16-6. Significant difference at the 1 percent level of significance.

16-7. Significant difference between the two variabilities at the 1 percent level of significance.

16-8. No significant difference in standard deviations.

16-9. Significant difference at the 1 percent level of significance.

16-10. $v = 1823.6 \pm 64.2 \text{ cm}^3$.

16-11. $s = 4.88$ m gives a better estimate of g.

16-12. $\sigma_v = 25.133 \text{ cm}^3$.

16-13. $\sigma_\delta = 0.00248$ mm.

16-14. 0.831 percent, 0.831 percent, e should be increased in accuracy.

16-15. (a) 0.115 mm/cycle, 0.0699 mm/cycle. (b) 0.125 mm/cycle.

16-16. Mean $= 143.6$ decibels, variance $= 32$ (decibels)^2.

16-17. First-order mean $V = 6.67$ m/sec, $\sigma_V^2 = 5.05$ (m/sec)^2, second-order mean $V = 8.13$ m/sec.

CHAPTER 17

17-1. $y = 9.669 + 1.157x$. $x = -8.113 + 0.846y$.

17-2. $y = 20.269 - (41.831/x)$.

17-3. (a) $y = -14.143 + 4.036x$. (b) 20.16 ± 5.33.

17-4. (a) $y = 10 + 2x$. (b) The hypothesis that $b = 0$ is not true at the 0.1 percent level. (c) No significant difference. (d) $(1.47, 2.53)$.

17-5. $y = -313.52 + 6.95x$, 15.31, 103.5, 68.6, (69.2, 137.8).

17-6. 240.49, 243.62, 246.19.

17-7. $A = 82°15'35''$, $B = 110°37'45''$, $C = 66°24'35''$, $D = 100°42'05''$, $(A + B) = 192°53'20''$.

17-8. (a) $\log y = 1.602 + 0.161x$. (b) 211. (c) 565, 79.

17-9. $y = 115.5 - 21.7 \log x$.

17-10. (a) $y = 5.074 + 0.882x$. (b) $y = 5.128 + 0.746x$. For (a) the value of $b = 0.882$ is significant. The value of $a = 5.074$ is significant. The slope is significantly different from 1.00. For (b) the value of $b = 0.746$ is significant. The value of $a = 5.128$ is significant. The slope is significantly different from 0.85.

17-11. $y = x^{0.801}/4.78$.

17-12. $57°35'15''$, $92°17'41''$, $75°53'22''$.

17-13. $+10.705$ m, -51.764 m, $+32.849$ m.

CHAPTER 18

18-1. 0.9152: the correlation is significant at the 1 percent level of significance.

18-2. r is 0.607. The correlation is significant at the 5 percent level.

18-3. The corresponding population correlation does not differ from zero at either level of significance.

18-4. At least 46.

18-5. $y = 29.612 + 2.838x$, 0.996. The slope is not significant at the 5 percent level of significance.

18-6. $r = -0.950$, limits for ρ: -0.991, -0.742.

18-7. H_0 cannot be rejected.

18-8. (a) $r^2 = 0.993$, $r = 0.996$. (b) H_0 is rejected. (c) Limits for ρ: 0.999, 0.981.

CHAPTER 19

19-1. (a) $y = 83.077 = 0.317x_1 + 0.552x_2 + 0.176x_3$.
    (b) $F = 3.26$; the null hypothesis that all the true partial regression coefficients are equal to zero cannot be rejected at the 5 percent level of significance.
    (c) t_a is 7.489, a is significant.
        t_{b_1} is 0.903, b_1 is not significant.
        t_{b_2} is 2.462, b_2 is significant.
        t_{b_3} is 0.329, b_3 is not significant.
    (d) 0.742. Not significant at the 5 percent level of significance.
    (e) $r_{yx_1} = -0.327$, $r_{yx_2} = 0.710$, $r_{yx_3} = 0.258$, $r_{x_1x_2} = -0.183$, $r_{x_1x_3} = 0.173$, $r_{x_2x_3} = 0.331$.

19-2. (a) $y = 94.213 - 0.333x_1 - 0.171x_2 + 0.971x_3$. (b) 74.482.
    (c) The null hypothesis that all partial regression coefficients are not significant cannot be rejected at the 5 percent level of significance.
    (d) t_a is 10.916, a is significant.
        t_{b_1} is 0.753, b_1 is not significant.
        t_{b_2} is 0.408, b_2 is not significant.
        t_{b_3} is 2.143, b_3 is not significant.
    (e) 0.5865. Not significant at the 5 percent level of significance.

19-3. (a) $\hat{y} = -2.491 + 0.099x_1 + 0.029x_2 + 0.086x_3$. (b) r is significant.
    (c) The null hypothesis is rejected. (d) Elevation.

19-4. The variables "temperature" and "pressure" have a significant influence on the tensile strength; however, their interaction does not at $\alpha = 0.05$.

CHAPTER 20

20-1. Significant difference at the 1 percent level of significance.

20-2. No significant difference.

20-3. No significant difference.

20-4. The type of terrain has no effect on runoff at the 5 percent level of significance.

20-5. Significant difference at the 5 percent level of significance.

20-6. No significant difference.

20-7. (b) No significant difference. **(c)** No significant difference.

CHAPTER 21

21-1. Warning limits for mean chart: 3657 kN/m², 3363 kN/m².
Action limits for mean chart: 3742 kN/m², 3278 kN/m².
Warning limits for range chart: 706 kN/m², 144 kN/m².
Action limits for range chart: 920 kN/m², 62 kN/m².

21-2. Warning limits for mean chart: 18.50, 10.32.
Action limits for mean chart: 20.87, 7.95.
Warning limits for range chart: 13.30, 1.10.
Action limits for range chart: 18.33, 0.25.

21-3. (a) Not in control. **(b)** Yes.

21-4. The control limits are (0, 5.72).
The probability limits are (0, 6.09).

21-5. (a) $s = 2.835$ MPa.
(b) MWL: 26.31 MPa, 21.33 MPa.
MAL: 27.74 MPa, 19.90 MPa.
RWL: 11.94 MPa, 2.44 MPa.
RAL: 15.56 MPa, 1.06 MPa.
(c) All points are within the limits.

21-7. (a) MWL: 534.1 N, 495.9 N.
MAL: 545.2 N, 484.8 N.
RWL: 77.6 N, 11.7 N.
RAL: 103.7 N, 4.0 N.
(b) $s = 19.5$ N.
(c) All welds meet the minimum specifications.

21-8. The control limits are (0, 5.72), no adjustments are necessary.

21-9. (a) The limits are (0, 5.17). **(b)** The limits are (0, 503).

21-10. The limits for $\bar{x}$ are (7.881, 8.318 ohm), the limits for R are (0.774, 0.03 ohm), the process cannot meet the specifications.

CHAPTER 22

22-1. (a) If the mean yield of 36 tests is greater than 10.1, reject the hypothesis that the processes are the same. **(b)** Since there is no overlap (from a practical point of view) the required probability is zero. **(d)** 38.

22-2. 6.

22-3. (a) $n = 25$ approximately. **(b)** The hypothesis is rejected.

CHAPTER 23

23-1. (a) 15.46.   **(b)** 4.86.   **(c)** 16.16.
   (d) No significant effect due to micrometers at the 1 percent level of significance. No effect due to different gauge blocks at the 1 percent level.
   (e) There is no significant effect due to different engineers at the 5 percent level.

23-2. (b) There is no significant effect due to "operator," significant effect due to "time-study engineer."
   (c) "Operator" variance = 10.45, "time-study engineer" variance = 80.08.

23-3. (a) Interaction is significant.   **(b)** Brand of gasoline is significant.
   (c) Car is significant.   **(d)** Error variance = 0.093.

23-4. Assuming no interaction: brand of gasoline is not significant, car is significant, error variance = 2.28.

23-5. The effect of the different shifts is significant at the 1 percent level of significance. There is a significant difference in the production figures during the four years at the 1 percent level.

23-6. The performance does not depend on the process at the 5 percent level of significance. The source affects the performance at the 5 percent level.

Index